HRM NELSON SERIES IN HUMAN RESOURCE MANAGEMENT

SEVENTH EDITION

MANAGEMENT OF OCCUPATIONAL HEALTH AND SAFETY

HRM NELSON SERIES IN HUMAN
RESOURCE MANAGEMENT

SEVENTH EDITION

MANAGEMENT OF OCCUPATIONAL HEALTH **AND** SAFETY

E. KEVIN KELLOWAY
SAINT MARY'S UNIVERSITY

LORI FRANCIS
SAINT MARY'S UNIVERSITY

BERNADETTE GATIEN
SAINT MARY'S UNIVERSITY

SERIES EDITOR:
MONICA BELCOURT
YORK UNIVERSITY

NELSON

NELSON

Management of Occupational Health and Safety, Seventh Edition
by E. Kevin Kelloway, Lori Francis, and Bernadette Gatien

VP, Product and Partnership Solutions:
Anne Williams

Publisher, Digital and Print Content:
Jackie Wood

Marketing Manager:
Dave Stratton

Content Development Manager:
Elke Price

Photo and Permissions Researcher:
Jessie Coffey

Production Project Manager:
Jaime Smith

Production Service:
MPS Limited

Copy Editor:
Karen Rolfe

Proofreader:
MPS Limited

Indexer:
MPS Limited

Design Director:
Ken Phipps

Managing Designer:
Franca Amore

Design Director:
Ken Phipps

Managing Designer:
Franca Amore

Interior Design:
Sharon Lucas

Cover Design:
Sharon Lucas

Compositor:
MPS Limited

Library and Archives Canada Cataloguing in Publication

Kelloway, E. Kevin (Edward Kevin), 1959-, author
    Management of occupational health and safety / E. Kevin Kelloway, Lori Francis, Bernadette Gatien.—7th edition.

First edition: Occupational health and safety / James Montgomery; second edition: Management of occupational health and safety / James Montgomery and Kevin Kelloway. Includes index. Issued in print and electronic formats. ISBN 978-0-17-665717-8 (paperback).—ISBN 978-0-17-676779-2 (pdf)

    1. Industrial hygiene—Management—Textbooks.
2. Industrial safety—Management—Textbooks.
3. Industrial hygiene—Textbooks. 4. Industrial safety—Textbooks. I. Francis, Lori D. (Lori Denise), 1974–, author II. Gatien, Bernadette, 1978-, author III. Montgomery, James, 1932–. Occupational health and safety. IV. Montgomery, James, 1932–. Management of occupational health and safety. III. Title.

HD7261.M65 2016   363.11
C2016-903707-X
C2016-903708-8

ISBN-13: 978-0-17-665717-8
ISBN-10: 0-17-665717-7

For Debra
(EKK)

With Memories of my Father, Ben.
(LF)

For Mackenzie, Sid, Josh, and Bruce
(BG)

BRIEF CONTENTS

About the Series   xxiii

About the Authors   xxiv

Preface   xxvi

Acknowledgments   xxxiii

PART 1   INTRODUCTION AND OVERVIEW   1
Chapter 1   Introduction   1
Chapter 2   Legislative Framework   28
Chapter 3   Workers' Compensation   50

PART 2   HAZARDS AND AGENTS   76
Chapter 4   Hazard Recognition, Risk Assessment, and Control   76
Chapter 5   Physical Agents   110
Chapter 6   Biological and Chemical Agents   133
Chapter 7   Psychosocial Hazards   160
Chapter 8   Workplace Violence, Aggression, and Harassment   188

PART 3   INTERVENTIONS   217
Chapter 9   Training   217
Chapter 10   Motivation and Safety Management Systems   243
Chapter 11   Emergency Planning   272
Chapter 12   Incident Investigation   291
Chapter 13   Disability Management and Return to Work   319
Chapter 14   Workplace Wellness: Work–Family and Health Promotion Programs   344

Glossary   377

Index   382

CONTENTS

About the Series xxiii

About the Authors xxiv

Preface xxvi

Acknowledgments xxxiii

PART I   INTRODUCTION AND OVERVIEW 1

Chapter 1   Introduction 1

Chapter Learning Objectives 1

Opening Vignette: Rail Disaster at Lac-Mégantic 2

Historical Development of Modern Occupational Health and Safety 6

    A Long History 6

    Changing Perspectives on Risk and Liability 7

    Developments in Canadian Legislation and OH&S Programs 8

Imperatives for Health and Safety 10

    Economic Considerations 10

    Legal Considerations 11

    Moral Considerations 12

The Stakeholders 12

Government 13

    Employers 14

    Employees 15

    Organized Labour 15

Barriers 15

Partnerships 16

Occupational Health and Safety Professionals 19

The Role of Human Resources 20

Safety Is Integrated in Other Human Resource Functions 20

Safety Requires Legislative Compliance 21

Safety Decreases Costs 21

Summary 22

Key Terms 22

Discussion Questions 23

Using the Internet 23

Exercises 23

OH&S in Action 24

Case Study 1: Production or Safety? 24

Case Study 2: Do We Need Health and Safety? 24

Notes 25

Chapter 2　　Legislative Framework 28

Chapter Learning Objectives 28

Opening Vignette: Small Fishing Vessel Regulations: Proposal for Change in a Dangerous Industry 29

The Scope of OH&S Legislation 32

Occupational Health & Safety Acts 33

Stakeholder Duties and Responsibilities 34

Joint Health and Safety Committees 36

Work Refusals 37

Stop-Work Provisions 39

Workplace Hazardous Materials Information System 40

Corporate Liability for OH&S Under the Criminal Code 41

Environmental Legislation 42

Transportation of Dangerous Goods 44

Summary 45

Key Terms 45

Discussion Questions 45

Using the Internet 46

Exercise 46

OH&S in Action 46

Case Study 1: Workplace Tragedy 47

Case Study 2: Work Refusal at Regional Hospital 47

Notes 47

Chapter 3   Workers' Compensation 50

Chapter Learning Objectives 50

Opening Vignette: Firefighters Battling and Police Fighting, But It's Not What You Think 51

Historical Roots 52

Workers' Compensation in Canada 53

   Administration and Responsibilities 53

   Prevention 55

   Compensation Rates and Methods 57

Medical Aid and Incident Prevention 59

Social Goals of Workers' Compensation 60

   Provision for Second Injuries 60

   Rehabilitation 60

Occupational Diseases and Workplace Stress 62

Assessments 64

   Experience Rating 65

Reporting Requirements 67

   Noncompliance 72

Summary 72

Key Terms 72

Discussion Questions 72

Using the Internet 73

Exercises 73

OH&S in Action 74

Case Study 1: The Employer's Duty 74

Case Study 2: A Stressful Job 74

Notes 75

PART 2   HAZARDS AND AGENTS 76

Chapter 4   Hazard Recognition, Risk Assessment, and Control 76

Chapter Learning Objectives 76

Opening Vignette: Rogue Wave 77

Terminology 78

Hazard Recognition and Identification 78

People 78

Equipment 79

Environment 79

Materials 80

Processes 80

Hazard Identification Programs 80

Components of the Hazard Identification Program 81

Risk Assessment 82

Follow-Up 85

Types of Injuries 85

Overt Traumatic Injuries 86

Overexertion Injuries 86

Hazard Control 89

Precontact Control 89

Point-of-Contact Control 90

Postcontact Control 90

Engineering Control 91

Substitution, Ventilation, and Isolation 91

Process Modification 92

Machine Guarding 92

Equipment Design 94

Administrative Control   95

    Safety Awareness   96

    Housekeeping   97

    Preventive Maintenance   99

Personal Protective Equipment   102

Source–Path–Human Controls   103

Monitoring/Auditing   104

Record Keeping   104

Summary   105

Key Terms   105

Discussion Questions   106

Using the Internet   106

Exercises   107

OH&S in Action   107

Case Study 1: Industrial Hazard Assessment   107

Case Study 2: Danger in the Grocery Store   108

Case Study 3: Hazard Control   108

Notes   109

Chapter 5   Physical Agents   110

Chapter Learning Objectives   110

Opening Vignette: How Is Blue Light Affecting You?   111

Radiation   111

    Ionizing Radiation   112

    Non-Ionizing Radiation   112

    Controlling Radiation   113

Noise   114

    Types of Hearing Loss   115

    Noise Control   117

Vibration   120

Health Effects of Vibration   120

Controlling Vibration   122

Thermal Stress   123

Heat-related Illnesses   124

Controlling Heat   125

Cold Environments   125

Controlling Cold   128

Summary   128

Key Terms   128

Discussion Questions   128

Using the Internet   129

Exercise   129

OH&S in Action   129

Case Study 1: Radiation   129

Case Study 2: Expensive Jewellery   130

Appendix: Hearing Protection Types or Classifications   131

Notes   132

Chapter 6   **Biological and Chemical Agents**   133

Chapter Learning Objectives   133

Opening Vignette: Ebola Outbreak of 2014   134

Biohazards   135

Chemical Agents   137

Toxicology: An Overview   139

Respiration (Inhalation)   140

Skin Absorption   142

Ingestion   142

Penetration   142

Characteristics and Properties of Solvents   143

Inorganic Solvents   146

Organic Solvents 146

Control of Exposures 147

    Engineering Controls 147

    Administrative Controls 149

    Work Practices and Procedures 154

    Personal Protective Equipment (PPE) 155

    Personal Hygiene Practices 156

Summary 156

Key Terms 156

Discussion Questions 157

Using the Internet 157

Exercise 157

OH&S in Action 157

Case Study 1: Firefighters and Cancer 158

Case Study 2: Unexpected Gas 158

Notes 158

Chapter 7   **Psychosocial Hazards** 160

Chapter Learning Objectives 160

Opening Vignette: Psychological First Aid 161

Stressors 163

    Stressors in the Workplace 164

Stress 166

    Stress Moderators 167

Strain 168

    Psychological Strain 168

    Physical Strain 169

    Behavioural Strain 169

    Organizational Strain 169

Recognizing, Assessing, and Managing Psychosocial Hazards 170

Primary Interventions 171

Secondary Interventions 172

Tertiary Interventions 173

Spotlight on a Stressor: Injustice at Work 173

Creating a Fair Workplace 174

Spotlight on a Stressor: Technology 174

Spotlight on a Stressor: Work–Family Conflict 176

Causes of Work–Family Conflict 178

Outcomes of Work–Family Conflict 178

Summary 179

Key Terms 179

Discussion Questions 180

Using the Internet 180

Exercises 181

OH&S in Action 182

Case Study 1: A Stressful Job 182

Case Study 2: Technology at Work 183

Case Study 3: A Toxic Workplace 183

Notes 184

Chapter 8   Workplace Violence, Aggression, and Harassment 188

Chapter Learning Objectives 188

Opening Vignette: Workplace Harassment 189

Defining Workplace Aggression and Violence 190

The Prevalence of Workplace Aggression 190

U.S. Prevalence Data 191

Canadian Data 191

Sources of Workplace Violence 192

Prevalence by Source 194

Risk Factors for Workplace Aggression 195

SAV-T(1) and SAV-T(2): The Risk of Violence   195

Imminent Risk   196

Prevention   198

Type I Violence   198

Type II Violence   199

Type III Violence   202

Type IV Violence   202

Organizational Policies and Programs   203

Harassment and Bullying in the Workplace   204

Investigation of Specific Incidents   206

Respectful Workplaces   206

Sexual Harassment   207

Sexual Harassment as a Health and Safety Issue   208

Summary   210

Key Terms   210

Discussion Questions   210

Using the Internet   211

Exercises   211

OH&S in Action   211

Case Study 1: Aggression Policy   211

Case Study 2: Addressing Inappropriate Email   212

Case Study 3: Offsite Harassment   212

Notes   212

PART 3   INTERVENTIONS   217

Chapter 9   Training   217

Chapter Learning Objectives   217

Opening Vignette: The Need for Training   218

The Role of Occupational Health and Safety Training   219

Health and Safety Training Programs   221

Needs Analysis 222

Training Design and Delivery 226

Training Evaluation 232

Common Safety Training Initiatives 236

Safety Orientation 236

First Aid Training 236

WHMIS Training 237

Summary 237

Key Terms 238

Discussion Questions 238

Using the Internet 238

Exercises 239

OH&S in Action 240

Case Study 1: The New HR Manager at A1 Manufacturing 240

Case Study 2: A Young Worker's Quandary 240

Notes 241

Chapter 10   Motivation and Safety Management Systems 243

Chapter Learning Objectives 243

Opening Vignette: YVR: Safety Comes First 244

Safety Behaviour 245

Motivating Safety Behaviour 247

Reinforcement Theory 248

Goal Setting 251

Self-Determination Theory 252

Increasing Opportunity for Safety Behaviour 253

Management Commitment to OH&S 253

Organizational Health and Safety Management Systems 257

Summary 263

Key Terms 263

Discussion Questions 264

Using the Internet   264

Exercises   264

OH&S in Action   265

Case Study 1: Noncompliance With Safety Standards   266

Case Study 2: Safety in the Bakery   266

Case Study 3: Working to Change Safety   266

Notes   267

Chapter 11   Emergency Planning   272

Chapter Learning Objectives   272

Opening Vignette: Fort McMurray   273

Emergency Preparedness   275

Precontact   277

Contact   281

Postcontact   285

Getting Back to Normal   286

Summary   287

Key Terms   287

Discussion Questions   288

Using the Internet   288

Exercises   288

OH&S in Action   289

Case Study: Biological Terrorism   289

Notes   289

Chapter 12   Incident Investigation   291

Chapter Learning Objectives   291

Opening Vignette: Workplace Fatality Investigation   292

Rationale for Incident Investigation   292

Critical Factors in the Investigative Process   293

Timing   293

Severity   293

Legal Requirements   294

Types of Information Collected   294

Human Factors   295

Situational Factors   296

Environmental Factors   297

Who Investigates?   297

Investigative Methods   297

Observations or Walkthroughs   298

Interviews   298

Re-enactments   300

Investigative Tools   301

Incident Reports   301

Incident Analysis   302

The Swiss Cheese Model   305

The Psychology of Incidents: Cognitive Failures   306

Summary   306

Key Terms   307

Discussion Questions   307

Using the Internet   307

Exercise   307

OH&S in Action   308

Case Study 1: Incident Investigation   308

Case Study 2: Office Incident   308

Appendix: Incident Report Forms   309

Notes   318

Chapter 13   Disability Management and Return to Work   319

Chapter Learning Objectives   319

Opening Vignette: Return to Work: High-Profile Style   320

Motives for Disability Management   321

  Financial Motives   321

  Moral and Social Motives   322

  Legal Motives   322

Disability Management   324

  Assessing Disability Management Programs   325

  Best Practices in Disability Management   326

Return-to-Work Planning   329

  Work Accommodation   329

  Physical Demands Analysis   331

  Functional Ability Assessment   332

Stakeholders in Disability Management   332

Barriers to Return to Work   334

Summary   336

Key Terms   336

Discussion Questions   337

Using the Internet   337

Exercises   337

OH&S in Action   338

Case Study 1: Forgotten Orders: A Case of Memory Impairment
  in a Restaurant   338

Case Study 2: Out of Contact at Widgit   339

Notes   339

Chapter 14   Workplace Wellness: Work–Family and Health
             Promotion Programs   344

Chapter Learning Objectives   344

Opening Vignette: Snoozing on the Job: Not Such a Bad Idea
  After All?   345

Work–Family Conflict: Family-Friendly Policies in the Workplace   347

    Family-Friendly Policies   348

Family-Friendly Policies: An Evaluation   352

Health Promotion Programs   354

    Employee and Family Assistance Programs (EFAPs)   354

    Stress Management Programs   356

    Effectiveness of Stress Management Training   357

    Worksite Health Promotion: A Focus on Lifestyle Changes   358

    Developing a Successful Worksite Health Promotion Program   362

Summary   366

Key Terms   366

Discussion Questions   366

Using the Internet   367

Exercises   368

OH&S in Action   369

Case Study 1: Mandatory Aerobics   369

Case Study 2: Evaluating the Benefits of WHPS   369

Case Study 3: Job Sharing in a Telecommunications Firm   370

Notes   370

Glossary   377

Index   382

ABOUT THE SERIES

The management of human resources has become the most important source of innovation, competitive advantage, and productivity, more so than any other resource. More than ever, human resources management (HRM) professionals need the knowledge and skills to design HRM policies and practices that not only meet legal requirements but also are effective in supporting organizational strategy. Increasingly, these professionals turn to published research and books on best practices for assistance in the development of effective HR strategies. The books in the *Nelson Series in Human Resources Management* are the best source in Canada for reliable, valid, and current knowledge about practices in HRM.

The texts in this series include:

- Managing Performance through Training and Development
- Management of Occupational Health and Safety
- Recruitment and Selection in Canada
- Strategic Compensation in Canada
- Strategic Human Resources Planning
- Industrial Relations in Canada

The *Nelson Series in Human Resources Management* represents a significant development in the field of HRM for many reasons. Each book in the series is the first and now best-selling text in the functional area. Furthermore, HR professionals in Canada must work with Canadian laws, statistics, policies, and values. This series serves their needs. It is the only opportunity that students and practitioners have to access a complete set of HRM books, standardized in presentation, which enables them to access information quickly across many HRM disciplines. Students who are pursuing the Certified Human Resource Professional (CHRP) designation through their provincial HR associations will find the books in this series invaluable in preparing for the knowledge exams. This one-stop resource will prove useful to anyone looking for solutions for the effective management of people.

The publication of this series signals that the HRM field has advanced to the stage where theory and applied research guide practice. The books in the series present the best and most current research in the functional areas of HRM. Research is supplemented with examples of the best practices used by Canadian companies which are leaders in HRM. Each text begins with a general model of the discipline, and then describes the implementation of effective strategies. Thus, the books serve as an introduction to the functional area for the new student of HR and as a validation source for the more experienced HRM practitioner. Cases, exercises, and endnotes provide opportunities for further discussion and analysis.

As you read and consult the books in this series, I hope you share my excitement in being involved and knowledgeable about a profession that has such a significant impact on the achievement of organizational goals, and on employees' lives.

Monica Belcourt, Ph.D., CHRP
Series Editor
October 2016

ABOUT THE AUTHORS

E. Kevin Kelloway

Dr. Kelloway is the Canada Research Chair in Occupational Health Psychology and a Professor of Psychology at Saint Mary's University, Halifax. He was the founding director of the CN Centre for Occupational Health and Safety and a founding principal of the Centre for Leadership Excellence.

Dr. Kelloway is a prolific researcher, having published more than 150 articles, book chapters, and technical reports. He is a Fellow of the Association for Psychological Science, the Canadian Psychological Association, the International Association of Applied Psychology, and the Society for Industrial and Organizational Psychology. In 2015, he received the Canadian Society for Industrial and Organizational Psychology's "Distinguished Contribution" award and in 2016 he was named the Distinguished Psychologist in Management by the Society of Psychologists in Management. His research interests include occupational health psychology, leadership, the development and measurement of work attitudes and values, unionization, and innovation in organizations. He is co-author of *The Union and Its Members*: *A Psychological Approach* (Oxford University Press), *Using Flexible Work Arrangements to Combat Job Stress* (Wiley), *Management of Occupational Health and Safety* (Nelson), and *People and Work in Canada: Introduction to Industrial/Organizational Psychology* (Nelson), and the author of both *Using LISREL for Structural Equation Modeling*: *A Researcher's Guide* (SAGE) and *Using Mplus for Structural Equation Modeling: A Researcher's Guide* (SAGE). With Dr. Julian Barling (Queen's University), he edited the book series *Advanced Topics in Organizational Psychology* (Sage) and has co-edited *Young Workers*: *Varieties of Experience* (APA). He also co-edited *Handbook of Work Stress* and *Handbook of Workplace Violence* (both Sage), *Occupational Health and Safety for Small and Medium Sized Enterprises* (Elgar), *Workplace Well-being: How to Build a Psychologically Healthy Workplace* (Wiley), *The Psychology and Management of Project Teams* (Oxford University Press) and *Leading to Occupational Health and Safety* (Wiley).

Dr. Kelloway frequently reviews for academic journals or conferences and serves on the editorial boards of the *Journal of Leadership and Organizational Studies, Organizational Dynamics,* the *Canadian Journal of Administrative Science* and *Canadian Psychology.* He is Associate Editor of *Work & Stress,* the *Journal of Occupational Health Psychology* and the *Journal of Organizational Effectiveness: People and Performance.* Dr. Kelloway also maintains an active practice consulting with private- and public-sector organizations on issues related to leadership and occupational health psychology.

Lori Francis

Lori Francis holds a Ph.D. in industrial/organizational psychology from the University of Guelph. She is a Professor in the Department of Psychology at Saint Mary's University in Halifax. Dr. Francis has broad research interests in occupational health psychology, including work stress, workplace aggression and violence, and health-related interventions in the workplace. Her Ph.D. dissertation on organizational injustice as a workplace stressor was awarded the International Alliance of Human Resources Researchers best doctoral dissertation award. She sits on the board of directors for the CN Centre for Occupational Health and Safety. Dr. Francis also has an extensive consulting record, having worked with government, military, and private industry.

Bernadette Gatien

Bernadette Gatien holds a M.Sc. and a Ph.D. in industrial organizational psychology from Saint Mary's University. Her research interests include safety culture and climate assessment, safety culture improvement, safety training and development, and the impact of leader behaviours on employee safety behaviours. Dr. Gatien has conducted applied research with various organizations in both the public sector and private industry. In addition to teaching in Saint Mary's Department of Psychology, she continues to provide consulting services to organizations from various industries including construction, health care, hospitality, and information technology.

PREFACE

Although occupational health and safety (OH&S) has long been considered the preserve of safety engineers and technical experts, in most organizations health and safety is housed within the human resources management function. Therefore, human resources managers must have a solid understanding of health and safety issues, legislation, and programs. Like the previous six editions of this text, the seventh edition is intended to give the HR manager and the HR professional a basic understanding of the elements that combine to create an effective occupational health and safety program.

We think of the seventh edition as comprising three relatively distinct areas relevant to health and safety. In the first set of chapters, we set the stage by providing an *overview* of and *introduction* to health and safety with specific reference to historical context, stakeholders, and the human resource function (Chapter 1), the legislative context of health and safety in Canada (Chapter 2), and the workers' compensation system (Chapter 3).

The next set of chapters focuses on the types of *hazards* in the workplace, with special reference to techniques for recognizing, assessing, and controlling those hazards (Chapter 4). Chapter 5 considers physical agents such as radiation, noise, vibration, and temperature. Chapter 6 focuses on chemical and biological agents in the workplace. Chapter 7 extends the focus on hazards to include psychosocial hazards in the workplace. Chapter 8 examines workplace violence as a particular hazard in the workplace. While these are arguably the most technical chapters in the book, we have tried to maintain a nontechnical focus and to present the information in a way that is most useful to human resources managers and others who are interested in the management of occupational health and safety.

The last chapters in the book speak more directly to human resources managers and those interested in management aspects of occupational health and safety. These final chapters outline some of the major ways in which they become actively involved in health and safety *interventions and programs* in the workplace. Chapter 9 focuses on training—one of the most popular, and arguably the most effective, health and safety interventions. Chapter 10 focuses on motivating safe working behaviour and workplace safety management, along with a consideration of safety climate and safety leadership. Chapter 11 presents an overview of emergency response planning, while Chapter 12 summarizes incident investigation techniques. Chapter 13 addresses the issues of disability management and return-to-work programs. Finally, Chapter 14 summarizes attempts to promote employee health and wellness in the workplace.

Throughout the text we have attempted to provide students with current examples, clear definitions of technical terms, and links to the vast amount of information found on the Internet. The nature of OH&S legislation in Canada, and the existence of jurisdictional differences, mean that the information presented in this text will need to be supplemented with (for example) provincial or territorial standards and legislative requirements. We hope students will find this book useful in and of itself and will also use it as a guide to other resources.

In addition to the new material and updating, the seventh edition retains several of the features that accompanied the previous edition of this book, including opening vignettes, Using the Internet, and Exercises.

As a part of the process needed to earn a professional HR designation, granted by the HR provincial associations, applicants must undergo two assessments: one is a knowledge-based exam, and the second assessment is based on experience. Because the competencies required for the knowledge exams may differ by province, we have not provided lists or links in this edition. Those interested in obtaining an HR designation should consult the HR association in their province.

// NEW TO THIS EDITION

Every new edition of the book brings changes and this edition is no different. Each chapter of the book now includes an "OH&S in Action" exercise that grew out of our own experiences in teaching with the book. Essentially the goal of these exercises is to simulate the work of an occupational health and safety professional in an organization. Students are presented with a situation, current issue, or occupational health and safety problem and asked to create a response in the form of a plan or a briefing to senior management. Our experience has been that students enjoy these exercises that allow them to apply the content of the course. One practice we use to further increase realism is to impose the restriction that students must respond within two pages as a written memo; this is a realistic constraint based on organizational practice that requires responses to be both focused and concise.

The following list of specific chapter changes highlights some of the new key and updated topics and examples that have been included in the seventh edition.

CHAPTER 1: INTRODUCTION

- New opening vignette about the rail disaster at Lac-Mégantic
- Broader introduction to basic OH&S concepts such as classes of hazards, with an OH&S Today feature to illustrate with examples
- Incorporated recent happenings and directions in OH&S into the historical context component of the chapter
- Expanded coverage of the role of occupational health and safety professionals
- Expanded discussion of broad range of OH&S stakeholders
- Updated all relevant statistics, including workplace fatalities, lost-time injuries, and economic costs associated with work-related injury

CHAPTER 2: LEGISLATIVE FRAMEWORK

- New opening vignette highlights fishing safety regulations
- Updated coverage of legislation, including OH&S Notebook 2.1, Occupational Health and Safety Legislation in Canada
- Updates to introduce WHMIS 2015 with main content and related figures moved to Chapter 6, Biological and Chemical Agents
- Updated material on OH&S and the Criminal Code of Canada

- Strengthened coverage of joint health and safety committees, including new OH&S Notebook 2.3, When Do Organizations Need a Joint Health and Safety Committee?
- New coverage of corporate social responsibility in OH&S Today 2.4, Corporate Social Responsibility: The Intersection of Safety and Environmental Concerns
- Updated OH&S Notebook 2.4, Building Awareness of the Statutes Relevant to OH&S in Canada

CHAPTER 3: WORKERS' COMPENSATION

- New opening vignette discusses battles for fair compensation
- Updated coverage of legislation including new "presumptive provisions" and PTSD legislation (see OH&S Today 3.1, Legislative Updates)
- Added information on noncompliance of reporting
- Expanded discussion on occupational and workplace stress
- Updated all relevant statistics, including workers' compensation premiums and WCB industry assessment rates

CHAPTER 4: HAZARD RECOGNITION, RISK ASSESSMENT, AND CONTROL

- New opening vignette illustrating the complexity of hazard and risk assessments
- Expanded discussions to include various types of industries and jobs (e.g., customer service, retail)
- Updated hazard control information
- Expanded coverage of audits, reports, risk assessment, overexertion injuries
- New OH&S Notebook on preventive maintenance

CHAPTER 5: PHYSICAL AGENTS

- New opening vignette on the impact of blue light from cellphones and tablets on health
- Expanded description of electromagnetic radiation and placement of coverage to the beginning of the chapter
- New OH&S Today feature on diagnosing the hazardous effects of vibrations
- Updated information on categories of heat stroke, including newly released criteria for heat exposure standards according to the National Institute for Occupational Safety and Health
- New case study on radiation added

CHAPTER 6: BIOLOGICAL AND CHEMICAL AGENTS

- New opening vignette on the 2014 Ebola outbreak discusses global epidemics
- Significant reorganization and revision of biohazard coverage, including chain of infection information as well as new glossary terms: reservoir, mode of transmission, portal of entry, portal of exit, and susceptible host
- Added a new section on WHMIS 2015, including new figures illustrating WHMIS Classes and Categories, WHMIS Supplier Label, and WHMIS 2015 Pictograms
- Updated introduction to chemical agents
- New OH&S box on cancers afflicting firefighters

CHAPTER 7: PSYCHOSOCIAL HAZARDS

- New opening vignette and discussions of emerging stressors in organizations
- Expanded coverage of mental health issues at work, including the CSA standard for psychological health and safety in the workplace
- Updated work–life balance statistics

CHAPTER 8: WORKPLACE VIOLENCE, AGGRESSION, AND HARASSMENT

- Expanded discussion of aggression and harassment in organizations, including new opening vignette on workplace harassment
- New coverage of cyberaggression and cyberbullying in Harassment and Bullying in the Workplace
- Three new end-of-chapter case studies and one new Using the Internet question added

CHAPTER 9: TRAINING

- New opening vignette on the need for establishing an effective training program
- Expanded discussion of the use of technology and new OH&S Today feature covering digital safety
- Strengthened coverage of how to design and implement specific courses as part of an occupational health and safety program, and how to develop a training program to meet the training needs of the organization
- Added cross-reference to the CSA management standard for training

CHAPTER 10: MOTIVATION AND SAFETY MANAGEMENT SYSTEMS

- Updated chapter title to include safety management systems, which have been incorporated over recent editions of the book

- New opening vignette covering the framework for safety at the Vancouver Airport Authority
- New OH&S feature covering peer learning, support, and safety groups
- Updated section on OH&S management systems, including a description of the CSA-Z1000-14 model

CHAPTER 11: EMERGENCY PLANNING

- New opening vignette covering the 2016 fire in Fort McMurray, Alberta
- Updated content and references throughout the chapter and examples of CSR added
- New OH&S Notebook on toxic fumes

CHAPTER 12: INCIDENT INVESTIGATION

- New opening vignette on workplace fatality and the goal of incident investigation
- Revised discussion of the domino model to reflect original and modern terminology
- Moved incident report forms examples (short and long reports, and physician and witness reports) out of the chapter to a new end-of-chapter appendix

CHAPTER 13: DISABILITY MANAGEMENT AND RETURN TO WORK

- Updated and expanded overview of workplace injuries across Canada
- New coverage and OH&S Today discussing absence management
- New discussion on the Accessibility for Ontarians with Disabilities Act (AODA) and its implications for OH&S
- New section on return-to-work planning, including physical demands analysis and functional ability assessments

CHAPTER 14: WORKPLACE WELLNESS: WORK–FAMILY AND HEALTH PROMOTION PROGRAMS

- Opening vignette revised to include coverage of NASA studies, nap rooms, and nap pods
- Updated Canadian statistics and references throughout the chapter
- Updated information on company wellness programs and trends related to promoting employee mental health, growing employee engagement in health initiatives, and increasing health awareness among the workforce
- New OH&S Notebook on wellness programming in small businesses
- Expanded focus on Canadian companies that have implemented comprehensive workplace wellness programs and the return on investment, including new OH&S Today on best practices in workplace wellness at Rogers Communications

// INSTRUCTOR RESOURCES

The **Nelson Education Teaching Advantage (NETA)** program delivers research-based instructor resources that promote student engagement and higher-order thinking to enable the success of Canadian students and educators. Visit Nelson's **Inspired Instruction** website at http://www.nelson.com/inspired to find out more about NETA.

The following instructor resources have been created for *Management of Occupational Health and Safety*, Seventh Edition. Access these ultimate tools for customizing lectures and presentations at www.nelson.com/instructor.

NETA TEST BANK

This resource includes over 350 multiple-choice questions written according to NETA guidelines for effective construction and development of higher-order questions. Also included are true/false, short answer questions, and problems.

The NETA Test Bank is available in a new, cloud-based platform. **Nelson Testing Powered by Cognero®** is a secure online testing system that allows instructors to author, edit, and manage test bank content from anywhere Internet access is available. No special installations or downloads are needed, and the desktop-inspired interface, with its drop-down menus and familiar, intuitive tools, allows instructors to create and manage tests with ease. Multiple test versions can be created in an instant, and content can be imported or exported into other systems. Tests can be delivered from a learning management system, the classroom, or wherever an instructor chooses. Nelson Testing Powered by Cognero for *Management of Occupational Health and Safety* can be accessed through www.nelson.com/instructor.

NETA POWERPOINT

Microsoft® PowerPoint® lecture slides for every chapter have been created. There is an average of 25 slides per chapter, many featuring key figures, tables, and photographs from *Management of Occupational Health and Safety*. NETA principles of clear design and engaging content have been incorporated throughout, making it simple for instructors to customize the deck for their courses.

IMAGE LIBRARY

This resource consists of digital copies of figures, short tables, and photographs used in the book. Instructors may use these jpegs to customize the NETA PowerPoint or create their own PowerPoint presentations. An Image Library Key describes the images and lists the codes under which the jpegs are saved. Codes normally reflect the Chapter number (e.g., C01 for Chapter 1), the Figure or Photo number (e.g., F15 for Figure 15), and the page in the textbook. C01-F15-pg26 corresponds to Figure 1-15 on page 26.

NETA INSTRUCTOR GUIDE

This resource is organized according to the textbook chapters and addresses key educational concerns, such as typical stumbling blocks student face and how to address them. Other features include suggested answers to discussion questions, using the Internet questions, exercises, OH&S in Action, and cases.

MINDTAP

MindTap®

Offering personalized paths of dynamic assignments and applications, **MindTap** is a digital learning solution that turns cookie-cutter into cutting-edge, apathy into engagement, and memorizers into higher-level thinkers. MindTap enables students to analyze and apply chapter concepts within relevant assignments, and allows instructors to measure skills and promote better outcomes with ease. A fully online learning solution, MindTap combines all student learning tools—readings, multimedia, activities, and assessments—into a single Learning Path that guides the student through the curriculum. Instructors personalize the experience by customizing the presentation of these learning tools to their students, even seamlessly introducing their own content into the Learning Path.

// STUDENT ANCILLARIES

MINDTAP

MindTap®

Stay organized and efficient with **MindTap**—a single destination with all the course material and study aids you need to succeed. Built-in apps leverage social media and the latest learning technology. For example:

- ReadSpeaker will read the text to you.
- Flashcards are pre-populated to provide you with a jump start for review—or you can create your own.
- You can highlight text and make notes in your MindTap Reader. Your notes will flow into Evernote, the electronic notebook app that you can access anywhere when it's time to study for the exam.
- Self-quizzing allows you to assess your understanding.
- Videos provide additional insights to topics discussed in the textbook.

Visit http://www.nelson.com/student to start using **MindTap**. Enter the Online Access Code from the card included with your text. If a code card is *not* provided, you can purchase instant access at NELSONbrain.com.

ACKNOWLEDGMENTS

For taking the time to review, we thank the following instructors who provided us with insightful and constructive feedback over the past few editions that led to many changes and improvements:

Bob Barnetson, Athabasca University
John Barker, Lambton College
Anna Blake, York University
Michael Byerley, University of Ontario Institute of Technology
Nita N. Chhinzer, University of Guelph
Wenlu Feng, Centennial College
Cathering Fitzgerald, Okanagan College
Lisa Guglielmi, Seneca College
Karen Hamberg, Kwantlen Polytechnic University
Suzanne Kavanagh, George Brown College
Martine Legare, Saskatchewan Polytechnic
Richard McFadden, Georgian College
Jody Merritt, St. Clair College
Colleen Morrison, College of the North Atlantic
David A. Morrison, Durham College
Bill Reid, Fanshawe College
Carol Ann Samhaber, Algonquin College
Aaron Schat, McMaster University
Julie Aitken Schermer, University of Western Ontario
Kate Windsor, University of Waterloo
Deborah M. Zinni, Brock University

Your insights are reflected in the current edition of the book, and we are appreciative of your efforts.

We would especially like to thank Catherine Fitzgerald of Okanagan University College for her comments and suggestions for exercises to include in the book. We would like to thank our colleagues at the CN Centre for Occupational Health and Safety (Vic Catano, Arla Day, Danielle Durepos, Mark Fleming, Debra Gilin-Oore, Camilla Holmvall, Catherine Loughlin, Jennifer Martinell, Margaret McKee, James O'Brien and Anthony Yue) and Valerie Wadman as well as Connie Clarke at Saint Mary's for their support. We acknowledge our network of colleagues across the country who are making significant contributions to the human resources side of occupational health and safety. These include Julian Barling (Queen's University), Kate Dupré (Carleton University), Aaron Schat (McMaster University), Mike Teed (Bishop's University), Jane Mullen (Mount Allison University), Sean Tucker (University of Regina) and Nick Turner (University of Calgary). The late Rick Iverson (Simon Fraser University) was a colleague, a friend, and a scholar who made major contributions to understanding issues of worker safety. His death is a loss to the safety community and to us all.

We are also grateful for the support and guidance of Monica Belcourt (York University), Jackie Wood (Publisher), and Elke Price (Content Production Manager) at Nelson, as well as those who worked on the book manuscript with us—Jaime Smith (Production Project Manager), and Karen Rolfe (freelance copy editor), and Gaurav Prabhu (Project Manager).

We also wish to thank James Montgomery, who made important contributions as an author on previous editions.

E. Kevin Kelloway, Ph.D.
Canada Research Chair in Occupational Health Psychology
Saint Mary's University

Lori Francis, Ph.D.
Professor of Psychology
Saint Mary's University

Bernadette Gatien, Ph.D.
Saint Mary's University

INTRODUCTION

CHAPTER LEARNING OBJECTIVES

AFTER READING THIS CHAPTER, YOU SHOULD BE ABLE TO:

- explain how occupational health and safety affects us all
- define occupational health and safety, occupational injury, and occupational illness
- describe the financial and social costs associated with occupational injuries and illnesses
- trace the development of modern models of health and safety management
- list and describe the roles of the major stakeholders in occupational health and safety
- explain the connection between human resource management and occupational health and safety
- describe the links between human resource practices and health and safety

In July 2013 the Quebec town of Lac-Mégantic, located 250 kilometres west of Montreal, was brought to its knees. Sixty-three driverless railways cars filled with crude oil derailed in the town's downtown area leading to massive fires and explosions. Residents compared the explosions to an atomic bomb. The aftermath was unimaginable. In the end 47 people were dead. Much of the town was destroyed, leaving many evacuated.

How does such an event happen? Even in the immediate aftermath, people questioned railway safety. In particular, people questioned how the train's brakes had been secured in Nantes, a town 12 kilometres from Lac-Mégantic. There had been a fire on the train in Nantes that night, before it began its downhill run into Lac-Mégantic. The Transportation Safety Board of Canada (TSB) conducted an investigation.

In its report the TSB concluded that several precipitating factors contributed to the incident. Its investigation was far reaching and thorough. It considered what caused the fire on the locomotive in Nantes; the braking force on the train; the type of rail cars involved; the safety culture at the operator, Montreal, Maine & Atlantic (MMA); Transport Canada's monitoring of rail safety; and safety regulations around single-person rail crews.

The TSB concluded that in total 18 different factors contributed to the disaster at Lac-Mégantic. These 18 factors can be grouped as originating with the locomotive, the tank cars, the operating company, Transport Canada, the train securement process, the derailment, and the operating company. Specific factors highlighted in the report include a weak safety climate at MMA, ineffective handbrakes, an improper test of the brakes, limited auditing and follow-up on safety deficiencies by Transport Canada, and unremedied mechanical problems with the locomotive.

Three years later the people of Lac-Mégantic still feel the effects of this unprecedented disaster. Many have lasting psychological effects such as post-traumatic stress disorder, anxiety, and persistent fear. There are concerns about the lasting environmental effects on the soil and water. Many charges remain before the courts, with the train engineer from the night of the derailment, the operations manager for the rail company, the railway traffic controller, and the now-defunct MMA charged with 47 counts of criminal negligence causing death. Several employees of the now-bankrupt MMA also face charges for violations of the railway safety and fisheries acts.

The tragedy at Lac-Mégantic spotlights some core issues in occupational health and safety. The importance of safety systems and oversight in the workplace and the potential for horrific outcomes when there are failures in those processes become very clear in light of this disaster. We will address these realities in this book.

Sources: Transportation Safety Board of Canada, "Lac-Megantic Runaway Train and Derailment Investigation Summary." Found at: http://www.tsb .gc.ca/eng/rapports-reports/rail/2013/r13d0054/r13d0054-r-es.asp (accessed March 25, 2016); *The Globe and Mail*, "Lac-Mégantic Derailment: Anatomy of a Disaster." Found at: http://www.theglobeand mail.com/news/national/lac-megantic-derailment-anatomy-of-a-disaster/ article20129764/ (accessed March 26, 2016); *National Post*, "One Dead, Many Missing as Explosions Demolish Part of Quebec Town Following Train Derailment. Found at: http://news.nationalpost.com/news/canada/ fiery-explosions-rock-quebec-town-as-train-carrying-crude-oil-derails -hundreds-evacuated (accessed March 26, 2013); *National Post*, "Hope Fading for 40 Missing in Quebec Train Disaster, Officials Confirm Five Dead." Found at: http://news.nationalpost.com/news/canada/we-know -there-will-be-more-deaths-death-toll-climbs-to-three-in-quebec-train -explosion (accessed March 26, 2016); CBC News, "Lac-Mégantic Residents Still Suffering 2 Years After Deadly Derailment." Found at: http://www.cbc.ca/news/canada/montreal/lac-megantic-study-findings -feb4-1.3433215 (accessed March 26, 2016); *The Globe and Mail*, "Study Shows High Pollution at Lac-Mégantic: One Carcinogen 394 444 Times the Limit." Found at: http://www.theglobeandmail.com/news/national/study -shows-high-pollution-at-lac-megantic-one-carcinogen-394444-times -above-limit/article13749318 (accessed March 26, 2016); *The Globe and Mail*, "Lac-Mégantic Criminal Negligence Case Delayed Until April." Found at: http://www.theglobeandmail.com/news/national/lac-megantic-criminal -negligence-case-delayed-until-april/article27544533 (accessed March 26, 2016); *The Globe and Mail*, "Six Former Railway Employees Charged in Lac-Mégantic Disaster." Found at: http://www.theglobeandmail.com/news/ national/ottawa-says-its-laying-new-charges-in-lac-megantic-derailment/ article25055238 (accessed March 26, 2016).

Courtesy of Sûreté du Québec.

The July 2013 train derailment in Lac-Mégantic, Quebec left 47 people dead and devastated the community.

The derailment, fire, and explosions at Lac-Mégantic provide a haunting reminder how occupational health and safety affects us all. In this case, several elements of occupational health and safety–safety climate, safety management systems, regulatory oversight, and auditing–factored into an occupational health and safety incident that left 47 people dead, untold psychological strain for the living who experienced the event, and continued environmental concerns for the community. This incident is a convincing example that occupational health and safety is indeed a matter of public safety.

Most of us go to work each day expecting to return home in more or less the same condition as when we left. However, for a distressingly high number of workers, this is not the case. Workplace accidents continue to occur, with consequences ranging from minor property damage to death.

Figure 1.1 illustrates the number of workplace fatalities in Canada. The most recent published national data suggest that between 2004 and 2014, somewhere between 900 and 1100 workers in Canada each year die as a result of workplace incidents. That's about three people per day. As one might expect, workplace fatalities are concentrated by industry. In Canada, construction, manufacturing, and transportation are the most dangerous industries in terms of workplace fatalities.[1]

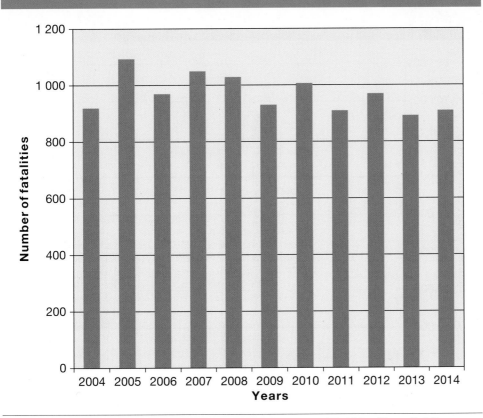

FIGURE 1.1

WORKPLACE FATALITIES IN CANADA: 2004–2014

Source: Association of Workers' Compensation Boards of Canada (AWCBC), National Work Injury/Disease Statistics Program (NWISP). Table 22: Number of Fatalities, by Jurisdiction, 1993–2014. Found at: http://awcbc.org/wp-content/uploads/2016/02/Fatalities-by-Jurisdiction-1993-2014.pdf (accessed March 22, 2016).

People also face serious injuries at work. In 2014, there were 239 643 injuries serious enough to warrant missing time from work—in occupational health and safety terms, a **lost-time injury**.[2] **Figure 1.2** illustrates the numbers of these injuries across the 12 workers' compensation jurisdictions in Canada. These raw numbers need be interpreted with the size of the total workforce of each jurisdiction in mind. Provinces like Ontario, Quebec, and British Columbia have substantially larger populations than provinces or territories such as Newfoundland and Labrador, Prince Edward Island, and Yukon. An additional consideration when interpreting the numbers of lost-time injuries across the country is that each provincial and territorial board may differ in its processes and procedures for compensating lost-time injuries. For example, the number of days an injured worker must be away work before a claim can be submitted varies across the country.

A further consideration when interpreting the noted statistics surrounding workplace fatalities and injuries is that the available numbers are generated by reports from workers' compensations boards across the country. Not all workers are covered by workers' compensation programs. For example, farm workers are currently excluded under Alberta's workers' compensation plan, but they are included in other jurisdictions.[3] Therefore, the numbers reported may in fact underestimate the incidence of death and injury in Canadian workplaces.

FIGURE 1.2

NUMBER OF LOST-TIME INJURIES BY JURISDICTION, 2014

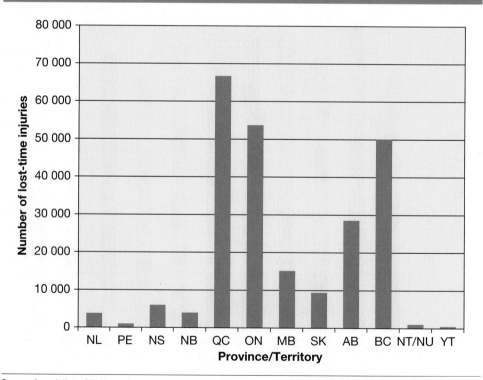

Source: Association of Workers' Compensation Boards of Canada (AWCBC), National Work Injury/Disease Statistics Program (NWISP), Table 1: Number of Accepted Time-Loss Injuries, by Jurisdiction, 1982–2014. Found at: http://awcbc .org/wp-content/uploads/2016/02/Lost-Time-Claims-by-Jurisdiction-1982-2014.pdf (accessed March 22, 2016).

This chapter is the start of your journey of learning about occupational health and safety. Let's lay the groundwork by considering some of the core terminology that you'll see used in this book and more broadly in discussions workplace safety. **Occupational health and safety (OH&S)** is the recognition, assessment, and control of hazards associated with the work environment. A hazard is any source of potential adverse health effect, damage, or harm on something or someone under certain conditions at work. In this book we will discuss chemical, biological, physical, and psychosocial workplace factors that can be hazards across a range of industries. Perhaps you have the sense that OH&S is pertinent to only high-risk industries where obvious hazards abound. After all, we can easily identify the hazards associated with jobs like fishing, logging, or radiation therapy. **OH&S Today 1.1** details the types of hazards that can be present in one such environment, a meat packing plant. However, there are hazards associated with just about every job. Part of our goal in this text is to help you think about how hazards present and can be managed across all types of jobs. Here are some examples to get you thinking. A hormone-mimicking chemical called BPA is

> **occupational health and safety (OH&S)** the identification, evaluation, and control of hazards associated with the work environment

OH&S TODAY 1.1

TAINTED MEAT IN A TAINTED WORKPLACE?

One of the largest meat recalls in Canadian history resulted from *Escherichia coli (E. Coli)*–contaminated meat that sickened numerous consumers in 2012. XL Foods in Brooks, Alberta—one of the largest beef packing plants in the country—was shut down for a month and thousands of workers were laid off as a result of the recall. A class action settlement of $4 million has been approved for victims who became ill and those who endured other costs during the recall. A government of Canada–sponsored independent report on the XL Foods beef recall describes a weak safety culture at the plant and with the Canadian Food Inspection Agency. XL Foods was taken over by JBS, which reported several changes in safety procedures upon reopening of the plant.

The focus of publicity was on the consumers of meat products, but there are also questions about the workers in the plant who are also exposed to tainted products. As an industry, meat packing can be both dirty and dangerous work. Workers in this industry deal with a variety of hazards and work in sometimes terrible conditions. They are at risk for biological exposures because the carcasses they work with may be in contact with blood, bodily fluids, and feces. There are physical hazards such as heavy lifting and sharp equipment, but the plants can be both hot and humid—making it uncomfortable to wear personal protective gear such as safety glasses or gloves.

There are chemical hazards from chemicals used in processes such as refrigeration and disinfecting. On top of these hazards, workers may also experience psychosocial hazards because of the need to kill other living things as part of their jobs, which can result in traumatic stress. Furthermore, the volume of work means that production lines have to keep moving—to the extent that workers may not follow safe work procedures in order to keep up with the line. Further increasing safety risks, employees in meat packing plants may represent vulnerable worker groups. For example, at XL Foods about one-third of the employees were temporary foreign workers. Temporary foreign workers may not receive adequate safety training or be fully versed in their occupational health and safety rights in Canada.

These issues raise numerous questions about risk, responsibility, and accountability. Some might argue that hazards are part and parcel of a slaughterhouse work environment. Such an argument might point out that sharp machinery, chemical disinfectants, biological by-products, and psychological stress are realities in such a workplace. As you move deeper into this book, you'll find discussions about this issue. For example, how are safety considerations balanced with the need for private-sector companies to produce products profitably? How much responsibility for protecting workers is borne by

(continued)

management? By the workers themselves? What is the role of government in establishing and enforcing safety standards? One major point to keep in mind when considering hazards is how workplaces can minimize exposure to unnecessary hazards and minimize the risks of negative outcomes when facing unavoidable hazards. Examples include by keeping machinery in good repair, following safety regulations, following up on inspection reports, providing appropriate personal protective equipment, and ensuring workers receive safety training.

Sources: Jean Lian, "Silence on the Floor," *Daily News* (January 10, 2013). Found at: http://www.ohscanada.com/news/silence-on-the-floor/1001981474 (accessed March 29, 2016); Ronald John Lewis, André Corriveau & W. Ronald Usborn. "Independent Review of XL Foods Inc. Beef Recall 2012" (May 2013). Found at: http://www.foodsafety.gc.ca/english/xl_reprt-rapprte.asp#b (accessed March 28, 2016); CBC News. "New Owner of Infamous XL Foods Plant Touts Changes" (July 20, 2013). Found at: http://www.cbc.ca/news/canada/calgary/new-owner-of-infamous-xl-foods-plant-touts-changes-1.1371904 (accessed March 29, 2016); OSHA, Health and Safety Topics, Meat Packing Industry. Found at: https://www.osha.gov/SLTC/meatpacking/hazards_solutions.html (accessed March 29, 2016). Food in Canada, "$4 Million Settlement in XL Foods Class Action Approved for Distribution" (February 17, 2016). Found at: http://www.foodincanada.com/food-in-canada/4-million-133286 (accessed March 29, 2016).

present in some types of cash-register receipts and may present an unexpected chemical hazard for store clerks and customers.[4] Daycare workers may be concerned about exposure to various germs as a biological hazard. Tax accountants may be exposed to very heavy work overload during tax season, which can present a psychosocial, or psychological as it's sometimes called, hazard. Office workers may be concerned about the physical hazard of unsecured shelving that houses office supplies. Hair stylists might be concerned about the physical toll of repetitive hand and arm motions and chemical exposure from hair care products.

OH&S programs incorporate efforts to identify potential workplace hazards and to control workers' exposure to them. The goal of an organization's health and safety program is to reduce occupational injuries and illnesses. An **occupational injury** is any cut, fracture, sprain, or amputation resulting from a workplace incident. So, a broken arm after falling from a ladder is one example of an occupational injury. Keep in mind that injuries can also result from repetitive motions. For example, a data entry clerk may be at risk for hand and arm injuries. An **occupational illness** is any abnormal condition or disorder caused by exposure to environmental factors associated with employment. For example, firefighter might develop cancer following exposure to chemicals in fire retardants or a solider may experience post-traumatic stress disorder, a psychological condition, following active deployment.

occupational injury any cut, fracture, sprain, or amputation resulting from a workplace accident

occupational illness any abnormal condition or disorder caused by exposure to environmental factors associated with employment

// HISTORICAL DEVELOPMENT OF MODERN OCCUPATIONAL HEALTH AND SAFETY

A LONG HISTORY

Occupational injuries and illnesses have been with us throughout history. Documented cases of work-related illnesses go back as far as ancient Egypt, when stonemasons and potters experienced respiratory problems. As societies became more technologically advanced, cases of vomiting, copper-induced dermatoses (skin diseases), and hepatic (liver) degeneration began to occur. Labourers who worked with iron and in various alloying operations risked symptoms such as high fever, coughing, and headache, as well as diseases like lung cancer.[5]

With the advent of the Industrial Revolution, machinists and others working in the new industries were exposed to oils used for lubrication during the cutting and removing of metal. These oils, in conjunction with poor personal hygiene practices, resulted in serious dermatoses, such as acne and skin melanomas. When the spinning and weaving industries were mechanized, the resultant dust from hemp and flax caused *byssinosis* (**brown lung**).

> **brown lung**
> a disease of the lungs caused by excessive inhalation of dust; the disease is in the pneumoconiosis family and often afflicts textile workers

CHANGING PERSPECTIVES ON RISK AND LIABILITY

For much of their long history, occupational illness and injury were considered to be exclusively workers' problems. Until the early 20th century, the dominant model of dealing with hazards in the workplace was the legal doctrine of **assumption of risk**. In essence, the assumption of risk stated that when a worker accepted employment, he or she also accepted all the normal risks associated with that occupation. Under this doctrine, employers bore little or no responsibility for worker health and safety. Indeed, employers were not responsible for providing compensation to injured workers unless the accident was *solely* the fault of the employer. Given that workplace incidents rarely have only one cause, it is not surprising that cases in which workers were compensated were few.

> **assumption of risk**
> the belief that a worker accepted the risks of employment when he or she accepted a job

Associated with the assumption-of-risk doctrine was the belief that occupational injuries were caused by worker carelessness. In its most extreme form, this notion was expressed as a belief in the accident-prone personality. The concept of **accident proneness** was a focus of research for most of the 20th century; it was based on the assumption that some individuals are inherently more likely to be involved in accidents than are others and that therefore most workplace accidents are caused by a small proportion of workers. Because workers in dangerous occupations or workplaces do tend to have more accidents than others, the belief in accident proneness appears to be supported. But this is like saying that Ontario drivers are the worst in Canada because of the high number of accidents on Highway 401. When we consider that the volume of traffic on the 401 exceeds that of all other highways in Canada, the higher number of accidents can be seen in perspective. It is now recognized that the concept of accident proneness has little empirical support. Modern health and safety programs have moved beyond these early beliefs, having recognized that enhancing occupational health and safety requires cooperation among multiple stakeholders, such as government, employers, and employees.

> **accident proneness**
> the notion that some individuals are inherently more likely than others to be involved in accidents, as a result of individual characteristics

Much has changed in the way of protective equipment and views on responsibility and risk at work since this historical photo captured loggers at work.

DEVELOPMENTS IN CANADIAN LEGISLATION AND OH&S PROGRAMS

In Canada, concern for occupational health and safety was first evident in the late nineteenth century, when Ontario passed legislation that established safety standards—for example, by mandating guards on machines. Quebec soon followed suit, and by the early 20th century every jurisdiction in Canada had passed factory laws to regulate heating, lighting, ventilation, hygiene, fire safety, and accident reporting. Factory inspectors were appointed in each province and territory to enforce these standards and to conduct regular inspections of workplaces.

The Royal Commission on the Relations of Capital and Labour in Canada (1889) had an important influence on the development of health and safety regulations. First, the commissioners made several recommendations for improving health and safety by establishing standards and mandating regular inspections. Second, the commissioners were the first to recommend a system for compensating victims of industrial accidents, regardless of who was at fault. Finally, the commissioners recommended that a labour bureau be created to oversee these activities.

The 1960s and 1970s were an important time for health and safety in Canada. Those decades saw the implementation of the Canada Labour (Standards) Code and the Canada Labour (Safety) Code. In 1974, the Ontario government formed the Royal Commission on the Health and Safety of Workers in Mines. Chaired by Dr. James Ham, this commission was the first to articulate the three principal rights of workers. These are:

- the right to refuse dangerous work without penalty
- the right to participate in identifying and correcting health and safety problems
- the right to know about hazards in the workplace

These three rights are still enshrined in current legislation and are the basis for many of Canada's health and safety programs. In 1988, for example, legislation was passed that established the Workplace Hazardous Materials Information System (WHMIS). Through federal and provincial cooperation, WHMIS has been established in every jurisdiction in Canada. In every jurisdiction, it is based on the fundamental right of workers to know about potential hazards in the workplace.

There continue to be developments occupational health and safety. These changes have be prompted by many different factors, including the legal, moral, and economic concerns we highlight later in this chapter. However, often change comes following serious workplace incidents involving fatalities that draw broad attention to matters of workplace safety. Sometimes, a single incident leaves such an impression that it prompts major change. One such case is the Westray mine disaster described in **OH&S Today 1.4.** The inquiry report called for more accountability for company officers and directors in occupational health and safety incidents. As we'll discuss further in Chapter 2, changes to federal criminal law resulted allowing individuals to be prosecuted criminally for OH&S violations.[6]

Other times, it is a generalized concern following a series of workplace events or suggestions that serious workplace incidents and fatalities in a particular sector or region are on the rise that bring about change. For example, in 2010 an expert advisory panel appointed by the Ontario Minister of Labour conducted a review of Ontario's occupational health and safety system. In Ontario, people were concerned about workplace fatalities, particularly regarding issues such as regulatory compliance and enforcement and how to prevent workplace incidents. The panel consulted diverse stakeholder groups across the province. The panel's final report offered numerous recommendations for the province, including creating a prevention-focused organization within the Ministry of Labour, tough enforcement after willful contravention of occupational health and safety laws, and incorporating occupational health and safety into the grade school curriculum.[7] An increasing focus on prevention efforts is one of the major trends of OH&S today.

The current scope of occupational health and safety incorporates a focus on mental as well as physical health in the workplace. Canada now has a voluntary national standard on psychological health and safety in the workplace (CSA-Z1003-13). The standard can help employers realize a workplace that promotes workers' psychological well-being.[8] There have also been ground-breaking trends in workers' compensation claims for disability resulting from psychological injury.[9] You can learn more about the integration of physical and psychological safety promotion as part of the healthy workplace movement, as shown in **OH&S Today 1.2**.

OH&S TODAY 1.2

THE HEALTHY WORKPLACE MOVEMENT

Occupational health and safety is increasingly seen in a broader context of establishing an overall healthy workplace. The World Health Organization defines a healthy workplace in terms of four elements: (a) health and safety, (b) the psychosocial environment, (c) personal health resources, and (d) enterprise community involvement.

The healthy workplace movement recognizes that workplaces have wide-reaching effects on worker health. Moreover, the healthy workplace movement is based on the belief that organizations must go beyond simply not harming individuals to the active promotion of workers' health and well-being. While this sounds like a laudable but idealistic goal, the available data increasingly suggest that there is a very real "business case" for this belief. Organizations that implement healthy workplace programs can derive substantial economic benefits from their investment. For example, one study illustrated that every dollar spent on workplace wellness programs saved organizations $2.73 in lowered absenteeism costs alone.

There are many resources available to help Canadian organizations that wish to join the healthy workplace movement. In fact, Healthy Workplace Week was launched in Canada in 2001 and has now grown into Canada's Healthy Workplace Month® (CHWM). The CHWM program is managed by Excellence Canada, an organization that helps promote and recognize excellence in Canadian organizations. Celebrated in October, Canada's Healthy Workplace Month promotes awareness of comprehensive efforts for workplace health. Its programming reflects four elements for a healthy workplace, including healthy lifestyles, workplace culture and mental health, physical environment, and corporate social responsibility. You can read about their healthy activity ideas and their showcase of successful initiatives on the website.

Sources: J. Burton, *WHO Healthy Workplace Framework and Model: Background and Supporting Literature and Practice* (Geneva: WHO, 2010). Found at: http://www.who.int/occupational_health/healthy_workplace_framework.pdf (accessed March 24, 2015); K. Baicker, D. Cutler, & Z. Song (2010) "Workplace Wellness Programs Can Generate Savings," *Health Affairs* 29, 304–311; Canada's Healthy Workplace Month. Found at: http://healthyworkplacemonth.ca/en/about/about (accessed April 6, 2016); Excellence Canada. Found at: https://www.excellence.ca/en/home (accessed April 6, 2016).

// IMPERATIVES FOR HEALTH AND SAFETY

Effective OH&S programs have important and far-reaching benefits for both employers and employees. Employers, employees, and the public should care about occupational health and safety for economic, legal, and moral reasons. The Institute for Work and Health in Ontario conducted a series of case studies looking at the major influences that prompted "breakthrough changes" in occupational health and safety improvements in four workplaces. The influences that led to these intentional and sustained safety improvement map nicely onto the economic, legal, and moral categorization of imperatives described here. One organization engaged in change when the owner became very concerned for the safety of young workers in a retail setting. A manufacturing environment engaged in OH&S improvements after it failed a safety audit. A social services organization recognized the economic costs of injuries and focused on safety improvements in pursuit of organizational excellence. Sector requirements pertaining to safety prompted changes in a manufacturing workplace that had been highly focused on productivity.[10] Let's consider each of these imperatives.

ECONOMIC CONSIDERATIONS

The economic costs associated with work-related injury are both direct and indirect. The example given in **OH&S Today 1.3** shows some of the direct and indirect costs that can result from a work-related injury. Note that the costs illustrated in this one example are repeated hourly across the country. Cost calculations for specific injuries and workplaces can be estimated using an online calculator provided by WorkSafeBC.

OH&S TODAY   1.3

DIRECT AND INDIRECT COSTS OF INJURY

A construction worker falls 3 metres off an unguarded scaffold and lands on the main floor, breaking his ankle and forearm. The direct costs of the injury include the time spent in investigating the incident, damaged equipment, and the finding/training of a replacement worker, and are estimated at $2530. This estimate does not include the indirect costs. Indirect costs includes things like a potential increase in Workers' Compensation Board assessment and the potential fines and legal costs associated with allowing an unsafe condition in the workplace. These indirect costs can be more than 10 times the direct costs of the incident. Note as well that these costs come right from the bottom line—every dollar in cost is a dollar lost in profit. The *direct* costs of this one incident will take 25 days' profit from the firm.

There are other costs to consider. A significant one is an injured worker's lost-time injury claim to the Workers' Compensation Board. Such claims are paid by all employers through their assessment rates. Of course, the injured worker experiences many costs in the form of pain and suffering and the possible long-term effects of the injury. This fictitious claim's cost was derived by inserting fictional facts and data into the WorkSafeBC Safety Calculator. That calculator can be found at http://www.worksafebcmedia.com/media/calculators_html5/WICC/index.html. The actual cost of a claim may differ owing to variables such as time involved and the hourly rates used in the calculator. You too can experiment with injury costs by looking at the other scenarios provided at the website and inserting your own details.

Source: http://www.worksafebcmedia.com/media/calculators_html5/WICC/index.html (accessed March 22, 2016).

The International Labour Organization (ILO) estimates that the global economic costs of workplace injuries and illnesses runs at 4% of the worlds' gross domestic product (GDP) (that is a dollar amount in the range of $US1.25 trillion).[11] Consider Ontario as a specific Canadian jurisdiction. The economic burden of workplace injuries reported to the province's Workers' Safety and Insurance Board was estimated at $6 billion for the year 2011.[12]

These estimates of direct and indirect estimates must be considered underestimates of the true costs of workplace illness and injury. First, there is considerable evidence that workplace injuries are not accurately reported. Indeed, studies have suggested that the number of reported injuries may represent only one-tenth of actual injuries.[13] Recall that the $6 billion estimate for Ontario was based on reported workplace injuries only and did not include those injuries that go unreported, nor workplace fatalities. Second, in Canada, workplace injury statistics are typically tracked via workers' compensation boards, and therefore do not include injuries experienced by those not covered by workers' compensation. Third, the available occupational injury statistics do not adequately capture the extent of illnesses that are caused or exacerbated by exposure to workplace conditions. Deaths that *might* be attributable to occupational illnesses are not typically accounted for in statistical analyses of occupational fatalities.

It is clear that safety problems cost every person in Canada hundreds of dollars annually based on the direct and indirect costs of occupational injuries. But these figures represent costs associated with an injury only once it has occurred. Other costs to the employer can include work stoppages and or labour strikes due to unsafe working conditions.

Another indirect cost to companies is that of negative publicity when a death, accident, or serious health problem becomes public. It is easy to generate scenarios where a highly public workplace incident could influence a company's reputation in the community. Would you choose to eat a restaurant or a shop at a store that is known for having a poor safety record or experienced a high-profile workplace incident? Would you choose to work for a construction company that is facing legal charges for safety violations? However, managers who are committed to safety can turn adverse publicity into a marketing and recruitment advantage by advertising their commitment to employee safety.

Employers who are not concerned about the health and safety of their employees affect other employers and taxpayers. Workers' compensation rates are determined by industry sector and a negligent employer can force others in the sector to pay higher rates. Unsafe working conditions cause insurance premiums to escalate and health expenditures to increase. Clearly, organizations have an economic interest in lowering the number of safety incidents and providing a safe working environment.

LEGAL CONSIDERATIONS

Legal considerations have been identified by occupational health and safety professionals as a major driver of OH&S activities in workplaces.[14] Every worker has the legal right to safe working conditions under OH&S acts. The Occupational Health and Safety Act of Ontario, section 25(2)(h), requires an employer to "take every precaution reasonable in the circumstances for the protection of a worker." The legal term for this requirement is **due diligence**.

From a legal perspective, due diligence is defined as the measure of prudence to be expected from, and ordinarily exercised by, a reasonable and prudent person under the particular circumstances depending on the relative facts of the special case. In other words, due diligence is a standard of conduct measured by what could be expected of a reasonable person in the same circumstances. Due diligence requires a business to foresee

due diligence
an expected standard of conduct that requires employers to take every reasonable precaution to ensure safety

all unsafe conditions or acts and requires it to take precautions to prevent accidents that can reasonably be anticipated.[15] Similarly, a worker is required to work in compliance with health and safety legislation. The penalties associated with safety violations and workplace incidents are increasing in Canada. For example, in 2013 Vale Canada Limited was fined a total of over $1.3 million following a double fatality at its Sudbury, Ontario mine, which was a record-setting OH&S related fine for Ontario. In Saskatchewan, the maximum corporate fine for serious safety offences has increased from $300 000 to $1.5 million.[16] Safety legislation in Canada is discussed at length in Chapter 2.

MORAL CONSIDERATIONS

Aside from legal and economic considerations, employers have a moral obligation to employees and their families to provide the safest working environment possible. Ethical arguments for safety initiatives as the right thing to do influence occupational health and safety professionals.[17] Two decades of research have provided consistent evidence that management commitment to health and safety results in higher levels of employee motivation to work safely and better organizational safety records. Similarly, workers have a moral responsibility to learn about safety and health, to follow recommended workplace practices, and to be alert and responsible. The perception that managers, supervisors, and coworkers are committed to and support health and safety predicts employees' willingness to participate in health and safety programs and speak up about safety at work.[18] Clearly, the economic, human, and social costs associated with workplace injury and illness are intolerable, and both employers and employees must work together to enhance occupational health and safety.

// THE STAKEHOLDERS

As we considered in our opening vignette, we are all stakeholders in occupational health and safety. Workplace incidents carry far-reaching effects for workers, companies, communities and so forth. At this point in our discussion it is helpful to identify a list of specific stakeholders in occupational health and safety. **Table 1.1** provides a list of stakeholders in occupational health and safety. What do you think about this list? Are there

TABLE 1.1

IDENTIFYING STAKEHOLDERS AND OCCUPATIONAL HEALTH AND SAFETY		
STAKEHOLDERS IN OCCUPATIONAL HEALTH & SAFETY		
Governments	Employers	Employees
Organized Labour/ Unions	Supervisors, managers, and senior-level executives	Occupational health and safety professionals
Contractors	Public organizations (e.g., workers' compensation boards)	Industry-specific OHS associations (e.g., farm safety organizations, construction safety groups)
Families	Communities	Health care providers

THE INTERNAL RESPONSIBILITY SYSTEM

The basis for most health and safety legislation in Canada is the internal responsibility system (IRS). Nova Scotia was the first province to define the internal responsibility system in its health and safety legislation. Under the IRS, each "actor" or stakeholder (employees, employers, supervisors, etc.) takes personal responsibility for safety. The idea is that individuals in the workplace are in the best position to ensure health and safety. Though government has a regulatory and legislative role to play, the primary responsibility for health and safety resides in the workplace.

Thinking about the meaning of each word in the term "internal responsibility system" can help you understand this approach to safety. It is "internal" in that responsibility for health and safety is internal to the workplace and not dependent on external regulation. Safety is also internal in the sense that it is the way we do our work—safety is not an add-on, it is an intrinsic feature of the way we work. As Peter Strahlendorf, an expert on the internal responsibility system notes, we do not talk about "safety" versus "production" we talk about "safe production."

Responsibility in the context of the IRS means that each person in the organization—from the CEO on down—has specific and personal responsibilities for safety that vary according to the nature of their role in the organization. Individuals can take ownership for safety in their workplaces. If a person notices a safety concern that she can fix right then

There are many groups of stakeholders in workplace safety. Here, a supervisor and group of employees discuss health and safety matters related to their upcoming tasks.

and there, she should fix it. For example, imagine a restaurant server who notices a high traffic area is slippery; she should mop the area. If it a person does not have the authority to fix the issue, she needs to report it to someone who can.

The IRS is a "system" that is both (1) based on people in the system interacting and (2) self-correcting. Self-correcting mechanisms that are frequently enshrined in legislation would include procedures for work refusals or work stoppages and the institution of joint occupational health and safety committees.

Sources: P. Strahlendorf, "Is Your Committee Effective?" *OHS Canada*, Vol. 23 (2007): 24–31; L. Johnson. "Internal Responsibility System Leads to Safer Workplace: Strahlendorf." *Canadian Occupational Safety* (December 11, 2012). Found at: http://www.cos-mag.com/safety/safety-stories/internal-responsibility-system-leads-to-safer-workplace-strahlendorf.html (accessed March 30, 2016); and Workplace Safety North, "A Theory of Incident: You Are Your Brother and Sister's Keeper." (June 3, 2013). Found at: https://www.workplacesafetynorth.ca/news/news-post/theory-incidents-you-are-your-brother-and-sister%E2%80%99s-keeper (accessed March 30, 2016).

others you would add? **OH&S Notebook 1.1** describes the internal responsibility system, which illustrates that many groups share in the health and safety of our workplace.

Let's consider the roles, responsibilities, and influence of some of these stakeholder groups as they relate to various elements of health and safety in the workplace.

> **internal responsibility system (IRS)**
> the system of shared responsibility for health and safety that is the basis for most Canadian OH&S legislation

// GOVERNMENT

In Canada, Ontario was the first province to enact compensation legislation with the passage of the Workmen's Compensation Act in 1914. This legislation provided lost-time wages to almost every injured worker, thereby removing the right of workers to sue

Hero Images/Getty Images

their employers. After the First World War, the federal and other provincial and territorial governments began to enact legislation to protect workers. The two main goals of this legislation were (1) to ensure that injured workers received compensation and that employers accepted liability, and (2) to prevent accidents and illness by establishing safe work environments.

In Canada, we have seen the number of compensated lost-time workplace injuries decline from 479 558 in 1982 to 239 643 in 2014.[19] One interesting study compared the trends in number of work versus non-work injuries reported at emergency rooms in Ontario.[20] The results showed that while there was no change in the number of non-occupational injuries each year from 2004 to 2011, the number of occupational injuries declined by more than 30% over the same time frame. The observed downward trend in work injuries, but not in other types of injuries, is attributed at least in part to the efforts of government regulatory agencies and workers' compensation boards.

Besides passing laws, governments solicit or conduct research on health and safety issues and disseminate information. Ontario, Nova Scotia, and British Columbia are world leaders in the development of chemical-exposure standards that are as strict as reasonably attainable based on hard scientific evidence. The federal government has created the Canadian Centre for Occupational Health and Safety (CCOHS) as a vital health and safety research and resource organization. CCOHS accesses a number of databases from around the world besides creating and maintaining its own comprehensive database. This organization's goal is to provide health and safety information to any worker who requests it.

CCOHS has developed an online information service called CCINFOWEB (http://ccinfoweb.ccohs.ca). This program's vast database contains information on the toxicological effects of chemicals and biological agents, as well as material safety data sheets (MSDS) and the health and safety laws for all of Canada's jurisdictions. CCOHS also produces a wide variety of safety publications.

EMPLOYERS

Though every player has a role in occupational health and safety, that of a company's management team is the most pivotal. Managers have the means and the authority to monitor the workplace and to ensure compliance with safe practices. Moreover, organizations have the resources to hire occupational health and safety professionals.

The employer is responsible for preparing a written OH&S policy and for ensuring that it is prominently displayed in the workplace. Employers are also required to

- provide and maintain equipment, materials, and protective devices;
- ensure that the manner in which the work is performed is safe and that the environment is free from hazards and serious risks;
- monitor their workplace and report minor, critical, disabling, and fatal injuries, as well as occupational illnesses and toxic substances (and to maintain the records of these occurrences for many years);
- establish health and safety committees with strong employee representation; alert employees to any known or perceived risks and hazards in the workplace; and
- provide employees with health and safety training.

Managers must be trained to recognize and control unsafe work environments; they cannot monitor and control what they do not recognize as unsafe. Supervisors who participated in a study of 70 construction sites failed to recognize 44% of the workplace hazards and felt that another 64% did not fall within their jurisdiction. Furthermore, these supervisors stated that 20% of the hazards were inevitable.[21] Clearly, in order to fulfill their responsibilities, managers must receive health and safety training.

EMPLOYEES

Employees of an organization have a role to play in occupational health and safety both as individuals and as members of organized labour groups. As individuals, employees are required to perform their duties and tasks in a safe and responsible manner and to wear protective equipment in compliance with company and legislative regulations. They are also required to report defective equipment and other workplace hazards to the occupational health and safety professional, the joint health and safety committee, or the manager. Any employees who feel that a particular activity will endanger them or others have the right to refuse to carry out the activity.

ORGANIZED LABOUR

Organized labour also has a role to play in ensuring the proper management of safety at work.[22] Researchers have examined how unionization in a workplace influences safety outcomes. One study reported in the mining sector reported that the presence of a union was associated with fewer traumatic and fatal injuries. Conversely, unionization has been associated with higher reported non-traumatic injuries; however, one explanation offered to explain these apparently contradictory patterns is that those unionized settings may be more likely to report even minor injuries when they happen.[23]

What are some of the tangible ways that a union influences safety? Certainly, the union participates in the joint occupational health and safety committee. Another role for organized labour is to bring emerging problems and issues in health and safety to the attention of government and employers and to pressure other stakeholders to take corrective action. Organized labour and professional associations have also used the collective bargaining process to incorporate health and safety provisions in many contracts. These labour contracts attempt to formalize voluntary measures and extend legislative programs. For example, some contracts state that a union must have a full-time safety representative in all plants. Others bargain for more training on safety measures or more information on exposure to known toxic chemicals.

// BARRIERS

Though all stakeholders support the concept of safe working conditions, not everyone is committed to implementing OH&S programs. There may be several reasons for stakeholders' lack of action in this area. Employers may be more concerned with production quotas than with safety records, because the costs of production are more visible. Employers may clean up their locations just before an announced safety inspection, thus ensuring a pass. Sometimes managers do not even recognize unsafe conditions, or

A PREDICTABLE PATH TO DISASTER AT WESTRAY

It is a day that shaped a community, impressed on the occupational history of a province, and prompted major changes in how occupational health and safety violations are viewed in Canadian law. On May 9, 1992, at 5:20 a.m., the Westray coal mine in Plymouth, Nova Scotia, exploded. Despite extensive rescue efforts involving more than 170 mine rescue workers, 26 miners died in the mine. Charged with investigating the cause of the disaster, Justice Peter Richard titled his final report *The Westray Story: A Predictable Path to Disaster,* emphasizing that the disaster that rocked the community had been entirely preventable.

Justice Richard documented many causes of the disaster, but he focused in particular on a management style that emphasized production over safety and that showed disdain for safety concerns: workers were not provided training in safe mining procedures; supervisors did not have the authority to correct unsafe conditions; and dangerous shortcuts were taken in the performance of mine tasks. Work procedures (e.g., the use of 12-hour shifts for miners) were also in violation of safety regulations. Despite excessive levels of gas and coal dust in the mine, unsafe procedures (e.g., the use of torches) were condoned, if not encouraged. No meaningful dialogue existed on safety matters at the Westray mine—the joint health and safety committee did not function effectively. As Justice Richard noted, the operation of the mine defied every principle of safe mining.

The explosion at Westray provides a cautionary tale for human resource managers—it illustrates what happens when management does not make safety a priority and does not promote a culture of safety. We'll consider the lasting impacts of the Westray mine disaster on Canadian OH&S laws in Chapter 2.

Source: Government of Nova Scotia, "The Westray Story: A Predictable Path to Disaster." Found at: http://www.gov.ns.ca/lwd/pubs/westray (accessed March 24, 2016).

they feel unable to do anything about those they do identify. Similarly, employers may be unaware of the methods and instruments by which rigorous monitoring of the workplace can be achieved. This situation is compounded by the fact that health and safety is rarely mentioned in management research, composing less than 1% of such research.[24] As a result, managers and prospective managers receive little or no training in health and safety issues. Also, those issues may be addressed in an industrial relations climate that emphasizes conflict between management and the union. In such an environment, health and safety issues may be seen as another bargaining chip.[25]

Another barrier to the implementation of OH&S programs is that the general medical establishment is not always well-versed or well-trained in OH&S issues and occupational medicine. For instance, the effects of some industrial diseases are not apparent for years and may be complicated by factors such as the worker's lifestyle and failure to follow safety regulations such as wearing protective equipment.

// PARTNERSHIPS

One way to overcome the barriers to the implementation of OH&S programs is to form alliances among OHS stakeholders. For example, three of the core parties in safety—employers, employees, and unions—have the same goal: the reduction of injuries and illnesses. It is a win–win situation in bargaining. The employer, by investing in health and safety programs, gains economically through a reduction in direct and indirect costs; it also gains through an improved public image that may strengthen employee loyalty and increase marketing opportunities. Employees gain through reduced risk of work-related injuries and illnesses. Unions gain through their ability to successfully champion the health and safety interests of their clients.

Other groups of stakeholders may also cooperate to promote safety. For example, workers' compensation boards may partner with industry safety associations to share data and work to reduce certain types of injuries. Community-focused safety groups may engage the public in safety campaigns to highlight workplace safety concerns. As we saw in **OH&S Today 1.5** with the case of young workers, advocacy groups that share common experiences can come together to program workplace health and safety.

Looking ahead, in Chapter 2 we will further consider how groups of stakeholders work together to meet legislative requirements. For example, the federal and most provincial and territorial governments require every organization with 20 or more employees to establish a joint health and safety committee (i.e., one that includes employers *and* workers). In some provinces, such as Ontario, there are no articulated requirements regarding the minimum number of employees if a designated substance— such as asbestos—is present. These joint committees of workers and managers respond to accidents; monitor the workplace; notify authorities about serious hazards, critical injuries, or deaths; hear complaints; and make recommendations.

OH&S TODAY 1.5

YOUNG WORKERS AT RISK

Young workers are at risk for workplace fatality and injury. The Association of Workers' Compensation Boards of Canada (AWCBC) tracks workplace fatality and injury data by age. Between 2012 and 2014, 100 young workers under the age of 25 were killed on the job in Canada. The many Canadian young people who have lost their lives to workplace incidents include Dean Smith, 23, although recognized as having a safety-first approach to life, was killed while contracting a job at an Alberta pulp mill in November 2015. Alan Fraser, 21, fell six stories to his death at a construction site in Halifax, Nova Scotia, in November 2013. Ashley Richards, 18, was working her first shift as a flag person at a Saskatchewan road construction site when she was struck and killed by a car in August 2012.

The AWCBC recorded more than 30 000 lost-time injuries among workers under age 25 in 2014 alone. A 2014 study by Canadian OH&S researchers suggests that this number may underestimate the rate at which young people are injured at work. Sean Tucker, from the University of Regina, and his colleagues found that 21% of a large sample of young Canadian workers had experienced a work injury that caused lost work time. However, only 50% of the injured workers reported that injury to the employer or to a doctor. The workers noted several reasons that they did not report their injuries, including blaming themselves for the injury, fearing the reactions of employers/coworkers, feeling that reporting was too much of a hassle, and protecting their self-identity (e.g., fearing that an injury would make them look weak or childish).

Why are young people at particular risk in the workplace? First, a lack of experience and training means they may not recognize hazards in the workplace. Second, they may not be aware of their right to a safe working environment and their right to refuse unsafe work; they may not want to "rock the boat." Finally, as part-time or short-term employees, they may not be offered the same level of safety training as full-time employees.

In recent years, Canadians have become more aware of the health and safety risks faced by young workers. There are many champions behind the campaign for increased awareness around young workers and safety.

(continued)

Young workers face risks of injury and illness at work. Here, a young worker operates a traffic signal on a road construction site.

Many of them have a tragic connection to the message they so passionately share. Rob Ellis founded "Our Youth at Work," a program that promotes safe workplaces, after his 18-year-old son, David, was killed on his second day of work at a bakery. Paul Kells began his mission as a champion for young worker safety after his son, Sean, was killed on his third day at work. The efforts of champions for young workers' safety like Rob Ellis and Paul Kells are invaluable. Increasing recognition of the hazards faced by young people in the workplace has resulted in efforts to ensure they know their rights and responsibilities. Programs such as the Young Worker Awareness Program are designed to integrate this training in high-school curricula. Workplace programs to reduce injury among young workers are gaining ground in workplaces and focus matters such as helping young workers understand their rights, targeting safety training to young workers, and mentoring in safe behaviour at work.

Sources: Association of Workers' Compensation Boards of Canada (AWCBC), National Work Injury/Disease Statistics Program (NWISP), Table 24—Number of fatalities, by Age and Jurisdiction and Table 3—Number of Accepted Lost Time Claims, by Age and Jurisdiction, 2012–2014 (accessed April 9, 2016); Ian Harvey, "Young Workers: Accident Prevention," Seton Job Safety (April 1, 2013). Found at: http://jobsafety.seton. ca/young-workers-accident-prevention (accessed April 9, 2016); S. Tucker, D. Diekrager, N. Turner, & E K. Kelloway (2014). "Work-related Injury Underreporting Among Young Workers: Prevalence, Gender Differences, and Explanations for Underreporting," *Journal of Safety Research*, 50, 67–73; Meagan Campbell, "Dean Jason Stewart Smith, 1992–2015," *Maclean's* (January 16, 2016). Found at: http://www.macleans.ca/society/dean-jason-stewart-smith-1992-2015 (accessed April 9, 2015); CBC News, "Alan Fraser's Workplace Hit with Safety Orders Before Fatality" (October 28, 2014). Found at: http://www.cbc.ca/news/canada/nova-scotia/alan-fraser-s-workplace-hit-with-safety-orders-before-fatality -1.2814745 (accessed April 9, 2015); Prince Albert Now, "SUV Passed Traffic in Orange Zone Before Killing Flag Worker" (August 14, 2014). Found at: http://panow.com/article/527814/suv-passed-traffic-orange-zone-killing-flag-worker (accessed April 9, 2016); Parachute: Preventing Injuries, Saving Lives, "Our History." Found at: http://www.parachutecanada.org/corporate/item/our-history (accessed April 9, 2016); My Safe Work, "Our Story." Found at: http://www.mysafework.com/our-story (accessed April 9, 2016).

// OCCUPATIONAL HEALTH AND SAFETY PROFESSIONALS

One way to develop an effective OH&S program is to employ health and safety professionals. Managers and human resource experts cannot be expected to develop, manage, and evaluate an OH&S program, particularly when the issues cover the spectrum from chemical hazards to workplace violence. To help managers operate an OH&S program, various types of safety and health experts may be hired or consulted. These people can be found through their associations or safety associations and provincial departments. Be advised, however, that to date there are no legal requirements regarding the training or skills necessary to practice as occupational health and safety professional in Canada. That said, there are safety designations and certifications that can help identify individuals with relevant training and skills in OH&S. One such certification is the Canadian Registered Safety Professional (CRSP®) described in **OH&S Notebook 1.2**.

Occupational health and safety professionals may differ greatly in their educational backgrounds areas of expertise. Some are chemists focused on the safe handling of chemicals for use or transport. Others may have a background in occupational nursing, medicine, or related health professions and focus on the prevention and treatment of

---

OH&S NOTEBOOK 1.2

OCCUPATIONAL HEALTH AND SAFETY PROFESSIONALS

Someone who holds the Canadian Registered Safety Professionals (CRSPs®) designation is a recognized safety expert. In fact, many Canadian organizations require that individuals hold this designation to qualify for jobs in OH&S. CRSPs are trained in a variety of health and safety areas such as identifying and appraising workplace hazards; evaluating incident severity; developing and communicating hazard control policies, methods, and programs, devising motivational programs to integrate safety procedures into operations, and evaluating the effectiveness of these programs and revising them as necessary. To achieve certification, occupational health and safety professionals must meet specified academic, experience, and examination requirements.

Among CRSP, you will find a diverse array of professions, united by their training and interest in health and safety. One example of a safety profession is registered occupational hygienist. Registered occupational hygienists are educated in a variety of fields (with degrees in chemistry, engineering, physics, biology, or medicine) and are trained to evaluate and control workplace hazards that may lead to sickness, impaired health, significant discomfort, and inefficiency. A related group of professionals are Registered Occupational Hygienist Technologists who perform similar functions as registered occupational hygienists, but typically have a college diploma rather than a university degree.

CRSPs can enjoy working in a variety of settings and in various operational functions. Every industry has health and safety needs and thus, occupational health and safety professionals work in a variety of industries including the construction, services, and manufacturing sectors. Within those sectors, you'll find occupational health and safety professionals in roles such as consultant, project manager, inspector, quality assurance, and many others. You can learn more about the CRSP designation, careers in occupational health and safety, and occupational health and safety training programs by exploring the website of the Board of Canadian Registered Safety Professionals.

Source: Board of Canadian Registered Safety Professionals, https://www.bcrsp.ca (accessed March 24, 2016).

occupational injuries. Some have backgrounds in human resources or management and focus on the coordinating occupational health and safety programs in workplaces or delivering OH&S training. Some are social scientists who focus on issues such as workplace stress and work–life balance. Still others investigate safety incidents or conduct safety inspections. These are just a few examples of the types of jobs held by occupational health and safety professionals.

As noted above, employing occupational health and safety professionals is a sound investment for companies. In many cases organizations retain OH&S experts as part of their full-time staff roster. For example, a company that deals in petrochemical manufacturing will likely have experts such as occupational hygienists on its staff. A large and diverse workplace may have an occupational health and safety specialist as part of the human resources team. That said, in smaller workplaces organizations may delegate the OH&S portfolio to a human resources generalist. In those cases, it is important that the company is able to consult with outside health and safety specialists. For instance, the company could contract with an ergonomics specialist to conduct physical assessments of office workspaces to ensure that individuals have an appropriate desk, chair, and computer arrangement. At other times, companies will interact with OH&S specialists who represent government agencies, such as a health and safety inspector. Regardless of their specific area of focus or their status as employee or consultant, well-trained and certified OH&S professionals play a vital role in the creation and maintenance of healthy and safe workplaces.

// THE ROLE OF HUMAN RESOURCES

> **the three Es**
> a traditional approach to occupational health and safety that emphasized engineering, education, and enforcement

Traditional views of safety have emphasized **the three Es**. In the past, the goal was to develop *engineering* solutions to ensure safe work environments, equipment, and personal protective devices. To that end, occupational health and safety professionals were tasked with *educating* supervisors and employers in the use of the equipment. Finally, health and safety programs focused on *enforcing* existing regulations and practices. To a great extent, these approaches have succeeded in creating safer workplaces. However, we now recognize that the three Es do not provide a total solution and that focusing on the people side of the workplace is likely to result in a safer workplace.

Not surprisingly, you will find that occupational health and safety is almost exclusively "managed" under the human resource function. This placement makes sense for several reasons.

SAFETY IS INTEGRATED IN OTHER HUMAN RESOURCE FUNCTIONS

Safety is a people issue and effective safety programs depend on building people's skills, abilities, and motivation for safety. Certainly, these are the traditional concerns of human resource departments; for instance skills and abilities can be developed through orientation and other training programs.[26] Strategies such as compensation and awareness programs can help motivate safe working. Factors such as safety leadership[27] and safety climate[28] help promote workplace safety and predict safety outcomes (e.g., incidents, injuries). Failures to promote safety carry direct implications for work outcomes such as stress and turnover,[29] traditional areas of HR concern.

Indeed, safety must be strategically considered in all areas of human resource management.[30] For instance, areas of human resource practice such as job design,[31] high-performance work systems,[32] lean manufacturing,[33] and scheduling have implications for occupational safety. Research findings suggest that human resource decisions may affect safety even if safety was not considered at the time of the decision. For example, research shows that individuals who fear job loss are more likely to "cut corners," ignore safety rules, and work unsafely. Thus, a rumour of corporate restructuring or plans for a layoff may have an impact on safety even though the two are not obviously connected. As another example, consider that performance-based pay systems have been associated with increased injury rates while the implementation of teams in organizations may be associated with reduced injuries.[34] Clearly, the way we manage human resources has direct implications for occupational health and safety.

SAFETY REQUIRES LEGISLATIVE COMPLIANCE

As we have already seen, and will discuss in detail in Chapter 2, occupational health and safety is a very well developed area of labour law. Numerous standards and requirements are imposed on employers to maintain workplace safety. Administering compliance is a natural outgrowth of the human resource function. Human resource professionals already ensure compliance with other areas of labour law (e.g., employment equity, human rights legislation) and thus are well versed in dealing with such concerns.

SAFETY DECREASES COSTS

Workers' compensation premiums, long-term disability coverage, sick-time provisions, and health plans all add to the costs of doing business. It is the responsibility of human resources to see that such costs are minimized. This duty has assumed increasing importance in an era in which double-digit increases in benefit premiums are not uncommon. Aside from minimizing costs, human resources has a role to play in ensuring that the benefits an organization pays for are used most effectively to help injured workers and ensure a prompt return to health (and to work). That said, it can sometimes be challenging to get companies to view safety efforts as a way to decrease costs. See **OH&S Notebook 1.3** for a discussion of this dilemma.

OH&S NOTEBOOK   1.3

DOES COST MOTIVATE?

When an organization increases revenue (e.g., sales) by $1.00, its actual profit may be substantially smaller (e.g., $.05 to $.20). On the other hand, every dollar in cost reduction goes straight to the bottom line—that is, every dollar saved is another dollar in profit (assuming that the cost savings do not require additional investment). Therefore, it is not surprising that reduction in cost is generally seen as a powerful motivator among organizational decision makers.

Thus, there seem to be powerful economic reasons for businesses to improve occupational health and safety—by reducing the costs associated with injuries and incidents, they increase profitability. Indeed, research illustrates that financial decision makers respect the logic of the argument that money spent on safety has the potential for significant returns.

Despite its logical value, in practice it is not always easy to convince companies of the economic benefits of

(*continued*)

decreasing costs related to workplace injury. Some organizations may see health and safety-related costs as "fixed" or uncontrollable. In this view, organizations simply accept the increased costs of injuries and incidents; they incorporate them into their price structures (e.g., they pass the costs along to consumers) and do not attempt to improve safety to reduce costs. Moreover, companies may attempt to reduce costs in other areas in order to compensate for rising costs related to health and safety.

There is no clear resolution to this issue. The way an organization responds to increased costs may depend on the particulars of its situation. The point to remember here is that the premise that all companies will automatically concern themselves about health and safety in order to reduce costs is not necessarily always accurate. Not all companies will appreciate the logic of investments in OH&S as a way to control organizational costs. Therefore, occupational health and safety professionals and human resources practitioners may encounter challenges when presenting this case to some companies. It is important that efforts be made to help occupation health and safety professionals build an empirical, rather than intuitive, case for investments safety. This may include building tools such as computer software to help generate return on investment numbers. It also helps provide empirically sound studies that illustrate the multifaceted positive effects spending on safety initiatives on factors such as workplace climate and employee commitment.

Sources: P. Miller and C. Haslam (2009). "Why Employers Spend Money on Employee Health: Interviews with Occupational Health and Safety Professionals from British Industry," *Safety Science*, 47, 163–169; Y.H. Huang, T. B. Leamon, T. K. Courtney, P. Y. Chen, and S. DeArmond (2007), "Corporate Financial Decision-Makers' Perceptions of Workplace Safety," *Accident Analysis & Prevention*, 39, 767–775; K. Mearns, L. Hope, M.T. Ford, and L.E. Tetrick (2010) "Investment in Workforce Health: Exploring the Implications for Workforce Safety Climate and Commitment," *Accident Analysis & Prevention*, 42, 1445–1454; and J.B. Linhard (2005), "Understanding the Return on Health, Safety And Environmental Investments," *Journal of Safety Research*, 36, 257–260.

// SUMMARY

This chapter has established the importance of occupational health and safety. We began by defining terms such as occupational health and safety, occupational injury, and occupational illness and by pointing out the unacceptably high rates of workplace injuries and fatalities. Second, we described the financial and social costs associated with occupational injuries and illnesses, showing that direct *and* indirect costs can be substantial. Third, we traced the development of modern models of health and safety management and described the role of the major stakeholders in modern occupational health and safety. We emphasized the role of the internal responsibility system and the notion that all parties have a stake in improving occupational health and safety. We ended the chapter by explaining the connection between human resource management and occupational health and safety and describing the links between human resource practices and health and safety. The management of occupational health and safety is a core area of practice for human resources practitioners.

KEY TERMS

accident proneness 7
assumption of risk 7
brown lung 7
due diligence 11

internal responsibility system (IRS) 13
lost-time injury 4
occupational health and safety (OH&S) 5
occupational illness 6
occupational injury 6
the three Es 20

DISCUSSION QUESTIONS

1. Discuss the following statement: Occupational health is a concern for us all.
2. Why have people historically been more concerned about work-related injuries than work-related illnesses?
3. How has our understanding of personal liability for accidents changed over the years?
4. For what reasons, beside humanitarian ones, should workplace hazards be controlled?
5. Who are the stakeholders in health and safety? What roles do they play?
6. What types of roles do occupational health and safety professionals play in workplaces? How does the organization benefit from hiring someone highly trained in OH&S?

USING THE INTERNET

1. How do organizations treat occupational health and safety? Find the websites for some major corporations in your area. Search them for information on health and safety. Who in the organization administers health and safety programs? What kinds of programs are in place?
2. What types of programs and awards are available to support organizations to work towards and achieve their health and safety goals? Search the Internet to find out.
3. Find out more about the Westray mine disaster by searching the Internet for information on its history and how it has affected the community and the industry. Do you agree with Justice Richard that it was a "predictable path to disaster"?

EXERCISES

1. For one week, read the local newspapers and listen to the news. Make a note of the main topic of every article or item relating to occupational health and safety. What roles are the media playing? What OH&S issues are most likely to gain attention? Give reasons for your answers.
2. Interview a human resources manager about occupational health and safety. What is HR's role in the effective management of health and safety at work? What HR functions are involved in meeting the health and safety requirements?
3. Do a scan of job advertisements for OH&S jobs. What types of jobs are being advertised? What industries were they in? What are the educational and background requirements?

April 28 is Canada's annual day of mourning for workers who have died or suffered injury or illness from their jobs. Imagine you are an occupational health and safety professional with a safety association for a natural resources industry (you can pick which one). Create a poster or a press release to commemorate what this day means to workers in the industry you have chosen.

CASE STUDY 1   PRODUCTION OR SAFETY?

Atlantic Radiators Inc. manufactures automotive radiators. Demand for its products has resulted in an empty warehouse, and there is an urgent need to increase production to satisfy current customers. John Roberts is an employee of Atlantic Radiators. His job is to spray each radiator core with a dilute solution of hydrochloric acid and to bake the radiators in an oven.

John's supervisor has spoken to him several times about the need to speed up and not be the bottleneck in the production process. As a result, John has been taking some shortcuts, including neglecting to wear the proper eye protection. Today, he splashed some of the acid mixture in his eye and will now be off work for several days. As plant manager, you are responsible for reviewing this incident. Who is at fault here? What can be done to ensure that similar incidents will not occur in the future?

CASE STUDY 2   DO WE NEED HEALTH AND SAFETY?

As the newly appointed manager of Global Insurance Company, Anuradha Das was trying to learn as much as possible about her new workplace. She was surprised to note the absence of the traditional health and safety bulletin board, and she asked her manager how health and safety information was being communicated to employees. "Are you kidding?" he replied. "This is an office. Our employees are mostly data-entry clerks. We don't have machines or equipment—what do we need with health and safety programs?" If you were Anuradha, how would you reply?

// NOTES

1. Association of Workers' Compensation Boards of Canada (AWCBC), National Work Injury/Disease Statistics Program (NWISP), Table 22: Number of Fatalities, by Jurisdiction, 1993–2014. Found at: http://awcbc.org/wp-content/uploads/2016/02/Fatalities-by-Jurisdiction-1993-2014.pdf (accessed March 22, 2016).

2. Association of Workers' Compensation Boards of Canada (AWCBC), National Work Injury/Disease Statistics Program (NWISP), Table 1: Number of Accepted Time-Loss Injuries, by Jurisdiction, 1982–2014. Found at: http://awcbc.org/wp-content/uploads/2016/02/Lost-Time-Claims-by-Jurisdiction-1982-2014.pdf (accessed March 22, 2016).

3. B. Barnetson, "A Dirty Business: The Exclusion of Alberta Farm Workers from Injury Compensation," Parkland Institute (January 2015). Found at: http://www.parklandinstitute.ca/a_dirty_business (accessed March 29, 2016).

4. T. Mendum, E. Stoler, H. VanBenschoten, and J.C. Warner, "Concentration of Bisphenol A in Thermal Paper," *Green Chemistry Letters and Reviews*, 4 (2011): 81–86.

5. H.W. Janson, *History of Art,* 2nd ed. (Englewood Cliffs: Prentice Hall, 1985).

6. E. Tucker, "The Road from Westray: A Predictable Path to Disaster?" *Acadiensis, 28*(1) (1998): 132. Found at: https://journals.lib.unb.ca/index.php/Acadiensis/article/view/10837/11653 (accessed March 29, 2016).

7. Expert Advisory Panel on Occupational Health and Safety, *Report and Recommendations to the Minister of Labour* (December 16, 2010). Found at: http://www.labour.gov.on.ca/english/hs/prevention/report (accessed March 28, 2016); and Ministry of Labour, *Occupational Health and Safety Panel Recommendations* (December 16, 2010). Found at: https://news.ontario.ca/mol/en/2010/12/occupational-health-and-safety-panel-recommendations.html (accessed March 28, 2016).

8. M. Shain, "Tracking the Perfect Legal Storm. Converging Systems Create Mounting Pressure to Create the Psychologically Healthy Workplace," Mental Health Commission of Canada (2010). Found at: http://www.mentalhealthcommission.ca/English/system/files/private/Workforce_Tracking_the_Perfect_Legal_Storm_ENG_0.pdf (accessed March 31, 2016); and CSA Group, "CAN/CSA-Z1003-13 Psychological Health and Safety in the Workplace—Prevention, Promotion, and Guidance to Staged Implementation" (January 2013).

9. C.A. Edwards, "Ontario WSIAT Strikes Down Mental Stress Restrictions," *Canadian Occupational Safety* (26 September 2014). Found at: http://www.cos-mag.com/legal/legal-columns/4119-ontario-wsib-strikes-down-mental-stress-restrictions.html (accessed March 31, 2016).

10. Institute for Work and Health, "Breakthrough Change Case Study Series." Found at: https://www.iwh.on.ca/btc-case-study-series (accessed March 31, 2016).

11. International Labour Organization (ILO), *Safety in Numbers—Pointers for a Global Safety Culture at Work*, Geneva (2003).

12. Workers' Health & Safety Centre, "Hazard Prevention: A Sound Investment for Business and Society" (December 2012). Found at: https://www.whsc.on.ca/Files/Resources/Training-Compliance-Audit/Economic-Cost-of-Inaction-Fact-Sheet.aspx (accessed March 29, 2016).

13. J. Barling, E.K. Kelloway, and A. Zacharatos, "Occupational Health and Safety," in P.B. Warr, ed., *Psychology and Work,* 6th ed. (London: Penguin, 2002).

14. P. Miller and C. Haslam, "Why Employers Spend Money on Employee Health: Interviews with Occupational Health and Safety Professionals from British Industry," *Safety Science,* 47 (2009): 163–69.

15. P. Strahlendorf, *Occupational Health and Safety Law Study Guide* (Toronto: Ryerson Polytechnic University Press, 2000).

16. A. Miedema, "Record $1.050 Million Fine under Ontario OHSA," Canadian Occupational Health and Safety Law (September 18, 2013). Found at: http://www.occupationalhealthandsafetylaw.com/record-1-050-million-fine-under-ontario-ohsa_(accessed March 30, 2016); Government of Saskatchewan, "Penalties and Fines." Found at: https://www.saskatchewan.ca/business/safety-in-the-workplace/complaints-enforcement-and-reporting-incidents/penalties-fines (accessed March 30, 2016); and OHS Canada, "Sask Proposes Increasing Penalty Amounts to $1.5M. Found at: http://www.ohscanada.com/compliance-enforcement/sask-proposes-increasing-penalty-amounts-to-1-5m/1000812373 (accessed March 30, 2016).

17. P. Miller and C. Haslam, "Why Employers Spend Money on Employee Health: Interviews with Occupational Health and Safety Professionals from British Industry," *Safety Science,* 47 (2009): 163–69.

18. T. Cree and E.K. Kelloway, "Responses to Occupational Hazards: Exit and Participation," *Journal of Occupational Health Psychology* 2 (1997): 304–11; S. Tucker, N. Chmiel, N. Turner, M.S. Hershcovis, and C.B. Stride, "Perceived Organizational Support for Safety and Employee Safety Voice: The Mediating Role of Coworker Support for Safety," *Journal of Occupational Health Psychology,* 13 (4) (2008): 319–30.

19. Association of Workers' Compensation Boards of Canada (AWCBC), National Work Injury/Disease Statistics Program (NWISP), Table 1: Number of Accepted Time-Loss Injuries, by Jurisdiction, 1982–2014. Found at: http://awcbc.org/wp-content/uploads/2016/02/Lost-Time-Claims-by-Jurisdiction-1982-2014.pdf (accessed March 22, 2016).

20. A. Chambers, S. Ibrahim, J. Etches, and C. Mustard, "Diverging Trends in the Incidence of Occupational and Nonoccupational Injury in Ontario," 2004–2011. *American Journal of Public Health,* Vol. 105, No. 2 (February 2015): 338–43, doi: 10.2105/AJPH.2014.302223 and C. Mustard and A. Costante (June 2015) "Divergent Trends in Work-related and Non-Work-related Injury in Ontario," IWH Issue Briefing. Found at: http://www.iwh.on.ca/briefings/divergent-trends-in-work-related-and-non-work-related-injury-in-ontario. (accessed March 29, 2016).

21. P.K. Abeytunga and H.R. Hale, "Supervisor's Perception of Hazards on Construction Sites," paper presented at the 20th Congress of the International Association of Applied Psychology, Edinburgh, July 1982.

22. E.K. Kelloway, "Labor Unions and Safety," in J. Barling and M. Frone, eds., *Psychology of Occupational Safety* (Washington: APA, 2003).

23. A.D. Morantz, "Coal Mine Safety: Do Unions Make a Difference?" *ILR Review*, 66 (2013): 88–116; A. Donado, "Why Do Unionized Workers Have More Nonfatal Occupational Injuries?" *ILR Review*, 68 (2015): 153–83.

24. Barling, Kelloway, and Zacharatos, "Occupational Health and Safety."

25. Kelloway, "Labor Unions and Safety."

26. M.J. Burke and S.A. Sarpy, "Improving Worker Safety and Health Through Interventions," in D.A. Hoffman and L.E. Tetrick, eds., *Health and Safety in Organizations: A Multilevel Perspective* (San Francisco: Jossey-Bass, 2003).

27. J. Barling, C. Loughlin, and E.K. Kelloway, "Development and Test of a Model Linking Safety-Specific Transformational Leadership and Occupational Safety," *Journal of Applied Psychology* 87 (2002): 488–96.

28. D. Zohar, "A Group-Level Model of Safety Climate: Testing the Effect of Group Climate on Microaccidents in Manufacturing Jobs," *Journal of Applied Psychology* 85 (2000): 587–596; Idem, "The Effects of Leadership Dimensions, Safety Climate, and Assigned Priorities on Minor Injuries in Work Groups," *Journal of Organizational Behavior* 23 (2002): 75–92.

29. J. Barling, E.K. Kelloway, and R. Iverson, "Accidental Outcomes: Attitudinal Consequences of Workplace Injuries," *Journal of Occupational Health Psychology* 8 (2003): 74–85.

30. J.D. Shaw and J.E. Delery, "Strategic HRM and Organizational Health Interventions," in D.A. Hoffman and L.E. Tetrick, eds., *Health and Safety in Organizations: A Multilevel Perspective* (San Francisco: Jossey-Bass, 2003).

31. J. Barling, E.K. Kelloway, and R. Iverson, "High-Quality Work, Job Satisfaction, and Occupational Injuries," *Journal of Applied Psychology* 88 (2003): 276–83.

32. A. Zacharatos, J. Barling, and R. Iverson, "High-Performance Work Systems and Occupational Safety," *Journal of Applied Psychology* 90 (2005): 77.

33. D. Mehri, "The Darker Side of Lean: An Insider's Perspective on the Realities of the Toyota Production System," *Academy of Management Perspectives* 20 (2006): 21.

34. M. Kaminksi, "Unintended Consequences: Organizational Practices and Their Impact on Workplace Safety and Productivity," *Journal of Occupational Health Psychology* 6, no. 2 (2001): 127–38.

LEGISLATIVE FRAMEWORK

CHAPTER LEARNING OBJECTIVES

AFTER READING THIS CHAPTER, YOU SHOULD BE ABLE TO:

- articulate the three health and safety rights granted to workers in Canada
- describe the regulatory framework surrounding occupational health and safety
- outline the duties of the major stakeholders under occupational health and safety legislation
- discuss the nature of and limits placed on work refusals and work stoppages
- describe the structure and role of joint health and safety committees
- discuss WHMIS 2015 as it applies to the right to know about chemical hazards in the workplace
- explain how occupational health and safety fits into the Criminal Code
- express how environmental and transportation of dangerous goods legislation interacts with occupational health and safety concerns.

There is no doubt that fishing is a dangerous industry. Stories of lives lost, vessels capsized, and near misses from extreme circumstances have shaped the industry and the communities it supports. Life as a fisher comes with risks. In Canada, there are around 13 fatalities each year in fishing vessel incidents. Looking at Nova Scotia alone, in 2013 eight people lost their lives in commercial fishing. Most fishing fatalities are drownings, and most occur within 50 kilometres of the shoreline. Stability problems, with vessels capsizing, and falls overboard are the most common reasons for fishing-related fatalities.

Safety concerns in commercial fishing have long been on the radar of the Transportation Safety Board (TSB). It has made more than 40 safety recommendations and released about 100 safety advisories since 1992 and fatalities on commercial vessels have been included on the Board's Watchlist of the biggest safety risks. Although many of the recommendations have been enacted, analyses show that little has changed over the decades in the causes of incidents at sea, and the cost in lives lost remains far too high.

The TSB launched an investigation into safety incidents on commercial fishing vessels. Its investigation included widespread consultations with fishers and other relevant stakeholders including government agencies, safety organizations, unions, and safety researchers. The investigation identified safety issues in the industry including vessel stability, reliance on regulations to manage safety, barriers to training, financial costs of safety, unsafe work practices, and fisheries resource management approaches that do not consistently incorporate safety. For each safety issue the investigation also articulated a safety goal. Also noted was the fact that attitudes toward safety vary greatly in the industry.

In February 2016, proposed regulation amendments for small fishing vessel inspections were published by the federal Department of Transport. Small vessel regulations are under the statutory authority of the Canada Shipping Act. This would be the first significant change to the regulations since the 1970s. The proposed regulations address safety requirements for vessels based on risk, including factors such as vessel stability, type of fishing operations, and type of voyages undertaken. The regulations would be phased in over time, with the first phases focusing on requirements for written safe operating procedures, safety equipment, and vessel stability. The regulations could be in effect as early as 2017. Implementation of the changes will cost the industry a projected $14.9 million over a 10-year period, mostly for safety equipment purchases and stability assessments. The projected financial benefit to the industry (i.e., the vessel owners and operators), is more than $273 over the same 10 years. However, there is a much larger, and not quantifiable benefit to society: tragedies avoided, and a projected 5.23 lives and 16.43 vessels saved per year. Safety measures at sea can save lives and bring fishers home to shore safely, like the crew of the *Poseidon Princess*, a vessel that went down southwest of Nova Scotia in January 2015. The vessel's procedures and safety equipment, along with the crew's safety training and composure during the incident, are attributed with saving all four lives on board.

Sources: A. Silliker, "Lost at Sea," *Canadian Occupational Safety* (July 15, 2015). Found at: http://www.cos-mag.com/ppe/ppe-stories -exclusive/4579-lost-at-sea.html (accessed May 5, 2016); Transportation Safety Board, "Marine Investigation Report Safety Issues Investigation into Fishing Safety in Canada" (Report Number M09Z0001). Found at: http://www.tsb.gc.ca/eng/rapports-reports/marine/etudes-studies/ m09z0001/m09z0001.asp (accessed May 5, 2016); Government of Canada, Department of Transportation, "Regulations Amending the Small Fishing Vessel Inspection Regulations Statutory Authority Canada Shipping Act, 2001," *Regulatory Impact Analysis Statement*, Vol. 150, No. 6 *Canada Gazette* Part I (February 6, 2016). Found at: http://www .gazette.gc.ca/rp-pr/p1/2016/2016-02-06/pdf/g1-15006.pdf (accessed May 5, 2016); P. Withers, "New Fishery Safety Standards to Affect About 20,000 Canadian Boats" CBC (February 18, 2016). Found at: http://www .cbc.ca/news/canada/nova-scotia/canada-fishery-safety-standards -1.3452620 (accessed May 5, 2015); Safe at Sea Alliance, "Fishing Safety Now: A Plan by and for Nova Scotia's Fishing Industry" (2015). Found at: http://www.workplacesafetystrategy.ca/Portals/workplace safetystrategy/Fishing%20Safety%20Now_FINAL.pdf (accessed May 5, 2015); Workplace Safety Committee of Inshore Fisheries Ltd. "Report by the Workplace Safety Committee of Inshore Fisheries Ltd on the Sinking of MV *Poseidon Princess*." Found at: http://s3.documentcloud.org/documents/ 2714581/Poseidon-Princess-Report.pdf (accessed May 5, 2016).

The description of risk and loss at sea in the opening vignette illustrates how legal requirements can influence health and safety at work. Occupational health and safety is regulated under a variety of mechanisms, including acts, regulations, guidelines, standards, and codes. For instance, in the opening vignette we considered proposed amendments at the federal level to the *regulations* for small fishing vessels, which is part of the

Canada Shipping Act. Moreover, each province and territory publishes its own regulations, which augment the federal ones. **OH&S Notebook 2.1** contains a list of the federal and provincial acts for occupational health and safety. There are resources that can help workers and employers identify which legislation applies to them. About 90% of

---

OH&S NOTEBOOK   2.1

OCCUPATIONAL HEALTH AND SAFETY LEGISLATION IN CANADA

Below is a listing of the Canadian jurisdictions for occupational health and safety legislation, the relevant occupational health and safety act, and the agencies across Canada that are responsible for these acts and regulations.

JURISDICTION	LEGISLATION	GOVERNMENT AGENCY RESPONSIBLE
Canada (Federal)	Canada Labour Code, Regulations under Part II	Workplace Safety, Labour Program, Employment & Social Development Canada, Government of Canada
Alberta	Occupational Health and Safety Act	Occupational Health & Safety, Alberta Labour
British Columbia	Workers' Compensation Act, Occupational Health & Safety Regulations	WorkSafeBC
Manitoba	Workplace Safety and Health Act	SAFE Manitoba
New Brunswick	Occupational Health and Safety Act	WorkSafeNB
Newfoundland and Labrador	Occupational Health and Safety Act	Occupational Health & Safety Branch, ServiceNL
Northwest Territories and Nunavut	Safety Act	Workers' Safety and Compensation Commission of the Northwest Territories and Nunavut
Nova Scotia	Occupational Health and Safety Act	Occupational Health & Safety Division, Nova Scotia Labour & Advanced Education
Ontario	Occupational Health and Safety Act	Occupational Health & Safety Branch, Ministry of Labour
Prince Edward Island	Occupational Health and Safety Act	Safe Workplaces, Workers' Compensation Board of PEI
Quebec	Act Respecting Occupational Health and Safety	Commission des normes, de l'équité, de la santé et de la sécurité du travail (CNESST)
Saskatchewan	Saskatchewan Employment Act, Occupational Health and Safety Regulations	WorkSafe Saskatchewan
Yukon	Occupational Health and Safety Act	Yukon Workers' Compensation Health and Safety Board

Source: CANOSH, Canada's national occupational health and safety website, "Legislation." Found at: http://www.canoshweb.org/Legislation/All/ (accessed June 7, 2016); CCOHS, "Canadian Government Departments Responsible for OH&S—OSH Answers Fact Sheet" (as updated December 8, 2015). Found at: https://www.ccohs.ca/oshanswers/information/govt.html (accessed May 6, 2016).

Canadian workers are regulated by OH&S legislation of the province or territory where they work. The remaining 10% are under federal jurisdiction for occupational health and safety. For example, employees of the federal government fall under the federal jurisdiction. Federal laws also govern employees in sectors that operate across borders, such as airports, rail, and highway transport.[1] Thus employers and employees who operate in one area typically must be familiar and comply with its provincial or territorial safety standards. This section provides an overview of the regulatory framework for occupational health and safety.

An **act** is a federal, provincial, or territorial law that constitutes the basic regulatory mechanism for occupational health and safety. Each jurisdiction publishes an act that sets out the basic intent and the general rights and duties of individuals affected by the law. **Regulations** explain how the general intent of the act will be applied in specific circumstances. Regulations typically have the same force of law as the act. **Guidelines and policies** are more specific rules but are not legally enforceable unless specifically referred to in a regulation or act. Finally, **standards and codes** provide practical guidance on the implementation of occupational health and safety practices. For instance, a code or standard may outline recognized best practices to manage a specific hazard, such as the maintenance and operation of a crane or another type of heavy equipment. Codes and standards are not necessarily enforceable by law, unless they are explicitly identified as required within the OH&S Act. Standards are established by agencies such as the Canadian Standards Association (CSA), the International Labour Organization (ILO), the International Organization for Standardization (ISO), the National Institute for Occupational Safety and Health (NIOSH), or the American Conference of Governmental Industrial Hygienists (ACGIH). You can read about one such standard in **OH&S Notebook 2.2**.

act
a federal, provincial, or territorial law that constitutes the basic regulatory mechanism for occupational health and safety

regulations
explain how the general intent of the act will be applied in specific circumstances

guidelines and policies
more specific rules that are not legally enforceable unless referred to in a regulation or act

standards and codes
provide practical guidance on the implementation of occupational health and safety practices; often established by agencies such as the CSA or the ILO

OH&S NOTEBOOK 2.2

CANADIAN STANDARDS FOR SAFETY

In 2006 the Canadian Standards Association published CSA Z1000-06: Occupational Health and Safety Management. This standard was based on wide consultation and has been described as "Canada's first consensus-based approach to occupational health and safety." The purpose of the standard is to provide organizations with a model for implementing a health and safety program. The standard is voluntary and, while standards do not have the force of legislation, they do provide organizations with "best practices," and may provide the basis for a due diligence defence in the case of legal action. An updated version of the standard was released in 2014. CSA Z1000-14 maintains focus on helping organizations plan, implement, review, and revise health and safety management systems. However, it also considers how to include workers in safety management programming, clearly differentiates between corrective and preventive actions, and offers additional insight on planning for continual improvement. The Canadian Standards Association issues a wide variety of such standards dealing with issues ranging from workplace electrical safety (CSA Z462) to mental health issues in the workplace (CAN/CSA Z1003-13).

Sources: CCOHS, "Canada's First Consensus-Based Occupational Health and Safety Management Standard." Found at: http://www.ccohs.ca/headlines/text190.html (accessed May 3, 2016); OHS Insider. "CSA Z1000-06" (September 8, 2009). Found at: https://ohsinsider.com/focus-on/csa-z1000-06 (accessed May 3, 2016); CSA Group, "CAN/CSA-Z1000-14. Overview." Found at: http://shop.csa.ca/en/canada/occupational-health-and-safety-management/cancsa-z1000-14/invt/27024062014 (accessed May 3, 2016).

// THE SCOPE OF OH&S LEGISLATION

The scope of the OH&S legislation differs from jurisdiction to jurisdiction, but in all cases these statutes and regulations have been enacted to protect the rights of workers. Recall from Chapter 1 that in Canada, the three principal rights of workers are the right to refuse dangerous work without penalty; the right to participate in identifying and correcting health and safety problems; and the right to know about hazards in the workplace. **OH&S Today 2.1** illustrates what can happen when an employee's right to know is not respected. Statutes and regulations also establish duties that require compliance. Statutes provide the legal foundation, while regulations enacted under the statute establish the framework within which the employer will conduct business in order to comply with the law. All Canadian OH&S legislation includes the following elements:

- an act;
- powers of enforcement;
- the right of workers to refuse to do unsafe work;
- protection of workers from reprisals; and
- duties and responsibilities assigned to employers and others.

Other elements, which vary among jurisdictions, include mandatory establishment of joint labour/management health and safety committees, health and safety policies, accident-prevention programs, and advisory councils on occupational health and safety.

OH&S TODAY   2.1

THE RIGHT TO KNOW

A workplace incident resulted in the imposition of 18 work orders for a blueberry farm in British Columbia. In April 2012, 10 workers were spraying the blueberry fields with herbicide when the spray applicator tipped over and severely injured a worker. The injured worker was transported to the processing plant to receive first aid and eventually an ambulance was called. The injured man required knee surgery and spent a month in hospital.

However, it wasn't until the injured man went public with his story in August that the authorities became involved. The injured man did not know about his OH&S rights. In a chance encounter, a taxi driver told him about workers' compensation and his right to a file a claim.

The blueberry farm's owners had not notified the appropriate health and safety authorities, which is in contravention of BC's Workers' Compensation Act. Under the act, employers must report serious incidents. Work orders were issued for a variety of other problems including the inability of the employer to show that workers had been trained, the employer's failure to conduct an immediate investigation into the incident, the failure to have up-to-date first aid procedures, and the failure to issue and train workers in the use of proper respiratory protection. Consideration of these issues shows the wide range of duties imposed by OH&S legislation and the importance of compliance with that legislation.

Sources: Jean Lian, "Blueberry Farm Neglected to Report Worker Injury," OHS Canada (September 4, 2012). Found at: http://www.ohscanada.com/news/blueberry-farm-neglected-to-report-worker-injury/1001 666221 (accessed June 7, 2016); M. Martins. "Farm Worker Says Accident Has 'Broke Him Forever,'" *Maple Ridge News* (August 10/12, 2012). Found at: (accessed June 7, 2016); CBC. "Blueberry Farm Didn't Report Injured Worker's Accident" (August 2, 2012). Found at: http://www.cbc.ca/news/canada/british-columbia/blueberry-farm-didn-t-report-injured-worker-s-accident-1.1297559 (accessed June 7, 2016).

Human resources, occupational health and safety professionals, and others responsible for managing health and safety and workers' compensation should be familiar with the administrative structure as it relates to enforcement, education, and compensation in their particular jurisdiction. Multinational and transportation companies may fall under two or more jurisdictions, which increases the administrative complexities.

It is important to emphasize the general duty provision requiring employers to take *every reasonable precaution to ensure* employee safety is Canada-wide. In the federal jurisdiction, the duty is sufficiently broad in scope that an employer could be held liable for failing to ensure the health and safety of an employee even if there was an absence of a specific violation to a regulatory provision. The term "ensure" is applied in legislation across Canada and is accepted to mean the strongest responsibility possible short of a guarantee.

Labour legislation and standards relating to occupational health and safety are not static. Rather, they are continually being updated. As we saw in the opening vignette, regulation changes are proposed for fishing vessel safety. Changes may be limited and specific; for instance, changes to Ontario's noise protection requirements take effect in 2016. Or the changes can be more general; for example, Manitoba published new and substantially updated OH&S legislation in 2014. Based on an extensive review, Ontario enacted new Occupational Health and Safety Standards in 2012 that contain substantially enhanced duties of employees and employers around issues of health and safety. Thus, human resource practitioners, safety professionals, and employers need to maintain current awareness of standards, regulations, and legislation.

// OCCUPATIONAL HEALTH & SAFETY ACTS

Occupational health and safety acts across the county set the minimum requirements for occupational health and safety within each jurisdiction. For example, the PEI act notes that its purpose is to "secure workers and self-employed persons from risks to their safety, health and physical well-being arising out of, or in connection with, activities in their workplaces."[2]

Each act also state the boundaries of its application. For instance, the PEI act notes that it applies to "all workplaces within the legislative jurisdiction of the province." Exclusions to the act will also be noted. For example, there was a longstanding farming and ranching exemption in the Alberta Occupational Health and Safety Act, but these workers are now included under new legislation that went into effect in January 2016.[3]

The acts also outline mandatory components for OH&S within their jurisdictions. These will include activities and policies such as requirements for health and safety activities, occupational health and safety policies, and prevention programs. While components of the acts vary, some are quite consistent. For example, most acts articulate duties for the major stakeholders; most mandate joint health and safety committees, and those that do not have provisions for enacting them when needed; and most include workplace safety policies. Other components are more variable across jurisdictions; for instance, some involve input from advisory councils, some do not. Likewise, some jurisdictions mandate incident or hazard protection programs; others do note.

As introduced in Chapter 1, occupational health and safety legislation in Canada is largely based on the notion of an internal responsibility system. Within the internal responsibility system all major stakeholders in health and safety are assigned specific responsibilities. Thus, health and safety acts include statements of mandated duties for particular groups. In Chapter 1, we introduced a list of individuals who are stakeholders in OH&S. Recall that these include employers, contractors, supervisors, and workers. In this section we examine some of the major duties mandated in occupational health and safety acts.

STAKEHOLDER DUTIES AND RESPONSIBILITIES

DUTIES OF EMPLOYERS

Employers have a primary duty to provide a safe work environment. As stated earlier, the general duty provision requiring employers to take *every reasonable precaution to ensure* employee safety is represented in health and safety acts across Canada.

Other duties include providing supervision, education, training, and written instructions where applicable, as well as assisting the joint health and safety committee or representative and complying with statutes and regulations. These broad-based duties are called **general duties**, and are directly articulated in the occupational health and safety act.

In Ontario the employer's responsibilities are extensive. The general employer general duties, can be described as including the following:[4]

- Take every reasonable precaution to ensure employee safety.
- Appoint a competent supervisor.
- Provide information (including confidential information) in a medical emergency.
- Inform supervisors and workers of possible hazards.
- Post the OH&S act in the workplace.
- Prepare and maintain a health and safety policy and to be reviewed annually (you can see an example in **OH&S Today 2.2**).
- Prepare policies regarding workplace violence and workplace harassment.

All federal and provincial or territorial OH&S acts include **prescribed duties** that may come into effect by regulation at some time. These prescribed duties may include an employer's responsibility to establish occupational health services, or a description of the written procedures that may be required. To continue the example from above, in Ontario, prescribed duties for employers include assessing risk for workplace violence given the nature of their workplaces.

> **general duty**
> a primary duty directly articulated in the occupational health and safety act. The general duty provision requiring employers to take every reasonable precaution to ensure employee safety is represented in health and safety acts across Canada

> **prescribed duty**
> under OH&S legislation, a duty to be undertaken because of health and safety regulation

---

OH&S TODAY 2.2

NELSON EDUCATION LTD.'S SAFETY PHILOSOPHY

Nelson Education Ltd. regards our employees as the most valuable asset in our organization. We are committed to providing a safe and healthy work environment through a proactive occupational health and safety improvement process.

To fulfill this commitment, everyone must work together to provide and maintain a safe and healthy work environment that meets or exceeds all legislated and industry standards. We will apply the continuous improvement process to health and safety, and will strive to control or eliminate all reasonable foreseeable hazards that may result in accidents, personal injury/illnesses, fires, security losses or other property damage.

The corporation shares responsibility with managers, supervisors, employees, customers, guests, contractors, and subcontractors. We are all responsible for accident prevention. Supervisors are expected to ensure that safe and healthy work conditions are maintained within their assigned areas. Employees are expected to follow all safe work practices and procedures.

All members of management, the Joint Health & Safety Committee, and all workers must join together in making the health and safety an integral component of our activity here at Nelson. Health and Safety is a key requirement for our success and viability.

DUTIES OF CONTRACTORS

In health and safety legislation, a **constructor** or a primary contractor is a person or company that oversees the construction of a project and that is ultimately responsible for the health and safety of all involved workers. Constructors/primary contractors have responsibilities similar to those outlined for employers. For instance Yukon's Occupational Health and Safety Act specifies that "Every constructor shall ensure, so far as is reasonably practicable, that during the course of each project the constructor undertakes (a) the measures and procedures prescribed by this Act and the regulations are carried out on the project; (b) every employer and every person working on the project complies with this Act and the regulations; and (c) the health and safety of workers on the project is protected."[5] In some jurisdictions, when a construction project is scheduled to commence, a constructor/primary contractor has a duty to notify the authority within a specified time. Some jurisdictions require a written "Notice of Project" to be filed outlining the approximate cost, scope, commencement date, and duration of the project.

constructor
in health and safety legislation, a person or company that oversees the construction of a project and that is ultimately responsible for the health and safety of all workers

DUTIES OF SUPERVISORS

The OH&S duties assigned to supervisors are similar across Canada. "Supervisor" is broadly interpreted to refer to a person (with or without a title) who has charge of a workplace and authority over a worker. Supervisors can be union members, association members covered under a collective agreement, plant managers, general managers, lead hands, forepersons, school principals, or self-employed individuals. For instance, in Newfoundland and Labrador's occupational health and safety act, a supervisor is "a person authorized or designated by an employer to exercise direction and control over workers of the employer." Under this provincial legislation supervisors have a general duty to "ensure, where it is reasonably practicable, the health, safety and welfare of all workers under his or her supervision." Specific duties include advising workers of safety hazards, providing instructions about safety precautions, and ensuring that workers use protective equipment.[6]

DUTIES OF WORKERS

Duties of workers are included in the majority of statutes. In some jurisdictions the responsibilities are laid out by regulation. The inclusion of workers' responsibilities and duties is relatively new in health and safety legislation. Before the late 1970s, all responsibility for workplace health and safety rested with the employer. Now, though the employer is solely responsible for paying for health and safety activities, everyone is responsible for making them work. For example, worker duties under the Canada Labour Code, can be paraphrased to include:

- properly using the safety equipment and clothes provided;
- taking all reasonable precaution to ensure their own health and safety and that of those who may be affected by their work activities;
- reporting hazards, such as defective equipment, to the employer;

Talking about safety. Supervisors' duties include advising workers of safety hazards and instructing about safety precautions.

moodboard/Thinkstock

- reporting any contraventions of the act or regulations;
- reporting to the employer work-related incidents and occupational diseases; and
- cooperating with health and safety policy, committees, and persons carrying out duties required by the code.

STAKEHOLDER SUMMARY

As we can see from the above consideration of duties, the occupational health and safety acts across Canadian jurisdictions reflect the philosophy of the internal responsibility system. All individuals share responsibility for health and safety in the workplace. Together, the shared and specific duties for various stakeholder groups help enact the regulations designed to keep our workplaces safe.

JOINT HEALTH AND SAFETY COMMITTEES

Joint health and safety committees in the workplace are required by law in most jurisdictions in Canada. However, there are two exceptions where committees are mandated at the discretion of the agency, minister, or safety officer responsible for the health and safety act or by written expression of the workforce. **OH&S Notebook 2.3** details the requirements for when a joint health and safety committee is necessary in workplaces across Canada. Note that although in this text we use the label "joint health

---

OH&S NOTEBOOK   2.3

WHEN DO ORGANIZATIONS NEED JOINT HEALTH AND SAFETY COMMITTEES?

Whether a workplace must have a joint health and safety committee largely depends on its size and the occupational health and safety jurisdiction it falls under. Most health and safety acts require a joint occupational and safety committee in workplaces with 20 or more employees. These include the federal jurisdiction, British Columbia*, Manitoba, Ontario*, New Brunswick, Nova Scotia, Prince Edward Island, Yukon, and Northwest Territories/Nunavut*. That said, some of these jurisdictions, as indicated by an asterisk, have special provisions that can require a smaller organization to have a committee in place as a result of an order and/or when requested by the governing body. Ontario has additional provision for committees when designated substances are in use. Two jurisdictions, Newfoundland and Labrador and Saskatchewan, require a committee when there are 10 or more employees. Quebec's act permits the formation of health and safety committees when there are more than 20 employees. The committee is established by written notice by the certified association or 10% of the workers in the case of workplaces without certified associations. The CNESST also has the ability to require a committee in a Quebec workplace regardless of the number of workers. Alberta requires committees at the direction of the minister responsible for the Occupational Health and Safety Act.

Source: CCOHS, (February 2, 2016) "Joint Health and Safety Committee—What Is a Joint Health and Safety Committee?" Fact Sheet. Found at: https://www.ccohs.ca/oshanswers/hsprograms/hscommittees/whatisa.html (accessed June 7, 2016); Quebec. *An Act Respecting Occupational Health and Safety*, Chapter 4. Found at: http://www2.publicationsduquebec.gouv.qc.ca/dynamicSearch/telecharge.php?type=2&file=/S_2_1/S2_1 _A.html (accessed June 7, 2016); Nunavut Safety Act. Found at: http://www.wscc.nt.ca/occupational-health-safety/ohs-information/safety-legislation (accessed June 7, 2016).

and safety committee," these committee may be called by other names; for example, "joint occupational health and safety committee," "worksite safety committee," and others.

The joint health and safety committee helps enact the internal responsibility system. The inclusion of "joint" in the title reflects that both labour and management participate in the work of the committee. The primary function of the joint health and safety committee is to provide a nonadversarial atmosphere in which labour and management can work together to create a safer and healthier workplace. The committee can bring together knowledge of work tasks and company policies and procedures to improve health and safety.[7]

Occupational health and safety legislation regulates the formation and composition of the joint committee. Legislation typically mandates that joint committees are structured in such a way that equal or better representation is required from workers who do not exercise managerial responsibilities. For example, in New Brunswick, the committee size is to be agreed upon by the employer and employees. The committee must have equal representation from the employer and its employees and is co-chaired by an employer representative and an employee representative. The committee must meet once a month.[8] Additionally, most acts outline training requirements for committee members. For example, in British Columbia and Manitoba, committee members are entitled to an annual educational leave to attend training. In Saskatchewan employers are responsible to ensure that representatives receive training.[9] Training for committee members might include law, general safety, hygiene, inspections, job safety analysis, indoor air quality, chemical safety, certified workers' rights and duties, and joint committees' responsibilities.

What are the duties of a joint health and safety committee? These differ somewhat across the country, but duties can include things such as hazard recognition, risk assessment, responding to employee concerns, and ensuring that records are maintained and monitored.[10] Certified members may be involved in inspections, work refusals, and bilateral work stoppages when there is an imminent hazard to a worker. They may also investigate critical accidents, attend at the beginning of hygiene testing, and respond to worker concerns.

The existence of joint health and safety committees grows out of the idea of an internal responsibility system (IRS)—the suggestion that work and safety are inexorably linked and that all parties in the workplace have a responsibility to improve health and safety.[11] A review of the literature generally supports the effectiveness of joint committees in managing health and safety.[12] In particular, the existence of joint health and safety committees leads to a reduction in the number of workplace injuries.[13] However, the existence of a joint health and safety committee does not necessarily mean that the committee is effective.[14] Indeed, like any other workplace group, committees may take some time before they become effective. Joint committees can improve health and safety through prevention, education, and training, and by providing an ongoing forum for problem resolution.[15]

WORK REFUSALS

The right to refuse dangerous work without fear of reprisal is available to workers in every jurisdiction in Canada. Within that right, workers can refuse to operate equipment, work in a place, or engage in an activity if they have *reasonable* cause to believe that doing so would cause danger to themselves or others. Some hypothetical situations where

With permission from Canadian Union of Public Employees.

The right to refuse dangerous work without fear of reprisal is available to workers in every jurisdiction in Canada.

a worker might feel at risk for illness or injury and launch a work refusal include the following: A machinist refuses to operate a particular press at work owing to a missing safety guard. A crew of outdoor workers refuse to work outside under very cold conditions because they feel their required uniform does not provide adequate personal protection. A construction worker refuses work because there has been a safety recall on the company-provided hard hats.

There are established procedures for engaging in and investigating a work refusal. Here is a sketch of the general process of reporting and investigating a work refusal, although various jurisdictions may differ somewhat in the exact process. The employee should alert the employer to the danger and indicate the intention to refuse due to a reasonable assumption that the work is unsafe. The employer then investigates. Note that another employee cannot be asked to perform the work in the interim. Following the investigation, the employer writes a report. If the conclusion is that danger is present, corrective actions are to be taken. If the employer concludes there is no danger, the worker may opt to return to the task. However, if the worker disagrees and still refuses, the refusal is taken to a committee that conducts additional investigations and reporting. If the conclusion is the same, the refusal can be taken to the relevant government ministry. At this point, the employee may be assigned to other work while the investigation continues.[16]

Following appropriate procedures in work refusal situations is important. Case law shows when work refusals go through the appeals process, the courts will consider whether appropriate reporting and investigations took place. They will also examine whether the motivation for the refusal was in bad faith; for instance, avoiding discomfort or reflecting other labour concerns as opposed to true safety concern.[17] Some of the complexities in work refusals are explored in **OH&S Today 2.3**.

That said, there are exceptions or limitations to the right to refuse unsafe work. The specifics of these situation vary from jurisdiction to jurisdiction across the country. However, the essential theme is that a worker does not have the right to refuse unsafe work if such work is a normal condition of employment, or if the worker, by his or her refusal, places another person's safety in jeopardy. These conditions are noted in in the Canada Labour Code. Provincial jurisdictions may expand or specify these exceptions. For instance, Ontario specifically notes, in addition to the situations noted above, certain professions have a limited right of refusal. These groups include police officers, correctional workers, firefighters, and health care workers. This does not mean that workers in these groups never have a right to

THE RIGHT TO REFUSE UNSAFE WORK

Although the right to refuse unsafe work is well enshrined in occupational health and safety legislation, enactment of that right can be confusing for employees and employers alike. In fact, in 2014 changes to the Canada Labour Code took effect. These changes were in part to clarify confusion around work refusals. One change was to provide a more specific definition of danger so that work refusals are enacted only in light of a serious and imminent safety threat.

One area of complexity is differentiating work refusals based on safety concerns versus those based on a worker's level of comfort. For instance, in one case a technician refused to work alone in remote sites in rural Newfoundland and Labrador, citing that typically this job would involve a team of two workers for safety reasons. The refusal was denied and the worker suspended. Was this refusal for safety reasons or was it because the work was outside the worker's comfort zone? The court later overturned the suspension, saying that the worker had reason to believe the job in question was unsafe. However, in that same case the court specified that when workers refuse unsafe work they must be careful to distinguish between safety concerns as opposed to questions of comfort.

In another case, correctional workers at a jail in Hamilton, Ontario, were tasked with conducting a search of the cells for a missing piece of metal. Fearing that inmates could have made a knife out of the metal, workers refused to conduct the search unless they were allowed to wear protective vests while searching. The employer initially refused—arguing that wearing the vests would likely intimidate inmates. In this case, a Ministry of Labour investigation also concluded that there was no enhanced risk and vests were not needed. However, management eventually allowed the guards to don vests to conduct the search. Although the initial issue was resolved, the guards ended up locked out of the job when the union and ministry continued to debate the legitimacy of the safety complaint.

Sources: Government of Canada, "Changes to the Canada Labour Code, Part II Effective October 31, 2014." Found at: http://www.labour.gc.ca/eng/health_safety/PartIIchanges.shtml (accessed June 7, 2016); OHS Insider "When Is a Worker's Refusal Based on Comfort Rather Than Safety?" (September 8, 2009). Found at: https://ohsinsider.com/search-by-index/work-refusals/when-is-a-workers-refusal-based-on-comfort-rather-than-safety-2 (accessed June 7, 2016); and Sabrina Nanji (September 10, 2012), "Jail Guards Locked Out After Bulletproof Vest Brouhaha," OHS Canada. Found at: http://www.ohscanada.com/news/jail-guards-locked-out-after-bulletproof-vest-brouhaha/1001682264 (accessed June 7, 2016).

refuse dangerous work. For example, a firefighter has the right to refuse to use unsafe equipment during an exercise. However, a firefighter cannot refuse work on the basis of being exposed to the dangers of fires, which are an inherent aspect of the job. A nurse has the right to refuse to use equipment suspected to be defective until his or her concern has been investigated and resolved. However, a nurse does not have the right to refuse unsafe work if the lives of patients are placed in jeopardy as a result of the refusal.[18]

STOP-WORK PROVISIONS

Some Canadian occupational health and safety acts incorporate stop-work provisions. For example, in Ontario certain persons have authority to stop work under the health and safety act. Bilateral work stoppages allow certified members of the joint health and safety committee, representing both the employer and employee members of the joint health and safety committee, to agree to stop work in dangerous

circumstances that become apparent in the course of an inspection or investigation. If both sides do not agree that there are dangerous circumstances, the legislation permits unilateral work stoppages with the notification and involvement of the Ontario Labour Relations Board. The legislation defines "dangerous circumstance" as follows:[19]

- a provision of the act or the regulation is being contravened;
- the contravention presents a danger or a hazard to a worker; and
- the danger or hazard is such that any delay in controlling it may seriously endanger a worker.

// WORKPLACE HAZARDOUS MATERIALS INFORMATION SYSTEM

GHS
an international standard for the classification and labelling of chemicals being adopted by countries around the world

The Workplace Hazardous Materials Information System (WHMIS) is an important aspect of workers' right to know about hazards in their workplaces, particularly about hazards that may be associated with handling, storage, use, and emergency measures for chemicals used in the workplace, and, by extension, the community. WHMIS was legislated in Canada in 1988, and phased into force across the country between 1988 and 1990.[20]

The original 1988 WHMIS legislation was based on three elements: labels designed to alert the worker that the container contains a potentially hazardous product, material safety data sheets (MSDSs) outlining a product's potentially hazardous ingredient(s) and procedures for safe handling of the product; and employee training. Note that Ontario added three further elements to its legislation including hazardous materials inventory requirement, physical agents (such as noise), and the public's right to know.

More recently WHMIS has undergone substantial changes in structure to align with the Globally Harmonized System of Classification and Labelling of Chemicals (GHS). The **GHS** is an international standard being adopted by countries around the world, which eases global trade and business interaction. WHMIS 2015 incorporates elements of the GHS. There are changes in the classification criteria with some new classes added, new requirements for supplier labels, and new formatting and information requirements for Safety Data Sheets (which are no longer called Material Safety Data Sheets).[21] There will be a time of transition, projected to last until 2018, during which government jurisdictions will update regulations and acts to comply with WHMIS 2015 and businesses will transition to the new system. Substantial changes have already taken place at the federal level, with amendments to the Hazardous Product Act.[22] WHMIS 2015 is considered in more detail in Chapter 6.

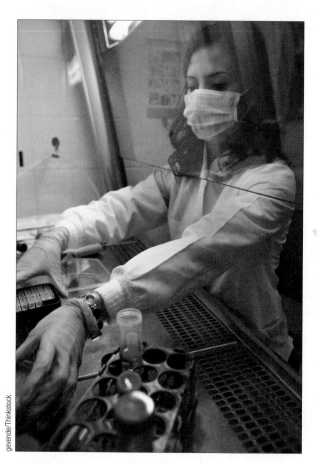

gevende/Thinkstock

WHMIS legislation, which focuses on chemicals in the workplace, enacts workers' right to know about the hazards in their workplace.

// CORPORATE LIABILITY FOR OH&S UNDER THE CRIMINAL CODE

In the past, directors and officers of incorporated entities were responsible solely to the corporation and shareholders; however, their zone of accountability now extends to the public at large. Environmental and OH&S statutes have been amended to include broad responsibilities for directors and officers of corporations. For example, directors and officers of corporations can be fined or imprisoned for environmental pollution and fined for failing to comply with regulatory legislation.

Although executives of a company could once hide behind the laws of incorporation when it came to occupational health and safety incidents, this is no longer the case. Changes to the Criminal Code of Canada mean that company executives can be found criminally negligent for serious occupational health and safety violations and face fines and prison time accordingly.

As mentioned in Chapter 1, these changes to the Criminal Code followed the 1992 Westray tragedy. This Nova Scotia mine explosion, which killed 26 miners, was determined to be attributable to corporate negligence. However, Canadian laws at the time did not permit criminal charges. Following Westray, a federal bill (Bill C-45) was proposed to address issue of corporate liability with respect to both fraud and occupational health and safety. The bill was passed by Parliament in 2003 and became law in March 2004. The passing of the bill into law meant the addition of sections to the Criminal

THE CANADIAN PRESS/Andrew Vaughan

Outrage following the mining tragedy at Westray helped prompt changes recognizing corporate criminal liability in the Criminal Code of Canada.

CHAPTER 2 Legislative Framework

Code of Canada. Specifically, it resulted in the addition of Section 217.1, which states that those in authority for workers have a responsibility to take reasonable steps to protect those workers from harm. Furthermore, Sections 22.1 and 22.2 specify that corporations can be criminally liable for negligence and other offences.[23] The act makes a company responsible for

- the actions of those who oversee day-to-day operations (e.g., supervisors and mid-level managers);
- managers (executive *or* operational) who intentionally commit, or have employees commit, crimes to benefit the organization;
- managers who do not take action when they become aware of offences being committed; and
- the actions of managers who demonstrate a criminal lack of care (i.e., criminal negligence).

These changes to the Criminal Code could lead to a corporation and its managers being criminally prosecuted for failing to provide an appropriate standard of occupational health and safety in the workplace if an employee died or was injured as a result of that negligence. This brings the notion of "corporate homicide" into the Canadian Criminal Code for the first time, which substantially raises the stakes for managers and corporations. Furthermore, companies cannot shift blame to frontline managers because the legislation details that companies are responsible for ensuring that frontline staff know the appropriate rules, regulations, and working procedures and that employees follow the procedures. It is no longer possible to claim that employees were derelict in their responsibility.

The passage of Bill C-45 was greeted with great fanfare; the first charges (relating to the death of a construction worker) were laid in 2004 but were subsequently withdrawn in 2005. There has been some concern that the law has no "teeth" in practice. Whenever charges could be laid under either the safety legislation (provincial) or the Criminal Code (federal), the preference seems to be for safety legislation to prevail. It seems that the Criminal Code is likely to be invoked in only the most severe, egregious, and atypical cases. Nonetheless, there have now been several convictions under the act. In one case, Transpave Inc., pled guilty to criminal negligence relating to a death of an employee and was fined $110 000. In a second case, a landscape contractor (Pasquale Scrocca) was sentenced to two years less a day to be served in the community for criminal negligence causing death when one of his employees was crushed by an improperly maintained backhoe. Merton Construction pled guilty to criminal negligence charges in relation to the staging collapse that killed four workers in Toronto on Christmas Eve, 2009. The company received fines of $230 000 with an additional $90 000 fine for the president of the firm. In January 2016, the project manager in the Merton case was sentenced to 3.5 years in prison for his role in the tragedy. Nevertheless, critics point to the fact that the penalties still do not reflect the seriousness of the charges.[24]

// ENVIRONMENTAL LEGISLATION

Environmental and occupational health and safety laws are closely linked. In recognition of this fact, many companies and institutions have occupational environmental health and safety departments. Some of the intersections between OH&S and environmental sustainability are explored in **OH&S Today 2.4**. The health and safety professional will be aware of the overlap in environmental and OH&S statutes and regulations. For example, chemicals that can cause damage to a worker may also cause damage to the ecosystem if released into the environment. Recall the rail tragedy at Lac-Mégantic explored in Chapter 1. Following the derailment and its associated explosions, there are concerns about the lasting environmental effects on the soil and water. Some of the changes faced by the individuals involved are under the Fisheries Act.[25]

By way of illustration, federal statutes relating to some aspect of environmental or health and safety management are listed in **OH&S Notebook 2.4**. Regulatory laws related to environmental assessment, public health, waste disposal, buried fuel tanks, and storage or use of pesticides have an impact on the environment, the public, and the occupational health and safety of employees. As the following scenario indicates, the practitioner is required to understand environmental and OH&S jurisdictions and the potential for overlap. If a release of a potentially hazardous substance occurs within a building (other than residential) it falls under the jurisdiction of the authority enforcing the health and safety legislation. If the release is outside the building, or if the potentially hazardous substance is released into the sewer, storm system, water, or air, it falls under the jurisdiction of the authority enforcing the environmental legislation. Any single occurrence may involve both authorities.

OH&S TODAY 2.4

CORPORATE SOCIAL RESPONSIBILITY: THE INTERSECTION OF SAFETY AND ENVIRONMENTAL CONCERNS

Via the corporate social responsibility movement, many organizations identify environmental protection and safety promotion as core organizational priorities. Under a corporate social responsibility philosophy, organizations make a purposeful effort to incorporate social and environmental considerations into their business decision-making frameworks. It is easy to see how the health and well-being of employees, community, and the planet are social responsibilities for organizations. Some organizations are putting this into practice and reflecting on their health and safety activities as part of their corporate social responsibility programming.

Consider TransCanada, an energy infrastructure company. In its 2014 Annual Corporate Social Responsibility Report, its President and CEO described the company as looking at "Corporate Social Responsibility (CSR) not as a facet of our business, but as a reflection of the way we conduct our business and an expression of our core values of integrity, responsibility, collaboration and innovation." The report incorporates asset management, health, safety and environmental activities, and performance.

Internationally, Denmark has legislation pertaining to mandatory reporting of corporate social responsibility activities. Developments in legislation, standards, and codes pertaining to corporations' social responsibilities will be something to watch for in the coming years.

Sources: M.J. Montero, R.A. Araque, & J.M. Rey (2009), "Occupational Health and Safety in the Framework of Corporate Social Responsibility," *Safety Science*, 47(10), 1440–1445; TransCanada, Corporate Social Responsibility Report 2014, (p. 3). Found at: http://www.transcanada.com/docs/Our_Responsibility/TransCanada-2014-Corporate-Social-Responsibility-Report.pdf (accessed June 7, 2016); and N. Keith (October 24, 2011), "Corporate Social Responsibility: An International Perspective," *OHS Insider*. Found at: https://ohsinsider.com/insider-top-stories/corporate-social-responsibility-an-international-perspective (accessed June 7, 2016).

You've likely determined at this point in the chapter that there are many statutes and regulations relevant to OH&S in Canada. First, each jurisdiction has its own occupational health and safety legislation. There are also considerations for OH&S in Canadian human rights and freedoms legislation. Human rights legislation is pivotal in protections and accommodations offered to injured or ill workers. However, we also see that there are overlaps in OH&S, environmental, and transportation spheres. Thus, statutes pertaining to the environment and transportation of dangerous goods also need to be on the radar of employers, OH&S professionals, employees, and other stakeholders in OH&S.

These are some of the federal statutes relevant to OH&S:

- Canadian Environmental Protection Act
- Hazardous Products Act
- Canadian Charter of Rights and Freedoms, Part I of the Constitution Act
- Canada Labour Code, Part IV

- Criminal Code of Canada
- Pest Control Products Act
- Transportation of Dangerous Goods Act
- Radiation Emitting Devices Act
- Canada Shipping Act
- Radiation Protection Regulations

There are also many relevant provincial and territorial statutes relevant to OH&S. These include the occupational health and safety acts, which we have considered throughout the chapter. Provinces and territories also have specific legislation around the protection of human rights and freedoms. Some provinces, such as Ontario and Manitoba, have specific acts pertaining to accessibility for persons with disabilities, which also have OH&S implications, particularly relating to workplace accommodations. In addition, there are provincial/territorial laws pertaining to the environment, waste management, and the transportation of dangerous goods that need to be considered as necessary.

// TRANSPORTATION OF DANGEROUS GOODS

The regulation of environmental hazards, occupational health and safety, and transportation of dangerous goods is not the exclusive domain of the federal, provincial, or territorial governments. Therefore, the OH&S professional should be familiar with the statutes relevant to his or her particular jurisdiction. In essence, the environmental and transportation legislation seeks to supply the framework within which society can protect itself from the risk that attends the transportation of inherently dangerous materials.

The federal legislation governing the transportation of dangerous goods applies to all persons who handle, offer for transport, transport, or import any dangerous goods. The provincial or territorial legislation does not always go this far, making it sometimes impossible to determine which statutes apply. Notwithstanding some provincial or territorial limitations, dangerous goods legislation applies to carriers, shippers, and transportation intermediaries such as freight forwarders and customs brokers. Various regulations exist with respect to identifying and placarding dangerous goods, controlling quantities, and training and certifying workers. The regulatory wording complements the WHMIS requirements and the OH&S responsibility of employers and supervisors to educate and train workers.

In *R. v. Midland Transport Ltd.* (1991) the New Brunswick Provincial Court made the following observation about the legislation: "The Transportation of Dangerous Goods Act and the Regulations thereunder with the act fall in the category of legislation which creates public welfare offences. Recognizing the potential dangers, it establishes safety guidelines for the handling of hazardous materials to ensure the protection of the public and the environment."

// SUMMARY

The complexities associated with OH&S legislation in Canada continue to increase. This chapter has outlined the scope of this legislation and the changing climate surrounding it. We began by reviewing the three principal rights of employees (the right to know, the right to participate, and the right to refuse) and how they are enacted in health and safety programs. We discussed the legislative framework of OH&S legislation. We paid particular attention to the duties of major stakeholders (employers, constructors, supervisors, employees) and their reflection of the internal responsibility system. We considered work refusals and work stoppages as concrete enactments of the right to refuse unsafe work. Further, we examined joint health and safety committees, which exemplify the right to participate in decision making around occupational health and safety. The elements composing WHMIS, a manifestation of the right to know, were reviewed with particular attention to the recent alignment with the GHS. We also explored corporate criminal negligence. Finally, we considered ancillary legislation (e.g., regarding environmental concerns and transportation of dangerous goods).

KEY TERMS

act 31
constructor 35
general duty 34
GHS 40
guidelines and policies 31
prescribed duty 34
regulations 31
standards and codes 31

DISCUSSION QUESTIONS

1. What are the three fundamental workers' rights that underlie most health and safety legislation?
2. What is the most fundamental general duty provision in occupational health and safety legislation across Canada? How do the general and prescribed duties in the legislation reflect the internal responsibility system?

3. Considering the health and safety legislation: (A) Provide an example of a situation in which a worker could reasonably refuse work. (B) Describe a situation in which a worker could not refuse unsafe work.

4. How does WHMIS reflect basic health and safety rights?

5. Describe the structure and role of joint health and safety committees. In your answer, reflect on how such committees enact the right to participate.

USING THE INTERNET

1. What OH&S legislation applies in your jurisdiction? Find the body responsible for occupational health and safety and review the legislation. What are the major provisions and their implications for employers? for employees? for human resource managers?

2. WHMIS training is widely available online. Using a search engine and keywords such as "WHMIS online training," find a local provider of online WHMIS training.

EXERCISE

1. Health and safety legislation can be crafted following different approaches. One approach is to "force" compliance by establishing standards, conducting rigorous inspections on a regular basis, and harshly punishing failures to meet the established standards. A second approach is to facilitate self-reliance by providing the parties with the information and resources necessary to monitor and enhance health and safety in their workplaces. What are the relative merits of these two approaches? What advantages and disadvantages accrue under each system? What is the appropriate balance between enforcement and encouragement?

OH&S IN ACTION

As a human resources manager at an urban property management firm, you've noticed a trend of an increasing number of young workers on your payroll. Some are students who are helping to cover their living costs by working part-time as on-site superintendents in their apartment buildings; some are summer workers who are hired to cover additional outside maintenance and landscaping work in the summer; and others are new full-time, permanent hires brought on in a recent expansion of your company's holdings. You're concerned that you are seeing an increase in worksite injury incident claims. When you interview many of these new, young workers you realize that they are often unaware of their workplace rights. Prepare a briefing note for your boss, the director of company operations, outlining the basic worker rights, why it is important for workers to understand them, and how you might increase awareness of these rights among your entire workforce, including young, short-term, and part-time workers. (Hint: You can easily find the details on the purpose and structure of a briefing note using an Internet search).

CASE STUDY 1   WORKPLACE TRAGEDY

An auto parts manufacturer employs 500 workers. The plant operates on three shifts, and its various lines include large punch presses, conveyors, paint spray booths, and overhead cranes. A worker has been killed following an accident on the overhead crane line. The worker was guiding the load hoisted by the crane when the load slipped, causing a failure of the supporting cables. The worker was killed when the falling load struck him. Though this is the most serious accident, there have been several others at the plant in the past. As plant manager, you are responsible for ensuring the safety of your employees. Outline the steps you plan to take to improve health and safety in the plant.

CASE STUDY 2   WORK REFUSAL AT REGIONAL HOSPITAL

Regional Hospital is a 100-bed acute care facility providing services to a mid-sized Canadian city. Recently, the hospital took advantage of a special government grant to develop and operate a Zika treatment ward. Though the ward is now open, there is considerable disquiet among the staff. Two nurses have refused to work their assigned shifts on the ward, claiming that it is their right to refuse unsafe work. Moreover, workers have been petitioning their certified representative on the joint health and safety committee to close the workplace because of the safety standard. As the HR representative for Regional Hospital, what is your planned response? How do you balance the workers' right to refuse unsafe work against the need to staff the ward?

// NOTES

1. CCOHS. "OH&S Legislation in Canada—Introduction. OSH Answer Fact Sheet" (July 8, 2008). Found at: https://www.ccohs.ca/oshanswers/legisl/intro .html (accessed May 5, 2016).

2. PEI Occupational Health and Safety Act. Found at: http://www.gov.pe.ca/ law/statutes/pdf/o-01_01.pdf (accessed June 7, 2016).

3. OHS Insider, "Alberta Moves to Include Farm & Ranch Workers under OHS Laws" (December 16, 2015). Found at: https://ohsinsider.com/search-by -index/industries/alberta-moves-to-include-farm-ranch-workers-under-ohs-laws (accessed June 7, 2016).

4. Ontario Ministry of Labour, "Guide to the Occupational Health and Safety Act. Part III: Duties of Employees and Other Persons." Found at: http://www.labour .gov.on.ca/english/hs/pubs/ohsa/ohsag_part3.php (accessed June 7, 2016).

5. Yukon Health and Safety Act, Section 4. Found at: https://www.wcb.yk.ca/ Document-Library/Legislation/LIB0054.aspx (accessed May 31, 2016).

6. Newfoundland and Labrador Occupational Health and Safety Act, Sections 2.k.1, 5.1, 5.2. Found at: http://www.assembly.nl.ca/legislation/sr/statutes/o03.htm#5_1 (accessed June 7, 2016).

7. CCOHS. "Joint Health and Safety Committee–What Is a Joint Health and Safety Committee?" Fact Sheet (February 2, 2016). Found at: https://www.ccohs .ca/oshanswers/hsprograms/hscommittees/whatisa.html (accessed June 7, 2016).

8. New Brunswick Occupational Health and Safety Act, Section 14. Found at: http://laws.gnb.ca/en/showdoc/cs/O-0.2/ga:s_14#anchorga:s_14 (accessed June 7, 2016).

9. CCOHS. "Joint Health and Safety Committee–What Is a Joint Health and Safety Creation?" Fact Sheet (February 2, 2016). Found at: https://www.ccohs .ca/oshanswers/hsprograms/hscommittees/creation.html (accessed June 7, 2016).

10. Ibid.

11. P. Strahlendorf, "Is Your Committee Effective?" *OH&S Canada* 23 (2007): 24–31.

12. E.K. Kelloway, "Labor Unions and Safety," in J. Barling and M. Frone, eds., *Psychology of Occupational Safety* (Washington: APA, 2003).

13. B. Reilly, P. Paci, and P. Holl, "Unions, Safety Committees, and Workplace Injuries," *British Journal of Industrial Relations* 33 (1995): 275–88.

14. D. Weil, "Are Mandated Health and Safety Committees Substitutes for or Supplements to Labor Unions?" *Industrial and Labor Relations Review* 52 (1999): 339–61.

15. Idem, "Mandating Safety and Health Committees: Lessons from the United States," *Proceedings of the 47th Annual Meeting of the Industrial Relations Research Association*, Madison, WI, 1995: 273–81.

16. Employment and Social Development Canada, "Information on Occupational Health and Safety–Pamphlet 4. Right to Refuse Dangerous Work" (2015). Found at: http://www.esdc.gc.ca/en/reports/health_safety/right_refuse.page#h2.3 (accessed May 3, 2016).

17. OHS Insider, "Heat Stress as Grounds for Refusing Work" (May 26, 2011). Found at: https://ohsinsider.com/insider-top-stories/heat-stress-as-grounds-for -refusing-work-2. (accessed May 3, 2016).

18. Employment and Social Development Canada, "Information on Occupational Health and Safety–Pamphlet 4. Right to Refuse Dangerous Work" (2015) Found at: http://www.esdc.gc.ca/en/reports/health_safety/right_refuse.page#h2.3 (accessed May 3, 2016); and Province of Ontario, Occupational Health and Safety Act, R.S.O. 1990, c. O.1, Section 43. Found at: https://www.ontario.ca/laws/statute/90o01 (accessed May 3, 2016).

19. Ontario Ministry of Labour, Guide to the Occupational Health and Safety Act. Part V: Right to Refuse or Stop Work where Health and Safety In Danger. Found at: http://www.labour.gov.on.ca/english/hs/pubs/ohsa/ohsag_part5 .php (accessed June 7, 2016).

20. CCOHS. "WHMIS 1988 General Fact Sheet." Found at: http://www.ccohs .ca/oshanswers/legisl/intro_whmis.html (accessed May 3, 2016).

21. Ibid.

22. CCOHS. "WHMIS 2015. An Overview." (November 2015). Found at: http://
images.ccohs.ca/products/whmisFactSheets/images/ghsFactSheet1Lrg.jpg
(accessed May 3, 2016); and CCOHS, "WHMIS 2015–WHMIS Program
Fact Sheet." Found at: http://www.ccohs.ca/oshanswers/chemicals/whmis
_ghs/program.html (accessed May 3, 2016).

23. CCOHS. "Bill C-45–Overview Fact Sheet." Found at: http://www.ccohs
.ca/oshanswers/legisl/billc45.html (accessed June 7, 2016); and Summary
of Bill C-45, An Act to Amend the Criminal Code (Criminal Liability of
Corporations). Found at: http://www.lop.parl.gc.ca/About/Parliament/
LegislativeSummaries/bills_ls.asp?ls=c45&Parl=37&Ses=2 (accessed
May 3, 2016).

24. N. Keith. "After 10 Years, Bill C-45 Yields Few Prosecutions" (April 23, 2014).
Canadian Occupational Safety. Found at; http://www.cos-mag.com/legal/
legal-columns/3900-after-10-years-bill-c-45-yields-few-prosecutions.html
(accessed June 7, 2016); CBC News, "Manager in Fatal Scaffolding Collapse
Sentenced to 3 1/2 Years" (January 11, 2016). Found at: http://www.cbc.ca/
news/canada/toronto/scaffolding-collapse-criminally-responsible-vadim
-kaznelson-1.3397597 (accessed June 7, 2016).

25. Government of Canada, "Charges Laid in Connection with Lac-Mégantic
Train Derailment" (June 22, 2015). Found at: http://news.gc.ca/web/article-en
.do?nid=990109 (accessed June 7, 2015).

CHAPTER

3

WORKERS' COMPENSATION

CHAPTER LEARNING OBJECTIVES

AFTER READING THIS CHAPTER, YOU SHOULD BE ABLE TO:

- outline the goals and methods of Workers' Compensation Boards (WCBs)
- discuss the problems associated with compensating for psychological conditions and occupational illnesses
- describe the assessment methods of WCBs

Typically when we think of firefighters battling something, it is fires and for police it is crime; however, these first responders are fighting for compensation. Firefighters in Ontario battled to have lung cancer added to the list of presumptive work-related diseases and they have won. This means that as of January 1, 2016, firefighters with a minimum of 15 years of service who have developed lung cancer will receive workers' compensation benefits without having to prove their cancer is work related. Presumptive provisions means that the usual requirements for determining whether an injury/illness is work-related are not required in special acknowledged or presumed circumstances (e.g., cancer).

This is a significant step for future and past firefighters. This change to the Ontario Workplace Safety and Insurance Act means that firefighters who received their diagnosis or on or after January 1, 1960 are eligible for compensation benefits. Family members of firefighters who have died during that time are also eligible to receive benefits. Significant progress has been made within the last couple of years regarding the list of presumptive work-related diseases for firefighters in Ontario. In 2014, breast cancer was added to that list and it is presumed that prostate and skin cancer will also be added. Firefighters in Ontario continue to work toward having post-traumatic stress disorder added to the list; however changes to workers compensation acts and benefits do not come easily nor quickly.

The Royal Newfoundland Constabulary Association (RNCA) is fighting for changes to benefits that would be a first of its kind in Canada. The RNCA has recommended that changes to injured officers' compensation benefits be such that their compensation be based on 100% of their pre-injury net earnings instead of the 80% they currently receive. Despite the RNCA's push, the Workplace Health and Safety Compensation Commission in Newfoundland did not pass the recommendation onto government. Reaction to these proposed changes is mixed. Firefighters in Newfoundland fully supported the proposed changes; however, some critics believe this would set an unfair precedent for those in other industries. These two situations raise very important questions about compensation policies and what should or should not be covered and to what extent. The needs of employers and employees must be considered and carefully balanced when changes are made in order to avoid any undue hardship, financial or otherwise, for either party or the compensation system as a whole. This chapter reviews the history of workers' compensation and the basic principles, policies and tenets of the various boards across Canada.

One recent study suggest that shift workers have longer recovery times compared to those who work day-time shifts.

Sources: Jeff Cotrill (January 12, 2016), "Lung Cancer Now an Occupational Disease for Ontario Firefighters," OHS Canada. Found at: http://www.ohscanada.com/health-safety/lung-cancer-now-deemed -an-occupational-disease-for-ontario-firefighters-2/1003349278 (accessed June 7, 2016); and Jason Contant (January 13, 2015), "Police Association Calls for Full Workers' Compensation for Officers," OHS Canada. Found at http://www.ohscanada.com/health-safety/police -association-calls-full-workers-compensation-officers/1003272663 (accessed June 7, 2016).

Workers' compensation is a form of insurance governed by an act of Parliament to help workers who are injured on the job to return to work. Consider the example of a construction labourer who has sustained an injury on the job and is now unable to work. Workers' compensation will ensure that the injured worker receives (1) first aid treatment, either on the job or at the nearest local treatment facility, (2) benefits while at home recuperating, and (3) proper treatment for any injuries. If necessary, rehabilitation will be provided to help the worker return to his or her former job or some modified version of it, if circumstances dictate.

// HISTORICAL ROOTS

Workers' compensation originated in Germany in 1884 but was not established in Canada until 1914, when the Ontario Workmen's Compensation Act was passed by the provincial Parliament (see **OH&S Notebook 3.1**). This time lag was something of an advantage, because it allowed for consideration of the American and European experience (the federal Employers' Liability Act had been passed in the United States in 1908). In 1900 the Ontario government inquired into the German system. This was followed between 1912 and 1914 by an intensive and prolonged study of existing laws in other European countries and in the United States, under the guidance of Sir William Ralph Meredith, chief justice of Ontario. On the basis of his findings, the first act in Canada was passed.

Acts were subsequently passed in all provinces and territories, and though they have been amended many times (largely for the purpose of increasing coverage and benefits), they have retained many of the principles set forth in the Ontario Act of 1914:

> **collective liability**
> where all employers in a class or other rate group are liable for the costs of any or all accidents and occupational diseases that occur in the operations of those employers

- **collective liability** for employers, with some recognition of risk in the amount of contribution paid by individual employers;
- compensation for workers regardless of the financial condition of the employer;
- compensation based on loss of earnings;
- a "no fault" system; and
- a nonadversarial process: little or no recourse to the courts (in Ontario, Schedule 2 can allow legal recourse).

OH&S NOTEBOOK 3.1

OVERVIEW OF WORKERS' COMPENSATION

Essentially, workers' compensation is an insurance plan in which the premiums (i.e., the cost of insurance) are paid by the employer. The plan is administered by a board typically known as the workers' compensation board. Each year the WCB sets a premium rate for each industry. The rate is usually expressed per $100 of payroll. For example, if you own a retail-based company that specializes in women's clothing and has an annual payroll of $300 000 in Ontario, you can use the calculator provided by the WSIB at http://www.wsib. on.ca/WSIBPortal/faces/WSIBPremiumEstimate by first selecting the service industry from the drop-down menu and then choosing the specific rate group titled women's clothing stores (Rate group 641) to derive your 2016 premium as $ 4770.00 paid in monthly installments of 397.50. A rate group is a method for categorizing companies based on the nature of their business (e.g.,

clothing retail). In some provinces a company's premium rate may be increased or decreased depending on its specific safety record. WCBs use this money to compensate injured workers, pay for medical treatment, engage in prevention activities, and fund safety associations (i.e., industry associations whose focus is promoting occupational health and safety).

If you are a worker who is injured in the workplace, your employer is required to file a report of the injury with the WCB. Assuming that your injury requires you to miss time from work, you will receive compensation to make up for lost income while you are off. Though the details vary by jurisdiction, the compensation is usually based on a percentage of your salary to a specified maximum. For example, in Prince Edward Island the 2016 maximum earning is $52,200; in Ontario the maximum earning is $88,000.

A workers' compensation system amounts to a trade-off for both workers and employers. Workers know they will be compensated for injury without having to undertake expensive and lengthy lawsuits; in return, they accept the WCB's authority to determine the amount of compensation. Employers are obliged to pay for the workers' compensation system but are also protected from litigation that could drive them into bankruptcy.[1]

// WORKERS' COMPENSATION IN CANADA

ADMINISTRATION AND RESPONSIBILITIES

The provincial and territorial acts throughout Canada are administered by the members of the WCB, who are appointed by the lieutenant governor in council. The provincial boards are empowered to fix and collect assessments, determine the right to compensation, and pay the amount due to the injured worker. In all these matters, the workers' compensation system has exclusive and final jurisdiction. In terms of its authority and power, the Ontario Act is representative of the legislation that exists in all jurisdictions. The regulations and responsibilities of workers' compensation boards are as follows:

- The injured worker will receive payment while off work and will have all medical bills paid if the injury happened at work and because of work.
- The injured worker will receive a pension if the injury is or becomes permanent.
- The injured worker will receive benefits if he or she cannot earn the same amount of money earned before the incident.
- The injured worker's immediate family and dependants will be entitled to benefits if the worker is killed or dies as a result of an injury on the job.
- The WCBs classify employers to ensure consistency.
- The WCBs decide whether an individual is classified as a worker, a subcontractor, or an employer, as each class has different conditions.
- The workers' compensation system can pay benefits if a worker is affected by an industrial disease that has resulted from his or her occupation.

In relation to most of the industries within the scope of the provincial or territorial acts, the system of compensation is one of compulsory and collective liability. Under collective liability, the various industries are classified according to their size and end product, and each employer is assessed a rate that is a percentage of its payroll. The percentage is determined by the injury cost of its classification. From the incident fund thus collected, payments are made for compensation, medical aid, rehabilitation, incident prevention, and administrative expenses. Each employer is liable for assessment, whatever the cost of injuries sustained by its workers. As a result, each is relieved of individual liability. In most jurisdictions, liability is further distributed by a disaster reserve fund.

Public authorities and certain large corporations such as railways and shipping or telegraph companies have a different liability approach from the collective liabilities scheme and are individually liable for compensation; however, all disputes are settled by the WCB. Such corporations contribute their portion of the cost of administering the various acts.

Because jurisdictions sometimes provide different benefits, most WCBs in Canada have entered into agreements among themselves to avoid duplicate assessments and to help the worker claim and receive compensation when two or more jurisdictions are involved. These agreements are intended to ensure that the worker receives the best possible benefits and that coverage is extended in a province or territory, often at the request of the injured worker.

The provincial and territorial acts generally cover all employment in industries such as lumbering, mining, fishing, manufacturing, construction, engineering, and transportation. Covered occupations include operation of electrical power lines, employment in waterworks and other public utilities, navigation, operation of boats and ships, operation of elevators and warehousing, street cleaning, painting, decorating, renovating, and cleaning. Those types of employment that are exempted from this list may be admitted at their own request.

Personal injuries resulting from incidents arising out of and in the course of employment are compensated, except when the incident is attributed to the worker's serious and willful misconduct. Workers' compensation systems also compensate for certain specified occupational diseases. The various compensation boards across Canada continually update and amend legislation to ensure and promote workplace health and safety. Many of those updates are to the presumptive work-related diseases—those diseases where the cause is presumed to be work related (see **OH&S Today 3.1**).

OH&S TODAY 3.1

LEGISLATIVE UPDATES

Over the last three to four years, many of the legislative updates include additions or changes to the list of presumptive diseases. On June 10, 2015, the government of Manitoba was the first province in Canada to amend the workers' compensation act to include presumptive provisions for post-traumatic stress disorder (PTSD). This legislative change allows any worker who endures a traumatic event while at work and is diagnosed with PTSD as a result to receive compensation. New Brunswick has also modified its legislation to provide compensation to first responders suffering PTSD.

While other provinces are working toward this (e.g., British Columbia), Manitoba has proven to be the leader thanks to efforts of the nurses, firefighters, first responders, and the Manitoba Government Employees Union, which fought to raise awareness and educate the public on the implications associated with PTSD.

In March 2014 the Yukon Workers' Compensation Health and Safety Board (YWCHSB) amended the Workers' Compensation Act to include cardiac arrests to the list of heart diseases on the presumptive provisions lists. Similarly in British Columbia (BC) the government tabled legislation to include cardiac arrests to the list of heart-related diseases covered. Forest firefighters, who are excluded from this list in some provinces, are included in BC.

Bill 35 in BC has also seen significant changes to the workplace in that it adds to the existing Bill 9, which strengthens WorkSafeBC's ability to enforce and promote compliance within the workplace. Effective January 1, 2016, this bill allowed for WorkSafeBC to:

- Require employers to immediately report all workplace fires or explosions that had the potential to cause serious injury;

- Require employers to provide preliminary and full employer investigation reports to the company's joint occupational health and safety committee, via a representative or by posting the investigations within the work site;

- Specify what is included as part of an employer and worker representative's participation in a work-related incident;

- Require joint occupational health and safety committees to advise the employer on significant proposed equipment and machinery changes that may affect worker health and safety; and

- Assist committees in resolving disputes over health and safety matters, even if the matter has not been formally reported to WorkSafeBC by the committee.

PREVENTION

Most WCBs, at one time, were responsible for the incident prevention or OH&S aspects of workers' compensation. In the 1970s and 1980s the combined role was seen as a conflict of interest by some governments, and these WCB functions were placed under a government department in most provinces and territories (e.g., the Department of Labour). Though the OH&S function is separate in most jurisdictions (with BC and NB being exceptions), all WCBs cooperate with the responsible government department by sharing information. Many jurisdictions across Canada include some type of prevention function to the WCB's traditional compensation functions. Other boards are offer premium reductions based on safety records. Compared to 2015, six jurisdictions in Canada decreased their average assessment rates, while five jurisdictions held them steady (see **OH&S Today 3.2**). In addition to this general premium reduction, employers in Alberta (and in some other provinces—see the discussion in this chapter on experience ratings) can achieve further premium reductions of up to 20% from the industry rate based on their safety performance. Conversely, organizations with a poor safety record may be charged a surcharge to reflect the increased costs of insurance. In Nova Scotia the surcharge program is a rate-setting

OH&S TODAY	3.2		
WORKERS' COMPENSATION PREMIUMS (AVERAGES PER $100 OF PAYROLL)			
		2015	**2016**
Alberta		0.97	1.01
British Columbia		1.70	1.70
Manitoba		1.30	1.25
New Brunswick		1.11	1.11
Newfoundland and Labrador		2.45	2.20
Northwest Territories/Nunavut		2.00	2.00
Nova Scotia		2.65	2.65
Ontario		2.46	2.46
Prince Edward Island		1.79	1.77
Quebec		1.94	1.84
Saskatchewan		1.46	1.34
Yukon		1.90	1.85

Source: Association of Workers' Compensation Boards of Canada, "Provisional average assessment rates, per $100.00 payroll." Found at: http://awcbc.org/wp-content/uploads/2013/12/Avg_Rates_History.pdf (accessed February 7, 2016).

model that responds to the safety performance of individual employers. This program is designed to place the onus of prevention and reducing rates on employers by encouraging them to take the necessary steps required to create a safe and healthy workplace. Employers who improve their safety records by preventing and reducing injuries will see a reduction rate and those who do not could be required to pay a surcharge.

A mandate for prevention also means that WCBs are actively involved in trying to prevent incidents and reduce costs to employers. WCBs provide a wide range of information for employers and employees regarding safety-related matters. For example, WorkSafeBC maintains a large online library of safety-related publications; the WCB of Newfoundland and Labrador provides workshops on how to prevent workplace injuries, and New Brunswick's WCB has the 5*22 Health and Safety Resources program. The WCBs in Alberta and Nova Scotia offer a Certificate of Recognition (COR) to organizations that have implemented safety programs that meet their standards. In many jurisdictions in Canada, WCBs provide extensive resources to both employers and individuals interested in health and safety issues. (See **OH&S Notebook 3.2** for individual WCB contact information.)

OH&S NOTEBOOK   3.2

CONTACT INFORMATION FOR THE PROVINCIAL AND TERRITORIAL WORKERS' COMPENSATION BOARDS

Workers' Compensation Board of Alberta
9912–107 Street
P.O. Box 2415
Edmonton AB T5J 2S5
Tel: 780-498-3999
Fax: 780-498-7999
http://www.wcb.ab.ca

WorkSafeBC
P.O. Box 5350
Vancouver BC V6B 5L5
Tel: 604-244-6181 (Lower Mainland—Employers & Assessment)
Tel: 604-231-8888 Claims call centre
Fax: 604-233-9777
http://www.worksafebc.com

Workers Compensation Board of Manitoba
333 Broadway
Winnipeg MB R3C 4W3
Tel: 204-954-4321
Fax: 204-954-4999
http://www.wcb.mb.ca

WorkSafe/Travail Sécuritaire New Brunswick
1 Portland Street
P.O. Box 160
Saint John NB E2L 3X9
Tel: 506-632-2200
Fax: 506-632-4999
http://www.worksafenb.ca

Workplace Newfoundland (WorkplaceNL)
146-148 Forest Road
P.O. Box 9000
St. John's NL A1A 3B8
Tel: 709-778-1000
Fax: 709-738-1714
http://www.whscc.nf.ca

Workers' Safety & Compensation Commission of the Northwest Territories and Nunavut
P.O. Box 8888
Yellowknife NT X1A 2R3
Tel: 867-920-3888
Fax: 867-873-4596
http://www.wscc.nt.ca

(*continued*)

Workers' Compensation Board of Nova Scotia

5668 South Street
P.O. Box 1150
Halifax NS B3J 2Y2
Tel: 902-491-8999
Fax: 902-491-8001
http://www.wcb.ns.ca

Workplace Safety and Insurance Board of Ontario

200 Front Street West
Toronto ON M5V 3J1
Tel: 416-344-1000
Fax: 416-344-4684
http://www.wsib.on.ca

Workers Compensation Board of Prince Edward Island

14 Weymouth Street
P.O. Box 757
Charlottetown PEI C1A 7L7
Tel: 902-368-5680
Fax: 902-368-5705
http://www.wcb.pe.ca

Commission des norms, de l'équité, de la santé et de la sécurité du travail (CNESST)

1, complexe Desjardins
Tour Sud, 31e étage
Case postale 3
Succursale Place-Desjardins
Montréal QC H5B 1H1
Tel: 1-866-302-2778
Fax: 514-906-3133
http://www.csst.qc.ca

Saskatchewan Workers' Compensation Board

200–1881 Scarth Street
Regina SK S4P 4L1
Tel: 306-787-4370
Fax: 306-787-4311
http://www.wcbsask.com

Yukon Workers' Compensation Health and Safety Board

401 Strickland Street
Whitehorse YK Y1A 5N8
Tel: 867-667-5645
Fax: 867-393-6279
http://www.wcb.yk.ca

Source: Association of Workers' Compensation Boards of Canada. Found at http://awcbc.org/?page_id=10 (accessed March 1, 2016).

COMPENSATION RATES AND METHODS

Two standards are in place for determining the amount of compensation. As of 2015 there were five jurisdictions that base the payment on a percentage (generally 90%) of net earnings; the remaining jurisdictions base payments on a percentage of average earnings that ranges from 75% to 85%. Jurisdictions such as Nova Scotia have used both methods depending on the date of the incident. In Nova Scotia the percentage is 75% for the first 26 weeks, after which it increases to 85%. A worker's average earnings are generally calculated on the basis of his or her earnings during the past 12 months. Since a large number of workers have not worked for the same employer for 12 months, other ways of establishing earnings are sanctioned. Each act also stipulates a maximum amount of earnings that can be used to determine the maximum amount of compensation. Though there are procedural variations across jurisdictions, workers' compensation is based on the individual's past salary record, not on the loss or potential loss of future earnings.

> **net earnings**
> salary after mandatory deductions (income tax, Canada Pension, and employment insurance)

One of the many stereotypes that exists regarding injured workers receiving compensation is that they do not want to work. This is especially pervasive if the injury or illness is not visible.[2] In order to dissuade anyone from exploiting the system, boards try to provide reasonable compensation without creating an incentive to avoid work.

The method used for determining the average wage of a worker is the one that gives the best representation of the worker's weekly earnings and that seems fair and reasonable. When work is made available and the worker still suffers an earnings loss, the payment for the continuing impairment may be adjusted, whether or not the worker accepts the work. A payment for non-economic loss (functional impairment) is also made in several jurisdictions. This figure is based on factors such as the worker's age, degree of impairment, and number of dependants. For example, a 40-year-old worker with three children would receive a larger payment than a 60-year-old worker with no children.

Compensation to employees can be provided using different methods including wage loss benefits, permanent disability benefits, dependency benefits, and rehabilitation. Wage loss benefits means that an injured employee receives a specific percentage of his or her typical wages (this varies by province). An employee typically receives permanent disability benefits if determined to have a permanent disability because of his or her work injury; he or she may receive additional or varied compensation depending on the province. In the event that an individual dies while on the job, his or her dependants (e.g., spouse or children) may be eligible to receive benefits. Finally, rehabilitation services and programs are provided to help workers get back to their pre-injury health and to get injured workers back to work.

Depending on the type of compensation—for example, wage loss—payments continue as long as an injury or impairment lasts, in accordance with the entitlement established by the province or territory. In cases of permanent partial impairment, the worker receives a life pension based on rating scales established by the boards. There are allowances for economic losses and non-economic losses. For a non-economic loss, an injured worker could receive payment is based on a percentage of impairment of the total person.

Wage or earnings loss refers to situations in which workers can no longer earn the same amount of money that they were earning before the incident as a result of their impairment. For a worker who was earning $20 per hour before the incident and now, as a result of the injury, is capable of earning only $10 per hour, the potential compensation is $10 per hour. The earnings loss is calculated and paid as long as the worker is unable to return to work paying the same wages as before the incident.

In the event of the death of a worker, the spouse may receive a pension in accordance with the schedules established by the various jurisdictions, and allowances are given to children. In addition, most provincial and territorial boards may allow an immediate lump sum payment and variable expenses. However, some workers are excluded from injury compensation; for example, Alberta excludes most farm workers (see **OH&S Today 3.3**).

OH&S TODAY 3.3

THE DANGERS OF FARMING

The agriculture industry is one of the most dangerous work environments. In many places farming has one of the highest fatality rates and is a work environment that exposes workers to various occupational diseases. Nonetheless, Alberta excludes the majority of farm workers from receiving injury and illness compensation. This means that if you are a farm worker injured while working, you are financially responsible for your own wage loss, medical aid, and any necessary vocational rehabilitation.

The Parkland Institute, which is affiliated with the University of Alberta, recently published a report that examined the reasons behind the exclusion of farms and strategies advocates can use to push for change. Those strategies include increasing the amount of political pressure by challenging the constitutionality of the exclusion and the differential treatment of farm workers, increasing the interest and buy-in of employers by encouraging injured workers to sue their employers and, by raising public awareness of the working conditions.

Source: Adapted from Bob Barnetson, Parkland Institute, "A dirty business: The exclusion of Alberta farm workers from injury compensation." Found at http://www.parklandinstitute.ca/a_dirty_business (accessed June 23, 2016).

Employers or injured workers who disagree with a WCB decision can turn to various appeal bodies and mechanisms. In many jurisdictions workers must appeal to the internal review board in order to have any decisions revaluated. The final level of appeal in most jurisdictions is the Workers Compensation Appeals Tribunal (WCAT). The WCAT is an independent administrative tribunal or board that has the legal authority to overturn decisions made by a worker's compensation board. However, not all jurisdictions in Canada have a WCAT; in provinces like Saskatchewan the WCB has various levels for a worker's appeal, but the final decision rests with the WCB Appeals Tribunal.

// MEDICAL AID AND INCIDENT PREVENTION

Accompanying compensation in all cases is the provision of medical aid. This aid includes medical and surgical care, hospitalization, nursing care, drugs and supplies, physical and occupational therapy, and the provision and maintenance of prostheses. An employee who sustains a work-related injury is compensated not only for loss of earnings but also for **loss of functional capacity**. Workers who, as a result of their injury, are no longer able to perform some of their duties on the job, such as lifting, twisting, or bending, are considered to have suffered loss of functional capacity for which benefits are payable.

Employers within a particular industry may form safety associations and make rules for incident prevention that, on approval of the WCB and the lieutenant governor, are binding on all employers in that industry. WCBs pay the expenses of these associations out of the incident fund and have the authority to investigate the premises of employers to ensure compliance with safeguards required by law. The goal of safety associations is to provide training in the area of incident prevention and health and safety (see **OH&S Today 3.4**).

> **loss of functional capacity**
> limit of ability or dexterity depending on the seriousness of an injury

---

OH&S TODAY   3.4

SAFETY ASSOCIATIONS

Health and safety associations are industry groups funded at least in part through the workers' compensation board (employers pay a levy or surcharge as part of their premium to fund the association). Associations provide training programs, prevention programs and other health and safety–related services (e.g., safety audits, certificates of recognition), to members of their industry, typically charging a fee for these services. They are not responsible for regulation, nor are they a government agency—rather, a safety association represents a specific industry and provides general and industry-specific safety knowledge to its members. Because workers' compensation premiums are initially set by industry, all employers in a given industry benefit if safety improves within that industry. This is the goal of safety associations. See below for some of the various safety associations found across Canada:

- Alberta Construction Safety Association https://www.acsa-safety.org /
- Aware-NS http://awarens.ca
- Service and Hospitality Safety Association (Saskatchewan) http://www.servicehospitality.com
- Northern Safety Association http://www.nsa-nt.ca
- Canadian Industrial Radiography Safety Association http://cirsa.ca

AWARE+NS
Nova Scotia Health + Community Services Safety Association

Aware-NS is a safety association dedicated to health and community service employees within the province of Nova Scotia.

Courtesy of Aware-NS, Nova Scotia Health + Community Services Safety Association.

// SOCIAL GOALS OF WORKERS' COMPENSATION

Workers' compensation is driven by two main social goals: (1) to provide services intended to prevent injuries or reduce the psychological impact of injuries when they occur, and (2) to provide the training and development necessary to prepare an injured worker to return to work. The various WCBs have come to look on compensation as a means for society to share with the worker the consequences of industrial incidents and to ensure the restoration of the worker to active participation in the life of the community. The focus is more on restoring earning power than on paying for its loss. In no sense is compensation considered a reward for being injured.

This social conception of compensation is grounded in the following standard provisions contained in the various acts:

- unlimited medical aid;
- artificial prostheses;
- a fund to encourage re-employment (known as the Second Injury and Enhancement Fund [SIEF] in some jurisdictions);
- liberal compensation; and
- rehabilitation maintenance income.

Canada's compensation system provides greater benefits than those of most other countries; it also ensures that benefits are not prejudiced by earnings after rehabilitation. In Canada, a permanently injured worker draws compensation for life and is able to keep his or her pension, even if the sum of the pension and the earnings supplements amounts to more than the wages earned before the injury. In contrast, many compensation laws in the United States hinder rehabilitation, either by cutting off compensation for permanent injury as soon as workers begin to earn as much money as they did before the injury or by paying compensation for only a limited period (which can leave workers stranded before they can be retrained).

PROVISION FOR SECOND INJURIES

In some provinces (e.g., Ontario) provisions may be provided to an employee who receives a second injury. The purpose is to facilitate the re-employment of disabled workers. Without a provision for multiple injuries, employers might be tempted to discriminate against workers with impairments, as an additional injury could make the employer responsible for a far more serious disability than if the worker had not had a prior injury. Thus, a worker who has lost one arm will be given a total disability rating if he or she loses the second arm. By charging the excess liability resulting from the cumulative effect of a prior disability and the subsequent injury to a disaster reserve fund, the various acts distribute the burden throughout industry as a whole rather than letting it rest on one particular class. In this way, employers are relieved of the extra risks associated with the employment of workers with disabilities.

REHABILITATION

Before the First World War, people with disabilities were often left to fend for themselves. Some were placed in poorhouses; others survived through begging. Gradually, society realized that people with disabilities could be productive; however, the first

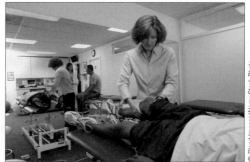

Injured workers receive physical, social, and psychological rehabilitation services as part of their compensation benefits.

attempts at drafting people with disabilities into the workplace proved to be difficult and frustrating. People with disabilities found that though they were given an opportunity to earn a living, they could do so only by accepting menial jobs that no one else wanted. However, when thousands of injured soldiers returned from the First World War, the need to provide rehabilitation programs was finally recognized. Rehabilitation is a financial necessity as well as a moral and social obligation. Only through effective rehabilitation can the future cost of the workers' compensation system be maintained at a reasonable level.

There are three types of rehabilitation. **Vocational rehabilitation** refers to the steps undertaken by WCBs to help injured workers return to their place of employment or find similar or suitable work elsewhere. Placement services, vocational testing, and retraining or training may all be part of this process. **Physical rehabilitation** refers to the steps taken to restore, fully or partially, the worker's physical function. **Social rehabilitation** refers to the psychological and practical services that help workers with severe disabilities cope with daily life (e.g., assistance with cooking, bathing, and household chores). An example of the full range of compensation benefits being provided to an injured worker is outlined in **OH&S Today 3.5**.

vocational rehabilitation
the steps undertaken by WCBs to help injured workers return to their place of employment or find similar or suitable work elsewhere

physical rehabilitation
the steps taken to restore, fully or partially, the worker's physical function

social rehabilitation
the psychological and practical services that help workers with severe disabilities cope with daily life

OH&S TODAY 3.5

WORKERS' COMPENSATION AT WORK

As a result of an industrial accident an employee lost his left hand in an industrial incident. Over the previous 10 years, he had risen from the position of delivery truck driver to plant manager at a small aluminum fabricator in northwest Toronto. Mr. Smith* had been thinking about a career change before the incident. Besides his duties as plant manager, he had begun to do some selling and marketing and found it was something he enjoyed. After the incident, he knew he would not be able to work in the plant again, so he began to consider retraining.

After his surgery, Mr. Smith spent four weeks in hospital recovering. A WCB representative came to see him two days after the incident and initiated his claim so that he could continue to pay his bills. Before Mr. Smith could be fitted with a prosthesis, his physical wounds had to heal. He spent the next couple of months getting better and receiving treatment.

Around this time, Mr. Smith decided to pursue a marketing career. Thanks to the sponsorship of the WCB, he enrolled in a marketing program. On graduation,

(continued)

Mr. Smith received further assistance from a WCB placement adviser. Within months, a job was located. After completing a training program with his new employer, Mr. Smith began work as a full-time marketing representative.

In this scenario the full range of compensation benefits was provided, including monetary benefits, medical aid, prosthetic device, vocational rehabilitation, placement services, and counselling in social services.

*Name has been changed.

Source: Joan Cushon-Boulet, "Vocational Rehabilitation of Injured Workers Downsview: A Rehabilitation Center?" *Journal of Law and Social Policy*, Vol 3 (January 1988). Found at: http://digitalcommons.osgoode.yorku.ca/cgi/viewcontent.cgi?article=1163&context=jlsp (accessed June 7, 2016).

// OCCUPATIONAL DISEASES AND WORKPLACE STRESS

A significant issue facing workers' compensation today concerns occupational diseases and the degree to which they are work related. Occupational diseases can include various cancers, skin diseases, and allergic reactions to materials and components in the workplace. Occupational disease compensation has been part of workers' compensation since six specific diseases were cited in Ontario Act of 1914. Since then, the act has broadened the definitions of "incident" and "injury," which has allowed for greater consideration of occupational disease claims. Today many occupational disease claims can be considered in the same way as any other claim. The requirement to isolate the point at which the disease was contracted has given way to a recognition that the disease could be the result of exposure or injury over time. Occupational disease claims, unless very straightforward, are often adjudicated by a special claim unit and may require additional expert medical opinion as well as exposure and employment histories. Some WCBs use separate claim forms for specific occupational diseases. The **latency period** is quite often a major factor in determining the acceptability of the claim.

> **latency period**
> the time between exposure to a cause and development of a disease

There has been an increased emphasis on the importance of good mental health in the workplace. In 2013, the Mental Health Commission of Canada released the standard for psychological health and well-being in the workplace. The standard is a voluntary set of guidelines and resources to help organizations promote employees' psychological health and prevent harm due to workplace factors. For more information see http://www.mentalhealthcommission.ca.

WCBs in many jurisdictions allow for stress-related disabilities to be claimed for compensation. Stress-related disabilities (impairments) can be divided into three groups: (1) physical injury or occupational disease leading to a mental disability, (2) mental stress resulting in a physical disability, traumatic occurrence, or series of occurrences, and (3) mental stress resulting in a mental condition. Generally, stress claims in the first group have been dealt with in the same way as any other claims. Those in the second group have been subject to some selection. If the disability (say, a cardiac attack) is acute, it will be considered for compensation. If the disability (say, an ulcer) is a result of accumulated stress, it will likely not be considered for compensation. With respect to the third group, an unusual incident that provokes the mental reaction and results in a disability will probably be considered for compensation; chronic stress resulting in a mental disability is seldom compensated. In Ontario, a worker is entitled to benefits for traumatic mental stress that is an acute reaction to a sudden and unanticipated traumatic event (e.g., violent act, armed robbery), that is suffered by the individual or suffered through direct contact with victims (e.g., 911 operators, first responders). While WSIB recognizes the potential for a cumulative effect of multiple traumatic events, the policy stipulates that compensation is provided for acute reactions. Workers may not claim benefits for stress that is the result of employer-based actions such as termination, demotions, and changes in work hours or performance expectations. (See **OH&S Notebook 3.3** for WCB claims process.)

The adjudication of stress claims is currently receiving a great deal of attention from various insurance companies. The courts and human rights tribunals have consistently maintained that stress-related disorders or other psychological disabilities are to be treated the same as physical disabilities in employment settings.[3] In 2014, the Workplace Safety Insurance Appeals Tribunal (WSIAT) in Ontario overturned a decision by the WSIB that denied a nurse's claim for psychological stress resulting from verbal abuse and bullying over a 12-year period. WSIAT sided with the nurse, stating the WSIB decision to deny her claim violated her rights as stated in the Charter of Rights and Freedoms. It remains to be seen whether workers' compensation schemes that continue to defend their exclusion of some stress-related disorders can be maintained into the future.

OH&S NOTEBOOK 3.3

THE WCB CLAIMS PROCESS

When a worker is injured, to process a claim a WCB generally needs information from three parties: the employer, the employee, and a physician. Although the specific details for the process may vary somewhat from jurisdiction to jurisdiction, it is helpful to consider an example of a claims process at a very general level.

As an illustration, let's look at the very basics of the claims process in PEI in the event of an injury or illness.

Employer

When a worker reports a work-related injury or illness, the employer must file Form 7 within three days. Form 7 requests information about the worker, the workplace, the injury/illness, the type of work performed by the work, hours of work, wages, the nature of the incident, and details regarding lost work time. The form also involves preparing for potential return-to-work reports. Beyond completing the form, the employer has responsibilities in terms of keeping in contact with the worker, finding safe employment options for the worker, and keeping the WCB up to date.

Employee

The employee needs to report the injury to his or her employer and file Form 6 with the WCB. Form 6 needs to be submitted even when there is no lost time from work. Form 6 collects information about the worker, the workplace, the injury/illness, the type of work performed by the work, hours of work, wages, the nature of the incident, and the details regarding lost work time. The worker has responsibilities to take an active role in treatment, cooperate with return-to-work options, and keep the employer and WCB informed.

Health Care Providers

During the initial and follow-up medical visits, the physician completes and submits Form 8 to the WCB. Reports from additional health care services, such as physiotherapy or assessment services to determine worker capabilities, must also be submitted to the WCB

Once all the forms are submitted, an entitlement officer assumes the file and makes a decision on the claim. If it is accepted, benefits begin. If claims are not accepted, there is a process for reconsideration and appeals. Claims that require more time for processing are moved to a case management team.

Source: Workers Compensation Board of PEI. http://www.wcb.pe.ca.

// ASSESSMENTS

Employers are grouped together according to the type of operation or industry in which they are engaged, and they are assessed on that basis. The groups are referred to as industries, classes, subclasses, or classifications. In some jurisdictions, the terms "unit" and "sector" are used; employers are not grouped by occupation, though occupation may help determine a subdivision of an industry or class.

Separate accounts are generally used when an employer is involved in more than one industry or when an industry or employer's operation includes several departments. Assessments are determined by the WCB at least once a year when the board sets a percentage or rate to be applied to the payroll of the employer. Payrolls are estimated; the employer is then required to submit a certified payroll statement (see **OH&S Notebook 3.4**).

The workers' compensation system in Canada is based on the concept of dividing employers into three categories: (1) those who contribute to the incident fund and benefit from its collective liability, (2) those who are individually liable for their own employees' incidents, and (3) those in certain low-risk industries, who are excluded under various acts across the country. Employers who pay directly for the incidents of their employees are generally public enterprises such as provincial or territorial and municipal governments and certain transportation and communication companies within Crown corporations.

All employers within a particular industry group are assessed at the same rate based on the injury experience of the group as a whole. Some organizations calculate their own experience rating in order to help manage their own health and safety (see **OH&S Notebook 3.5**). In most jurisdictions, within the general incident fund, a provision is

---

OH&S NOTEBOOK 3.4

ILLUSTRATIVE INDUSTRY RATES

The average workers' compensation assessment in Ontario for 2016 was $2.40 for every $100 in insurable earnings. However, there are dramatic differences in premium assessment rates across occupational groups. For some sample rates, see the table below.

RATE GROUP	DESCRIPTION	ASSESSMENT PER $100 OF INSURABLE EARNINGS
030	Logging	$13.04
608	Beer stores	$4.17
641	Clothing stores	$1.59
638	Pharmacies	$0.70
817	Education facilities	$0.36
858	Group homes	$3.14
875	Professional offices and agencies	$0.73

Source: Workplace Safety and Insurance Board of Ontario, "2016 Premium Rates." Found at: http://www.wsib.on.ca/WSIBPortal/faces/WSIBDetail Page?cGUID=WSIB061756&rDef=WSIB_RD_ARTICLE&_afrLoop=450845634958168&_afrWindowMode=0&_afrWindowId=16eu40o4zb_190# %40%3FcGUID%3DWSIB061756%26_afrWindowId%3D16eu40o4zb_190%26_afrLoop%3D450845634958168%26rDef%3DWSIB_RD_ARTICLE%26 _afrWindowMode%3D0%26_adf.ctrl-state%3D16eu40o4zb_206 (accessed June 7, 2016).

CALCULATING INJURY FREQUENCY AND SEVERITY RATES

Following a workplace injury, a copy of the incident analysis report about the injury may accompany the firm's workers' compensation claim form. Injury and frequency rates are often used by individual organizations to set benchmarks or to set targets that will help manage their health and safety.

Depending on the industry, there are various ways to assess injury frequency and severity rates. The frequency rate is often defined as the number of medical aid injuries (or recordable events) relative to the number of hours worked expressed in a ratio of 200 000 labour hours. Some firms and jurisdictions use a factor of 1 000 000 rather than 200 000. Using the 200,000 figure, the relationship becomes

$$\text{frequency} = \frac{\text{number of injuries}}{\text{total hours worked}} \times 200{,}000$$

Take, as an example, a company that employs 300 people who work 8-hour shifts for 250 days in one year. The total number of hours worked is

$$250 \text{ (days)} \times 300 \text{ (people)} \times 8 \text{ (hour shifts)}$$
$$= 600\,000 \text{ total hours worked}$$

This company has a record of 6 medical-aid injuries with no lost time, 15 minor injuries with 5 days lost, 3 major injuries with 55 days lost, and 7 property damage incidents with no lost time. The total number of injuries is

$$(6 + 15 + 3) = 24$$

The frequency is calculated as

$$\text{frequency} = \frac{24}{600{,}000} \times 200{,}000 = 8$$

Therefore, this organization has an injury frequency ratio of 8 per 200 000, or 8.

Severity of work-related injuries is the ratio of the number of days lost due to injuries to a factor of 200 000. Severity is sometimes calculated by using the relationship

$$\text{severity} = \frac{\text{number of days lost to injuries}}{\text{total hours worked}} \times 200{,}000$$

The severity, based on the total number of days lost due to injury in the above example, would be calculated as

$$\text{total lost days} = (5 + 55) = 60$$

$$\text{severity} = \frac{60}{600{,}000} \times 200{,}000 = 20$$

The injury severity for this company is 20, or a ratio of 20:200 000. If the company works two or three shifts instead of one, as the examples show, then the total hours worked will be increased twofold or threefold and the relationship will be the same.

These figures facilitate comparisons between various years of the company and among companies within the same product and size group. These values can help identify trends. Records of injuries caused by incidents can also be used as a basis for risk and fault tree analyses.

made for a rate stabilization and disaster reserve fund. One group by itself cannot sustain the heavy costs associated with a major disaster that might occur in any one year, or with a sharp decline in assessable payroll owing to massive layoffs in the industry. Continued financing can be provided by the rate stabilization and disaster funds, which are maintained by the various WCBs.

EXPERIENCE RATING

Experience rating in workers' compensation refers to an incident insurance premium pricing scheme that takes into account the clear cost experience of the individual employer. Under experience rating, the assessment for each firm may be higher or lower than the basic rate for the relative industry group. Firms with lower-than-average incident costs per worker pay lower premiums than firms with above-average incident costs. In essence, experience rating reduces or eliminates the cross-subsidization of relatively unsafe firms by relatively safe firms. Given two otherwise similar firms, a safer employer will face lower workers' compensation costs and hence lower production costs. Thus, the primary effect of the experience rating is to create a financial incentive for relatively unsafe firms to begin caring for their workforces (see **OH&S Notebook 3.6**).

Experience rating is intended to offer an incentive to employers to reduce injuries and to return workers to their jobs as early as possible. In this way, employers benefit because the amount of money spent on compensation is reduced; workers benefit because they return to their jobs quickly. Experience rating is thus a process of rewarding good performers and penalizing those organizations that are not making efforts to reduce incidents and return workers back to work as quickly as possible.

Generally, if an employer has an experience rating of a three-year average injury cost lower than that of the entire group, that employer will receive a rebate on the annual assessment. Conversely, employers who have an average injury cost higher than the group will receive demerit charges on top of their regular assessments.

One of the most important reasons for experience rating is to reduce industrial incidents and injuries and their costs. The profit-maximizing, cost-minimizing firm will respond to the incentive by investing in activities that reduce its workers' compensation claim costs to the point where the expected marginal benefits (i.e., incremental

---

OH&S NOTEBOOK 3.6

EXPERIENCE RATING PROGRAMS IN ONTARIO

New Experimental Experience Rating Program (NEER)

NEER automatically applies to companies that pay more than $25 000 per year in premiums and are not in a construction rate group. NEER allows companies to earn rebates on premiums by maintaining a good health and safety record. Alternatively, companies that have a poor health and safety record will be assessed a surcharge. To establish whether a company's record is better or worse than average, it is compared with similar companies (i.e., a company's costs are compared within its rate group over the past four years). Companies are not penalized for long-term conditions such as hearing loss or asbestosis.

CAD-7

CAD-7 applies to employers in the construction sector whose average annual premiums are more than $25 000. Similar to NEER, a company's claim history is compared with that of similar firms within a rate group to determine whether a surcharge or rebate is applicable. The plan

uses a rating factor to determine the extent to which an individual employer is held responsible for its own costs. The rating factor is based on person hours derived from employer's total insurable earnings from the last two years. Depending on the number of derived person hours within the last two years, this factor can range from .15 for employers with upwards of 21,000 hours to 1.0 for employers with upwards of 100,000 derived person hours. When the calculated factor is above the maximum, it is reduced; however, if the calculated factor is below the minimum, it is increased.

Merit Adjusted Premium (MAP) Plan for Small Business

MAP is similar to the foregoing programs but applies to firms paying between $1000 and $25 000 in annual WCB premiums). Generally, MAP decreases or increases to premiums do not take effect until after three years of continuous operations (though increases may be applied earlier if a significant number of claims are filed).

Source: Workplace Safety and Insurance Board of Ontario, 2011. "Experience Rating: NEER (New Experimental Experience Rating Plan)," *Operations Policy Manual*, #3, June 30, p. 488, http://www.wsib.on.ca. Accessed March 1, 2016.

reduction in the expected cost of injuries and incidents) equal the marginal costs. Given the existence of workplace risk, and assuming full information about such risk, the firm may allocate resources to safety practices or pay the costs associated with work injury. Profit-maximizing firms operating in competitive markets will strive to minimize some of the costs associated with workplace injuries and incidents, such as workers' compensation premium payments (including experience rating service charges/refunds as well as material costs), fixed employment costs, lost production time, and damage to equipment, by preventing incidents (i.e., reducing the probability of a hazardous state) as well as by engaging in activities that minimize costs when incidents do occur. Post-incident employer actions that can result in claim cost reduction include implementing early return-to-work programs and appealing WCB decisions on workers' benefits.

The workers' compensation boards in several jurisdictions (e.g., Ontario, Alberta, BC) operate experience rating plans with the goal of creating incentives for firms to reduce their claim rates. That is, the experience rating systems attempt to reward safe firms (through a rebate of assessment premiums) and to penalize unsafe firms (through a surcharge on premiums). Such programs provide some leverage to firms seeking to reduce their workers' compensation costs: to the extent that firms can establish and maintain better-than-average safety records, costs will be decreased.

Empirically, then, the question is whether experience rating schemes actually work. That is, do they decrease incidents or injuries in the workplace? This is an exceedingly complex question, and there does not appear to be a clear answer thus far.[4] Some evidence suggests that such plans are effective in improving workplace safety.[5]

// REPORTING REQUIREMENTS

In most jurisdictions, employers are required to report all workplace injuries to the workers' compensation board within a certain time. In Manitoba, for example, the requirement is to report within five days of learning of an injury. In New Brunswick, employers must report serious (e.g., fatality, loss of limb) incidents immediately; other incidents within 24 hours; or, if neither of these applies, within three days of learning of the incident. Each board provides a form for employer reporting. **Figure 3.1** shows the form used for employer reporting in Manitoba (note that each board has its own form, though all are very similar). Essentially the employer report is designed to collect information about (1) the nature of the employment relationship, (2) the employee's salary and hours of work, (3) the nature of the incident and injury, and (4) the extent of time loss and medical treatment. These elements will then enter into the determination of whether the employee is eligible for compensation and, if so, the amount and duration of this compensation.

Employees are also required to report to the WCB if they want to open a claim for compensation. Employees often do not want to complete an incident report if they do not plan to open a claim (e.g., have not incurred medical expenses, do not intend to miss time). Though not a requirement, it is a good idea for employees to file a report—one never knows when a seemingly minor injury will become something much more serious later on, and having the paper work filed will make subsequent claims easier to file. A typical employee report is presented in **Figure 3.2**; it collects basically the same information as the employer report.

Reporting requirements for employers and employees vary by province.

FIGURE 3.1

EMPLOYER INCIDENT REPORT, MANITOBA

WCB
Workers Compensation
Board of Manitoba

Please FAX this form IMMEDIATELY to:
954-4999 (Toll-free 1-877-872-3804)

or report this claim by calling:
954-4100 (Toll-free 1-800-362-3340)
333 Broadway • Winnipeg R3C 4W3

EMPLOYER'S INCIDENT REPORT

Claim No.		2

Employer Information

Business Name	Address (include Branch where applicable)		
City	Province	Postal Code	Firm Number	Industry Code	Telephone No. ( )

Worker Information

Last Name	First Name
Address	City
Province	Postal Code	Telephone No. ( )	Date of Birth DD / MM / YYYY
Social Insurance Number	Male ☐ Female ☐	Job Title

Incident Details

Date of Incident DD / MM / YYYY	Area(s) of Injury
Date Reported to Employer DD / MM / YYYY	Name and position of person to whom incident was reported.

Please describe the incident in as much detail as possible. (Use separate sheet if necessary)

City and province where incident occurred.

If the incident occurred out of province, is the worker's usual place of employment in Manitoba? ☐ yes ☐ no   Had the worker been employed outside of Manitoba for 6 months or longer at the time of the incident? ☐ yes ☐ no

Did the incident occur on your premises? ☐ yes ☐ no   If no, specify name and address of premises where incident happened.

Name and Address of Doctor(s) and/or Hospital(s) who Provided Treatment   (If known)

Name	Address
Name	Address

Time Loss & Wages (Only complete this section if the worker missed time from work beyond the date of the incident)

What was the last day and hour worked following the incident?	DD / MM / YYYY at HOUR ☐AM ☐PM
Has the worker returned to work? ☐ yes ☐ no If yes, when?	DD / MM / YYYY at HOUR ☐AM ☐PM
Are you continuing to pay the worker during time loss? ☐ yes ☐ no	What wages were paid to the worker on the last date worked? $
How many hours does the worker work per week? If it varies, please describe.	What are the worker's regular days off? If it varies, please describe.
What are the worker's regular gross earnings? (Specify weekly, bi-weekly, etc.) $	What are the worker's total gross earnings for the last calendar year? $
What date did the worker begin employment with your firm? DD / MM / YYYY	If employed less than one year, what are the worker's gross earnings for the period from the date of employment to the date of the incident? $
If employed more than one year, what are the worker's gross earnings during the twelve months prior to the date of the incident? $	Are you able to accommodate worker in alternate duties? ☐ yes ☐ no

WCB 2009   Aussi disponible en français

For Faster Claim Reporting, Please Call 954-4100

Page 1 of 2

FIGURE 3.1

EMPLOYER INCIDENT REPORT, MANITOBA (*continued*)

Worker's Name	Claim No.	2

Coverage

Was anyone not employed by you involved in the incident? ☐ yes ☐ no	If yes, give name and address.

Is the worker a partner, director or sole proprietor of the company? ☐ yes ☐ no

Please answer these questions if the incident occurred between Jan. 1, 1992 and Dec. 31, 2005

Is the worker a member of the employer's family (or if the employer is a corporation, a family member of the director of the corporation)? ☐ yes ☐ no

If yes, does the worker reside with the employer or director? ☐ yes ☐ no

Is the worker a sub-contractor? ☐ yes ☐ no   If yes, specify: ☐ Construction ☐ Logging   (Complete appropriate sections below)

Is the worker an owner operator? ☐ yes ☐ no   If yes, specify: ☐ Courier ☐ Trucking ☐ Towing   (Complete appropriate sections below)

Farming:

Is the worker related to the farm owner? ☐ yes ☐ no

Sub-Contractor or Owner Operator: (only complete if worker is a sub-contractor or owner operator)

Are you covering the worker under your WCB coverage? ☐ yes ☐ no	If no, is the worker registered with WCB? ☐ yes ☐ no	
Does the worker work in a partnership? ☐ yes ☐ no	Does the worker employ other workers? ☐ yes ☐ no	

Sub-Contractor in Construction

Does the worker supply any materials or equipment? ☐ yes ☐ no	If yes, please specify.

Sub-Contractor in Logging

Does the worker supply any materials or equipment? ☐ yes ☐ no	If yes, please specify.
Was the worker cutting on the firm's timber sale, timber permit or sawmill license? ☐ yes ☐ no	If no, on whose timber sale, timber permit or sawmill license was the worker cutting?

Owner Operator is a Courier

What is the gross vehicle weight? (This can be obtained from the Autopac registration)

Owner Operator in Trucking

Does the worker haul within a 16 km radius of the city or town in which the home terminal is located? ☐ yes ☐ no	Is the worker a long distance driver? ☐ yes ☐ no
Does the worker provide a vehicle? ☐ yes ☐ no	If yes, how many vehicles?

Name and Position of Person Completing Report	Date DD / MM / YYYY

Page 2 of 2

Source: Workers Compensation Board of Manitoba.

FIGURE 3.2

WORKER INCIDENT REPORT, MANITOBA

WCB
Workers Compensation
Board of Manitoba

To report your claim faster, please CALL:
954-4100   (Toll-free 1-800-362-3340)

or fax this form to:
954-4999   (Toll-free 1-877-872-3804)
333 Broadway • Winnipeg R3C 4W3

WORKER INCIDENT REPORT

Claim No.	
	3

Worker Information

Last Name	First Name
Address	City

Province	Postal Code	Telephone No. ( )	Date of Birth DD / MM / YYYY	PHIN ___ ___ - ___ ___ - ___

Social Insurance Number	Male ☐ Female ☐	Job Title

Employer Information

Business Name	Address (include Branch where applicable)

City	Province	Postal Code	Telephone No. ( )

Incident Details

Date of Incident DD / MM / YYYY	Area(s) of Injury
Date Reported to Employer DD / MM / YYYY	Name and position of person to whom incident was reported.

Please describe the incident in as much detail as possible. (Use separate sheet if necessary. If applicable, identify any witnesses.)

City and province where incident occurred.

Did the incident occur on your employer's premises?   ☐ yes ☐ no   If no, specify name and address of premises where incident happened.

Name and Address of Doctor(s) and/or Hospital(s) that Provided Treatment (Attach separate sheet if necessary)

Name	Address	Date of Visit DD / MM / YYYY
Name	Address	Date of Visit DD / MM / YYYY

Time Loss & Wages (Only complete this section if you have missed time from work beyond the date of the incident)

What was the last day and hour you worked following the incident?	DD / MM / YYYY at HOUR ☐AM ☐PM

Have you returned to work? ☐ yes ☐ no   If yes, when?   DD / MM / YYYY   at   HOUR   ☐AM ☐PM

Were you paid wages by your employer while you were off work? ☐ yes ☐ no	Do you have other sources of employment income? ☐ yes ☐ no
How many hours do you work per week? If it varies, please describe.	What are your regular days off? If it varies, please describe.
What is your current hourly wage? $	What are your regular gross earnings? (Specify weekly, bi-weekly, etc.) $

What is your marital status?
☐ Single ☐ Common-law ☐ Married ☐ Separated ☐ Divorced   If married/common-law, is your spouse/partner working? ☐ yes ☐ no

Are you personally allowed to claim a deduction on your current year Income Tax Return for:

Dependant children age 18 years or younger? ☐ yes ☐ no   If yes, how many dependants? _____

Disabled dependants age 18 years or older? ☐ yes ☐ no   If yes, how many dependants? _____

Child care expenses?   ☐ yes ☐ no   If yes, estimate total deduction for current tax year $ _____

Child support payments?   ☐ yes ☐ no   If yes, state monthly amount $ _____   Total for the year $ _____

Spousal support payments?   ☐ yes ☐ no   If yes, state monthly amount $ _____   Total for the year $ _____

Have you applied for income from other sources? (e.g. EI, CPP, Social Insurance, Co. Disability Plan, etc.)   ☐ yes ☐ no   If yes, please describe.

WCB 2009

For Faster Claim Reporting, Please Call 954-4100

Aussi disponible en français

Page 1 of 2

FIGURE 3.2

WORKER INCIDENT REPORT, MANITOBA (*continued*)

Worker's Name	Claim No.	**3**

Coverage

Was anyone not employed by your employer involved in the incident?	☐ yes ☐ no	If yes, give name and address.
Are you a partner, director or sole proprietor of the company? ☐ yes ☐ no		
Are you a sub-contractor? ☐ yes ☐ no	If yes, specify: ☐ construction ☐ logging	(Complete appropriate sections below)
Are you an owner operator? ☐ yes ☐ no	If yes, specify: ☐ courier ☐ trucking ☐ towing	(Complete appropriate sections below)

Please answer these questions if the incident occurred between Jan. 1, 1992 and Dec. 31, 2005

Are you a member of the family of your employer (or if the employer is a corporation, a family member of the director of the corporation)? ☐ yes ☐ no

If yes, do you reside with the employer or director? ☐ yes ☐ no

Farming:

Are you related to the farm owner? ☐ yes ☐ no

Sub-Contractor or Owner Operator: (only complete if you are a sub-contractor or owner operator)

Is your employer covering you under their WCB coverage? ☐ yes ☐ no		If no, are you registered with WCB? ☐ yes ☐ no	
Do you work in a partnership?	☐ yes ☐ no	Do you employ other workers?	☐ yes ☐ no

Sub-Contractor in Construction

Do you supply any materials or equipment?	☐ yes ☐ no	If yes, please specify.

Sub-Contractor in Logging

Do you supply any materials or equipment?	☐ yes ☐ no	If yes, please specify.
Were you cutting on the firm's timber sale, timber permit or sawmill license? ☐ yes ☐ no		If no, on whose timber sale, timber permit or sawmill license were you cutting?

Owner Operator is a Courier

What is the gross vehicle weight? (This can be obtained from the Autopac registration)

Owner Operator in Trucking

Do you haul within a 16 km radius of the city or town in which the home terminal is located?	☐ yes ☐ no	Are you a long distance driver?	☐ yes ☐ no
Do you provide a vehicle?	☐ yes ☐ no	If yes, how many vehicles do you provide?	

I understand that under *The Workers Compensation Act* the WCB can collect information about me to adjudicate and manage my claim and that information from my claim may be disclosed to my employer or employer representative for WCB program purposes, or may be released to others as authorized by legislation, including *The Workers Compensation Act, The Personal Health Information Act* and *The Freedom of Information and Protection of Privacy Act*. The information collected may be used to conduct WCB evaluations and surveys.

If you have any questions regarding the collection, use or disclosure of information on your claim, please contact the WCB's Access and Privacy Officer at 954-4557 or toll free at 1-800-362-3340 extension 4557.

Release for Medical Information
I authorize persons in possession of medical and other information that the WCB determines relevant to this claim to release same to the WCB upon request.

Release for Income Information from Canada Customs and Revenue Agency
This is your authorization to provide the Workers Compensation Board of Manitoba with copies of my complete income tax return(s) and other taxpayer information including all supporting information slips, schedules and financial statements. The information will be used:

(1) to assist in establishing my net average earnings and
(2) to determine and verify eligibility for benefits under the Workers Compensation Act.

This authorization is valid for the two taxation years prior to the year it was signed, the year it was signed, and each following taxation year where benefits are provided.

Signature of Worker	Date
X	DD / MM / YYYY

Page 2 of 2

Source: Workers Compensation Board of Manitoba.

NONCOMPLIANCE

When employers and employees fail to comply with the act in their jurisdiction, then penalties and fines can be applied. Penalties and fines vary slightly in that penalties do not require court proceedings. For instance, in Manitoba the WCB has the authority to levy penalties for those who fail to comply with provisions within the act. Employers can be required to pay upward of $50 000 for certain offences. Penalties can be imposed for various reasons including administrative violations. If an employer discourages an employee from filing a claim or punishes the worker for filing the claim then a penalty of $4000 can be imposed. Similarly, if an employee fails to report to WCB that he or she has returned to work, he or she can be penalized.[6] Reporting requirements can be found on each WCB provincial website (see **OHS Notebook 3.2**).

// SUMMARY

Workers' compensation was established in Canada in 1914 with the passage of Ontario's Workmen's Compensation Act. Since then, coverage and benefits have increased, as have the associated costs. Though the primary goal of workers' compensation is to ensure that injured workers receive appropriate treatment, compensation, and rehabilitation, WCBs often engage in promoting occupational health and safety and trying to prevent occupational injuries. WCBs fund these activities by collecting a premium (based on industry, amount of payroll, and previous claim history) from employers. Compensation for stress-related and chronic conditions still remains a challenge for many boards and while some industries are challenging current policies and practices, others are making gains. Workplace injuries are fundamentally about more than financial losses to workers and employers. Each and every individual has a moral and ethical responsibility to ensure he or she is working as safety as possible and providing a safe and healthy work environment.

KEY TERMS

collective liability 52
latency period 62
loss of functional capacity 59
net earnings 57
physical rehabilitation 61
social rehabilitation 61
vocational rehabilitation 61

DISCUSSION QUESTIONS

1. Imagine you work for a large grocery in the meat department. An incident with the meat grinder has left you with significant lacerations on your hand and you are unable to return to work. What type of assistance might you expect from

workers' compensation? What could your manager do to expedite your return to work?

2. Outline the responsibilities of WCBs today. Describe how these responsibilities have changed over the years since the inception of workers' compensation in 1914.

3. If you are employed, talk with the health and safety manager in your organization. (If you are a student, ask to speak to the safety officer at your school.) Obtain information about the organization's sector, assessment, and record-of-experience ratings.

USING THE INTERNET

1. Check the workers' compensation board in your area. What cost savings are available to firms that improve their health and safety record? What obligations exist to implement return-to-work procedures?

2. Most WCBs publish their current rates online. Pick a single industry and find the appropriate rate group assessment across the provinces and territories. Who pays the highest assessments? Who pays the lowest?

EXERCISES

1. Various jurisdictions have struggled with how employees should be compensated for stress-related disabilities. Using the workers' compensation websites listed in **OH&S Notebook 3.2**, check to see how the following scenarios are handled in your jurisdiction:
   a. mental–mental stress at work results in a psychological disorder (e.g., depression)
   b. mental/physical–mental stress at work results in a physical disorder (e.g., heart attack)
   c. physical/mental–an incident at work results in a psychological disorder (e.g., anxiety attacks)

2. Company X operates one 12-hour shift per day for 220 days per year. It employs 315 people. The company records show a history of incidents and injuries:
   • 3 medical aid injuries with no days lost
   • 15 property damage incidents with a total of 35 days lost
   • 11 equipment failures that caused a total of 20 days lost
   • 19 injuries requiring medical attention with a total of 75 days lost

3. Calculate the following (refer to **OH&S Notebook 3.4** for the formulas):
   a. frequency
   b. severity

4. Explain how the company's severity rate can have a significant increase while the frequency rate has a very minor increase.

CHAPTER 3 Workers' Compensation

OH&S IN ACTION

You have been hired to help revitalize a worker's compensation social media campaign that targets youth and new workers. The current board received feedback that its social media materials include very technical language that is difficult to understand and information youth do not feel is relevant. You need to revamp this material to ensure the information is accurate, engaging, positive, and informative, and reaches as many young and new workers as possible. Outline the following:

- What information about the worker's compensation system do you think should be included in these materials? What information can be excluded? Explain why.
- How will you make this information engaging to youth and new workers? Provide one to two example materials.
- What social media platforms will you use to target youth and new workers?
- How will you plan to evaluate the impact of your social media campaign?

CASE STUDY 1   THE EMPLOYER'S DUTY

Sulleman has worked for Speedy Courier for the past three years. Last Tuesday he was loading his truck when he suddenly screamed in pain. Apparently, he had injured his back while lifting a box that exceeded the weight limits. Sulleman was rushed to the hospital, where they could find no evidence of injury other than the pain expressed by Sulleman. Knowing that a lack of hard evidence is common in these types of injuries, you can assume that Sulleman will be off work for a considerable period. As the HR representative for Speedy Courier, you have been charged with fulfilling the company's responsibilities under the act. In this regard, senior management has expressed concern about the number of claims and the fact that most recent claims have been for extended periods (e.g., several exceeding 12 months). What do you need to do?

CASE STUDY 2   A STRESSFUL JOB

Carol is an emergency paramedic first responder in her city. She has always enjoyed the hustle of working with emergencies and the challenges of dealing with the unexpected. Lately, though, she has been worried about her own well-being. She has been very abrupt with her coworkers on several occasions and has had difficulty concentrating on her job. Though there have been no problems to date, she is worried that her deteriorating performance might cause a problem, given the critical nature of her work. She has not yet been to a doctor as she fears they will put her on medications for depression and worries that if she is told to take time off that workers' compensation won't cover her lost salary. She has come to you for help. As the HR professional, what would you advise Carol?

// NOTES

1. K. Roberts, "Using Workers' Compensation to Promote a Healthy Workplace," in D.A. Hoffman and L.E. Tetrick, eds., *Health and Safety in Organizations: A Multi-Level Perspective* (San Francisco: Jossey Bass, 2003), 367.

2. B. Kirsh, T. Slack, and C.A. King, "Nature, Impact of Stigma Towards Injured Workers," *Journal of Occupational Rehabilitation*, 22 (2012): 143–54.

3. E.K. Kelloway, L. Francis, V.M. Catano, J. Cameron, and A. Day, *Psychological Disorders in the Canadian Forces: Legal and Social Issues–Contractor's Report* (Ottawa: National Defence Headquarters, Director Human Resources Research and Evaluation, 2004).

4. K. Roberts, "Using Workers' Compensation to Promote a Healthy Workplace," in D.A. Hoffman and L.E. Tetrick, eds., *Health and Safety in Organizations: A Multi-Level Perspective* (San Francisco: Jossey Bass, 2003).

5. D. Durbin and R. Butler, "Prevention of Disability for Work-Related Sources: The Roles of Risk Management, Government Intervention, and Insurance," in T. Thomason, J.F. Burton, and D.E. Hyatt, eds., *New Approaches to Disability in the Workplace* (Madison: IRRA, 1998).

6. Workers Compensation Board of Manitoba, "Fines and Penalties." Found at: http://www.wcb.mb.ca/fines-and-penalties-0 (accessed June 7, 2016).

CHAPTER
4

HAZARD RECOGNITION, RISK ASSESSMENT, AND CONTROL

CHAPTER LEARNING OBJECTIVES

AFTER READING THIS CHAPTER, YOU SHOULD BE ABLE TO:
- define key terms used in the field of occupational health and safety
- identify the sources of workplace hazards
- describe the types of injuries caused by workplace hazards
- identify types of workplace hazards
- describe methods for systematically examining workplace hazards and risk
- describe the processes for controlling hazards and managing risk

ROGUE WAVE

On March 25, 2015, a whale watching tour off the coast of Tofino, Vancouver Island, BC, headed toward an area known for being rich with sea life. According to news reports, this was a trip the *MV Leviathan II*, its skipper, and three crew members had made many times before. The weather on this particular day was said to be moderate with light rain and relatively calm waters, a seemingly average day. Sadly, the excursion turned tragic when an apparent rogue wave struck the boat, causing it to capsize. The vessel sank, resulting in the drowning death of six passengers. Thanks to surrounding First Nations fishers and locals from the area, 21 of the passengers and crew were rescued. At publication time, the Transportation Safety Board of Canada (TSB) had yet to finalize its investigation; however, its initial findings, supported by witness accounts, indicate that a significant wave broadsided the tour boat, leaving no time for a mayday or distress call. The TSB is investigating various factors that may have contributed to this disaster such as operational procedures, weather, and whether the boat's stability was affected by majority of passengers standing on one side of the top deck of the converted 20 metre vessel.

According to the National Ocean Service of the National Oceanic and Atmospheric Administration in the United States a rogue wave is more than twice the size of surrounding waves, and is very unexpected and unpredictable in nature as it can appear from a direction that is counter to existing winds. Given the nature of rogue waves, how can marine-based organizations adequately assess and prepare for hazards such as rogue waves which are very rare and unpredictable in nature? Consider other environments wherein certain hazards are difficult to forecast (e.g., aviation, medicine). Hazard recognition and risk assessments are a proactive and systematic approach to identifying hazards as well as mitigating any negative consequences should those risks be realized. Will you be prepared if a particular event occurs? You may decide to continue with a course of action (e.g., continue with a whale watching tour), however you may alter your approach, or even implement a stricter set of procedures as a result. This situation not only highlights the importance of properly assessing risks and taking the appropriate measures to mitigate or control any potential consequences but also illustrates one of the many environments wherein hazard assessment and risk analysis can be very difficult and complex. Hazard identification, risk assessment and control are the backbone of workplace OH&S programs and are the focus of this chapter.

It is believed a rogue wave resulted in the capsizing of this tour boat in Tofino, British Columbia, which illustrates the complexity of hazard and risk assessments.

Source: CBC News (October 25, 2015), "5 dead, 1 missing after whale watching vessel sinks off Tofino, BC," CBC News British Columbia. Found at http://www.cbc.ca/news/canada/british-columbia/tour-vessel-sinks-off-tofino-with-fatalities-1.3288191 (accessed March 1, 2016); National Ocean Service http://oceanservice.noaa.gov/facts/roguewaves.html (accessed April 2, 2016).

Almost every workplace has recognizable hazards to which people are exposed. There are many different definitions of the term "hazard"; however, the term is typically defined as any source of potential adverse health effects, damage, or harm to something or someone under certain conditions at work.[1] Hazards within the work environment pose a risk to those within that environment and, in order to manage that risk, the hazard and its potential must be properly understood, assessed, and controlled using a systematic process known as hazard identification, risk assessment, and control.

// TERMINOLOGY

The explanations of hazard identification, risk assessment, and control involve very specific terms, some of which are often used incorrectly or interchangeably. Though the following terms might seem similar to one another, each has a distinctive use in the OH&S field:

- A **hazard** is any object, action, or condition that can be a source of potential adverse health effect, damage, or harm to people, processes, or equipment within the workplace. Examples of objects that can be considered workplace hazards are chemicals used to disinfect a surface, or sharp objects and machinery. Examples of hazardous conditions are icy steps, or an understaffed shift rotation. Examples of hazardous actions are not wearing personal protective equipment (e.g., gloves), or not following safety procedures.

- Generally the term **incident** is defined as an event or occurrence that had or could have had a negative impact on people, property, or processes. Events that could have had a negative impact are frequently referred to as close calls or near-miss incidents. A close call or near-miss incident is any unplanned event wherein harm or equipment loss almost occurred but was successfully prevented or mitigated. Examples of close calls include not wearing safety glasses when operating a power saw and nearly being hit by flying debris, or brushing against hot objects with unprotected hands without getting burned. Close calls or near-miss incidents involve the presence of a hazard but may or may not result in harm or loss.

- **Risk** is typically defined in terms of the probability or the extent to which a hazard is likely to cause harm to people, processes, or equipment. The concept of **risk perception** is based on the individual's interpretation of the potential for harm and his or her concern for the consequences based on social, physical, political, cultural, and psychological factors that then influence how an individual behaves in response to that hazard.[2]

// HAZARD RECOGNITION AND IDENTIFICATION

When hazards are being identified, one considers the sources: biological, chemical, ergonomic, physical, and psychosocial (discussed in detail in following chapters) followed by the specific type of hazard. There are five categories of hazard types—people, equipment, environment, materials, and processes—that should be considered during the hazard identification process.

PEOPLE

Humans create hazards in the workplace by their actions or inactions. Proper training, administration, leadership, and supervision are required to ensure that employees engage in the appropriate workplace behaviours. Incidents involving humans are referred to as unsafe acts. An **unsafe act** generally refers to a deviation from standard job procedures or practices that increase the potential for an incident and harm. A human action that may cause an immediate event of any type, and over which the person has control, is considered a direct, unsafe act (sometimes referred to as a *substandard practice*).

---

hazard
any object, action, or condition that can be a source of potential adverse health effect, damage, or harm to people, processes, or equipment within the workplace

incident
an event or occurrence that had or could have had a negative impact on people, property, or processes

risk
the probability or the extent to which a hazard is likely to cause harm to people, processes, or equipment

risk perception
an individual's interpretation of the potential for harm based on values, beliefs, and experience with a hazard

unsafe act
a deviation from standard job procedures or practices that increases a worker's exposure to a hazard

---

An example would be improper modifications to a respirator to allow a cigarette to be smoked through the filter cassette. An indirect, unsafe act is one in which the human action is only indirectly involved. Consider the following example: a designer of a machine who alters the braking system on a punch press that allows the machine to complete its operating cycle after the emergency stop is activated instead of immediately stopping. In this instance there is overlap between an indirect unsafe act and an unsafe condition. The machine defect started as an indirect unsafe act but resulted in an unsafe condition for the operators using the machine.

Unsafe acts are observable behaviours that are the direct outcome of a decision made by an individual. Unsafe acts that contribute to or cause an incident are labelled as human factors.

When a worker or another person causes an incident by commission (doing something), poor judgment, or omission (failing to do something), the cause is labelled a human factor. An example of a human factor would be when a physician does not engage in proper hand hygiene practices between patient visits even when there is minimal direct contact with the patient. When conducting hazard recognition and risk assessment process it is important to consider the role of human factors. Much of what incorporate into this process comes from what we have learned from the investigation process. A human action can be directly or indirectly involved in an event, and the purpose of an investigation is to determine what actions led to a particular outcome and how this information can be incorporated into the hazard recognition and risk assessment process. From the investigation perspective, the point of examining human factors is not to determine whether an individual had ill intent to cause harm; it is to determine how these factors can be prevented and incorporated into safe operations. No matter how many backup systems are in place, some shortcut or personal foible can cause the system to fail. The intent of hazard recognition, risk assessment, and control is to understand this and to take a proactive approach to managing our safety and the various possible outcomes.

EQUIPMENT

Under certain conditions or situations the tools, machines, or equipment people use and work near can be hazardous. Examples of equipment that can be hazardous include defective tools (broken ladder) and unguarded moving machinery (unguarded saw blades in a butcher shop). When considering the equipment in the workplace that can be hazardous it is important to carefully consider what is workplace equipment and to ensure that everyday equipment like office, lunchroom, or kitchen equipment are considered.

ENVIRONMENT

Some hazards can be created by the work environment and can be either naturally occurring (e.g., weather in outdoor work environments) or the result of an unsafe condition caused by poorly maintained equipment, tools, or facilities.

The following are examples of an unsafe work environment:

- Improper illumination—too dark or too much glare
- Poor exhaust or ventilation systems—the toxic vapours from a process hang in the air rather than being removed
- Defective equipment and materials—not to the required specifications

- Adverse temperature conditions—working around a furnace on a hot summer day
- Poor indoor air quality—odours and stuffiness

Environmental factors, which encompass sources of hazards such as physical, chemical, biological factors, and ergonomic factors, can play a direct *or* indirect role in incidents. For example, factors such as noise, vibration, and temperature extremes have an obvious relation to safety and exist within certain work environments. A noisy work environment, such as a kitchen, may prevent a worker from hearing approaching individuals or may damage hearing over time. Similarly, chemical factors such as airborne toxic gases not only may cause illness, but also may impair a worker's reaction, judgment, or concentration. Contact with biological agents such as viruses or parasites may cause either minor illness—a cold—or something more serious—hepatitis B.

MATERIALS

Materials are any workplace substance, matter, or provisions used in the workplace that have the potential to cause harm or loss especially if handled improperly. Examples of materials include supplies and raw materials such as wood within a carpentry shop, dry-cleaning chemicals, acetone or nail polish remover in a spa, or cleaning chemicals in a hotel. When materials are improperly handled or misused or if the wrong materials are used during production they can become a hazard or create hazardous conditions. For instance, certain cleaning materials such as ammonia and bleach should never be mixed together because the mixture results in a toxic chemical reaction. Ensuring the proper handling and use of workplace materials is very important and requires training (e.g., WHMIS training).

PROCESSES

When combining people, equipment, environment, and materials with the purpose of production of a good or service, a process is involved. Processes involve the flow of work and include factors such as design, pace, and organization of the various types of work via policies, procedures, and work processes. Work processes can result in various hazardous by-products when combined with people, equipment, environment, and materials. While the objects and equipment in and of themselves are types of hazards, when combined with a poor process or procedure then the process or procedure itself is a hazard.

// HAZARD IDENTIFICATION PROGRAMS

A hazard identification program (or hazard recognition) is simply a systematic means of identifying and recording hazards in the workplace. They are designed to integrate safe and healthy procedures into job tasks and procedures. The process of hazard identification should be completed by safety experts or employees who are trained to recognize hazards that might not be readily apparent to the casual observer. The hazard identification process can be as simple as a visible inspection of the workplace or as complex as taking air samples to test for suspected contaminants. There are various methodologies available for conducting a hazard identification; however, it is critical that a sequential and systematic process is used to ensure that no hazard is overlooked.

COMPONENTS OF THE HAZARD IDENTIFICATION PROGRAM

A safety professional can enter a worksite and, by walking through, note hazards. The utility of a **walk-through survey** is increased when the supervisor and a worker member of the joint health and safety committee (JHSC) accompany the safety expert. **Safety sampling**, often referred to as *behaviour* or *activity sampling*, is a systematic survey procedure undertaken by safety personnel, who record their observations of unsafe practices on a sampling document. They might observe, for example, workers without hardhats where they are required.

Actual and observable exposures to hazards are the focus of the survey. Following the walk-through survey, the safety personnel encode and count their observations. A report is then submitted to management to provide an objective evaluation of the type and number of unsafe acts and conditions.

Management can ask workers who represent a variety of tasks and jobs to identify hazards and unsafe conditions. Employees might report that they are required to adapt tools (thus rendering them potentially hazardous) in order to meet production quotas, or to make room for a new piece of equipment (e.g., photocopier) by placing paper boxes in a hallway for storage, rendering a corridor treacherous. Discussions with both the experts and the employees should be supplemented by an analysis of the job site and the work performed.

Additionally, the company should have a detailed layout of the plant or premises, showing the location of processes, machinery, equipment, and materials storage. Having this information available in printed format allows for quick retrieval in emergency situations.

walk-through survey
a survey in which a safety professional walks through a worksite and notes hazards

safety sampling
a systematic survey procedure undertaken by safety personnel who record their observations of unsafe practices on a sampling document

TASK AND JOB INVENTORY

A description of the job and its associated tasks should be obtained and organized by department, operation, or product. The human resource department can assist by providing **job descriptions**, the content and hierarchy specific to a particular job, and **job specifications**, which are the requirements necessary to perform the various functions of a job (e.g., ability to lift weight, education level).

Task analysis refers to the systematic examination of a job's many components. It consists of a list of tasks and the job of which they are a part, the number of workers who perform the same or similar tasks, the time spent on each task, the importance of the task to the job, the complexity and criticality of the job, the learning curve if complicated and repetitive, and the effort required. The analysis identifies the various demands on the worker, the tasks that are susceptible to worker error and stress, and potentially hazardous conditions. Industrial engineering methods are best for performing this kind of analysis.

job description
the content and hierarchy specific to a particular job

job specifications
the requirements necessary to perform the various functions of a job (e.g., ability to lift weight, education level)

AUDITS AND REPORTS

Workplace safety audits typically involve a comprehensive and systematic review of one or more components of an organization's health and safety–related programs and documents. Audits are designed to identify and correct any outdated or missing information and to ensure the reliability and effectiveness of the various workplace inspections, education of workers, policies, and procedures. Workplace inspections are a systematic process of investigating previous incidents and the current work environment looking for hazards and unsafe acts. A review of the reports filed after an incident, or injury, or as part of a safety inspection, will provide valuable information on hazards. Also, OH&S departments and safety associations can provide written information about the types of accidents in similar industries. Accident and injury rates published by governments are another source of information. For example, most workers' compensation boards (for a complete list, see Chapter 3) publish regular reports on accident statistics.

Workplace audits and inspection and investigation reports, which are obtained by reviewing records of all injuries, accidents, incidents, workplace design changes, and environmental sampling, are extremely useful sources for cataloguing hazards. Inspection reports typically include equipment and chemical inventories, diagrams of the work environment, and procedural or equipment checklists. The frequency of audits and inspections depends on factors such as legislation and the type of work, previous incidents, size of work operations, introduction of new work processes or equipment, and work hours/shifts. Consider the frequency with which a fitness facility may conduct safety audits compared to a local clothing retail company. How this information is stored, analyzed, and used is extremely important. Most large organizations use computers to store, analyze, and report on hazards and incidents, thus facilitating the identification of hazards by type or department.[3] Audit and inspection reports are a key component to identify hazards in the workplace before an incident.

HAZARD ANALYSIS

Hazard analysis is used to acquire specific hazard and failure information about a given system.[4] Hazard analysis is an orderly, analytical technique that examines a system for the most probable hazards having the severest consequences, for the purpose of establishing corrective or control mechanisms. The most common form of hazard analysis is the analytical tree, of which there are two types. The **positive tree** shows, graphically, how a job should be done. The more frequently used tree is the **fault tree**, which illustrates things that can go wrong. A typical fault tree structure is shown in **Figure 4.1**.

RISK ASSESSMENT

Once hazards have been identified, the risk of an incident or injury must be determined. Risk assessments are a critical aspect of occupational health and safety in every organization regardless of the industry. Risk assessments make employees aware of the hazards and risks they are exposed to and what they should be doing to manage the risk. Consider for a moment your most recent job or your current job and the various hazards you were exposed to; what risk did they pose to your health and safety? Regardless of whether you work or plan to work in customer service, manufacturing, telecommunications, information technology, or research, assessing the level of risk associated with workplace hazards is vital to your health and safety. However, determining risk is often difficult due to the nature of how it is defined and because there are various methods for assessing it. Furthermore, the nature of some hazards can make it extremely difficult to assess; consider the rogue-wave example from the opening vignette in this chapter.

It is important at this point to consider the concept of risk perceptions and the relationship between the actual risk of a hazard and an individual's perception of the risk. Risk can be assessed by rating the probability of an incident followed by rating the consequences and assigning a level of priority (e.g., very high risk). Risk can also be

FIGURE 4.1

EXAMPLE OF A FAULT TREE

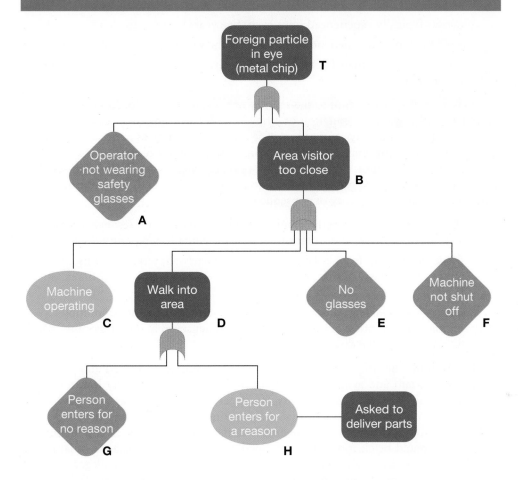

measured by consulting statistics (e.g., accident statistics) and calculating the probability of an event. Risk assessment methods that are based on numerical calculations are sometimes referred to as quantitative risk assessments while those not based on numerical calculations are referred to as subjective risk assessments. An argument can be made for choosing one type of risk assessment method over another given the subjective nature of risk perceptions; however, there is evidence to support that the actual or objective level risk and an individual's interpretation are not always disparate. Research involving offshore oil and gas platform employees showed that workers had "reasonably accurate perceptions of risk" and suggest that the factors that influence risk perceptions are similar to those which influence more objective assessment methods (e.g., quantitative risk assessment).[5] Regardless of the assessment method chosen, the necessity of conducting a risk assessment cannot be negated.

Probability refers to the chance or likelihood that an event will happen and will result in harm or loss. Within the context of workplace safety and risk assessments probability is typically expressed in terms describing the likelihood (e.g., very unlikely, likely, very likely); however there are numerous ways to express probability and it is up to the organization to ensure it are appropriate within a particular context,

> **probability**
> the chance or likelihood that an event will occur and will result in harm or loss

environment, or situation. The Canadian Centre for Occupational Health and Safety (CCOHS) provides the following terminology for probability:

- *Very likely*–Typically experienced at least once every six months by an individual.
- *Likely*–Typically experienced once every five years by an individual.
- *Unlikely*–Typically experienced once during the working lifetime of an individual.
- *Very unlikely*–Less than 1% chance of being experienced by an individual during his or her working lifetime.[6]

Consequences correspond to the severity of the injury, harm, or loss and can range from dust in the eye, to amputation of a finger, to death. Consequences of hazard can be expressed in various ways and can include the consequences of harm and or the loss to equipment. It is important for organizations to select terminology that is appropriate for a given job, situation, or context. Consequences are often expressed in terms of severity of harm or loss (e.g., slight harm, moderate, or extreme). CCOHS provides the following indicators of severity of consequences:

- *Slightly harmful* (e.g., superficial injuries; minor cuts and bruises; eye irritation from dust; nuisance and irritation; ill health leading to temporary discomfort).
- *Moderately harmful* (e.g., lacerations; burns; concussion; serious sprains; minor fractures; deafness; dermatitis; asthma; work-related upper limb disorders; ill health).
- *Extremely harmful* (e.g., amputations; major fractures; poisonings; multiple injuries; fatal injuries; occupational cancer; other severely life-shortening diseases; acute fatal diseases).[7]

Determining the risk level of hazard is done by gauging likelihood and the consequence of a hazard and assigning it a rating. Risk can be rated as very low, moderate, high, or very high. The rating or priority of risk can be determined by an organization; however, it is extremely important that each ranking or priority rating of risk be clear to all those who conduct risk assessments. In other words, employees conducting risk assessments should be clear on what is defined as "low risk." For instance, what is considered to be low risk in a book store at a university or community college? CCOHS provides guidance on defining risk (see **Table 4.1**) and is a useful resource that is based

consequences
the results or severity
of the injury

TABLE 4.1

RISK ASSESSMENT

LIKELIHOOD OF HARM	SEVERITY OF HARM		
	SLIGHT HARM	MODERATE HARM	EXTREME HARM
Very unlikely	Very low risk	Very low risk	High risk
Unlikely	Very low risk	Medium risk	Very high risk
Likely	Low risk	High risk	Very high risk
Very likely	Low risk	Very high risk	Very high risk

Source: CCOHS, "Risk Assessment," Table 2. Found at: http://www.ccohs.ca/oshanswers/hsprograms/risk_assessment.html (accessed June 7, 2016).

TABLE 4.2

SAMPLE HAZARD INVENTORY AND RISK EVALUATION

EXAMPLE OF RISK ASSESSMENT

TASK	HAZARD	RISK	PRIORITY	CONTROL
Delivering product to customers	Drivers work alone	May be unable to call for help if needed		
	Drivers have to occasionally work long hours	Fatigue, short rest time between shifts		
	Drivers are often in very congested traffic	Increased chance of collision Longer working hours		
	Drivers have to lift boxes when delivering product	Injury to back from lifting, reaching, carrying, etc.		

Source: CCOHS, "Risk Assessment," Table 1. Found at: http://www.ccohs.ca/oshanswers/hsprograms/risk_assessment.html (accessed June 7, 2016).

on the British Standards Institute (UK equivalent of ISO). For example, "very low risk" is defined as acceptable and does not require further action other than ensuring existing controls are maintained. CCOHS (see **Table 4.2**) provides a sample layout that can be used for hazard inventory and risk evaluation, which is also based on the British Standards Institute.

FOLLOW-UP

The information obtained through hazard identification and risk assessment should be communicated to the appropriate manager, the immediate supervisor, and the health and safety committee. Some reports may be forwarded to the Ministry of Labour (if the substance is under assessment), to the Ministry of Environment, or to the corporation's lawyers. Safety professionals and supervisors who do not pass on information about unsafe conditions to a responsible manager could be charged under the jurisdiction's occupational health and safety act.

When presented with information about hazards, management may decide to (1) take no action, (2) take corrective action, or (3) consider a cost–benefit analysis to determine whether the anticipated losses are worth the cost of correcting the problem.

// TYPES OF INJURIES

A look at the nature of workplace injuries will help us identify the types of workplace hazards we are concerned with. There are at least two broad classes of **injuries** in workplaces. **Overt traumatic injuries** (e.g., cuts, fractures, burns) typically result from

injury
any trauma, physical or mental, direct or indirect, acute or chronic, experienced by a human being

overt traumatic injuries
injuries resulting from coming into contact with an energy source

coming into contact with an energy source (e.g., falling, being struck by material). In contrast, **overexertion injuries** (e.g., sprains, back pain, tendonitis, carpal tunnel syndrome) typically are caused by excessive physical effort, repetitive motions, and, possibly, awkward working positions. From this observation it follows that hazard identification and control should focus on identifying and controlling sources of energy that can result in injury as well as in conditions of work that may lead to overexertion.

OVERT TRAUMATIC INJURIES

One of the most common causes of workplace accidents is individuals coming into contact with objects and equipment. For example, individuals may be struck by objects that are falling from overhead or may drop materials on themselves, resulting in crush injuries. Material may be flying through the air because of grinding or cutting operations. The use of compressed air in many industrial settings is a particular hazard, as the stream of compressed air may cause small particles of material to accelerate rapidly through the work environment. Individuals may also be struck by moving equipment such as the portable equipment or "crash" carts used in hospitals, or chair lifts and T-bars used at ski hills.

Another form of contact with equipment occurs when individuals become caught in, under, or between (CIUB) machinery. Industrial presses, for example, are often associated with crush injuries when individuals who are feeding the machine stock get their hands caught in the machinery as it presses. Conveyer belts and other power transmission systems (e.g., belts, pulleys) may have "pinch points" in which individuals can become entangled.

Falls are another significant source of workplace injury. This category includes falls from a height (e.g., off a ladder, or down a set of stairs) as well as falls on the same level (e.g., slipping on the floor). As we might expect, falls from a height are common in construction, where ladders and other temporary structures (e.g., scaffolding) are frequently used; however, consider other occupations where individuals are working from heights such as telecommunications technicians who climb towers or electricians who climb various structures. Falls on the same level often result from spilled material (e.g., oil) or from tripping over poorly placed material, uneven surfaces, and so on.

Overt traumatic injuries also result from coming into contact with sources of energy such as electricity, chemicals (e.g., chemical burns), and heat (e.g., touching a hot surface). Prolonged kneeling and the use of abrasives can result in abrasive injuries in which the skin is torn or rubbed raw.

In all situations, prevention focuses on (1) recognizing the source of the hazard (i.e., the potential energy source), (2) eliminating the hazard, and (3) protecting workers from exposure to the energy source (e.g., through personal protective equipment).

OVEREXERTION INJURIES

There are many types of overexertion or repetitive strain injuries. Most of them, though, have one of three basic causes: lifting, working in an awkward position, or repetition.

Workers like store clerks, merchandisers, or even continuing care assistants who might be working in a nursing home are frequently and repeatedly handling materials and clients that require lifting, carrying and lowering countless times during a shift. These frequently performed operations in many organizations can result in high-risk injuries through overexertion and poor posture, both of which are the primary cause of low back pain. According to the Canadian Centre for Occupational Health and Safety (CCOHS), training that focuses on how to lift properly is a controversial topic in the world of manual handling due to the fact that there is no best way to lift an object or materials and lifting can often be done in various ways.[8] The best way manage injuries such as lower back injuries from lifting is to do so with very specific and onsite training provided to workers; nevertheless, there are general lifting guidelines (see **OH&S Notebook 4.1**).

When lifting activities are identified as a workplace hazard, materials handling can be mechanized through the use of an ergonomic program or with equipment like conveyors and forklift trucks or other lifting devices. Work processes can be automated through the use of guided vehicles, which follow sensor lines on the floor, stopping as required to transfer their loads; or inventory systems can be installed that allow computer-controlled machines to pick up or stock inventory. In these ways, many of the risks associated with lifting can be greatly reduced. Some workers use supports (e.g. back belts) that force the back to remain straight but do not prevent the worker from lifting or handling heavier loads. Though the logic of using back supports is appealing, agencies such as NIOSH in the United States and CCOHS have suggested that there is no scientific evidence in favour of the use of such devices and does not recommend the use of them.[9]

REPETITIVE STRAIN INJURIES

Consider how many times in a day you grip, hold, bend, twist, clench, and reach for something. Performing these activities as part of our daily life may not contribute to an injury but consider the amount of time a student or office worker spends typing at a computer.

OH&S NOTEBOOK 4.1

GENERAL LIFTING GUIDELINES

Prepare to lift by warming up the muscles.

Stand close to the load, facing the way you intend to move.

Use a wide stance to gain balance.

Ensure a good grip on the load.

Keep arms straight.

Tighten abdominal muscles.

Tuck chin into the chest.

Initiate the lift with body weight.

Lift the load close to the body.

Lift smoothly without jerking.

Avoid twisting and side bending while lifting.

Do not lift if you are not convinced that you can handle the load safely.

Sources: Does Training Reduce Back Injuries, http://www.ccohs.ca/oshanswers/ergonomics/inj_prev.html, Canadian Centre for Occupational Health and Safety (CCOHS), 2007. Reproduced with the permission of CCOHS, 2016.

Tennis elbow, golfer's elbow, writer's cramp, and postal worker's shoulder are well-known examples of what is known as repetitive strain injury (RSI). Other conditions include carpal tunnel syndrome, thoracic outlet syndrome, and white fingers disease or Raynaud's syndrome.

Repetitive strain injuries are serious and it is the responsibility of employers and employees to minimize the impact. RSIs result in lost productivity, compensation costs and health care costs. More importantly, though, RSIs are painful and debilitating and can lower an individual's overall quality of life. While we can calculate the amount these injuries cost the economy, it is also important to consider the impact RSIs have on work and daily life (see **OH&S Today 4.1**).

The origins of RSI can be traced to the following four general conditions:

- *Unnatural joint position or posture.* Whenever a joint is forced to work in a position that is unnatural or stressed, the risk of RSI is increased. For instance, during keyboarding the wrists are forced out of axial alignment with the arm. The use of a hand tool such as a pair of pliers can force the wrist–arm axes out of line, creating a stress condition that could eventually cause joint irritation.

- *Force application to hinge joints.* When hinge joints are forced to carry applied loading, particularly when flexed, the joint load distribution of the cartilage is uneven, causing excessive stress in a small area of the joint. The wrist is a good example of a hinge joint. When performing a task such as lifting while bent, this joint can begin to ache. Repetition of the activity can result in a loss of strength.

- *Activity repetition.* Tasks such as keyboarding (computer operator) or using a hammer (carpenter) involve a repetitive flexing of the fingers and wrists. The action of typing applies low-load repetition to the fingers (touching the keys) and medium loading to the wrist (supporting the hand). The action of hammering applies a high-impact loading to the wrist, which is flexed into a non-aligned axis on impact. The shock effect increases the potential risk of tissue damage.

- *Pre-existing conditions.* Ailments such as arthritis and circulation disorders can have a synergistic effect on RSI conditions. For example, arthritis and inflammation of the joints can be aggravated by the stress associated with hammering or keyboarding.

OH&S TODAY 4.1

REPETITIVE STRAIN INJURY AWARENESS DAY

Did you know that February 29, 2016 marks the Repetitive Strain Injury Awareness Day? In years when there are only 28 days in February, the day is note on the 28th. The purpose of this day is raise awareness among workers, employers, and the general public of the impact of RSIs, and the importance of prevention. In Ontario, the Workers Health and Safety Centre held a training day designed to educate individuals about the impact of RSIs and the various ways that ergonomics can be used to prevent injuries.

Source: "Repetitive Strain Injuries: A Real Pain," http://www.ccohs.ca/newsletters/hsreport/issues/2012/02/ezine.html, Canadian Centre for Occupational Health and Safety (CCOHS), 2012. Reproduced with the permission of CCOHS, 2016.

AWKWARD WORKING POSITIONS

Strains and sprains can result from bending, twisting, and working in a variety of awkward positions. Frequently, the work position may compound or interact with other factors. For example, an individual may be lifting a load that normally would present no problem but be working in a restricted space that prohibits following safe lifting procedures, resulting in an injury.

Perhaps the most common types of injury result from bending or twisting the torso, extending the reach beyond the body, and working overhead with the hands and arms. As a general guideline, individuals should not have to reach below the knees or raise their arms above the shoulder for any length of time. Workstations and work procedures should be designed to ensure that individuals work in a comfortable position. Moreover, equipment and machinery should be adjustable to accommodate differences in body size.

Sprains and strains are often the result of awkward working positions.

// HAZARD CONTROL

Hazard control refers to the program or process used to establish preventive and corrective measures as the final stage of hazard recognition, risk assessment, and control. The goal of hazard control is first and foremost to eliminate hazards whenever possible; when this is not possible, then the goal is to reduce the exposure or point of contact with a hazards and to manage or control hazards so as to minimize any potential negative outcomes such as injuries and losses, , property damage, and time lost. It is useful to think of hazard control as comprising three levels of intervention (1) **precontact control** (addressing issues before an incident or accident occurs), (2) **point-of-contact control** manages hazards at the point of contact with the worker (e.g., using personal protective equipment to prevent the transfer of energy between hazard and worker), and (3) **postcontact control** manages the escalation of an incident and ensures further harm or damage does not occur, for instance putting in place medical and cleanup operations and ensuring that nobody else is hurt and no further damage to equipment occurs. Controls at each of these levels could comprise engineering controls, administrative controls, and control through personal protective equipment.

PRECONTACT CONTROL

Precontact control is the first method of controlling hazards by preventing hazards from reaching individuals within the workplace. Precontact control means using methods such as isolation, housekeeping, safe work policies and procedures, machine guarding, and replacing or retrofitting hazardous equipment. Precontact control of hazards involves various engineering, administrative, and personal protective equipment-based controls. It is important that organizations consult with their provincial occupational health and safety act and regulations because many precontact controls are legislated; for example, the Nova Scotia Department of Labour and Advanced Education provides information

hazard control
the program or process used to establish preventative and corrective measures

precontact control
addressing issues before an incident or accident occurs

point-of-contact control
managing hazards at the point of contact with the worker

postcontact control
manages the escalation of an incident and ensures further harm or damage does not occur

within the general occupational health and safety regulations for housekeeping and other methods for preventing contact with various hazards.

When precontact control measures are not feasible or practical given the work environment, then employers must engage point-of-contact controls that mitigate the risk associated with that hazard (e.g., using personal protective equipment). In some situations hazards result in an incident in which case post-contact control measures must be implemented.

POINT-OF-CONTACT CONTROL

If workers cannot avoid contact with a hazard (e.g., nurses working with a communicable disease) then they must do what they can to protect themselves and others engaged with that hazard.

Many point-of-contact controls fall under the engineering, administrative, and Personal Protective Equipment (PPE) categories and are legislated in many jurisdictions across Canada.

The main purpose of point-of-contact control is to ensure that the workers and emergency crews are not injured while they work. Steps to be taken can be grouped into the five following categories:

1. *Suppression*. Reduce or eliminate the ongoing hazard condition by using standard firefighting techniques; for example, (1) install fans to help clear the contaminants from the surrounding air, and turn off the power and utilities to the area, or (2) control dust from an explosion in a mining operation by spraying water at the rock surface.

2. *Barriers*. Install barriers between workers and sources of the emergency to keep unauthorized personnel out of the area.

3. *Modifications*. Identify and modify equipment or structures that need to be strengthened in order to prevent further damage from occurring, such as adding shoring to weakened walls to prevent collapse.

4. *Substitution*. Eliminate potentially harmful energies that have been unleashed by the event and replace them with safer, independent devices; for example, use portable floodlighting to replace the existing plant lighting if there is a possibility that damaged electrical equipment could cause a fire.

5. *Isolation*. Isolate energy sources from the emergency personnel and plant workers. Shut off all energy sources in the plant to prevent additional problems, and replace with outside equipment if possible, such as a portable air compressor to replace the one in the damaged area. Shut down any expensive equipment that could be damaged by energy surges.

POSTCONTACT CONTROL

If workplace, equipment, machines, or buildings are damaged as a result of an incident or if a hazard results in an emergency, then control of the hazard site is necessary so that no further hard or damage is done. The following are some steps that should be taken in the aftermath of an event:

1. Ensure that any injured worker receives immediate and thorough emergency care. The injury could be anything from a blow to the head to exposure to a

hazardous chemical. Provisions for first aid and emergency care should have been made during the precontact control process. The extent of these provisions will depend on the number of workers in an organization and the types of hazards they face.

2. Lock out the machinery involved until the accident investigation is complete and the damage is repaired.

3. Keep unauthorized people out of the area.

4. Determine what can be salvaged and what waste must be disposed of. Environmental regulations may prohibit the easy removal of certain hazardous wastes (e.g., PCB-contaminated oils from a damaged piece of lab equipment).

5. Apprise the JHSC, affected managers, and government agencies of the event. Fire, police, and paramedics will probably already know.

6. Complete all accident reports to determine what happened. Use report recommendations to ensure that the accident will not be repeated.

7. Review all company procedures and revise where appropriate.

8. Communicate with workers about the event. If necessary, implement safety retraining and possibly trauma counselling depending on the seriousness of the event.

As with the point-of-contact control measures, some of the above-mentioned postcontact control measures may be legislated by a ministry and/or a worker's compensation board.

// ENGINEERING CONTROL

Engineering controls are methods of modifying plants, workshops, factories, or other work environments through substituting equipment, isolating machinery, or ventilating a work environment. Engineering controls also involve modifying work processes and designing or redesigning equipment in order to minimize workers' exposure to the hazard.[10] Engineering controls should be built into the design of the work itself. Before equipment and materials are purchased, specifications for efficient and safe operations should be determined. For example, noise emission limits for noisy equipment can be specified before the equipment is purchased, thus reducing possible worker exposure. Engineering controls also refer to the installation of auxiliary equipment, such as physical barriers and ventilation systems, in order to reduce hazards involving the source and path. Because engineering controls avoid hazards or eliminate them entirely and because they work independently of workers, they are the first (i.e., most preferred) way to deal with hazards.

> **engineering control** modification of work processes, equipment, and materials to reduce exposure to hazards

SUBSTITUTION, VENTILATION, AND ISOLATION

Engineering controls often include substitution, ventilation, and isolation. Substitution involves replacing or changing out equipment or materials for less hazardous ones. Safety professionals can sometimes replace hazardous equipment or materials with those that are less hazardous. For example, replacing a light, fluffy powder with the same material in granular form will result in a reduction of airborne dust levels. Lead paints can be replaced with less toxic materials such as water-based coatings. Similarly, electric trucks can be substituted for gasoline-powered ones, with a resultant decrease in exposure to carbon monoxide. The substitute should, of course, be checked for other types of hazards. The introduction of electric trucks will reduce the serious risk of carbon monoxide exposure but increase less serious exposure to flammable hydrogen or electric shock from batteries. Ventilation is one that specifically targets the control of airborne hazards by removing the contaminated air and replacing it with uncontaminated air. Examples of this would be an exhaust system found in office buildings or sky scrapers (e.g., heating, ventilation, air conditioning unit, or HVAC). Isolation limits exposure to employees who are working within close proximity or directly with a hazard by enclosing the hazard in a containment structure, (e.g., closet). In this approach, the hazardous job or task is isolated from the employees in order to reduce their exposure. Isolation strategies may be as simple as putting a physical barrier around a chemical or noise source, or involve removing a hazardous operation to a separate facility. Robots can handle tasks that are too dangerous for humans.

PROCESS MODIFICATION

Sometimes changing the manner in which the work is done can increase safety. Moving from a manual operation to an automated one, or from batch processes to continuous processes, may result in fewer hazards.

Effective job design is key to worker safety and efficiency. Frederick Taylor (1856–1915), the founder of industrial engineering, tried to increase both by breaking a job into its basic components and then assigning to each task specific times and methods (motions). Taylor's ideas were applied to the shovelling of coal at the Bethlehem Steel Company in what was to become a classic motion study. This application demonstrated that a stoker could shovel more coal into the blast furnace by using a larger shovel and engaging in fewer work cycles. Decreasing the repetition of the task reduced fatigue and back strain.

Subsequent efficiency experts addressed the tedium associated with simple task repetition. In 1920 the managers at Hawthorne Works, a large manufacturing facility in Illinois, set out to determine whether employees were more productive in a well-lit work environment compared to a poorly lit work environment. The managers at the facility hired consultants and commissioned a study that indicated that employees were in fact more productive in well-lit conditions. Furthermore, the results of the study also indicated that modifying work processes by letting employees work in teams, having a clean work space, and allowing for regular breaks also increased worker productivity.[11]

Inspired by the Hawthorne studies of the 1920s, the socio-technological approach to work design was concerned with enhancing worker involvement and satisfaction. What has this to do with health and safety? The more interested and motivated the worker, the lower the probability of a serious accident or injury.

MACHINE GUARDING

Machine guarding is necessary to protect a worker from the hazards and energies created by moving machinery.

The following basic guidelines for machine guarding apply, regardless of the type or operation of the equipment:

- The guard must be sturdy enough to resist external source damage that would interfere with the operation of the machine, such as being struck by a forklift truck.

machine guarding
protection for workers
from the hazards and
energies created by
moving machinery

- The guard must permit required maintenance tasks without excessive dismantling or reassembly labour.
- The guard must be properly and securely mounted to prevent rattling, which is a distraction, or part interference, which can cause snags and force the operator to attempt to free them, possibly without proper precautions.
- There should be no parts that, if removed, would compromise the protection provided by the guard; there should always be some guarding left.
- Construction should be relatively simple so that problems can be immediately identified and corrected during an inspection.

Thoroughness in guard design is essential. An incomplete guard may be as much of a hazard as no guard at all. The guard must not create a false sense of security that may cause accidents and possible injuries. When the guard is in operation, all parts of the body must be excluded, and no access is permitted. The barrier or guard will prevent a worker from being caught in, on, or between moving equipment (kinetic energy), or from being struck by flying, sliding, or falling objects (gravity energy).

Floor barriers installed around pumps and other hazardous equipment must be strong enough to resist damage by, for example, forklift truck impact (mechanical energy), and high enough that a worker will not trip or fall over them. Expanded metal should fill the open spaces to prevent parts from rolling into the hazard area and fingers from being poked through.

Several devices can be used to control point-of-operation hazards. *Barrier* or *enclosure guards* prevent workers from entering a hazardous area. The barrier may be mechanical (a cage that covers the work action) or electrical (a photocell that will not permit the machine to cycle while the beam is broken). The emergency stop button is another form

Machine guards shield or cover hazardous areas of a machine to prevent contact with body parts or to control hazards such as debris or noise from exiting the machine.

CHAPTER 4 Hazard Recognition, Risk Assessment, and Control

of guard; for it to be effective, the machine must be equipped with a braking system that will stop the machine in mid-cycle.

Guarding by distance involves keeping workers physically removed from the machine hazard. One of the most common methods is the two-handed trip guard or control, which is located near but not in the midst of the hazard site. Both hands are required to press each button simultaneously for the machine to cycle.

Hand-removal devices are designed to physically remove the worker's hands and arms from the activated machine. The "hand pullout" is a harness-like system fastened to the worker's wrists at one end and to the machine at the other end. When the machine (say a punch press) is activated, the harness mechanism physically pulls the worker's hands out of the way. Short of removing the harness, the worker cannot win the ensuing tug-of-war.

The *sweep away* is a device with one or two arms (single sweep or double sweep) that, when activated by the machine cycle, will swing across in front of the worker, forcibly removing his or her hands from the danger area. A small panel attached to each arm screens the swept area to keep the worker's hands from re-entering the danger zone after the sweep arm passes. The sweep-away device is not a recommended guard.

The *photoelectric eye* is a light beam that, when broken, will not allow the machine to cycle. This type of device has the advantage of not adding to the machine any obstructions that can make maintenance difficult. It is generally expensive to install and maintain but very effective.

Feeding tools include hand-held tongs, push sticks, or clamps that allow the operator access to the machine while keeping his or her hands out of the way. Metal tools are usually made of aluminum or magnesium, which will crush easily if caught in the machine, thereby saving the die sets and not allowing the type of **kickback** that could direct the worker's hands into the machine. A press forge operator will use a set of special tongs to hold a red-hot piece of metal in place in the dies while the machine forms the part. In a similar manner, a set of handles secured to sheet glass or metal by vacuum will permit a worker to handle the material without being cut by sharp edges.

> **kickback**
> action of having a work piece suddenly thrown backward into the operator

EQUIPMENT DESIGN

Controls and displays can also be designed to reduce confusion. Automobile instrument panels and machine operating panels should exhibit the following four characteristics:

1. *Visibility.* The display must be within the worker's field of vision, with no obstructions. Characters should be of a readable size, with high contrast.

2. *Legibility.* Characters must be adequately spaced as well as distinguishable (a "3" should not look like an "8"). No more than one line or pointer should appear on each display.

3. *Interpretability.* The displays must be interpreted in the same way by all observers. Universal symbols help but can lead to misunderstandings. For example, the red exit symbols may be confused with the red glow that means "stop." In Europe, exit symbols are green.

4. *User-friendliness.* Each control must be a different shape and have a different operating direction in order to be easily distinguished from adjacent controls. Picture the controls in your car: the radio volume rotates, while the station change button is pushed; the most important controls—the fuel gauge and the speedometer—are displayed most prominently.

Engineering controls can also be applied to any environment; for instance an office environment where you might be doing your banking, or even a call centre. Many employees spend long periods seated at their workstations. A poor sitting position or posture can restrict blood circulation, increase blood pooling in the legs and feet, and add to the compressive load on the spine. Correct chair design will minimize the concentration of pressures under the thigh and the back of the knee. Work seating must be completely adjustable in all directions and planes. A forward-tilting seat may be preferred by employees who must lean over a workstation.

The backrest should be curved on the vertical and horizontal planes. It should also be vertically adjustable (so that the point of contact fits the small of the back in the lumbar region) as well as horizontally adjustable. Armrests are recommended unless a wide variety of arm movements are required. The chair base should provide stability and mobility. Five casters with a wide spread will prevent tipping.[12] Visit http://www.ccohs.ca/oshanswers/ergonomics/sitting/sitting_position.html for illustrations and information on recommended chair settings and body positions.

Lighting within an office environment is also extremely important and has two main purposes: to illuminate the tasks, and to increase the safety and comfort of the worker. Bright overhead lighting can produce glare and annoying reflections on a computer screen, resulting in eyestrain and headaches. Choosing the correct lighting for a workplace will involve consideration of the following factors:

- *Intensity:* the amount of light given off by a source.
- *Luminance:* the amount of light uniformly reflected or emitted from a surface and the background.
- *Reflectance:* the amount of light reflected from a surface (luminance) and the amount of light falling on the surface (illuminance). A dull black surface has 9% reflectance, while a shiny white surface has closer to 100% reflectance.
- *Luminaire:* a complete lighting device.
- *Contrast:* the relationship between the amount of light from a surface and the background.
- *Glare:* the reduction of visibility caused by brightness differences between an object and its background.

Both the quantity and the quality of light must be considered. In the context of workstation design, quantity refers to the correct amount of light needed to perform a task. Quality is more complex and includes measures of distribution (or spread), glare, diffusion, shadows, contrast, and colour.

// ADMINISTRATIVE CONTROL

Administrative controls are the changes to work practices, policies, procedures, training, and rules. Administrative controls direct or provide guidance on the safest method for completing a job or task. Relative to engineering controls, administrative controls can be more complex as they do involve removing a hazard and involve various individuals within the organization, require coordination, and resources (e.g., employee training and rotation, environmental sampling, and medical surveillance) to protect individuals.[13] Administrative controls is the second level of priority for worker protection, after engineering controls but before personal protective equipment. Administrative controls

administrative control
management involvement, training of employees, rotation of employees, environmental sampling, and medical surveillance to protect individuals

CHAPTER 4 Hazard Recognition, Risk Assessment, and Control

can have some effect in minimizing hazardous conditions. The most serious failure of this method relates to a company's reluctance or lack of appreciation for the hazards, and of the impact administrative controls can have. Using administrative controls, the HR practitioner can be effective by (1) introducing preplacement assessments so that employees who have suitable characteristics (e.g., the ability to lift materials) are chosen for the job; (2) scheduling job rotations so that workers spend time in less hazardous jobs, thereby reducing exposures (e.g., working with toxic materials in the morning and with nontoxic materials in the afternoon); (3) moving workers to other permanent jobs after exposure to toxic materials; and (4) performing periodic monitoring.

Some common examples of administrative control include safety awareness programs, incentive programs, housekeeping programs, preventive maintenance, and the development of policies and training modules for unique situations such as confined space entry.

SAFETY AWARENESS

Safety awareness refers to programs that attempt to inform workers about health and safety issues and to remind them of the importance of health and safety. Awareness programs are done in various ways; you might be most familiar with public awareness campaigns (e.g., Repetitive Strain Injury Awareness Day).

VISIBLE REMINDERS

There are many ways to remind workers of the importance of safety:

- Posters and signs at worker entrances and other points of entry are one way to promote safety awareness.
- A company-designed booklet dealing with health and safety issues can be issued to employees.
- Safety messages through emails, text messages, and messages via social media (e.g., Twitter, Facebook) are also used to provide reminders to employees.
- Place mats and napkins in the dining area can be imprinted with safety messages.
- Decals (self-adhesive or magnetic) can be applied to specific objects as safety reminders.
- Safety displays can be set up at entrances and in cafeterias. These displays can feature photographs of the Safe Employee of the Month or brief statements by workers who were saved from injury by, for example, correct use of personal protective equipment (e.g., safety glasses).
- Newsletters, bulletin boards, and billboards are other vehicles for promoting safety awareness.

Safety campaigns can be used to target specific hazards or unsafe practices. These efforts and presentations, though, will not be effective unless senior managers are fully behind the programs.

SPECIAL EVENTS

Numerous special events and campaigns have been developed to promote safety awareness in the workplace (e.g., National Safe Driving Week). In general, the intent of these

OH&S TODAY 4.2

CCOHS YOUNG WORKERS ZONE

In response to the high rate of injuries among young workers, many jurisdictions have begun to address the issue of young workers' health and safety by specifically targeting youth about safety issues, the importance of health and safety, and their rights under the law. CCOHS has recently created a website called the Young Workers Zone, which is designed to help educate young people about their roles and responsibilities in worker safety. This website provides information to youth about programs and incentives they can access as well as various safety-based contests they can participate in. Parents can access information about what they should be asking their children about their work environment, and what they should be doing to ensure their child is safe while at work. The website also targets employers and teachers and provides information about rights, responsibilities, and resources designed to help engage youth, as well as various teaching tools and techniques.

Source: Canadian Centre for Occupational Health and Safety, "Young Worker Zone." Found at http://www.ccohs.ca/youngworkers/resources/initiativesprograms.html (accessed June 7, 2016).

special events is to increase awareness of safety issues in the workplace by focusing on safety or a specific element of safety in the workplace (see **OH&S Today 4.2**).

AWARDS AND INCENTIVES

Safety awards are another vehicle for increasing awareness of safety. By establishing an award, the sponsoring agency or company creates an "event" comprising a presentation and a media announcement. The resulting publicity can be used to raise safety awareness. Safety award programs have been created by industrial associations, governments, and agencies to recognize achievements in safety.

Within organizations, individual employees can be given incentives to maintain good safety performance. However, safety awards and incentive programs must be very carefully designed and executed to ensure that employees and employers are engaging in safe work behaviours for the right reasons and not simply because they are rewarded for doing so (see Chapter 10 for behaviour-based safety programs that involve incentives).

HOUSEKEEPING

Ensuring that the worksite is clean and that workers have access to cleaning facilities will contribute to the control of hazards. A clean, orderly workplace can reduce hazards and at the same time increase efficiency. Every worksite contains potentially hazardous tools and equipment. For example, a plant site may have containers of chemicals such as solvents, tools such as drills, and processes that generate dust or scrap material. Maintaining a clean and orderly job site reduces the risk of injury due to falls, fires, and so forth. Furthermore, it is easier to locate first aid equipment or exits in an environment in which all tools and equipment are in their assigned places (see **OH&S Notebook 4.2**).

PREVENTING SLIPS AND FALLS THROUGH HOUSEKEEPING

Have you walked into a service station bathroom and notice a sheet of paper on the back of the door that identifies the last time the washroom was cleaned and by who? Have you ever walked into a coworker's office and had to navigate your way around stacks of books and papers? Consider the area where you study; do you ever feel like you study better when your space is clean? Good housekeeping practices are perhaps the simplest and most effective way to prevent slips and falls in the workplace, and clean, well- maintained workspaces often help boost employee morale and productivity. Housekeeping programs should involve information, policies, and procedures about how to manage dust, dirt, and waste removal; storage of materials and supplies; work surface lighting; and so forth. Housekeeping programs should be built into a typical work routine and should specifically identify the following:

- who is responsible for clean up during the shift
- day-to-day cleanup
- waste disposal
- removal of unused materials
- inspection to ensure cleanup is complete

Source: CCOHS, "Why Should We Pay Attention to Housekeeping at Work?" Found at: http://www.ccohs.ca/oshanswers/hsprograms/house.html (accessed June 7, 2016).

Housekeeping is not just a good practice; it is a legal requirement under most health and safety legislation. Though legislation varies across jurisdictions, the Canadian Health and Safety Regulations under the Canada Labour Code are typical:

1. Every exterior stairway, walkway, ramp, and passageway that may be used by employees shall be kept free of accumulations of ice and snow or other slipping or tripping hazards.

2. All dust, dirt, waste, and scrap material in every workplace in a building shall be removed as often as is necessary to protect the health and safety of employees and shall be disposed of in such a manner that the health and safety of employees is not endangered.

3. Every travelled surface in a workplace shall be

   a. slip resistant; and

   b. kept free of splinters, holes, loose boards and tiles, and similar defects.[14]

The cleaning process itself should be evaluated. Besides the obvious hazards posed by solvents used for cleaning, other hazards may be involved in operations such as dust removal. Workers using compressed air may be tempted to blow dust off work surfaces and even clothing; however, compressed air can be forced through the skin, enter the bloodstream, and cause death.

Organizations that employ workers who handle toxic materials should ensure that washing facilities are located close to the work area. Workers should wash before drinking or eating to prevent the ingestion of toxic materials. No food or drink should be permitted at the worksite. Workers exposed to chemicals should have showers and change clothes before leaving the worksite. Where appropriate, hazardous material (hazmat) suits should be available and workers should be trained in their use.

PREVENTIVE MAINTENANCE

Preventive maintenance refers to the orderly, continuous, and scheduled protection and repair of equipment and buildings. The primary goals of preventive maintenance are to determine potential problems and to implement corrective actions. The main benefits of this process are uninterrupted production and the reduction of potential hazards caused by equipment failure. See **OH&S Notebook 4.3**.

Generally speaking, equipment failures do not happen without warning. We are all familiar with the atypical noises that our cars or air conditioners produce as signals that something needs to be fixed. However, maintenance should enter the picture before warning signs emerge. It is more cost-effective to perform maintenance routinely while the equipment or machines are still operating than it is after they have failed, necessitating shutdown of the entire operation. Checking the level of oil in your car at every second fuel stop is preventive maintenance. To let the oil level drop and the engine seize is expensive and unnecessary.

Record keeping is essential to any preventive maintenance program. Maintenance information should be recorded at the time the maintenance work is done. Pertinent data will include part replacement and frequency, lubrication, bearings and drive repairs, electrical failures, and cleanliness. Once the historical information is available, failure trends can be anticipated and addressed. (This approach is often referred to as failure mode analysis or maintenance hazard analysis.)

> preventive maintenance
> the orderly, continuous, and scheduled protection and repair of equipment and buildings

LOCKOUT PROCEDURES

When maintenance or adjustment is performed on any machine, the machine must be shut off and locked out. For example, replacing the signal light on a residential stove involves accessing the appliance's interior. Shutting off the stove entails turning off the switches; locking it out entails turning off the power at the main fuse box or circuit breaker and removing the appropriate fuses in either the power panel or the stove. With these precautions, no one can turn the stove on and cause an electrical shock or burn injury. For a more complicated appliance such as a furnace, not only must the fuses be removed, but also the fuel lines must be shut off, and the supply flange joint must be disassembled.

X video shown on this — must know the 5 steps

OH&S NOTEBOOK   4.3
PREVENTIVE MAINTENANCE

Preventive work plans are often completed according to a specific schedule with the overall goals of avoiding wear and tear and any sudden equipment failures. Preventive maintenance plans increase equipment reliability, decrease replacement costs and downtime, and reduce injuries to workers. Preventive maintenance plans include planned replacement of equipment or exploratory maintenance wherein workers will stop a work process and or system and look for any parts or components that are showing signs of wear or are in need of replacement.

Source: Health and Safety Ontario, "Preventive Maintenance." Found at http://www.wsps.ca/WSPS/media/Site/Resources/Downloads/Preventative-Maintenance_Final.pdf?ext=.pdf (accessed June 7, 2016).

The following are some of the precautions that must be taken during the lockout process:

- Only one person should be in charge of the lockout procedure.
- The worker must ensure that the machine is shut off completely; that all internal pressure sources (hydraulic, air, steam) are bled off to atmospheric levels; that the valves are locked open; and that any movable parts, such as flywheels or rams, are immobilized.
- After the machine has been shut down, all the disconnect points, such as the electrical panel, must be left open.
- Before work begins, complete testing must be undertaken to ensure that all energy sources are inoperative.
- The worker must use an approved lockout tag and single-key padlock to secure the equipment.
- Only the workers who installed each lock are permitted to remove that lock, in the reverse order to the lock installation, beginning and ending with the project manager.
- Each worker must sign off the work permit as his or her lock is removed.

When the project is finished, the equipment will be activated in the reverse sequence to the shutdown. Checks must be made to ensure that guards are in place, isolation devices have been removed, all tools are accounted for, energy controls have been closed and put back into operating condition, and tags and locks have been removed. The last lock removed is that of the manager of the project from the shift on which the lock was applied.

WORK PERMITS

Before any high-risk work is undertaken, a series of work permits must be in place, one for each type of activity. These permits are, in effect, in-house licences to perform dangerous work. Permits are required for confined space entry, electrical work, excavation work, safety valve work, scaffolding work, radiation work, and equipment-disconnecting work (lockout procedures). "Hot work" permits may be required for activities such as cutting, welding, and soldering wherein the heat involved may trigger the fire alarm system or present a fire hazard. A sample work permit for scaffolding is shown in **Figure 4.2**.

CONFINED-SPACE ENTRY

confined space
any space that is enclosed or partially enclosed and restricts entrance and exit by the location and size, and is potentially deficient in oxygen or could contain toxic gases

Confined space refers to a space that is enclosed or partially enclosed and restricts entrance and exit by the location and size, and is a space that is potentially deficient in oxygen or could contain toxic gases. Some typical examples are city sewers, holding tanks on fishing vessels, boiler rooms, walk-in fridges and freezers in restaurants, and ditches. Other examples include any long, small tunnel; shower stalls; and some specialty rooms such as computer equipment rooms that are completely independent from any adjacent spaces.

FIGURE 4.2

EXAMPLE OF SCAFFOLD USE PERMIT

SIRTE OIL COMPANY — **SCAFFOLDING PERMIT**

DATE

TIME FROM: TO:

PLANT:

EQUIPMENT & LOCATION:

DESCRIPTION OF WORK TO BE DONE:
☐ ERECTION
☐ REMOVAL

SCAFFOLD DUTY: ☐ LIGHT ☐ GENERAL ☐ HEAVY

HEIGHT = ___ M WIDTH = ___ M ☐ CONSULT CIVIL ENG. GROUP

ANSWER WITH (X) WHERE APPLICABLE: YES
1. FAMILIAR WITH AREA HAZARDS/SAF. RULES? ☐
2. SCAFFOLD TYPE/MATERIAL AGREED TO? ☐
3. SCAFFOLD ANCHORING POINTS APPROVED? ☐
4. FOUNDATION/FOOTING PREPARED? ☐
5. HAZARD CREATED TO/FROM TRAFFIC? ☐
6. AREA FREE OF COMB./TOXIC GAS? ☐
7. ACCEPTANCE APPROVAL NEEDED? ☐

SPECIAL PROTECTION REQUIRED
☐ MONITOR FOR _____
☐ LIFTING DEVICE APPROVAL
☐ BARRIERS/ROPING OFF
☐ SAFETY BELTS/LINE
☐ STANDBYS
☐ (SPECIFY)

THE EQUIPMENT AND/OR LOCATION WHERE THE WORK IS TO BE DONE HAS BEEN INSPECTED & POINTS 1-7 ABOVE HAVE BEEN INVESTIGATED TO MY SATISFACTION.

SIGNATURE OF PERSON AUTHORIZING THIS PERMIT

I UNDERSTAND THE HAZARDS INVOLVED IN THE ABOVE PERMITTED WORK AND THE LIMITATIONS REQUIRED HAVE BEEN EXPLAINED TO ME.

7-3 SHIFT | 11-7 SHIFT

SIGNATURE OF AUTHORIZED CRAFTSMAN

PERMIT CLOSED OUT | WORK COMPLETED
DATE TIME | ☐ NO ☐
AUTHORIZED CRAFTSMAN | OPERATING SUPERVISOR
APPROVAL FOR USE OF COMPLETED SCAFFOLD | NAME | SIGNATURE | DATE

SIDE 1

CHECKLIST FOR THE AUTHORIZED CRAFTSMAN PREPARATIONS

☐ SPECIFICATIONS/DRAWING PROVIDED?
☐ FOUNDATIONS/FOOTING PREPARED?
☐ LIFTING DEVICES NEEDED?
☐ ERECTION PERSONNEL EXPERIENCED?
☐ SUPERVISION APPOINTED? COMPETENT?
☐ AREA HAZARDS/SAF. RULES KNOWN?
☐ ADDITIONAL JOB DEMONSTRATION NEEDED?
☐ STRUCTURE INSPECTION/APPROVAL BY A COMPETENT PERSON NEEDED?

STABILITY & CONSTRUCTION
☐ ANCHORING POINTS SELECTED? APPROVED? SUFFICIENT?
☐ SCAFF. MATERIAL INSPECTED? SELECTED? IN GOOD CONDITION?
☐ FOOTING FIRM?
☐ STANDARDS SPACING ADEQUATE?
☐ BRACING USED? SUFFICIENT?
☐ PLATFORMS FULL? TRIPPING? OPENINGS?
☐ GUARDRAILS? TOE BOARDS?
☐ ACCESS ADEQUATE? LADDERS FIXED?

IN USE
☐ STRUCTURE INSPECTED DAILY?
☐ TRAFFIC HAZARDS?
☐ OVERLOADING?
☐ USE OF PERSONAL PROTECTION?
☐ RESPONSE TO EMERGENCY KNOWN?

DISMANTLING
☐ METHOD AGREED TO?
☐ HAZARD CREATED TO SURROUNDING?
☐ FINAL SITE CLEARING ENSURED?

SPECIAL INSTRUCTIONS

SIDE 2

At home, cleaning the bathroom shower stall with the door closed and using a tile cleaner will trap the vapours from the cleanser. These vapours may accumulate near the floor where the work is being done, displace oxygen, and cause drowsiness or fainting.

Entry into industrial confined spaces is addressed in various OH&S regulations. One of the first things to determine is whether the space to be entered is, in fact, a confined space. CCOHS provides helpful information on identification of a confined space, how to manage the space, and how to develop a confined-space safety program.

Once it has been established that a confined space exists, the following steps should be taken:

1. Issue a proper work permit and follow all the lockout procedures.
2. Determine the ease of access to and from the space and develop appropriate contingency plans for worker emergencies.

Confined space entry poses a number of hazards and requires very specific training and special work permits.

3. Make sure that all the proper tools and equipment are on hand to do the job.

4. Communicate to workers that no smoking or open flames are to be permitted at or near the worksite.

5. Purge the space of all contaminants and test the air quality several times to ensure that all impurities have been removed.

6. Ensure that a constant forced airflow into the space is provided.

7. Clean the interior of the space to ensure that no hazardous scale or deposits are present.

8. Post a trained safety lookout outside the space. (The inside workers should be kept in full view at all times.)

9. Attach a lifeline to each worker in the space. (The free end should be controlled by the safety lookout.)

On completion of the confined-space work, equipment startup can be undertaken in the reverse order to the shutdown. The permit and lockout systems should be followed without deviation.

// PERSONAL PROTECTIVE EQUIPMENT

In some cases it is not possible to fully protect individuals by applying engineering and administrative controls. The third line of defence in occupational health and safety is the use of personal protective equipment (PPE) (point-of-contact controls). PPE consists of clothing, helmets, goggles, and other devices designed to protect the individual from specific hazards. A construction worker, for example, might wear steel-toed safety boots (typically with a nonconductive, nonslip sole), a helmet, safety glasses or goggles, work gloves, and hearing protection.

It is relatively easy to control the wearing of some PPE. For example, in many industries the use of steel-toed safety boots/shoes is a standard policy. Since most of us don't remove or change our shoes during the working day, a worker who puts on safety boots is likely to continue to wear them. The use of other PPE can be more variable. Safety goggles or glasses (for example) can steam up on a hot day, and workers may find that they are uncomfortable. Hearing protection can make it difficult to converse with coworkers. Moreover, workers can simply forget to use PPE. For example, when working on a construction site it is easy to forget to put on your safety glasses before using a saw. Individuals may opt for wearing PPE in a way that reduces its effectiveness; for example, one often sees construction workers wearing helmets with the peak to the back or perched improperly on the head. Helmets worn in an improper position do not provide the same level of protection as when properly worn.

Though PPE offers protection to workers, its use can be highly variable because of factors like this. As a result, the use of PPE is recognized as the least preferred means of controlling hazards. Though PPE of one sort or another is required in many workplaces, it is most properly considered to be an adjunct or backup to other methods of control. It should never be the sole means of protecting workers from hazards.

// SOURCE–PATH–HUMAN CONTROLS

Hazards can be controlled or eliminated by identifying and attacking the source of the hazard, the path it travels, and the employee or recipient of the hazard. The strategies discussed in this chapter can be regrouped along these lines, as shown in **Figure 4.3**. This schematic provides a useful summary of the information on hazard control.

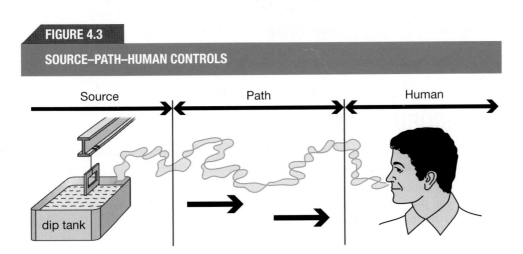

FIGURE 4.3

SOURCE–PATH–HUMAN CONTROLS

Source: Hazard Control, http://www.ccohs.ca/oshanswers/hsprograms/hazard_control.html, Canadian Centre for Occupational Health and Safety (CCOHS), 2016. Reproduced with the permission of CCOHS, 2016.

Placing control strategies in categories is less important than having a thorough understanding that hazard control is necessary and possible.

// MONITORING/AUDITING

Monitoring is an important part of hazard control and is a continual process that occurs at various points in time with regularity. Audits are done to ensure that hazard controls are functioning effectively and to identify new hazards. Monitoring can be done daily by supervisors and maintenance personnel, weekly by department heads, monthly by health and safety committees, and as needed by compliance officers.[15] An audit program can be used to evaluate health and safety performance and security in the workplace. For example, the Natural Sciences and Engineering Research Council (NSERC) and Social Sciences and Humanities Research Council (SSHRC) recently completed a corporate internal audit of the physical security of their information, assets, and services to ensure they were protected against compromise and threats, and to ensure individuals were protected against workplace violence.[16]

A number of audit methods are available. One very effective technique, which involves applying total quality control methodologies and trend analysis, relates the number of incidents to a predetermined goal. If it seems from the number of events in a particular time frame that a safety goal failure is imminent, steps can be taken to prevent the occurrence. The audit program should:

1. ensure that safety programs are being carried out without restrictions
2. ensure that safety programs are up to date and that deficiencies are documented
3. be carried out by people with some understanding of both the audit methods and the material being examined (the various members of the JHSC should be able to carry out this inspection)
4. stimulate discussion among all managers and workers, and ultimately produce conclusions and recommendations
5. be conducted at least annually by companies with high-risk hazards
6. include all documentation (WSIB/WCB statements, Ministry of Labour citations, air sampling results, first aid and incident reports, hazard analyses, discipline records, cost-benefit studies, etc.)

// RECORD KEEPING

Information obtained at all stages of the hazard control process should be stored in a database. These records are used to identify frequency of events as well as trends in hazards. They are also a source of information on worker training and equipment maintenance. The provision of monthly updates to managers will assist them in their efforts at ongoing hazard control. The length of time that records should be kept varies with the nature of the record. Records on individual employees should be kept for as long as that individual is with the company. In some cases (e.g., individual records of exposure to radiation) records may have to be kept for the length of employment plus an additional period (e.g., 10 years).

// SUMMARY

In this chapter we introduced the concepts of hazard recognition, risk assessment, and control. A hazard was defined as any source of potential damage, harm, or adverse health effects on something or someone under certain conditions at work. Hazards typically involve exposure to some kind of energy, and hazard recognition involves the systematic identification of the hazards and risks associated with them. We discussed various tools for hazard recognition. Risk assessment refers to the evaluation of the likelihood of harm posed by the hazard. Such an assessment needs to consider the probability of an adverse event, and the potential consequences. If the decision is made to control the hazard, there are three basic approaches: engineering, administrative, and PPE. Engineering controls typically involve redesigning the work (e.g., the tools, machines, or substances) so as to reduce or eliminate the hazard. Administrative controls involve strategies such as training, education, and management techniques to reduce exposure to the hazard. In this case, the hazard is still present but the exposure of the individual worker is substantially reduced or controlled. PPE includes items such as helmets, safety glasses, and hearing protection. These devices do not reduce exposure but do reduce the probable consequences of being exposed to a hazard. There is a hierarchy of hazard control such that engineering controls are the preferred solution (i.e., reduce or eliminate the hazard), administrative controls are the second line of defence (i.e., reduce exposure to the hazard), and PPE is the last option (i.e., reduce the consequences). That said, all three forms of control have a place in OH&S programs and can be thought of as providing multiple layers of protection for workers.

KEY TERMS

administrative control 95
confined space 100
consequences 84
engineering control 91
fault tree 82
hazard 78
hazard analysis 82
hazard control 89
human factor 79
incident 78
injury 85
job description 81
job specifications 81
kickback 94
machine guarding 92
overexertion injuries 86
overt traumatic injuries 85
point-of-contact control 89
positive tree 82
postcontact control 89
precontact control 89
preventive maintenance 99
probability 83

CHAPTER 4 Hazard Recognition, Risk Assessment, and Control

risk 78
risk perception 78
safety sampling 81
unsafe act 78
walk-through survey 81

DISCUSSION QUESTIONS

1. Explain why hazard control at the precontact stage is better than hazard control at the other stages.

2. An instrumentation technician has been hired to find out why an electrical panel that monitors water temperature and flow to and from various tanks around a large aquarium at a local zoo continues to malfunction. To access the panel the technician must crawl into one of the connected pipes after it has been flushed of all water. The technician is not familiar with the aquarium environment that she will be working in. She calls and asks you for advice about any necessary equipment and procedures for entering and exiting from the pipe. Briefly outline your response.

3. When a worker does not wear PPE or wears it incorrectly, who is responsible? The company? The individual?

4. Examine any office supply catalogues or office supply store websites to determine how many methods and accessories are available to prevent keyboard-related RSI. How many of these devices do you have in your own workstation?

5. Outline all of the methods that a manager of a small office could use to identify hazards. What could a safety professional add to this manager's hazard identification program?

6. Choose any operation in your workplace or at school and identify the hazards associated with it. Perform a risk assessment to determine whether these hazards are dangerous. Outline the changes that could be made to reduce the level of risk associated with the hazards.

USING THE INTERNET

1. Human resources managers are responsible for ensuring that workplace safety inspections take place regularly. Using your text and online resources, describe how you would conduct an effective safety inspection program. (Hint: Go to http://www.worksafebc .com/publications/health_and_safety/by_topic/assets/pdf/safety_inspections.pdf).

2. Using the Web, determine (a) what safety awareness events are celebrated or implemented in your local area and how.

3. Lifting limits can be established by calculations developed by the National Institute for Occupational Safety and Health (NIOSH) in the United States. An online calculator for the equations is found at http://www.ccohs.ca/oshanswers/ergonomics/niosh/ calculating_rwl.html. Use the calculator to assess the lifting limits for a retail employee who has to lift a shipment of clothing weighing approximately 16 kg onto a shelf that is 60 cm (horizontally) from where he or she is standing (assume the vertical distance of their hands from the ground is 50 cm and that horizontal distance from the midpoint between the ankles to the hands while holding the object is 30 cm). The worker must lift each box a vertical distance of 50 cm. The lift is repeated once each minute for 30

minutes. Keep in mind the employee must twist at an angle of 30 degrees giving them a fair grasp on the boxes of clothing. Determine the acceptability of the operation.

EXERCISES

1. In law, the "thin skull argument" refers to a perfectly healthy person whose minor trauma resulted in serious injury. Were it not for the trauma, the individual would not have been hurt. However, other individuals who experience the trauma are not hurt. Imagine, for example, four workers who are struck on the head by flying objects. Three workers suffer no injury whatsoever; the other (perhaps because of an abnormally thin skull) suffers serious brain damage. Is the damage a result of the hazard or the individual's pre-existing condition? How should health and safety programs account for individual variability like this?

2. Identify a hazard at your workplace (or a workplace with which you are familiar). List all the approaches you could undertake to control or minimize the hazard.

OH&S IN ACTION

Using the example risk assessment found in **Table 4.1**, compete a risk assessment and fault tree diagram on a task or job you are familiar with. Once you have completed this, outline how your individual risk perceptions may have influenced your assessment and how it might be different from a classmate's evaluation.

CASE STUDY 1   INDUSTRIAL HAZARD ASSESSMENT

A plant worker in a textile manufacturing plant is experiencing some difficulties with a clamping device on a holding fixture that keeps a material in position while it is fed into an automatic stencilling machine. The clamp does not always allow the material to be fed into the machine properly aligned with the stencil. The worker who was operating the machine had 32 years' experience with this type of equipment. While attempting to make the necessary adjustments for smooth operation without shutting off the power, she had to reach into the machine. She placed her left hand between the feed-in mechanism levers while her right hand was positioning the misaligned part between the open clamps of the fixture.

Unfortunately, the one-button actuating control was located immediately to the left of the worker's body, about hip level. The worker inadvertently depressed the button with her leg while reaching into the machine. The machine cycled-the feed mechanism slid forward while the fixture clamps closed. The worker's sleeve was pinched in the clamps and her arm was pulled partly into the machine before a coworker was able to hit the emergency stop button. You have been asked to investigate and as part of that investigation you have been asked to list the following:

a. the unsafe acts
b. the unsafe conditions
c. the energies involved
d. the steps to be taken to prevent this situation from recurring

CHAPTER 4 Hazard Recognition, Risk Assessment, and Control

Tadao works as a butcher in a large chain grocery store. His primary responsibility is cutting up meat using large (and very sharp) knives. He's been on the job now for four years and has never had a health and safety complaint. Lately, though, he's been experiencing some difficulties. Actually, it started a couple of years ago when Tadao noticed that his right hand was painful at the end of the day and that he was unable to use the hand for several hours after work. The pain and fatigue didn't last long, and Tadao assumed that he was just overworking the hand (Tadao is right-handed). In the past month or so, the pain has escalated; it often lasts all night and makes sleep difficult. Tadao also experiences numbness and tingling in the hand. Tadao has begun to avoid activities that require using his right hand, including shaking hands with people.

Last Tuesday, Tadao came to work and could not pick up the knife in his right hand—he had to pick up the knife with his left hand and place it in his right hand to begin work. Watching him go through this procedure, a coworker observed, "Well, it looks like you've developed butcher's claw—it comes from doing the same motion over and over again. It happens to us all and there's not much you can do about it." As an HR professional responsible for health and safety, do you have a better answer for Tadao?

A new plating machine had been installed and was being checked for proper operation. During this check it was discovered that the bearings on the caustic solution circulating pump were defective and had to be replaced. The pump was removed and repaired and was being reinstalled. An electrician was assigned to make the electrical connections, while a plumber performed the necessary pipe connections on the same pump.

The electrician finished the assignment except for checking the direction of shaft rotation. Since the plumber was out of the area, the electrician asked the company representative supplying the equipment if the pump was ready to be tried out. The representative stated that it was. The electrician walked to the end of the plater to start the motor, just as the plumber appeared. The plumber's shouts to the electrician not to start the pump were too late—the pump had already been turned on. At that moment, hot caustic solution showered out of the pipe flange, which had not been tightened after reassembly. The solution splashed onto the plumber, two engineers in the area, another plant engineering employee, and the vendor representative. The plumber received burns requiring immediate hospitalization and was off work for about two months. One engineer required subsequent hospitalization for eye burns and was off work for more than a week. The other three involved received minor burns.

What would you recommend for contact and postcontact control?

// NOTES

1. Canadian Centre for Occupational Health and Safety, OHS Answers, "Hazard and Risk." Found at: http://www.ccohs.ca/oshanswers/hsprograms/hazard _risk.html (accessed June 7, 2016).

2. M. Fleming, R. Flin, K. Mearns, and R. Gordon, "Risk Perceptions of Offshore Workers on UK Oil and Gas Platforms," *Risk Analysis* 18: 103–10.

3. G. Rampton, I. Turnbull, and G. Doran, *Human Resources Management Systems*, (Toronto: Nelson, 1996).

4. R.J. Firenze, *The Process of Hazard Control* (Dubuque: Kendall/Hunt, 1978).

5. M. Fleming, R. Flin, K. Mearns, and R. Gordon, "Risk Perceptions of Offshore Workers on UK Oil and Gas Platforms," *Risk Analysis* 18: 103–10.

6. CCOHS, "Risk Assessment," Table 2. Found at: http://www.ccohs.ca/ oshanswers/hsprograms/risk_assessment.html (accessed June 7, 2016).

7. Ibid.

8. Canadian Centre for Occupational Health and Safety, OHS Answers, "Lifting Guidelines." Found at: http://www.ccohs.ca/oshanswers/ergonomics/inj_prev .html (accessed June 7, 2016).

9. The National Institute for Occupational Safety and Health, "Back Belts: Do They Prevent Injury?" Found at: http://www.cdc.gov/niosh/docs/94-127 (accessed (accessed June 7, 2016).

10. Canadian Centre for Occupational Health and Safety, OHS Answers, "Engineering Controls." Found at: http://www.ccohs.ca/oshanswers/ hsprograms/hazard_control.html (accessed June 7, 2016).

11. R. Gillespie, *Manufacturing Knowledge, A History of the Hawthorne Experiments*, (New York: Cambridge University Press, 1991).

12. Canadian Standards Association, "Office Ergonomics," CSA Standard, CAN/ CSA Z412-M89, section 5, 1995.

13. S. DiNardi, ed, *The Occupational Environment—Its Evaluation and Control*, 2nd ed. (Fairfax: American Industrial Hygiene Association, 1997).

14. Canada Occupational Health and Safety Regulations (SOR/86-304). Found at: http://laws-lois.justice.gc.ca/PDF/SOR-86-304.pdf (accessed June 7, 2016).

15. P.M. Laing, ed., *Accident Prevention Manual for Business and Industry: Administration and Programs*, 10th ed. (Washington: National Safety Council, 1992).

16. NSERC/SSHRC "Audit of Physical Security Management" Found at: http://www.nserc-crsng.gc.ca/_doc/Reports-Rapports/Audits-Verifications/ PhysicalSecurity_e.pdf (accessed June 7, 2016).

CHAPTER
5

PHYSICAL AGENTS

CHAPTER LEARNING OBJECTIVES

AFTER READING THIS CHAPTER, YOU SHOULD BE ABLE TO:

- identify common physical agents within the workplace
- explain how and when many of the commonly found physical agents can be considered hazardous
- identify methods of controlling physical agents within the workplace

Take a minute to consider how often you interact with an electronic device such as a mobile phone or tablet. Now consider at what point during the day you use them. Have you ever used them before bed to wind down before going to sleep? Consider how much time you spend sitting in front of a computer screen while at work and for leisure activities. Perhaps you use your tablet to study or play games? Many of these sorts of electronic devices emit what is referred to as blue light. Visible light is made up of electromagnetic particles that travel in waves; these waves emit energy and vary in length and in strength, making up what is referred to the visible light spectrum. Blue light, which is part of this spectrum, has a much shorter wave than other colour lights (e.g., red) resulting in a higher energy level, reaching further into our retinas, and having a greater impact on us. Researchers and scientist have conducted studies over the last number of years and have found that while blue light has a number of benefits, exposure to it before sleep can be detrimental to our health. For instance, the Harvard Medical School indicates the dangers of blue light as significant for those who work night shifts and for those who regularly use electronics before sleep. Being exposed to blue light negatively affects the body's ability to produce melatonin, a hormone that impacts circadian rhythms, resulting in a greater risk for a poor night's sleep. The risks associated with many of the physical agents we are exposed to in our daily environment are complex, and mitigating those risks can be as equally complex. The first step in managing these risks is ensuring that employees are able to identify them, understanding the potential consequences and knowing the proper controls.

Source: Harvard Medical School, Harvard Health Publications, "Blue Light Has a Dark Side." Found at http://www.health.harvard.edu/staying-healthy/blue-light-has-a-dark-side.

demaerre/Thinkstock

Is blue light affecting your sleep cycle?

In this chapter we consider the effects of physical agents in the workplace and how best to control them. **Physical agents** are sources of energy that may cause injury or disease if they are not controlled or managed properly. Examples include noise, vibration, radiation, and extremes in temperature and pressure. Each of these agents may be **ambient** or acute (i.e., resulting from a single exposure).

// RADIATION

Every minute of every day we are exposed to radiation, some that occurs naturally, and some of which is created. The exposure comes from various sources including the LED lights in our houses, various foods we eat, basements we live in, medical equipment we use, and the offices and buildings where we work. Although we have almost-constant exposure, not all radiation has the same effect on our health.

Radiation in general is the emission of electromagnetic energy, and is divided into two distinct groups—ionizing and non-ionizing. These two types of radiation are identified primarily by wavelength range—short for ionizing and long for non-ionizing—and by their action on tissue. This section will be general since any worker employed

physical agents
sources of energy that may cause injury or disease

ambient
all-encompassing condition associated with a given environment, being usually a composite of inputs from sources all around us

by a company involved in radiative processes or materials must undergo extensive, specialized training.

IONIZING RADIATION

Ionizing radiation is any form of electromagnetic energy capable of producing ions through interaction with matter. Types of ionizing radiation include X-rays, gamma rays, alpha particles, beta particles, and neutrons. X-radiation is most commonly found in medical facilities. The other forms of ionizing radiation are commonly found in nuclear operations or research companies. All of these forms, except X-rays, occur naturally as well as in manufactured states. Natural radiation is found in ground-grown food, building materials such as concrete, and fertilizers such as phosphorus. Most of these sources are measurable with very sensitive instruments but are insignificant from a health standpoint. Some harmful ionizing radiation, which might occur in basements and mines, is radon.

Radiation exposure or dosage is usually measured in a unit called a rem (*r*oentgen *e*quivalent *m*an). Natural radiation is approximately 125 mrem (millirem) per year. A dose of approximately 75 rem (75,000 mrem) per year can cause serious health effects.

Manufactured ionizing radiation can be found in a number of products or operations other than nuclear energy. Most home smoke detectors use a source that emits alpha particles, which are harmless; older "glow in the dark" watch faces were painted with very low radioactive paint. In industry, ionizing radiation can be found in bulk-material measuring devices, high-voltage electronic devices, and medical equipment such as X-ray machines or scanners; none of these poses a health hazard to the general population.

The effects of electromagnetic radiation upon humans and animals depends upon the power and frequency of the radiation. The biological effects of equal amounts of different radiations depend on several factors, including whether the exposure is whole body or local (e.g., the arm), acute, or chronic. Genetic effects can include cell mutation, burns, and radiation sickness. Control of exposure will include regular monitoring, shielding, job rotation, protective equipment, and extensive training. This is why the dentist places a lead apron over your body and neck when taking X-rays.

NON-IONIZING RADIATION

Non-ionizing radiation refers to electromagnetic radiation that does not have energies great enough to turn matter into ions. Non-ionizing radiation is made up of photons, which are bundles of electromagnetic energy that travel at the speed of light. Non-ionizing radiation includes extremely low frequency (ELF) radiation, microwave frequency, radio frequency (RF) infrared radiation (IR), visible light radiation (light that is part of the visible light spectrum), and ultraviolet radiation (UV).

Even though non-ionizing radiation does not have the ability to ionize matter, it can still have a negative impact on our health; however, we can be exposed to it without causing significant impairments or damage to body tissues.[1] The impact of non-ionizing radiation on our bodies depends on a number of factors such as the amount of exposure, the power density of the field of beam, and environmental conditions.[2] Do you wear sunscreen before going outdoors? Do you know how long it lasts before you start to burn? What about on a cloudy day? If you wear sunglasses,

FIGURE 5.1

GENERAL ABSORPTION PROPERTIES OF THE EYE FOR ELECTROMAGNETIC RADIATION

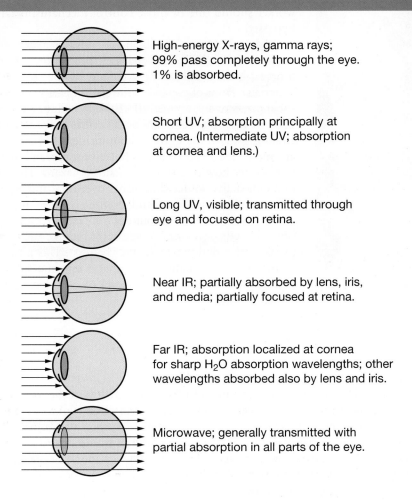

High-energy X-rays, gamma rays; 99% pass completely through the eye. 1% is absorbed.

Short UV; absorption principally at cornea. (Intermediate UV; absorption at cornea and lens.)

Long UV, visible; transmitted through eye and focused on retina.

Near IR; partially absorbed by lens, iris, and media; partially focused at retina.

Far IR; absorption localized at cornea for sharp H_2O absorption wavelengths; other wavelengths absorbed also by lens and iris.

Microwave; generally transmitted with partial absorption in all parts of the eye.

do you wear them for style or protection, or both? If your answer is style only, then consider that the sun can be a source of all types of radiation and the eye is the primary organ at risk from non-ionizing radiation (see **Figure 5.1**). The impact of non-ionizing radiation is a significant research topic and in some cases debate (e.g., the impact of cellular telephones).

CONTROLLING RADIATION

Chapter 4 outlines the various ways in which the risks associated with hazards can be controlled or mitigated. Controlling the health risks of radiation often includes a combination of precontact, point-of-contact controls and postcontact controls, which would include various engineering and administrative controls. For instance, a company may implement a specially designed piece of equipment that prevents access to radiation. Engineering controls can include shields, walls, locked doors, warning

Electronic personal dosimeters allow workers to measure the levels of ionizing radiation they are exposed to.

indicators, displays, and ventilation systems. Typically in an environment wherein the risk of exposure is high, multiple engineering controls are in place in order to protect a worker should one of those control mechanisms fail or be bypassed.

Administrative controls include regular inspections and maintenance schedules, operating procedures, as well as proper labelling and inventory of any radioactive devices or materials. Point-of-contact controls primarily include personal protective equipment (PPE). PPE includes lead aprons, vests, or air purifying respirators as well as eye protection such as sunglasses. In the event that an incident has occurred and an employee is exposed to a radioactive source, it is important to consider how that source remains a hazard. The intensity of a radioactive source diminishes over time and, as a result, radioactive atoms decay and eventually form more stable atoms. To measure the amount of time required for the intensity of a radiation from a radioactive source to be reduced by half is referred to as radiation half-life. This measure tells us the amount of radioactivity that is left in a substance or object, thereby indicating the level of risk or danger that is associated with it.

// NOISE

Noise is defined as any unwanted sound and is often referred to as the most common workplace hazard. Technically, it refers to "the auditory sensation evoked by the oscillations in pressure in a medium with elasticity and viscosity," such as air.[3] Sound and noise differ by definition in that that noise is unwanted sound. It would be difficult to find a profession where employees are not exposed to some type of sound or noise; however construction workers, cafeteria workers, and farmers are among some of the professions most at risk for hearing damage, specifically, **early warning change**, as a result of noise. A Canadian study published in 2015 found that approximately 4.6 million Canadians aged 20 to 79 (19%) had hearing loss significant enough to negatively affect their ability to hear normal speech.[4]

early warning change a deterioration of hearing in the upper frequency—the earliest detectable sign of noise-induced hearing loss

What makes the issue of noise within the workplace so complex is the fact that a sound considered to be noise by one individual may not be considered to be noise by another, meaning various circumstances can change whether a sound is considered to be noise and therefore harmful. Furthermore, there are characteristics about the ear that add to the complexity of managing noise in the workplace. For instance, one major characteristic of the human ear and hearing is that we do not hear everything in a nice, neat fashion. If sound were measured electronically, the sound spectrum might appear more or less as a straight line. However, what the human ear hears or perceives is significantly different. Sound is often assessed using a unit of measurement known as Hertz or Hz (equal to one cycle per second). The human hearing range of frequencies is approximately 20 Hz to 20 000 Hz. Thus, a person can hear a bass note from a tuba or a shrill note from a piccolo, but not a dog whistle. This has direct implications for human hearing problems. Just because we cannot hear the sound does not mean that it is not present and possibly causing hearing damage.

The response of the human ear to sound is usually represented as a graph that illustrates the threshold of hearing. The term "threshold of hearing" refers to the envelope or range of sound that the human ear can perceive or hear. The standards for the measurement of noise use the unit of a decibel, or dB (also referred to as sound pressure level). Decibels are measured on a logarithmic scale so that very small differences in the numbers can translate into very large actual differences. For example, a 3 dB difference (e.g., going from 80 to 83 dB) represents a doubling of the "loudness" (83 dB is twice as loud as 80 dB), and a 10 dB difference represents a tenfold difference (90 dB is 10 times louder than 80 dB). A 20 dB difference is a 100-fold increase (90 dB is 100 times louder than 70 dB). Thus, when the human response is involved, the unit becomes dB (A) or A-weighted decibel. This response is built into the sound meters used for measuring noise exposure in the workplace.

Human hearing response is conditional on three characteristics: frequency, duration, and loudness. Any noise-level investigation must take into account these three elements. Most noise sources and sounds, such as music, are made up of a variety of frequencies, which the ear blends to create a pleasant or not-so-pleasant sound. As noted earlier, noise beyond the range of human hearing response can be damaging even though not "heard." Similarly, certain frequencies in a noise that is made up of a variety of frequencies can be extra-loud and thus damaging without being noticed, even within the human range. It is important to consider frequency response when dealing with hearing protection.

The duration of the sound is one of those conditions that the human ear responds to in a strange way. A loud noise of very short duration, like a gunshot, is perceived to be "quieter" than the same sound level heard for a longer duration. They can both be damaging, but only the latter one "sounds" like it. The short-duration noise is referred to as impact or impulse noise, which has a duration of about 1 millisecond (1/1000th of a second). The third characteristic of human response is loudness. This term is self-explanatory. The louder (volume) the noise, the more problems it can cause.

TYPES OF HEARING LOSS

Noise can affect humans in three ways: by causing physiological damage that affects hearing also known as noise-induced hearing loss (NIHL), by causing more general physiological effects in some cases referred to as sociological effects, and by causing psychological effects. In terms of the first effect, physiological damage, there are two basic types of hearing loss. The first is *conductive*, and restricts the transmission of sound to the cochlea or inner ear (see **Figure 5.2**); the second is *sensorineural* (sometimes referred to as nerve deafness), and affects the cochlea and is usually irreversible. Conductive hearing loss can be caused by wax buildup, infection, or trauma. From an industrial standpoint, it can be caused by the unhygienic application of hearing protectors or the improper cleaning of these devices.

More prevalent in industry, however, is the sensorineural type of hearing loss. This type of NIHL can occur randomly in workers, that is to say that noise may affect two workers differently.[5] NIHL is typically a cumulative process wherein the loudness and the amount of exposure are factors. Two indications of exposure to excessive noise levels at work are ringing in the ears (tinnitus) and raising the volume on the radio or television after work. The volume of the radio or television will seem very high the next morning because temporary hearing loss diminishes with rest and removal from exposure. Causes of workplace NIHL can be caused by various pieces of equipment (e.g., hairdryers, drills, fans, and so forth) and careful measurements must be taken to ensure workers are not exposed to dangerous levels.

FIGURE 5.2

THE AUDITORY SYSTEM

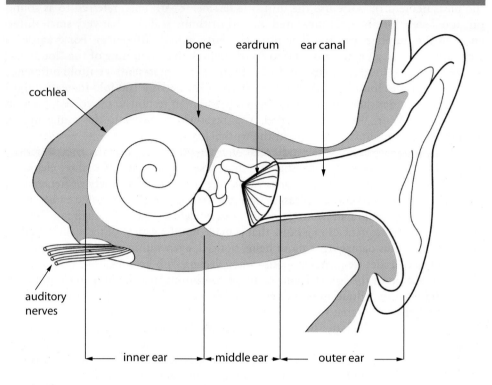

Gradual hearing loss, known as temporary threshold shift (TTS), can sometimes be reversed by removal from the noise source. Permanent threshold shift (PTS) identifies a hearing disability that is permanent and may not be correctable. In many cases, a hearing aid can bring about some improvement. However, such a device is of little assistance when the hearing loss has been caused by noise exposure or sensorineural loss because the hair cells in the cochlea have been destroyed.

The second effect of noise is also physiological but a slightly different category of physiological in that it is more general. It is sometimes referred to as sociological hearing loss and causes extra-auditory effects such as a startled response to a loud, unexpected noise; cardiovascular, neurologic, endocrine, and biochemical changes; and nausea, malaise, and headaches.[6] Other laboratory and field studies have demonstrated **vasoconstriction**, **hyperreflexia**, fluctuations in hormonal secretions, and disturbances in equilibrium and visual functions. In the past companies, would hire workers with hearing loss to work in high-noise environments on the notion that the damage was already done; however, it is now known that noise can cause more general physiological effects.

The third effect deals with human psychology. Many people are affected and disturbed by certain sounds that are not loud enough to present any serious physiological problem. These are day-to-day noises that tend to bother us, such as a patron talking during a movie, a helicopter flying overhead, or a tap dripping. Though the actual noise level may be well below acceptable standards and may not be measurable with a sound level meter, it is nonetheless very real (often referred to as "selective hearing") and can cause stress and other possible non-auditory effects (see **OH&S Notebook 5.1**).

vasoconstriction
the process of causing a constriction of the blood vessels

hyperreflexia
the condition of unusually quick reaction by the nerves to some external stimulus

NOISE EXPOSURE STANDARDS AND HEARING CONSERVATION PROGRAMS

Noise exposure standards vary across provinces and territories in terms of their relative stringency. The standards are based on worker exposure during a defined time frame. This relationship is referred to as dose, which describes the amount of noise absorbed by or impinged on an organ (the ear or the body) in a given unit of time. The exposure limits in Canadian jurisdictions are available at: http://www.ccohs.ca/oshanswers/phys_agents/exposure_can.html.

To support employers with understanding how to manage and control noise in the workplace, various organizations across Canada have hearing conservation programs. These programs provide various resources and tools for employers to ensure they are following legislation, performing their due diligence, and caring for employees. The workers compensation board in British Columbia (WorkSafeBC) offers a comprehensive hearing conservation program that employers can adopt and implement in their workplaces. This program includes information about noise measurement, legislation, controls, hearing protection, and resources needed for education and training. The University of Calgary in Alberta implements a hearing conservation program designed to educate and protect university employees. This program also contains information about the importance of avoiding hearing loss, the legislative requirements, testing, record-keeping and so forth. For more information about both of these programs, visit the following websites:

WorkSafeBC: http://www2.worksafebc.com/topics/hearinglossprevention/HearingLossPreventionProgram.asp

University of Calgary: https://www.ucalgary.ca/safety/programs/hearing-conservation

Sources: CCOHS, "Noise—Occupational Exposure Limits in Canada." Found at: http://www.ccohs.ca/oshanswers/phys_agents/exposure_can.html (accessed June 7, 2016).

NOISE CONTROL

Noise can be controlled by using various methods, but the process for control follows the source–path–human strategies used by health and safety professionals. The first strategy is always elimination; however, when that is not possible the next course of action would be to change the source and make the source quieter. There are a number of possible approaches. If the problem consists of a noisy machine, for instance, it may be possible to make the machine quieter by adding sound-absorbing materials, placing vibration padding under it, redesigning the operation so that the machine performs in a different manner, isolating the machine in a separate room or sound-deadening enclosure, or purchasing a new machine. (See **OH&S Notebook 5.2**.)

The second strategy—*path*—involves moving the worker away from the source or erecting sound barriers between the noise and the worker, or both. Based on the physics of noise, as the distance from the sound source is doubled, the noise level will drop by a fixed amount. For example, if a noise level of 90 dB is measured 5 metres away from a machine (a point source) and the distance is increased to 10 metres, the noise level will be **attenuated** or lowered by 6 dB. This is called a "free field effect," which simply means that nothing like a wall is around to reflect the sound back on the worker. Objects such as the walls of the building and other machines will cause reflections that can reduce the amount of attenuation from this fixed amount. Nevertheless, the principle is still valid, and this process is usually less costly than the source approach.

> **attenuated**
> reduction of noise at one location compared to another farther from the source

NOISE IN THE WORKPLACE: SIGNS AND LEVELS

Though nothing will replace accurate measurement of noise levels in the workplace, the Canadian Centre for Occupational Health and Safety suggests that a workplace might be too noisy if:

- people have to raise their voices to be understood
- employees have ringing in the ears at the end of the workday
- employees find that they have to turn their radio up on the drive home (compared with the volume on the way to work)
- individuals who have worked in the workplace for years have difficulty understanding conversations at parties or restaurants

If any of the above statements are true, a noise assessment or survey of the workplace should be undertaken. Noise exposure tests can be done by an outside specialist or by a trained person on staff using various pieces of equipment including:

- a sound pressure level meter to measure gross noise levels
- an octave band analyzer to measure noise level in each frequency range
- a dosimeter to measure a person's exposure to noise as a percentage for one shift
- an audiometer to determine the sensitivity of a person's hearing or degree of hearing loss

Source: CCOHS, "Noise—Basic Information." Found at: http://www.ccohs.ca/oshanswers/phys_agents/noise_basic.html#_1_3 (accessed June 7, 2016).

The third strategy—*human*—involves the use of personal protective equipment (PPE). This approach is the least costly and the one most commonly used. Although it is not always the best method, in many cases some companies are not well-enough informed to undertake other approaches such as job rotation, relocation, isolation, automation,

© Hero Images Inc./Alamy Stock Photo

Various types of hearing protection are available to workers; PPE should be carefully selected to ensure proper protection.

rest periods, and site design. The two basic classes of hearing protection available are earplugs, which are inserted into the ears, and circumaural muffs or earmuffs, which are worn over the ears. A description of the various types of industrial hearing protection is provided in **Table 5.2** in the chapter appendix. Note that whatever strategies are used to decrease noise exposure, personal protective devices may still be necessary in conjunction with other methods (see **OH&S Notebook 5.3**).

OH&S NOTEBOOK 5.3

CHOOSING HEARING PROTECTORS

For each application and to be properly fitted for maximum protection, there are 10 factors to consider when deciding on the most effective hearing protection.

1. *Comfort:* Earmuffs in particular can be hot in warm conditions. The spring band can generate a feeling of the head being squashed. Workers who are claustrophobic may experience feelings of confinement.

2. *Visibility:* It is important that hearing protection be visible so that supervisors can ensure that the worker is wearing the protection and using it in the required manner.

3. *Size:* People have heads of different sizes and shapes. It is imperative that hearing protective devices be fitted properly. Additional types of paraphernalia such as face shields used in conjunction with hearing protection must also be examined.

4. *Weight:* Generally, the lighter the protection, the greater the comfort.

5. *Ease of donning:* A device that is easy to put on will gain more acceptance among workers.

6. *Cost:* The actual dollar cost will depend on the application, the required degree of attenuation, and the style of device. Earmuffs are more costly than earplugs. The specific noise protection required could necessitate both plugs and muffs.

7. *Effective attenuation:* Most modern hearing protection devices use a noise reduction rating (NRR) system to indicate the degree of attenuation based on laboratory evaluation. The NRR value is usually accompanied by a chart showing attenuation by octave band frequencies. Generally, the higher the number, the greater the level of attenuation. A good rule-of-thumb relationship is expressed with the equation below:

$$NRR = L_{actual} - L_{standard} + 7$$

where Lactual is the noise level measured in the workplace and Lstandard is the noise standard for an eight-hour period. Thus, if a worksite has a noise level of 97 dB(A) and the standard is 90 dB(A) for eight hours, the required NRR for hearing protectors would be $97 - 90 + 7$, or 14 dB(A).

8. *Hygiene:* This requirement is the most critical and most abused. It is not uncommon to observe a hearing protection device hanging from a hook in a dirty environment. Care must be taken to keep the personal item clean and stored in a sanitary location to avoid ear infections, which could cause more damage than the noise does.

9. *Useful life:* Disposable plugs or inserts do not last long but require no maintenance; muffs last longer but require maintenance.

10. *Maintenance:* All non-disposable hearing protection devices require ongoing maintenance and care. They must be cleaned regularly with soap and warm water, not alcohol, and checked periodically for wear. The foam seal pads on circumaural units must be regularly maintained because skin oils and sweat will cause embrittlement and surface failure. Once the seal is damaged, the attenuation effectiveness is reduced.

Sources: E.H. Berger, W.D. Ward, J.C. Morrill, and L.H. Royster, eds., *Noise and Hearing Conservation Manual*, 4th ed. (Akron: American Industrial Hygiene Association, 1988); CCOHS, "What Is Personal Protective Equipment?" Found at: http://www.ccohs.ca/oshanswers/prevention/ppe/designin .html (accessed June 7, 2016).

// VIBRATION

Another physical agent within the workplace that can be hazardous, but may not be thought about as often, is vibration. Vibration refers to the oscillating motion of a particle or body moving about a reference position.[7] Vibration is measured by examining the frequency, amplitude, and acceleration of an object. Vibration has a number of mechanical causes, including the dynamic effects from machine tolerances, clearances, rolling or rubbing contact, and out-of-balance conditions with rotary or reciprocating parts.

Vibrations are often easily detectable but determining the amount that is hazardous is difficult and, because of that, vibration exposure must be measured and carefully monitored. Vibration enters the body from the part in contact with the vibrating equipment. Vibrations are classified into two categories: low frequency (discussed above) and high frequency. Vibrating effects fall into two separate conditions. As noted earlier, the first concerns low-frequency vibrations. The second deals with higher frequency vibrations, which can happen so quickly that the body cannot respond. When the higher frequencies occur, the effects of wave velocity and acceleration take precedence. Vibratory effects are evaluated with a vibration meter, which is often a variation on a sound-level meter, using measurements of velocity and acceleration caused by the source.

HEALTH EFFECTS OF VIBRATION

An employee who is required to operate a handheld piece of equipment that vibrates (e.g., jackhammer) typically feels it in the hands and arms. This is often known as segmental vibration or hand–arm vibration. An employee who is required to sit or stand on a vibrating floor area such as a seat or piece of equipment will experience vibration in his or her entire body, which is known as whole-body vibration. The impact on health is largely dependent upon the average amount of exposure and must be properly assessed. An evaluation takes into account the intensity and frequency of the vibration, the duration (years) of exposure, and the part of the body that receives the vibration energy.

Vibration can be a health hazard for three reasons. As mentioned above, it can cause whole-body vibration, segmental vibration, and noise. Similar to noise, vibration is transmitted through a medium, though in this case the medium is usually solid (e.g., steel or brick). The health effects will vary with the frequency and amplitude of the vibration. At low frequencies —say, up to 15 Hz —the body will experience whole-body vibration. In this instance, the complete human body will "shake" with the source. We have all experienced or witnessed this condition of motion sickness in an automobile or onboard a ship. Whole-body vibration can also result in fatigue, nausea, stomach problems, headache, and "shakiness" and some situations may be connected to bowel, respiratory, circulatory, and back disorders.[8] Additionally, health effects of whole-body vibration can include inhibition of muscular reflexes, impaired or blurred vision, and alterations of brain electrical activity. Whole-body vibration effects can result from driving a motorcycle, truck, or tractor, or from working near large machines such as air compressors or punch presses. See **OH&S Today 5.1**.

As the frequency of vibration increases, parts of the body—not the whole body—will be affected by a process called segmental vibration. Segmental vibration effects include sore neck and shoulder muscles and sore joints; Raynaud's phenomenon, or white fingers, caused by restricted blood circulation in the fingers; neuritis and degenerative alterations of the central nervous system; fragmentation, **necrosis**, and **decalcification** of the carpal bones; and muscle atrophy and tenosynovitis (see **OH&S Notebook 5.4**).

segmental vibration
vibrations that affect only parts of the body

whole-body vibration
vibrations that affect the whole body as a unit

necrosis
death or decay of tissue

decalcification
loss of lime salts (calcium) in the bones

WHO DIAGNOSES VIBRATION EFFECTS?

The acceptance of vibration syndromes as an industrial disease has been encumbered by the fact that not all physicians have the training and expertise to diagnose vibration-related injuries and illnesses, the causes are often unidentifiable or complex in nature, and there is no objective method or measurement technique to determine the level of impairment to a worker. Furthermore, the progression of vibration-related diseases and conditions can take a long time before it impairs an individual's ability to work. The Health and Safety Executive in the United Kingdom provides a number of resources for workers, employers, and occupational health specialists in order to support accurate, early diagnosis and intervention. These resources include information about the nature of vibration-related injuries and illnesses as well as various tools that support proper diagnosis and measurement of the effects. For more information, visit http://www.hse.gov.uk/vibration/index.htm.

Source: Canadian Centre for Occupational Health and Safety, "Why Is It Not Easy to Diagnose Vibration-related Diseases?" Found at http://www.ccohs.ca/oshanswers/phys_agents/vibration/vibration_effects.html (accessed June 7, 2016).

HAND–ARM VIBRATION SYNDROME (HAVS)

Working with handheld power tools (particularly in cold weather) can result in vibration-induced white finger (VWF)—or, more generally, hand-arm vibration syndrome (HAVS). HAVS results from changes in blood circulation and the nervous system associated with vibration and is characterized by:

- tingling in the fingers
- loss of sensation in the fingers (numbness)
- loss of sense of light touch
- whitening (blanching) of the fingers when exposed to cold
- loss of grip strength
- development of cysts in fingers and wrists

HAVS is a progressive disorder and is also known as Raynaud's phenomenon. Prevention efforts focus on reducing vibration, using ergonomically designed tools, keeping hands warm and dry, and taking rest breaks.

Sources: J. Mason, "Bad Vibrations," *Occupational Health*, Vol. 55, No. 7 (2003): 24; E. Weir and L. Lander, "Hand–Arm Vibration Syndrome," *Canadian Medical Association Journal*, Vol. 172, No. 8 (2005): 1000–001.

One term that often arises in discussions of vibration is **resonance**, which refers to the effect that occurs when an object reacts strongly to some particular frequency. If you sing in a tiled shower stall, you will occasionally hear a note that sounds louder than most, which means that the space is resonant to that note. Parts of the human body can resonate when exposed to some lower frequencies. For instance, the head and shoulders can resonate at 20 Hz to 30 Hz, while the eyeballs resonate at 60 Hz to 90 Hz.[9] If your vision becomes blurry when you have been working with a power tool such as a belt sander, you are experiencing minor levels of eyeball resonance, which is harmless unless prolonged.

> **resonance**
> the effect that occurs when an object reacts strongly to some particular frequency

CONTROLLING VIBRATION

The first step in controlling vibration in the workplace is being knowledgeable about the standards or exposure limits. The CCOHS website contains information about exposure limits and can be found at http://www.ccohs.ca/oshanswers/phys_agents/vibration/vibration_effects.html.

Being knowledgeable of the standards helps determine which control mechanisms are required for minimizing any negative impact. By using the proper engineering and administrative controls as well as the correct personal protective equipment, the impact of vibration, whether whole body or segmental, can be greatly reduced.

One example of an engineering control includes ergonomically designed equipment or equipment features such as special grips or properly designed seating that helps absorb or decrease the vibrations felt by the worker. The frequency response associated with vibrating systems is directly related to the system's mass. In the simplest terms, vibration can be dampened by increasing mass or weight. An example: the increased weight on the outer flange of a flywheel (typically a large wheel designed to regulate the speed of machinery) smooths out much of a machine's vibration. A flywheel is one method for reducing health effects of vibrations. Segmental vibration effects are caused by vibrating tools such as riveters, sanders, saws, air hammers, or hammer drills. The most serious segmental effects are those associated with hand–arm vibrations. Vibrating hand tools produce a catch-22 situation: to properly control a vibrating hand tool, one must grip it securely; but the tighter the hand grips the tool, the more severe the effects of segmental damage from vibration. The human resource professional should also be aware that vibration has chronic effects that must be managed.

Examples of administrative controls include policies or rules around the duration and amount of exposure (e.g., shift rotations) as well as regular maintenance of equipment. Finally personal protective equipment like padding, gloves, or floor mats can help reduce the amount of vibration that is felt by the individual. For more specific methods for controlling vibrations, see **OH&S Notebook 5.5**.

OH&S NOTEBOOK 5.5

CONTROLLING VIBRATION

Strategies for whole-body and segmental vibration control include implementing a number of safe work practices, maintaining equipment, using PPE, and educating workers about the impact of vibrations on their health. Employers can reduce the risk of vibrations by:

- avoiding the source by revising the task
- using equipment that produces lower vibrations
- adding dampening devices to equipment to reduce vibrations
- maintaining equipment properly
- decreasing worker exposure time
- isolating the worker from the source

Source: CCOHS, "How Can You Measure Vibration?" Found at: https://www.ccohs.ca/oshanswers/phys_agents/vibration/vibration_measure.html (accessed June 7, 2016).

// THERMAL STRESS

Thermal stress conditions involve cold and hot temperature extremes. The human body can be seen as a machine that takes in chemical energy (food) and converts it to mechanical energy (muscles) and heat (see **Figure 5.3**). The balance of this heat generation, referred to as homeostasis, is the basis for examining the effects of heat and cold on the body. Simple thermodynamic theory shows that temperature, like water, flows from the high point to the low point. Thus, in cold climates, heat will flow from the body into the surrounding environment, making the person feel cold. Similarly, in hot climates, heat will be absorbed by the body, making the person feel hot. Adding physical work to either of these situations will increase body heat and shift the thermal balance. When an imbalance occurs, the body is stressed thermally. This body thermal balance can be illustrated by the mathematical model below:[10]

$$S = (M - W) \pm R \pm C \pm V - E$$

where S is the body heat storage or loss, M is the metabolic heat production of the body, W is the work output, R is the radiative heat gain or loss, C is the convective heat gain or loss, V is the respiratory heat gain or loss, and E is the evaporative heat loss.

When there is heat, the body will gain heat if R, C, and V are positive; similarly, when there is heat loss, then R, C, V, and E are negative and the body will lose heat. In medical terms, heat gain is referred to as *hyperthermic*; heat loss is referred to as *hypothermic*; and a condition of neither gain nor loss is known as balance (see **OH&S Notebook 5.6**).

There are three methods of heat transfer that apply to the body, as well as to any other thermal condition. The first method, conduction, occurs when two surfaces are in contact (e.g., the skin touches a hot stove, resulting in a local burn). The second method, convection, occurs when one surface adds heat to the surroundings (e.g., the skin is close to air flow emanating from a flame or a heater). The third method, radiation, occurs when energy is transmitted by electromagnetic waves (e.g., the skin is exposed to sunlight).

homeostasis
the balance of heat generation

conduction
heat transfer occurring when two surfaces are in contact

convection
heat transfer occurring when one surface adds heat to the surroundings

radiation
heat transfer occurring when energy is transmitted by electromagnetic waves

FIGURE 5.3

THE BODY AS A MACHINE SYSTEM

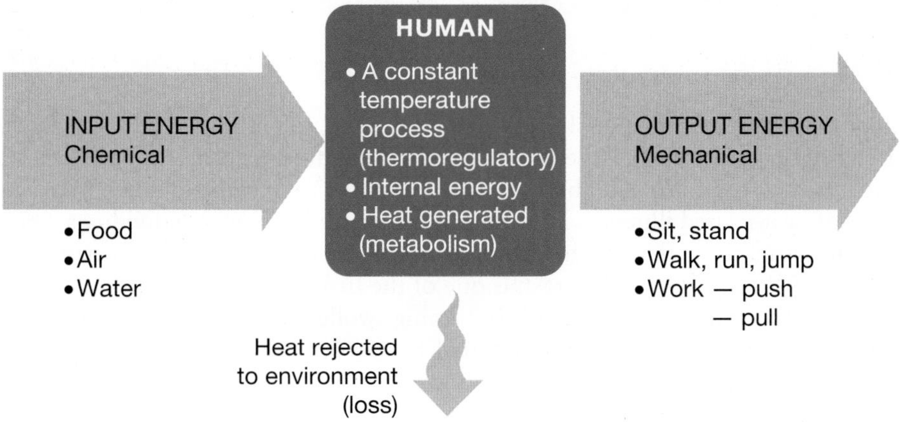

INPUT ENERGY
Chemical

- Food
- Air
- Water

HUMAN
- A constant temperature process (thermoregulatory)
- Internal energy
- Heat generated (metabolism)

OUTPUT ENERGY
Mechanical

- Sit, stand
- Walk, run, jump
- Work — push
  — pull

Heat rejected to environment (loss)

Thermal stress is measured using the wet bulb globe temperature (WBGT) index. This index measures the effect of heat and humidity on a worker.

HUMIDEX RANGE (°C)	COMFORT
20–29	Comfortable
30–39	Some discomfort
40–45	Great discomfort; avoid exertion
46 and over	Dangerous; heat stroke possible

Source: CCOHS, "Humidex Rating and Work," Table 1. Found at: http://www.ccohs.ca/oshanswers/phys_agents/humidex.html; and CBC, http://www.cbc.ca/news/canada/the-humidex-the-flawed-canadian-way-to-calculate-summer-discomfort-1.1394673.

The body has remarkable temperature control, with the blood system and the skin being the major players. As body heat increases, blood flow increases, capillaries move closer to the surface of the skin (they actually open up), and sweating increases, thereby allowing increased heat exchange to the atmosphere. As body heat decreases, blood flow slows and the capillaries withdraw from the skin surface, thus reducing the amount of heat transferred to the atmosphere.

The effects of heat and cold on health are well recognized by anyone who spends a lot of time outside in summer and winter. The focal point of most thermal stress and control is at the body core—from the neck to the groin and between the shoulders. The body core temperature range is 35°C to 38.5°C, with "normal" being 37°C. Fluctuations in the body's core temperature typically stay within 1°C and occur during various times of the day or when engaged in a physical activity or an emotionally arousing situation. In some situations the environment can cause the body's core temperature to increase more than 1°C. We typically see greater changes in the body's core temperature when an individual is ill. When the core temperature goes outside the normal range, serious problems can result.

HEAT-RELATED ILLNESSES

A number of factors influence the risk that heat poses to an individual. For instance, health, weight, age, low fitness level, and medical conditions such as high blood pressure are factors that influence the risk that heat poses to an individual.[11] There are a number of heat-related illnesses. Heat edema occurs most often in individuals who are not acclimatized to working in hot environments and typically results in parts of the body swelling (e.g., ankles). Heat rash is one of the first signs of the body's intolerance to heat and results in the sweat glands becoming swollen and plugged. Small red spots appear on the skin and cause an individual to feel a tingling sensation or itchiness. Heat cramps occur in the muscles of the body and may or may not occur in conjunction with other heat-related illnesses such as heat rash. Heat cramps are the result of an imbalance of salt in the body and are often felt in the arms and legs first. Heat syncope or fainting is the result of an inadequate amount of blood in the brain due to lowered blood pressure and often occurs while an individual is standing or working. Fainting as a result of heat often occurs in individuals who are not acclimatized; however, recovery is typically rapid after a period of rest in a cool area. Heat exhaustion occurs when an individual is sweating excessively and loses too much body water. Individuals suffering from heat exhaustion exhibit one or more of the following symptoms: excessive sweating, dizziness, blurred vision, nausea, headache, vomiting, heart palpitations, and numbness in the hands and or feet. Heat stroke and heat hyperpyrexia occur when the body is unable to control its thermal balance, resulting in a dangerous rise in core temperature (above 41°C). Symptoms of heat stroke include either a partial or complete loss of consciousness while the symptoms of heat hyperpyrexia are similar but the skin remains moist or wet. Heat stroke and heat hyperpyrexia are the most serious of heat-related illnesses and require immediate first aid; if left untreated, they can result in damage to the brain, kidneys, and heart. As part of the newly released criteria for heat exposure standards, the National Institute for Occupational Safety and Health in the United States defines two categories of heat stroke: classic heat stroke and exertional heat stroke. Classic heat stroke includes major disruption to the central nervous system functions and often includes a lack of sweating. Exertional heat stroke occurs in individuals who are physically active and may still continue to sweat. In that latter category, skeletal muscle can rapidly break down and can result in kidney and heart failure.[12]

CONTROLLING HEAT

Provincial legislation requires that employers take every reasonable precaution to prevent heat-related illnesses and the risks of heat exposure. If employees are at risk for heat-related illnesses the employer is required to conduct heat assessments and implement the proper controls.[13] Engineering controls are the most effective method for controlling heat exposure; however, they are often impractical in certain environments such as outdoors. Examples of engineering controls include insulating heat sources or hot surfaces, shielding or protecting workers, providing air conditioning, or increasing ventilation. When engineering controls are not feasible then administrative controls should be put into place. Administrative controls include reducing worker activity, proper supervision, arranging for work–rest cycles, and implementing work methods or requirements that help acclimatize workers (e.g., physical fitness, water drinking). Personal protective equipment, including eye protection, cooling vests, hats, and sunblock is also useful and an effective method for minimizing the risk of heat-related illnesses; however, PPE should be used in combination with other administrative and engineering control mechanisms.

COLD ENVIRONMENTS

When we think of workers in cold environments we often think of the outdoors (e.g., construction workers, ski patrol); however, cold environments can include industrial freezers at restaurants or food manufacturing plants, temperature-controlled rooms for IT equipment, etc. Cold environments can be very hazardous to an individual's health and require similar precautions as hot environments. (See **OH&S Today 5.2**.)

MEN AND WOMEN IN THE COLD

How we react to cold temperatures varies not only from person to person but also between men and women. CCOHS studies have demonstrated that while women's core body temperature decreases more slowly than men's, women are not able to create as much body heat through activities such as exercise and shivering. This is an important consideration for both employees and employers.

Source: Adapted from CCOHS, "Cold Environments—General." Found at: http://www.ccohs.ca/oshanswers/phys_agents/cold_general. html (accessed June 7, 2016).

COLD-RELATED INJURIES AND ILLNESSES

Similar to heat-related illnesses, a number of factors or conditions influence the extent to which individuals are at risk for cold-related illnesses. For example, age, gender, fatigue, diseases, health conditions such as Reynaud's syndrome, consuming drugs or alcohol, or smoking are all factors that increase the risk of suffering from a cold-related illness. Interestingly, the human body does not become acclimatized to the cold in the same way it does in hot environments; however, certain body parts (e.g., hands) are able to develop a tolerance to the cold.[14] Key factors influence the human body's response to the cold: air temperature, wind speed, humidity, physical activity, work schedule, and protective clothing.

Cold-related injuries are labelled as non-freezing injuries or freezing injuries. Non-freezing injuries happen when body parts such as hands and feet cool but do not freeze. Non-freezing injuries can occur in temperatures above the freezing mark and include chilblains, immersion foot, and trench foot. Chilblains are a mild injury caused by reduced circulation in the extremities after prolonged exposure to temperatures above freezing. Chilblains result in redness, swelling, and tingling in the hands and feet. Immersion foot is an injury that occurs after an individual's foot or feet have been wet but not frozen for prolonged periods of time (e.g., days, weeks). Similar to chilblains, immersion foot results in tingling, numbness, itching, pain, and swelling in the feet and legs, and the skin may turn blue or purple. Trench foot is similar to immersion foot and is caused by prolonged exposure to colder (up to 10°C) wet conditions. The onset of symptoms, after hours or days, are similar to immersion foot and if left untreated can result in muscle tissue or nerve damage.[15] Freezing injuries occur in colder temperatures and are caused by local freezing of muscles and tissues. Examples of freezing cold injuries include frostnip and frostbite. Frostnip is the mildest form of a cold injury and can affect the ear lobes, nose, cheeks, fingers, and toes after exposure to temperatures below freezing. Symptoms of frostnip include the top layer of skin freezing, which results in numbness, tingling, and the skin turning white and hard.

Frostnip occurs when the top layer of skin freezes; it often occurs to exposed skin such as hands and feet.

Frostbite is similar to frostnip except the underlying tissues and the outer layer of skin freeze. Frostbite occurs after exposure to freezing temperatures, frozen objects, or cold compressed gases. Frostbite results in restricted blood flow to the tissue and, in severe cases, can cause permanent tissue damage, blisters, infection, and gangrene if left untreated.

Hypothermia occurs when cold causes the body's ability to regulate its thermal temperature to fail and the body is not able to compensate for the loss of heat. Hypothermia sets in after the body's core temperature falls below 33°C and is life-threatening if left untreated. Hypothermia requires immediate first aid and treatment of symptoms. The first symptoms of mild hypothermia include an overall feeling of cold and pain in exposed extremities. As time passes, moderate hypothermia sets in and feelings of cold and pain subside due to an increase in numbness. This is followed by muscle weakness and drowsiness. Eventually, severe hypothermia sets in, resulting in heart and respiratory failure and eventually death. See **Table 5.1** for the signs and symptoms of hypothermia.

TABLE 5.1

SIGNS AND SYMPTOMS OF HYPOTHERMIA

STAGE	CORE TEMPERATURE	SIGNS AND SYMPTOMS
Mild hypothermia	37.2–36.1°C (99–97°F)	Normal, shivering may begin.
	36.1–35°C (97–95°F)	Cold sensation, goose bumps, unable to perform complex tasks with hands, shivering can be mild to severe, hands numb.
Moderate hypothermia	35–33.9°C (95–93°F)	Shivering, intense, muscle incoordination becomes apparent, movements slow and laboured, stumbling pace, mild confusion, may appear alert. Use sobriety test, if unable to walk a 9-metre (30-foot) straight line, the person is hypothermic.
	33.9–32.2°C (93–90°F)	Violent shivering persists, difficulty speaking, sluggish thinking, amnesia starts to appear, gross muscle movements sluggish, unable to use hands, stumbles frequently, difficulty speaking, signs of depression, withdrawn.
Severe hypothermia	32.2–30°C (90–86°F)	Shivering stops, exposed skin blue or puffy, muscle coordination very poor, inability to walk, confusion, incoherent/irrational behaviour, but may be able to maintain posture and appearance of awareness
	30–27.8°C (86–82°F)	Muscle rigidity, semiconscious, stupor, loss of awareness of others, pulse and respiration rate decrease, possible heart fibrillation.
	27.8–25.6°C (82–78°F)	Unconscious, a heartbeat and respiration erratic, a pulse may not be obvious.
	25.6–23.9°C (78–75°F)	Pulmonary edema, cardiac and respiratory failure, death. Death may occur before this temperature is reached.

Source: CCOHS, "Cold Environments—Health Effects and First Aid." Found at: https://www.ccohs.ca/oshanswers/phys_agents/cold_health.html (accessed June 7, 2016).

CONTROLLING COLD

There are also engineering, administrative, and PPE mechanisms that reduce the risk of suffering from a cold-related injury or illness. Engineering controls include equipment such as heaters and shields that protect an individual from the cold environment or object. Administrative controls include work and rest schedules and cold-weather procedures such as shutdown or closure requirements. Clothing is one of the most effective methods for reducing the risk of a cold-related injury or illness. Protective clothing should be carefully selected based on what is required by legislation, the conditions of the environment, and the nature of the work being performed.

// SUMMARY

This chapter has focused on four physical agents that are commonly encountered in industry—noise, vibration, thermal stress, and radiation. Industries in which agents such as ionizing radiation are encountered have implemented extensive, specialized training programs and procedures. In most situations, however, simple prevention policies and programs are adequate for reducing and controlling worker exposure to physical agents.

KEY TERMS

ambient 111
attenuated 117
conduction 123
convection 123
decalcification 120
early warning change 114
homeostasis 123
hyperreflexia 116
necrosis 120
physical agents 111
radiation 123
resonance 121
segmental vibration 120
vasoconstriction 116
whole-body vibration 120

DISCUSSION QUESTIONS

1. Workers in a manufacturing division in your jurisdiction have made a formal complaint that three machines are too noisy. Noise measurements are taken: the results are 83 dB, 87 dB, and 88 dB. Do the workers have a legitimate complaint?

2. What are the health risks associated with vibrations?

3. All jurisdictions in Canada have access to the same science. Yet jurisdictions vary in legislated standards. Why might different standards apply in different jurisdictions?

4. Many occupations involve inherent exposure to a physical agent resulting in excessive exposure to noise, vibration, thermal conditions, and so on. Outline the steps an employer can take to protect employees when avoiding the exposure is not possible.

USING THE INTERNET

1. Working outside in the Canadian winter can be a hazard for many workers. Using Internet resources, determine the health and safety regulations and guidelines for outdoor work in your jurisdiction. Compare regulations across several provinces or territories. Which jurisdictions have developed the most extensive sets of guidelines for outdoor work?

EXERCISE

1. OH&S legislation establishes standards for exposure to various forms of physical agents in the workplace. Think of common forms of after-work entertainment (e.g., movies, bars, restaurants, malls). What physical agents are present in these settings? What risks do they pose for customers? What about the employees of these establishments?

OH&S IN ACTION

You are the HR manager in your organization. An employee believes he is suffering the ill effects of regular exposure to vibration. He has been to a doctor; however, the physician is skeptical and tells the patient to go home and rest. The employee is not convinced that rest will be helpful over the long term. The employee is frustrated and asks you for help and to conduct an assessment of his work environment. Identify a plan for helping this employee including:

- how you would measure the vibrations he is exposed to
- any controls that might be necessary and helpful
- whether there is an expert on the health effects of vibrations in your area

CASE STUDY 1   RADIATION

Sidney loves technology and uses it regularly for work and at home. For approximately 8–10 hours a day, Sidney is either in front of a computer screen, using a tablet, or using his smartphone. Recently the software developers of his smartphone released an update, which was designed to decrease the amount of blue light emitted by the phone during night time hours. Curious about this, Sidney did some research and found various articles that indicated that computers, tablets,

(continued)

and smartphones emit blue light and use of these devices during night time hours or in dark environments can cause potential health effects; in particular, blue light can have a negative effect on an individual's sleep cycle.

The next day while at work Sidney asks his supervisor whether she knows anything about the impact of blue light on employees. Mackenzie, Sidney's supervisor, tells him that she read an article on the topic a number of years ago; however, at the time the research was inconclusive. Sidney expresses his concern about how blue light could be having an impact on his health and the health of his coworkers. Mackenzie agrees to look into this further and get back to Sidney with respect to what she finds.

Upon consulting with the health and safety manager Josh, Mackenzie learns he too is unaware of any potential hazards associated with blue light radiation. Both Josh and Mackenzie decide they need to investigate further. Josh agrees to conduct more research and consult with experts on the topic and get back to her within the next two weeks. Two weeks later Josh informs Mackenzie that blue light can, in fact, have potentially negative effects on sleep cycles by affecting the production of sleep hormones; however, testing for this is extremely complex and not something that can be done locally. Given that a number of employees including Sidney are required to work shift work, you are concerned about the impact this could be having. As both Josh and Mackenzie, how would you handle this situation? Should you take greater steps to learn more about radiation from technology and what you should or could you do to measure the impact? Discuss with classmates.

CASE STUDY 2   EXPENSIVE JEWELLERY

As a newly hired human resource specialist, you are touring the floor of the manufacturing plant. You are surprised to see that many workers are wearing their hearing protectors around the neck like a necklace instead of covering their ears. Moreover, the style seems to be to wear safety glasses perched on top of the head rather than in a position that would protect eyes. Employees working with acids are doing so in street clothes and barehanded, although rubber gloves and safety aprons are hanging on hooks next to the workstations. Even from your brief tour, it is clear that the company has invested in the best personal protective equipment available. Yet workers do not seem to be using the equipment to protect themselves. One of your new responsibilities is health and safety programming. What do you do?

APPENDIX
HEARING PROTECTION TYPES OR CLASSIFICATIONS

The early part of this chapter noted that there are two basic styles of hearing protection devices: plugs and muffs. **Table 5.2** shows a more detailed breakdown of the styles and their designations.

TABLE 5.2

TYPES OF INDUSTRIAL HEARING PROTECTION

CLASS	TYPE	DESCRIPTION
Earplugs	A1	Preformed earplug, the fitting of which should be done professionally.
	A2	User-formable earplug made of soft spongelike materials that the user rolls between the fingers for insertion into the ear canal.
	B1	A stethoscope configuration with the spring headband holding earplugs in position in the ears. Easy to observe, and the band may be worn in several positions on the head.
Circumaural	D1	An earmuff that surrounds the complete ear with a headband that sits only on the top of the head. Often best for comfort and optimum attenuation.
	D2	An earmuff similar to D1 but with a headband system that can be worn in many positions on the head. Attenuation may vary with headband position.
	D3	An earmuff attachment for a hardhat, which can be permanently attached or field applied. Usually used in construction settings.
Nonlinear protectors	F1	A specialty device with an electronic amplifier. A system that allows only certain sound levels and frequencies to pass unimpeded.
	F2	A specialty device with a mechanical "ear valve" on each ear that responds to impact noise and causes attenuation.
Combination		Many of the above types may be used in combination.

// NOTES

1. Kwan-Hoong Ng, "Non-Ionizing Radiations—Sources, Biological Effects, Emissions and Exposures," Proceedings of the International Conference on Non-Ionizing Radiation at UNITEN (October 2003): 1–16.

2. Kwan-Hoong Ng, "Non-Ionizing Radiations—Sources, Biological Effects, Emissions and Exposures," Proceedings of the International Conference on Non-Ionizing Radiation at UNITEN (October 2003): 1–16.

3. E.H. Berger, W.D. Ward, J.C. Morrill, and L.H. Royster, eds., *Noise and Hearing Conservation Manual*, 4th ed. (Akron: American Industrial Hygiene Association, 1988).

4. K. Feder, D. Michaud, P. Ramage-Morin, J. McNamee and Y. Beauregard, "Prevalence of Hearing Loss Among Canadians aged 20 to 79: Audiometric Results from the 2012/2013 Canadian Health Measures Survey," *Health Reports* (Statistics Canada) Vol. 26, no. 7, (July 2015): 18–25.

5. Canadian Centre for Occupational Health and Safety, "What Are the Characteristics of Noise-induced Permanent Hearing Loss?" https://www.ccohs .ca/oshanswers/phys_agents/noise_auditory.html (accessed March 12, 2016).

6. M.M. Key, A.F. Henschel, J. Butler, R.N. Ligo, I.R. Tabershaw, and L. Ede, *Occupational Diseases: A Guide to Their Recognition*, rev. ed. (Cincinnati: U.S. Department of Health, Education, and Welfare, 1977).

7. Canadian Centre for Occupational Health and Safety: OHS Answers "Vibration." https://www.ccohs.ca/oshanswers/phys_agents/vibration/ vibration_intro.html (accessed May 31, 2016).

8. Canadian Centre for Occupational Health and Safety: OHS Answers "Vibration Health Effects," http://www.ccohs.ca/oshanswers/phys_agents/ vibration/vibration_effects.html, (accessed March 24, 2016).

9. R.D. Soule, *Vibration in the Industrial Environment—Its Evaluation and Control* (Cincinnati: U.S. Department of Health, Education, and Welfare, 1973).

10. W. Hammer, *Occupational Safety Management and Engineering*, 4th ed. (Englewood Cliffs: Prentice Hall, 1989).

11. "Hot Environments: Health Effects," Canadian Centre for Occupational Health and Safety Answers, http://www.ccohs.ca/oshanswers/phys_agents/ heat_health.html (accessed January 19, 2013).

12. B. Jacklitsch, W.J. Williams, K. Musolin, A. Coca, J-H. Kim, and N. Turner, "Criteria for a Recommended Standard Occupational Exposure to Heat and Hot Environments," Department of Health and Human Services Centers for Disease Control and Prevention, 2016.

13. Canadian Centre for Occupational Health and Safety OHS Answers, "Hot Environments: Control Measures." Found at: http://www.ccohs.ca/ oshanswers/phys_agents/heat_control.html (accessed March 23, 2016).

14. Canadian Centre for Occupational Health and Safety OHS Answers, "Cold Environments-General." Found at: http://www.ccohs.ca/oshanswers/phys _agents/cold_general.html (accessed March 23, 2016).

15. Canadian Centre for Occupational Health and Safety: OHS Answers "Cold Environments-Health Effects and First Aid." Found at: http://www.ccohs.ca/ oshanswers/phys_agents/cold_health.html (accessed March 24, 2016).

CHAPTER 6

BIOLOGICAL AND CHEMICAL AGENTS

CHAPTER LEARNING OBJECTIVES

AFTER READING THIS CHAPTER, YOU SHOULD BE ABLE TO:
- define the numerous terms relating to chemical and biological agents
- discuss the management of chemical and biological agents
- outline the actions of chemical and biological agents on human physiology
- outline control mechanisms

In 2014, West Africa endured the most devastating and widespread outbreak of the Ebola virus in history. Unfortunately this outbreak was not the first. According to the Center for Disease Control (CDC) the first outbreak of the virus occurred in 1976, killing 280 people. Outbreaks occurred again in 1995, 2000, and 2007. These prior outbreaks were reported in countries in regions closer to central Africa (e.g., Democratic Republic of Congo, Uganda) and resulted in reported cases and deaths in the hundreds. Sadly, the latest outbreak spread to more countries, and infected and killed significantly more people. The 2014 outbreak spread across multiple countries in Western Africa and resulted in 28 646 reported cases and 11 323 deaths. The World Health Organization explained that the latest outbreak was unlike previous outbreaks in that many of the countries affected had no experience with the virus, were some of the poorest countries in Africa, and consequently did not have the means to diagnose, treat, or contain the spread of it. As such, the response to this outbreak was also different from previous responses. In previous outbreaks there was a rapid and concerted focus on isolating those infected to prevent the disease from spreading. The response to the 2014 outbreak involved rapid isolation but, due to the number of people already infected, the response also required aggressive treatment and clinical care.

Individuals infected by Ebola Virus Disease (EVD) exhibit signs and symptoms that can include fever, fatigue, muscle pain, weakness, vomiting, and hemorrhaging (severe bleeding). While the virus is not always fatal, an individual's chances of survival depend on a number of factors including the health of his or her immune system and receiving a proper diagnosis and proper medical treatment. The CDC indicates that the diagnosis of EVD is very difficult as signs and symptoms can take up to 21 days to appear in an infected individual and many of the signs and symptoms are non-specific to EVD, meaning they also appear in other more common diseases for that part of Africa (e.g., malaria).

EVD is rare and the virus is not a biological agent that many of us will be exposed to. Consider when your last cold was, or perhaps you know someone right now who has the flu. Have you ever contracted food poisoning, had pneumonia, or a sinus infection? Whether at work, at home, or in the community, we are exposed to biological and chemical agents that have the potential to cause us harm. Take a moment to consider how many germs and chemicals you might be exposed to over the course of a work shift, or even a work week.

In Chapter 4, you read about hazard identification, risk assessment, and hazard control measures. Now reflect on how each of those topics applies to the management of the various biological and chemical agents you will learn about in this chapter.

Source: Center for Disease Control, "About Ebola." Found at: http://www.cdc.gov/vhf/ebola/about.html (accessed April 20, 2016); and World Health Organization, "Factors That Contributed to Undetected Spread of the Ebola Virus and Impeded Rapid Containment." Found at: http://www.who.int/csr/disease/ebola/one-year-report/factors/en (accessed April 20, 2016).

John Moore/Getty Images News

In 2014, Ebola Virus Disease or EVD, a rare biological agent, infected over 28,000 people in Africa.

biohazards
hazards created by exposure to infectious microorganisms, proteins, or nucleic acids

chemical agent
hazards created by exposure to chemicals

In the previous chapter we discussed the nature of physical hazards that appear in our work environments and our everyday lives; however, physical hazards make up only some of the hazardous materials we encounter. Biological materials are made up of microorganisms, proteins, or nucleic acids, and those that are infectious and result in disease or are hazardous to our health are frequently referred to as **biohazards**. Chemicals are compounds that are purified, often artificially, using chemistry. Chemicals that pose a risk to our health and safety are referred to as **chemical agents**. It is important to note that not all biological material and chemicals are hazardous to our health; in fact, some are beneficial. However, the focus of this chapter is the significant number of **agents** that are hazardous to our health. OH&S legislation includes specific sections in order to deal with biological and chemical materials that pose a risk to humans. The majority are addressed under the Workplace Hazardous Materials Information System (WHMIS) and the Global Harmonized System (GHS). Many occupational diseases–such as asbestosis, silicosis, various types of dermatitis, respiratory problems and some occupational injuries (e.g., burns) that result from spills and splashes–are related to exposure to biological and chemical materials. This chapter provides an overview of the problems associated with biohazards and chemical agents and the measures that can be taken to manage and control them.

> **agents**
> any substances—chemical, biological, or physical—to which a human may be exposed at work or at home

// BIOHAZARDS

Biological agents are often referred to as biohazards when they pose a risk to our health and safety. Biohazards can result in disease, allergic reactions, and infections. Examples of biohazards include bacteria, viruses, fungi, prions (proteins or proteinaceous infectious particles), toxins, genetically modified organisms, nucleic acids, tissue samples, specimens, and live vaccines that may contain microorganisms, bacteria, or viruses. In many cases, biohazards are very difficult to see or are invisible to the naked eye, making it extremely difficult to perceive the risk associated with them (see **Table 6.1**).

TABLE 6.1

BIOLOGICAL AGENTS

AGENT GROUP	AGENT/ILLNESS	SOURCE	OCCUPATION
Bacterial	Anthrax (*bacillus anthracis*)	Direct contact with infected animals, hides, and wool	Veterinarians, farmers, butchers, wool workers
	Salmonellosis (*salmonella species*)	Oral exposure, usually from unsanitary food conditions (food poisoning)	Travellers, patient-care workers, chefs
	Staphylococcal food poisoning (*staphylococcus species*)	Ingestion of improperly stored or leftover food or food infected by workers	Food workers, health care workers, home storage
Viral	Serum hepatitis (*hepatitis B virus*—HBV)	Direct contact with infected material by puncture, abraded skin, or onto mucous membrane surfaces	Hemodialysis workers, surgeons, dentists, health care workers
	Infectious hepatitis (*hepatitis A virus*—HAV)	Fecal–oral transmission (from contaminated water)	Travellers, primate handlers, dentists
Fungal	Dermatophytosis (*trichophyton species*)	Contact with people infected by soil, animals, or humans	Gardeners, military personnel (athlete's foot), farm workers (cattle ringworm), health care workers
	Histoplasmosis (*histoplasma capsulatum*)	Inhalation or ingestion of dust from areas that have been bat or bird habitats	Construction workers, bird or chicken farm workers
Prion	Creutzfeldt-Jakob disease (*Protein*)	Transmitted via contact with infected tissue, body fluids, or contaminated medical instruments.	Physicians, medical technicians, patients

chain of infection
the process and conditions by which biological agents are spread from one host to another

reservoir
the home or environment where the biological agent grows and multiplies

portal of exit
the path by which a biohazardous agent leaves its host

mode of transmission
the means or channel by which an agent is carried from one host to another

portal of entry
the path by which a biohazardous agent gains access to a new host

The people most at risk of exposure to biohazards tend to be employed in unique or specialized fields, such as medicine, research, and farming. However, the general public is also at risk (e.g., through salmonella food poisoning, influenza, or the common cold). Nonetheless, in order for a biohazard to infect an individual, certain conditions must be met. These conditions make up what is referred to as the **chain of infection**. The chain of infection outlines the specific links and process by which an infectious agent is spread from host to host. All of the links or conditions must be met in order for infection to occur and it is only by breaking these conditions, or interrupting the links, that transmission is stopped.

The process of transmission starts with a biohazard or an agent such as a bacterium or virus leaving its host or *reservoir* through a *portal of exit*. It is then transported via *a mode of transmission* until it enters via a *portal of entry* on a *susceptible host* (see **Figure 6.1**). The CDC defines each of these links as follows: A **reservoir** is the home or environment where the biological agent grows and multiplies (e.g., humans, animals, and the ground). A **portal of exit** is the path by which an agent leaves its host and often corresponds to where the agent is located within the host (e.g., chest infections typically exit via the respiratory tract). **Modes of transmission** are the means or channel by which an agent is carried. Modes of transmission can be through direct contact (e.g., skin to skin) with an infected host, or indirectly via the air (e.g., droplet spread). Food, water and bodily fluids can also be vehicles. Insects are also known to be a mode of transmission and are referred to as vectors (e.g., West Nile virus and malaria are spread via mosquitos). Once an agent has been transported, it must gain access to the tissues and cells via a **portal of entry**, which is similar to an exit route (e.g., respiratory tract)

FIGURE 6.1

CHAIN OF INFECTION

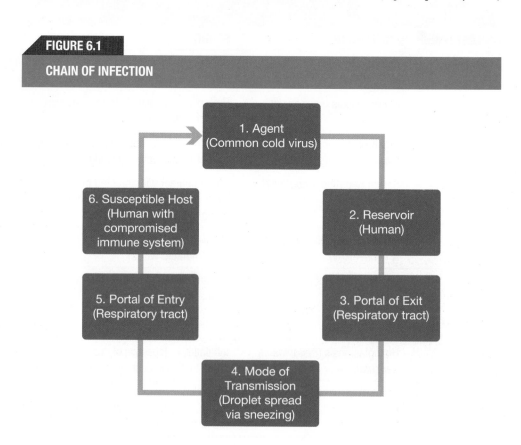

1. Agent (Common cold virus)
2. Reservoir (Human)
3. Portal of Exit (Respiratory tract)
4. Mode of Transmission (Droplet spread via sneezing)
5. Portal of Entry (Respiratory tract)
6. Susceptible Host (Human with compromised immune system)

of a **susceptible host** or person. The factors that determine whether new hosts are susceptible are their genetics, the health of their immune system (e.g., antibodies) and the sensitivity of their sneeze and coughing reflex. If an individual is infected by an agent and is unable to fight it off, he or she may become ill; however, not everyone infected will show symptoms. An individual who does not become ill can be a carrier of the agent, and transmit it to another.[1]

// CHEMICAL AGENTS

Regardless of the industry, every workplace contains chemical agents and if they are not handled and stored properly, they can be harmful. Chemical agents can be intentionally used for a specific purpose like cleaning or production. For instance, common chemicals used in office buildings are cleaners, photocopier toner, and printer ink. Other industries such as agriculture use pesticides and fertilizers (e.g., potash). A common chemical agent used in industries like steel manufacturing, pharmaceutical, food, and oil production is hydrochloric acid. Other chemical agents within workplaces can be a side effect or a by-product of process. The number of chemical agents currently in existence is difficult to determine because there are various databases and registries used around the world for commercial, research, or even environmental purposes (e.g., Chemical Abstract Service in the United States). Chemicals are a necessary part of our everyday lives and in order to minimize any negative impact on our health they must be carefully managed; part of this means understanding how they affect our health.

The specific effects of some chemicals are well documented, while those of many others are still unknown. Health problems created by chemical exposures are more prevalent in the workplace than in any other environment. For instance, dermatitis is a common workplace condition wherein the skin becomes irritated after exposure to a chemical. The Health and Safety Executive in the United Kingdom reports that up to 70% of hairdressers, at some point over the course of their career, suffer from skin damage.[2] Health care workers, construction workers, and caterers who are required to wash their hands repeatedly are also at a very high risk for dermatitis.

Chemical agents may be hazards in and of themselves, but they can also interact *synergistically* with lifestyle or environmental factors. Synergistic effects occur when the result of two factors taken together is greater than the sum of the two. For example, a lifestyle factor such as smoking can have a synergistic effect on some materials. An asbestos worker is four times more likely than a non-asbestos worker to develop lung cancer; the probability rises to 80 to 90 times more likely if the asbestos worker smokes. For the sake of simplicity, this chapter will discuss single chemical exposures; however, most of the exposures that take place in the workplace are more complex.

To understand chemical agents, we must be familiar with the associated hazards each possesses. The hazard associated with a material is defined as the likelihood that it will cause injury in a given environment or situation. The potential degree of seriousness of the hazard is determined by its **toxicity** (i.e., its ability to cause injury to human biological tissue) or its explosive properties, which are defined in terms of flammability and reactivity. The extent to which a potentially toxic substance is an actual health hazard will depend on other factors, such as the concentration of the chemical and the length of time the employee is exposed to it.

Chemicals exist in three main states: solid, liquid, and gas. Having knowledge of the physical state of a chemical helps you understand the health risks it poses to the human body. The physical state of a chemical determines its route of entry into the body; for example, chemicals in a gaseous state are more likely to enter the human body via inhalation whereas liquids and solids are more likely to enter the body via skin absorption or ingestion. Throughout a work process the physical state of a chemical can change (e.g., liquid to a gas) and therefore change the health risks associated with that chemical. Consequently, it is extremely important to take into consideration the physical state of a chemical in the context of routes of entry into the human body.[3]

Every chemical has its own melting, freezing, and boiling points. Typically, more than one of these states may be present at the same time. Consider an open container of boiling water: the water is in the liquid state, while the steam is entering the gas state. Similarly, ice may feel hard (solid), be wet (liquid), and actually have evaporated water surrounding it (vapour). Most chemical-related health problems result from contact with chemicals in the liquid or gas (vapour) state. Most of the negative effects of exposure are derived from airborne respiratory contaminants known as **aerosols** (see **OH&S Notebook 6.1**).

A workplace health hazard is posed by exposure to one or more of these airborne respirable particulate forms. For instance, the white cloud that rises from a welding operation usually consists of the following: fumes resulting from the condensation of

aerosols
airborne respirable contaminants, such as liquid droplets or solid particulate, dispersed in air, that are of a fine enough particle size (0.01 to 100 micrometres) to remain suspended for a time

---

OH&S NOTEBOOK 6.1

TYPES OF CONTAMINANTS (AEROSOLS)

Listed below are seven types of contaminants:

1. *Dust.* Airborne respirable particulate that is solid particles generated by some mechanical means such as grinding, crushing, or sanding. The heavier particles tend to settle out of the air under the influence of gravity. The lighter or smaller the particle, the longer or greater the settling rate.

2. *Fume.* Airborne respirable particulate formed by the evaporation of some solid materials (e.g., steel, where the parent metal will vaporize on the application of weld-level heat and the vaporized metal will condense on contact with cooler ambient air). This condensed particulate is a *fume*. (This term is often confused with *vapour.*) Particle size is usually less than 1 micron or micrometre in diameter. Other examples of fume include plastic extrusion and automobile exhaust, which can include fumes (from the metallic additives) and vapours (from the unburned fuel).

3. *Smoke.* Airborne respirable particulate originating from the products of combustion, usually less than 0.1 micron in size. An example would be tobacco smoke or smoke from a fire.

4. *Mist.* Airborne respirable particulate in the form of liquid droplets generated by condensation from the gas state or by the breaking up of a liquid into a dispersed state of finely divided droplets. Spray paint and hair spray are two sources of mist generation.

5. *Vapour.* The airborne respirable contaminants in a gaseous form of any substances that are normally in the solid or liquid state at room temperature and pressure. An example would be the airborne contaminant present above any solvent.

6. *Gas.* An airborne respirable contaminant that is one of the three states of matter created where the temperature is above the boiling point. Carbon dioxide and oxygen are two examples.

7. *Liquid.* Chemicals are sometimes found in a liquid form from which, though not airborne, respirable particulate can come in contact with the skin and the eyes—for instance, when there is a splash or spill during manual mixing or pouring operations.

Source: J. B. Olishifsky, "Overview of Industrial Hygiene," *Fundamentals of Industrial Hygiene*, 4th ed. (Chicago: National Safety Council) 1995.

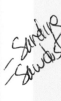

BAKERS' ASTHMA

If you were to think about the various occupational hazards that bakers are exposed to you might think of the industrial mixers, or heat or the cleaning chemicals, but what about flour? Flour is one of the most important ingredients for many of the foods we eat and when flour becomes airborne it creates a very fine dust that can easily be inhaled. Imagine inhaling flour dust week after week, month after month, and year after year. Without the proper precautions, flour and other similar ingredients like wheat or rye are known to cause a type of occupational asthma referred to as "Bakers' asthma." According to the Occupational Health Clinics for Ontario Workers,

individuals who suffer from this type of asthma may not even realize their symptoms are work related as the signs and symptoms can also occur as a result of other conditions, and they often subside after leaving the workplace. Signs and symptoms include coughing, shortness of breath, wheezing, and chest tightness, and typically worsen over the course of a shift as exposure increases. Bakers are not the only occupations at higher risk for occupational asthma. Other occupations include people working in nail and hair salons, farmers, people working in snow crab processing plants, and people who work in the automotive manufacturing industry.

Source: Occupational Health Clinics for Ontario Workers, 2005. "Baker's Asthma." Found at http://www.ohcow.on.ca/uploads/Resource/General%20 Handouts/bakersasthmafactsheet.pdf (accessed April 20, 2016); Occupational Health Clinics for Ontario Workers (2005) "General Handouts." Found at http://www.ohcow.on.ca/generalhandouts (accessed April 20, 2016).

the parent metal and the weld rod metal and coating; smoke resulting from combustion of oil and other surface contamination; and vapours resulting from the evaporation of some of the oils and solvents on the metal surface (see **OH&S Today 6.1**).

// TOXICOLOGY: AN OVERVIEW

Toxicology is the scientific study of poisons. For the purposes of this chapter, toxicology is part of understanding chemical-related occupational illnesses (see **OH&S Notebooks 6.2** and **6.3**). Similar to biological agents, chemicals may enter the body

OTOTOXIC EFFECTS OF WORKPLACE CHEMICALS

When you consider typical causes of hearing loss, most individuals would think of noise; however, certain chemicals are known to have ototoxic effects. Ototoxicity is defined as having an adverse or harmful effect on the nerves and or bones required for hearing and balance. Chemicals known to have ototoxic effects include those

used in the manufacturing of plastics, perfumes, and dyes, and certain medications (e.g., antibiotics) can also cause hearing loss or damage (e.g., tinnitus or ringing in the ears). A proper assessment of the work environment should be conducted if there are concerns about possible noise or ototoxic hazards.

Source: CCOHS, "Chemicals and Noise: A Hazardous Combination." Found at http://www.ccohs.ca/newsletters/hsreport/issues/2009/10/ezine.html (accessed April 20, 2016).

TOXICITY TERMINOLOGY

- *Dose.* The degree of exposure and possible reaction with time. The dose is usually the basis for the values that are developed for threshold limit values (TLVs), which are used as a control measure in the workplace. For example, the TLV for carbon dioxide is 5000 parts per million (ppm), based on an eight-hour exposure time.

- *Acute toxicity.* An effect that manifests itself immediately following exposure or very shortly thereafter. Burning your hand on a hot surface, for example, results in immediate pain and discoloration, and, later, blisters.

- *Chronic toxicity.* An effect that manifests itself sometime after the exposure (possibly months or even years). Examples include sensitization from isocyanates; occupational cancer, such as leukemia, from benzene exposure; and mesothelioma from asbestos exposure.

- *Local toxicity.* The effect of an exposure at the point of contact. Cleaning your hands with paint thinner will cause dry, grey skin at the point of contact; this will be an immediate reaction.

- *Systemic toxicity.* An effect that occurs at some location remote from the point of contact. For example, inhaling a chlorinated solvent such as trichloroethylene can cause damage to the liver; and inhaling carbon monoxide, which interrupts oxygen transfer to the blood, can cause asphyxiation and death.

Source: *Threshold Values for Chemical Substances and Physical Agents in the Workplace* (Cincinnati: American Conference of Governmental Industrial Hygienists, 1994).

Aerosol cans release contaminants that can remain suspended in the air, resulting in inhalation into the lungs.

turbinates
spiral or spongy sections of the respiratory system that have a centrifugal effect to help remove aerosols

by one of four portals of entry. In order of risk and normal contact, they are respiration (inhalation), skin absorption, ingestion, and skin penetration.

RESPIRATION (INHALATION)

An average-sized human breathes approximately eight litres of air per minute while at rest; this quantity increases with any activity.[4] Most human exposure to chemicals comes from breathing airborne contaminants. The respiratory system (see **Figure 6.2**) does a very efficient job of distributing these contaminants throughout the body during the normal air exchange process.

There are five basic levels of protection or defence within the respiratory tract. The first is the nose. The nose, or upper respiratory tract, is lined with hairs, or cilia, which act as a coarse filter medium. The second is the interior of the nasal passage, where turbinates are found, which act as humidifiers and heat exchangers. The third is farther back in the throat, where the hairs or cilia are coated with a thick fluid called mucus. This mucus/cilia system entraps the finer particulate. The trapped contaminant is removed by blowing the nose and/or clearing the throat. Everyone has experienced these conditions after cleaning the garage, dusting a room, or sanding wood for refinishing. The fourth level is the lung passages such as the bronchi and

FIGURE 6.2

THE RESPIRATORY SYSTEM

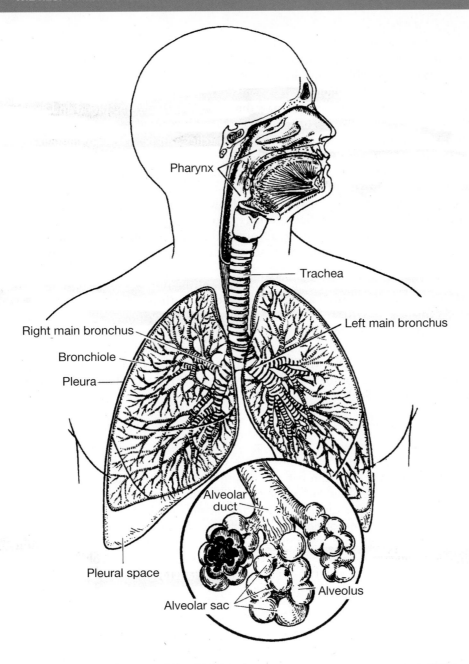

Pharynx

Trachea

Right main bronchus

Left main bronchus

Bronchiole

Pleura

Alveolar duct

Pleural space

Alveolus

Alveolar sac

the bronchiole. Here, the flow of air and its turbulence from breathing allow much of the larger particulate that bypassed the earlier defences to be expelled with normal exhalation. The fifth level of defence consists of myriad tiny air sacs, called **alveoli**, located at the ends of the lungs' air passages, called the alveolar ducts. These sacs (which are the source of oxygen transfer from the lungs to the bloodstream) contain

alveoli
tiny air sacs

small cells called macrophages (Greek for "big eater"), which dispose of any impurities via the lymph system.

SKIN ABSORPTION

In many workplaces and at home, chemical contact with the skin is a common occurrence. Many fat-soluble chemicals are readily absorbed, and most gases can pass through the skin very quickly. Chlorinated solvents such as carbon tetrachloride (e.g., industrial cleaners or degreasing agents) can pass through the skin into the blood and eventually reach the liver, where tissue damage may occur. Dimethyl sulphoxide, found in solvents and some medical applications such as skin patches, can be absorbed through the skin in less than a minute following contact.

A chemical's ability to easily pass through the skin is often closely associated with its level of toxicity. For example, the toxicity of DDT is about the same for insects and humans when it is injected. However, it is much less toxic to a person when applied to the skin, because it is poorly absorbed through the skin. Other pesticides are much more rapidly absorbed through human skin. Many agricultural workers have died following skin absorption of pesticides, particularly organophosphate insecticides.

Chemicals that are not rapidly absorbed through the skin may produce a localized irritation (dermatitis) at the point of contact through a process called defatting, which causes the skin to become white and dry (e.g., when cleaning your hands with paint remover) and thus more permeable to water vapour, leading to tissue water loss and cracking. Burns or blisters can result from contact with acids or alkalis (chemical action). Skin disorders can result from contact with certain plants (biological action). Skin damage can result from contact with radiation or heat (physical action).

INGESTION

For many solvents, entry through the mouth and digestive system is not as major an issue as entry through the skin or the lungs. That said, poor personal hygiene can contribute to poisoning, as can eating, drinking, or smoking in an area where solvents are used. Ingestion of most solvents will cause damage to the lining of the digestive system. The ingested solvent may also be absorbed into the bloodstream and carried to target organs, where it will produce toxic effects. Worse still, the ingested solvent may be aspirated into the lungs where it can destroy the surfactant layer, cause a chemical pneumonitis, and collapse the alveoli.[5]

PENETRATION

Penetration occurs when the skin is cut or punctured by any sharp object. The type of contamination on the source, such as a knife or needle, will determine the possible trauma or illness. Cuts can occur when contact is made with sharp metal, glass materials, or other pointed instruments. Workers such as doctors, nurses, and veterinarians can easily be punctured by a hypodermic needle. The disorders range in seriousness from low-grade infections to HIV (human immunodeficiency virus).

target organs
tissues or organs that are most affected by exposure to a particular substance

surfactant layer
layer of liquids in the digestive tract and elsewhere (e.g., the cardiovascular system) that modify or reduce the surface tension within the conductors—intestine, blood vessels—to allow material—blood, food, stools, and so on—to move easily

// CHARACTERISTICS AND PROPERTIES OF SOLVENTS

The majority of solvents were developed by the science of organic chemistry, and they are the most common of those products used both at work and at home. There are eight general characteristics or properties that make solvents effective but at the same time hazardous and toxic (see **OH&S Notebook 6.4**).

1. *Low surface tension.* This property allows a solvent to spread evenly and quickly and to provide excellent wetting of the contact surface. The higher the wetting factor, the better the wetting effect. But the wetting factor allows a spilled solvent to flow into cracks and joints and remain there, creating vapours that may be toxic. It also allows for more effective skin absorption.

2. *High vapour pressure.* Vapour pressure increases with temperature; this in turn increases the volume or concentration of a generated vapour or gas. This property of solvents allows efficient cleaning in processes such as degreasing systems because of the high vapour generation at the high operating temperatures. It can, however, create an inhalation hazard, the risk of which increases with temperature. This is not considered a problem as long as the container is kept closed. In a fire situation, the pressure increase can cause an explosion.

3. *Low boiling point.* The lower the **boiling point**, the greater the rate of evaporation or generation of vapours from a liquid. This property is useful when cleaning or painting because the solvents can evaporate quickly at room temperature, allowing the article to dry or tack off efficiently. However, the lower the boiling point, the greater the health risk since vapour can be generated at lower temperatures. Chemicals with boiling points close to room temperature or lower, such as ammonia (BP = 22°C) or hydrogen cyanide (BP = 25°C), can be a special problem since they can evaporate readily and are highly toxic.

4. *Low heat of vaporization.* This relates to the amount of heat or energy required to change a liquid into a gas or vapour. The less heat required, the less costly the process in an industrial environment. But, similarly, the lower the amount of heat necessary, the greater the risk of exposure if the material is not properly controlled.

5. *High volatility.* The main test of a solvent's effectiveness is the speed at which it will evaporate. The greater the volatility, the faster the evaporation, and the greater the health and fire risk.

6. *Ability to dissolve fats.* The more effectively a solvent dissolves fats or oils, the more useful it can be. However, when solvents are in contact with the skin, the skin's surface oils are dissolved. The unprotected skin then becomes susceptible to infection and other trauma. Skin contact with solvents is one of the major causes of **dermatitis**.

7. *Flammability.* This is one of the main hazards associated with solvent use, since all organic solvents are flammable. Care must be taken to ensure that there are no sources of ignition present during use. Chemical specifications usually list four characteristics that relate to flammability.

   a. *Flash point.* This is defined as the lowest temperature at which a liquid gives off enough vapour to form an ignitable mixture with air and produce a flame with a source of ignition. If the flash point is close to room temperature, the danger of ignition can be very great.

boiling point
temperature at which the vapour pressure of a liquid equals atmospheric pressure

dermatitis
the inflammation of the skin from any cause

CLASSIFICATION OF TOXIC SUBSTANCES

Toxic materials are many and varied and have a variety of health effects on humans. In this section, organic and inorganic solvents are enumerated, because they are common at home and at work, and because they can have widespread health effects based on their properties. The overall effects of toxic materials can be grouped under the following 9 classifications.

1. *Irritants.* Irritants, sometimes referred to as "primary irritants," produce tissue or other damage at the point of contact. They are divided by route of entry into two groups:

   a. *Inhaled irritants.* These refer to airborne respirable contaminants or aerosols (including vapours, gases, and solid particulate) that are inhaled into the lungs, causing damage wherever they settle. Ammonia is dissolved into body fluids and absorbed by the mucous membranes of the upper airways and can result in symptoms such as headache, nausea, salivation, and burning of the throat. Bronchitis may follow a very severe exposure, if the patient survives.

   b. *Contact irritant.* A contact irritant is any material that causes some sort of irritation, such as a rash or itch, at the point of contact. An example would be using Varsol to clean paint from your hands or coming into contact with poison ivy. In most cases, the skin is the organ most affected.

2. *Asphyxiants.* Any material that interferes with the oxygen supply to the blood and body tissues is referred to as an asphyxiant. Normal air contains approximately 21% oxygen and 79% nitrogen. The average person uses about 3% of the oxygen in air when breathing. If the oxygen content of the air falls below 15%, the body will be asphyxiated. There are two major types of asphyxiants:

   a. *Simple asphyxiants.* Any airborne respirable chemical that reduces the quantity of oxygen in the inhaled air by displacement is referred to as a simple asphyxiant. Examples are methane, propane, and nitrogen.

   b. *Chemical asphyxiants.* If an airborne and inhaled chemical interferes with the transport of oxygen by the blood hemoglobin or with the ability of the body cells to use oxygen, it is called a chemical asphyxiate. Examples of such chemicals are carbon monoxide, which interferes with the ability of the hemoglobin to transport oxygen and can result in tissue hypoxia and death, and hydrogen sulphide (rotten gas), which can interfere with the ability of the body cells to use oxygen and, after acute exposure, can result in immediate coma and possible death.

3. *Anesthetics and narcotics.* Any chemical that affects the central nervous system (CNS) can be considered to belong to this class. Most of these chemicals can, on exposure, cause headaches; interfere with the ability to concentrate; and act as a depressant. Examples include ethyl alcohol, acetylene, acetone, and toluene. In fact, all organic solvents can produce narcotic effects. Many of us have experienced some of these symptoms after consuming alcohol.

4. *Systemic poisons.* Systemic poisons can cause damage to one or more internal organs, as well as cell and neuron damage. Chlorinated materials such as DDT, endrin, chloroform, and trichloroethylene can cause damage to the liver and kidneys, usually as a result of chronic exposure. Benzene can cause damage to the blood-forming cells (the homeopathic system). Carbon disulphide is believed to damage the neurons. Other common systemic poisons include heavy metals such as lead, cadmium, and mercury, and chemicals such as arsenic and fluoride.

   a. *Liver toxicants.* This grouping includes any chemical that will cause direct damage to the liver. The toxic action may be chemical (caused by alcohol) or metabolic (caused by benzene). In most instances, slight damage can be repaired. Cirrhosis is the most common disease.

   b. *Kidney toxicants.* Kidney toxicants, like liver toxicants, include chemicals that cause damage to the kidneys, usually through the process

(*continued*)

of metabolic-transformation whereby harmless chemicals are rendered harmful or vice versa. Heavy metals such as lead, cadmium, and mercury, in addition to some solvents, can have this effect.

c. *Neurotoxins.* As the name indicates, these chemicals can cause damage to the nerves in the body. Hexane, a component of gasoline, can produce a condition called peripheral neuropathy—a disease affecting the nerves of the extremities—that can result in numbness and loss of feeling. This condition is dose related.

5. *Sensitizers.* Sensitizers, which can be chemical or biological, cause the body's immune system to respond abnormally by producing antibodies. Examples of sensitizers are isocyanates and poison ivy. The result is an allergy to the specific chemical whereby even casual exposure will cause an allergic reaction. Workers thus affected may have to change jobs, if not employers. Though sensitization is usually chronic, a very large acute exposure can sometimes bring it on. Farmer's lung, humidifier fever, nickel itch, and nickel fume fever are common examples of sensitization.

6. *Lung toxicants.* Toxic chemicals that can affect the lungs include irritant gases such as hydrogen chloride and ammonia, vapours such as isocyanates, and respirable solids such as asbestos, platinum, and silica. These materials can cause a variety of diseases, from simple pneumoconiosis (an accumulation of dust in the lungs and the tissue reaction to the presence of such dust) to cancer.

7. *Mutagens.* These include any chemicals that can lead to changes or mutations in DNA. The actions of chemicals such as lead, nickel, zinc, and manganese usually cause the death of cells but may in some cases allow the distorted cells to multiply, creating a potentially malignant tumour.

8. *Teratogens.* Chemicals such as lead, DDT, and PCB can damage germ cells or create defects in a developing fetus. The most infamous of these chemicals, thalidomide, is a well-known cause of gross abnormalities or birth defects in the fetus.

9. *Carcinogens.* Carcinogens are agents that cause or promote the formation of cancers. Well-known carcinogens include vinyl chloride, which can cause a liver cancer called angiosarcoma; benzene, which can result in leukemia; and asbestos, which can lead to mesothelioma. Following exposure to the carcinogenic chemical, there can be a latency period of five to 15 or more years.

Sources: University of Toronto, Environmental Health and Safety. "Health Effects of Toxic Chemicals." Found at http://www.ehs.utoronto.ca/resources/whmis/whmis6.htm (accessed April, 14, 2016); M.M. Key, et al., eds. *Occupational Diseases: A Guide to Their Recognition*, rev. ed. (Cincinnati: U.S. Department of Health, Education, and Welfare, 1977).

b. *Lower explosion limit* (LEL; also known as lower flammability limit, LFL). This is defined as the smallest fuel–air mixture that is ignitable, expressed as a percentage. Carbon monoxide has an LEL of 12.5% by volume, which is equivalent to 125 000 parts per million (ppm). The upper exposure value for health exposure is 50 ppm, as shown in various standards. If the exposure to carbon monoxide in the workplace is maintained well below the health limit, there is no risk of ignition from that source.

c. *Upper explosion limit* (UEL; also known as the upper flammability limit, UFL). This is defined as the highest fuel–air mixture that is ignitable, expressed as a percentage. Carbon monoxide has a UEL of 74% by volume, or 740 000 ppm. The LEL and UEL spread indicates that carbon monoxide could be ignited through a wide range of fuel–air mixtures, which could be an advantage if the gas were to be used for some heat applications.

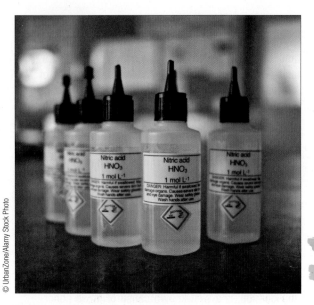

Acids require special care and treatment.

d. *Auto-ignition temperature.* This is defined as the lowest temperature at which a flammable fuel–air mixture will ignite from its own heat source. An example is spontaneous combustion in moist hay in a barn or in paint-soaked rags stuffed in a pail.

8. *Vaporization.* Most solvents will form very large volumes of vapour from a small amount of liquid. For instance, turpentine can form 112 litres of vapour for each litre of liquid at standard temperature and pressure conditions.

INORGANIC SOLVENTS

Inorganic solvents fall into two classes: acids and bases. These are the simplest of chemical groups and are the oldest known such groups. The difference between an acid and a base is expressed in terms of pH, a unit that notes the degree of acidity or alkalinity of a solution, having a scale of 1 to 14. A pH value of 7 is considered neutral (e.g, neither an acid nor a base). A pH of 1 indicates extreme acidity, while a pH of 14 indicates extreme alkalinity.

1. *Acids.* Materials such as hydrochloric acid (HCl), sulphuric acid (H_2SO_4), and chromic acid (H_2CrO_4) are some of the most common. All are highly corrosive and are used for refining and processing metals. The plating process makes extensive use of these acids. The health effects are predominantly burns resulting from inhalation and skin contact. The eyes are the most susceptible body part and are exposed usually as a result of splashing. Chromic acid is a known carcinogen and a sensitizer. The most common indicator of chromic acid exposure is the presence of chrome holes in the surface of the skin. These are ugly, black holes left when the skin has been corrosively attacked. Their size depends on the amount of exposure and personal hygiene practices.

2. *Bases.* Sometimes referred to as alkalines, these chemicals include potassium hydroxide (KOH), sodium hydroxide (NaOH), and sodium chloride (NaCl; also known as table salt). Sodium chloride in its refined state is a requirement of a normal diet. In its less refined form, it is used to keep roads free of ice. The other two alkalines are used to etch or dissolve a variety of materials. All are toxic in certain concentrations.

ORGANIC SOLVENTS

Organic solvents, which are petrochemically based, are manufactured by combining the carbon atom with a great many other elements. These solvents can be identified by their molecular structure and can be grouped under 10 classifications (see **Table 6.2**).

TABLE 6.2

ORGANIC SOLVENTS

NUMBER	CLASSIFICATION	EXAMPLE	TOXIC EFFECTS	USES
1	Aliphatic hydrocarbons	Paraffin, acetylene, methane	Simple asphyxiants, CNS, irritants	Fuels, refrigerants, dry cleaning, propellants
2	Aromatic hydrocarbons	Benzene, toluene, xylene	CNS, dermatitis, leukemia (benzene)	Plastics, resins, dyes, pharmaceuticals
3	Halogenated hydrocarbons	Chlorine, iodine, fluorine, carbon tetrachloride	CNS, dermatitis, cancer (carbon tetrachloride)	Fire extinguishers, fumigants, aerosol propellants
4	Nitro-hydrocarbons	Nitroglycerin, pitric acid	Irritants, skin sensitizers	Explosives
5	Esters	Methyl acetate, banana oil	Irritants	Plastics, resins, artificial flavours, perfumes
6	Ethers	Ethylene oxide	Irritants, anesthetics, nausea, respiratory difficulties	Antifreeze, chemical synthesizers, cancer treatment (ethyl ether-anesthetic)
7	Ketones	Acetone, methyl ethyl ketone (MEK)	Narcotic, irritants, vertigo, nausea	Acetate rayon, artificial silk, lubricants
8	Alcohols	Ethyl alcohol (grain alcohol), methyl alcohol (wood alcohol)	Narcotic, dermatitis, headache, nausea, tremors, blindness	Ethyl-liquors; methyl-solvent for inks, embalming fluids
9	Glycols	Ethylene glycol, cellosolve	Intoxication; blood, brain, and kidney disorder	Antifreeze, disinfectants, drugs
10	Aldehydes	Formaldehyde	Sensitizers, CNS, allergic response	Dyes, perfumes, flavourings, vinegar

// CONTROL OF EXPOSURES

The safe use and handling of chemical and biological agents can be ensured only through the active employment of a variety of precontact, and point-of-contact measures. **Figure 6.3** outlines the various control measures that can be used to ensure the safe handling of both chemical and low-level biological agents. These controls are the subject of the sections that follow.

ENGINEERING CONTROLS

The best method for mitigating the risk associated with chemical and biohazards is elimination. When that is not possible, the next best line of defence is to reduce the risk by finding a less harmful alternative. Unfortunately, within the context of biohazards this may not be practical or even possible. For chemical agents, a thorough investigation should be

FIGURE 6.3

ENGINEERING, WORK PRACTICES, AND MEDICAL CONTROL MEASURES

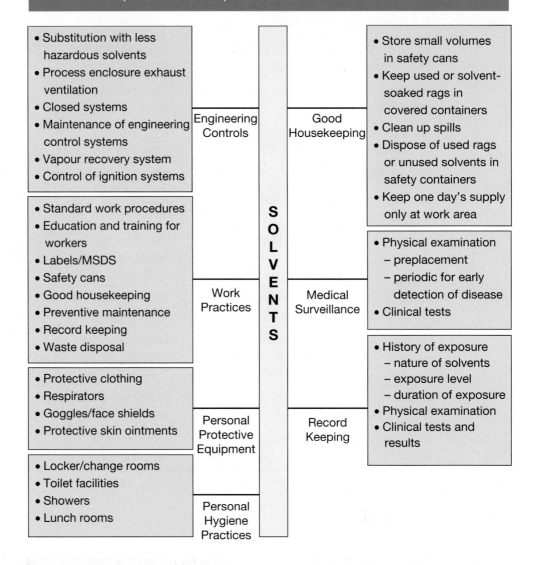

Engineering Controls
- Substitution with less hazardous solvents
- Process enclosure exhaust ventilation
- Closed systems
- Maintenance of engineering control systems
- Vapour recovery system
- Control of ignition systems

Work Practices
- Standard work procedures
- Education and training for workers
- Labels/MSDS
- Safety cans
- Good housekeeping
- Preventive maintenance
- Record keeping
- Waste disposal

Personal Protective Equipment
- Protective clothing
- Respirators
- Goggles/face shields
- Protective skin ointments

Personal Hygiene Practices
- Locker/change rooms
- Toilet facilities
- Showers
- Lunch rooms

Good Housekeeping
- Store small volumes in safety cans
- Keep used or solvent-soaked rags in covered containers
- Clean up spills
- Dispose of used rags or unused solvents in safety containers
- Keep one day's supply only at work area

Medical Surveillance
- Physical examination
  - preplacement
  - periodic for early detection of disease
- Clinical tests

Record Keeping
- History of exposure
  - nature of solvents
  - exposure level
  - duration of exposure
- Physical examination
- Clinical tests and results

conducted to ensure that the proposed substitute meets the intended purpose, does not contain dangerous properties, and is compatible with existing materials in use. If solvents are being used, areas should be properly enclosed to prevent or minimize the escape of vapours, and an effective exhaust system should be in place. Because some of the chemicals used may be a source of ignition, it is equally important to ensure that appropriate fire-extinguishing equipment is on hand and that combustibles are isolated from sources of ignition. Materials should not be stored adjacent to highly reactive chemicals.

Engineering controls for biohazards include built-in protective systems, equipment or supplies, which often require they be planned ahead of time and built into the design of a workspace. Common examples include ventilation systems (e.g., HVAC systems), construction seals, sharps disposal containers for needles, or automated equipment like toilets and sinks (e.g., in hospitals, restaurants).

ADMINISTRATIVE CONTROLS

Perhaps the single most important administrative function is the education and training of all employees in safe work practices. Employees should receive training in safe operating and emergency procedures, in the use and care of PPE, and in the handling and control of agents. Training must be conducted on an ongoing basis, given that new solvents and other agents are continually entering the workplace. Finally, workers must be familiar with all aspects of Workplace Hazardous Material Information System (WHMIS) legislation.

WORKPLACE HAZARDOUS MATERIALS INFORMATION SYSTEM

WHMIS is a comprehensive communication system designed to outline the safe use of hazardous products via product labels, safety data sheets (SDS), and worker education and training programs. WHMIS began in the United States in the early 1980s in the form of the Hazard Communication Standard. WHMIS was the brainchild of industry, labour, and government representatives committed to developing regulations that meet the right-to-know standard. WHMIS legislation came into force across Canada between 1988 and 1990. Initially, all jurisdictions were involved in creating the first Canada-wide health and safety legislation. To ensure the desired consistency in regulations, the federal government created a model OH&S regulation, which was then used by the provincial and territorial governments. As of 2015, WHMIS was adopted to incorporate the Globally Harmonized System (GHS) of Classification and Labelling of Chemicals for workplace chemicals due to the various methodologies used around the world. The overall goal in adopting the GHS is to develop consistent policies, practices, and standards with other countries that use the GHS. In addition to adopting the GHS, the federal government released an amended Hazardous Products Act (HPA) and released the new Hazardous Products Regulations (HPR), which replaced the Controlled Product Regulations. The act and the regulations define which materials (i.e., hazardous products) are included in WHMIS 2015 and what information suppliers must provide to employers for controlled products used in the workplace.

WHMIS 2015 is based on three elements:

- labels designed to alert the worker that the container contains a potentially hazardous product
- safety data sheets outlining a product's potentially hazardous ingredient(s) and procedures for safe handling of the product
- employee training

The main differences between WHMIS 1998 and WHMIS 2015 include:

- new rules for classifying hazardous workplace chemicals: two main hazard classes—physical hazards and health hazards
- new label requirements, including pictograms instead of symbols that correspond to hazard classes
- a different format for safety data sheets (formerly material safety data sheets MSDS)

HAZARD CLASSES AND CATEGORIES Hazards identified within WHMIS 2015/GHS are organized by group, class, and category or type. There are two groups of hazards: physical and health. GHS outlines an additional environmental group; however, this is not included within the latest changes made to WHMIS 2015. The physical hazard group is based on physical and chemical properties (e.g., flammable). The health hazard group identifies hazards that have the ability to cause negative health effects (e.g., irritations). Hazards within these two groups can be further organized into a *hazard class*, which clusters hazards with similar properties together (e.g., flammable gases, aerosols, and gases under pressure).

Once hazards are classified, if necessary, they are categorized by number. Numbers are assigned to categories according to how dangerous they are, meaning that category 1 is more hazardous than category 2, and category 2 is more dangerous than category 3. Each hazard class has at least one category associated with it; however, further categories (i.e., 2 and 3) may not be necessary. If a particular category needs to be further grouped it is done so by type, which is assigned a letter (see **Figure 6.4**). It is important to note that some of the hazard classes included in WHMIS are not included within GHS. Hazards such as explosives are covered under separate legislation in Canada; thus, it is extremely important employers ensure they are complying with their provincial or territorial requirements under the appropriate legislation and regulations.

LABELS All products within the workplace that meet the criteria for being classified as a hazardous product as outlined in the act and regulations must be labelled. There are two specific types of labels: supplier and workplace labels. Supplier labels must be attached by the supplier or provider. For example, if you work in a lab all hazardous agents received from a supplier by a lab must have a supplier label (see **Figure 6.5**). Workplace labels are required when a hazardous product is made and used within a workplace, when a hazardous product is poured or transferred to another container, or when a supplier label is lost or unreadable. Workplace labels are not required when a hazardous product is poured into a container and will be used immediately or when one worker pours a material into another container and will be the only person using it for that shift. If another worker will be using that container, or if it is to be stored, then a workplace label must be applied. Workplace labels must contain the product name, outline measures for safe handling, and refer to the safety data sheet if one is available. It is important to note that each provincial and territorial jurisdiction has specific requirements that must be followed and, as such, it is the responsibility of individual employers to ensure they are up to date on when changes or modifications to WHMIS in their area are adopted.

FIGURE 6.4

WHMIS CLASSES AND CATEGORIES

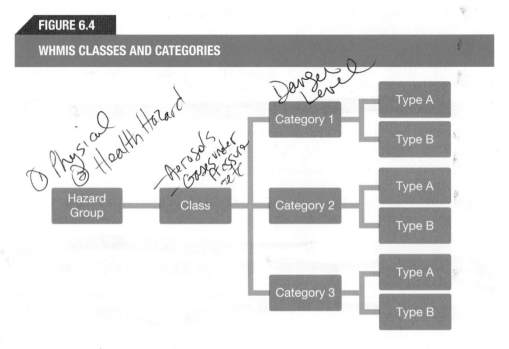

FIGURE 6.5

WHMIS SUPPLIER LABEL

Product K1/Produit K1

Danger	**Danger**
Fatal if swallowed. Causes skin irritation.	Mortel en cas d'ingestion. Provoque une irritation cutanée.
Precautions: Wear protective gloves. Wash hands thoroughly after handling. Do not eat, drink or smoke when using this product.	**Conseils:** Porter des gants de protection. Se laver les mains soigneusement aprés manipulation. Ne pas manger, boire ou fumer en manipulant ce produit.
Store locked up. Dispose of contents/containers in accordance with local regulations.	Garder sous clef. Eliminer le contenu/récipient conformément aux réglements locaux en vigueur.
IF ON SKIN: Wash with plenty of water. If skin irritation occurs: Get medical advice or attention. Take off contaminated clothing and wash it before reuse. IF SWALLOWED: Immediately call a POISON CENTRE or doctor. Rinse mouth.	EN CAS DE CONTACT AVEC LA PEAU: Laver abondamment á l'eau. En cas d'irritation cutanée: Demander un avis médical/consulter un médecin. Enlever les vétements contaminés et les laver avant réutilisation. EN CAS D'INGESTION: Appeler immédiatement un CENTRE ANTIPOISON ou un médecin. Rincer la bouche.

Compagnie XYZ, 123 rue Machin St, Mytown, ON, N0N 0N0 (123) 456-7890

Source: WHMIS 2015—Labels, https://www.ccohs.ca/oshanswers/chemicals/whmis_ghs/labels.html, Canadian Centre for Occupational Health and Safety (CCOHS), 2015. Reproduced with the permission of CCOHS, 2016.

Supplier labels must include the following information in both English and French:

- *Product identifier*—the brand name, chemical name, common name, generic name or trade name of the hazardous product.
- *Initial supplier identifier*—the name, address and telephone number of either the Canadian manufacturer or the Canadian importer. When distributors are selling

a product, the distributor may replace the name, address, and telephone number of the initial supplier with the distributor's own contact information. When an importer brings in a hazardous product for its own use, it is not required to replace the foreign supplier's information with their own.

- *Pictogram(s)*–hazard symbol within a red "square set on one of its points."
- *Signal word*–a word used to alert the reader to a potential hazard and to indicate the severity of the hazard (e.g., "danger" or "warning").
- *Hazard statement(s)*–standardized phrases that describe the nature of the hazard posed by a hazardous product (e.g., "Extremely flammable gas" or "May cause cancer").
- *Precautionary statement(s)*–standardized phrases that describe measures to be taken to minimize or prevent adverse effects resulting from exposure to a hazardous product or resulting from improper handling or storage of a hazardous product (e.g., "Wear protective clothing" or "protect from sunlight").
- *Supplemental label information*–some supplemental label information is required based on the classification of the product. For example, the label for a mixture containing ingredients with unknown toxicity in amounts higher than or equal to 1% must include a statement indicating the percentage of the ingredient or ingredients with unknown toxicity.

Using the GHS, labels must now include pictograms, which are standardized graphic images that help a user to quickly identify the type of hazard he or she are using or is exposed to. Most of the pictograms used within the GHS are identifiable as a square that has been turned 45 degrees and has a red border. There are nine pictograms used within WHMIS 2015; they are located on supplier labels as well as on the safety data sheets (see **Figure 6.6**).

The objective of safety data sheets (SDS) is to identify potentially harmful materials, to present information about the nature of the materials and their harmful effects, and to provide guidance on how to handle safely.

The manufacturer or supplier must develop an SDS for each product supplied for use in the workplace. The requirement for supplying SDSs is twofold. Suppliers are regulated by the federal legislation under the Hazardous Products Act and provincial or territorial regulations, while employers are regulated only under provincial or territorial regulations. Should an employer also be a manufacturer or produce research products not intended for sale, the responsibility for creating an SDS becomes an employer's.

The SDS must contain information as set out by the Hazardous Products Act, and the Hazardous Products Regulations. The SDS must be provided to the buyer on or before the date of sale or delivery of the product. The information on the SDS must be current at the time of sale or delivery, and the SDS must be dated no more than three years before the date of sale or delivery.

The following 16 items must appear on an SDS; however, items 12 to 15 are not required by law in Canada to be filled in.[6]

1. Identification
2. Hazard identification
3. Composition/Ingredients
4. First aid

FIGURE 6.6

WHMIS 2015—PICTOGRAMS

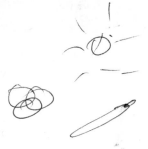	**Exploding bomb** (for explosion or reactivity hazards)	**Flame** (for fire hazards)	**Flame over circle** (for oxidizing hazards)
	Gas cylinder (for gases under pressure)	**Corrosion** (for corrosive damage to metals, as well as skin, eyes)	**Skull and Crossbones** (can cause death or toxicity with short exposure to small amounts)
carcinogen	**Health hazard** (may cause or suspected of causing serious health effects)	**Exclamation mark** (may cause less serious health effects or damage the ozone layer*)	**Environment*** (may cause damage to the aquatic environment)

Biohazardous Infectious Materials
(for organisms or toxins that can cause diseases in people or animals)

must know for exam

* The GHS system also defines an Environmental hazards group. This group (and its classes) was not adopted in WHMIS 2015. However, you may see the environmental classes listed on labels and SDSs. Including information about environmental hazards is allowed by WHMIS 2015.

Source: WHMIS 2015—Pictograms, http://www.ccohs.ca/oshanswers/chemicals/whmis_ghs/pictograms.html, Canadian Centre for Occupational Health and Safety (CCOHS), 2015. Reproduced with the permission of CCOHS, 2016.

5. Firefighting
6. Accidental release measures
7. Handling/Storage
8. Exposure controls/Personal protection
9. Physical/Chemical properties
10. Stability/Reactivity
11. Toxicology information
12. Ecological information
13. Disposal considerations
14. Transportation information
15. Regulatory information
16. Other information (e.g., last time SDS was revised)

EDUCATION AND TRAINING WHMIS education refers to providing information about how the WHMIS/GHS is structured, its purpose and objectives, and the hazards associated with each material. For instance, WHMIS education teaches workers about the various hazard classes and why a material belongs to a particular class.

Training can be viewed as more job-specific information and covers the procedures for handling, storage, use, disposal, and emergency procedures within that particular work environment. Companies and organizations that use hazardous products as outlined in the HPA must have a WHMIS program in place. Any and all individuals who use or directly work with (e.g., workers), or are exposed to but do not directly work with a hazardous product (e.g., supervisors, emergency personnel), must receive WHMIS education and training. The requirements for WHMIS education and training are outlined according to each province and territory, and it is imperative that employers stay up to date on changes and amendments to the legislative requirements in their area.

WORK PRACTICES AND PROCEDURES

Senior managers must ensure policies and procedures are enforced at all times (see **OH&S Today 6.2**) and by everyone. Situations where employees do not follow policies must be handled appropriately, and in cases where employees willfully neglect policies and practices, a disciplinary structure must be put in place.

Good housekeeping is essential workplace practice when handling, storing, or using agents. This is important for breaking the chain of infection. Ensuring that surfaces such as doorknobs and faucets are properly disinfected is extremely important. Laboratories, hospitals, and clinics must ensure that each area exposed to biohazards is kept clean and orderly. For chemical hazards, if containers are leaking, the agents they contain must be transferred immediately to sound containers. Spills must be cleaned up properly, and employees who may be exposed to the hazard must wear protective equipment. Solvent-soaked rags should be disposed of in airtight, all-metal containers and removed daily.

OH&S TODAY 6.2

NEEDLESTICK INJURIES: A DECREASE IN RATES

Needlestick injuries have been a health and safety concern for many years. A needlestick injury occurs when a sharp object, such as a needle, lancet, scalpel, or IV delivery system, which is potentially carrying blood-borne pathogens, punctures the skin of a care provider. For example, a nurse changing an intravenous (IV) may inadvertently stick the used needle in his own hand. For some occupations, there has been a decrease in the incidence of sharps injuries. Researchers in Ontario have found that needlestick injury rates have decreased significantly. However, needlestick injuries are a worry for other occupations—workers at recycling centres.

Many communities have adopted recycling programs that involve (at least in part) individuals working at a recycling centre sorting through various types of recyclable material (glass, plastic, etc.). Items such as syringes are often discarded in the recycling bins, and recycling plant workers run the risk of a needlestick injury as they sort through the material to identify what can be recycled.

The solution to the problem involves both prevention and protection. First, communities with recycling programs must educate citizens in the proper procedures for disposing of needles and similar items. Second, employees should be provided with protective gear (e.g., heavy leather gloves over latex) to offset the exposure to needles. These policies and procedures must also be followed by all employees at all times.

Sources: Canadian Centre for Occupational Health and Safety, OHS Answers "What Are Needlestick Injuries?" Found at http://www.ccohs.ca/oshanswers/diseases/needlestick_injuries.html (accessed April 1, 2016); A. Chambers, C. Mustard, and J. Etches, "Trends in Needlestick Injury Incidence Following Regulatory Change in Ontario, Canada (2004–2012): An Observational Study," *BMC Health Research 15* (2015): 127.

Each municipality has its own guidelines for the disposal of wastes, and employees must be familiar with the guidelines that apply to them.

Preventive maintenance must be conducted regularly to ensure that no potential dangers exist. For example, air filters on exhaust or ventilation equipment may become damaged or plugged and pose a potential danger in an enclosed area in which solvents or biohazards are used. Employees should understand the procedures for maintaining equipment and documenting all repairs.

Thorough recordkeeping is essential. Though provinces and territories vary in terms of requirements for recordkeeping, all demand that records be kept of employee exposure, workplace air monitoring, and equipment breakdowns and repairs.

MEDICAL SURVEILLANCE Medical surveillance programs, an administrative control, are implemented to ensure that employees who are exposed to agents are not subjected to situations in which their health will be jeopardized. For such programs to be effective, pre-employment and preplacement medical examinations should be conducted to establish a baseline of the employee's health and exposure to agents in previous workplaces. Follow-up medical examinations should be conducted periodically. Examinations may include a chest X-ray, pulmonary function tests, and blood workups. Finally, recordkeeping is an important aspect of medical surveillance programs. The types of exposures employees face and their health records before and after exposure should be included in this process.

PERSONAL PROTECTIVE EQUIPMENT (PPE)

Personal protective equipment (PPE) is one of the most important point of contact control mechanisms for many hazards, and because inhalation is the most common and hazardous route of entry for chemical and biological hazards, the most commonly used protection device is a respirator. Respiratory protection is more specialized for biohazards than it is for chemical agents, since a biological airborne contaminant can be much smaller than a chemical one. PPE for hands, face, and other body parts must be provided where necessary. No single protective device, such as a facemask, will adequately address all conditions for all workers. Each device must be matched to the chemical or biological exposure, and it is imperative that the device be properly fitted to the individual. (One size does not fit all!)

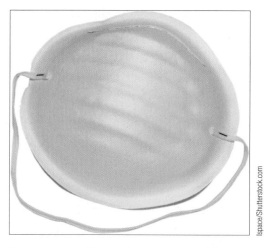

lspace/Shutterstock.com

science photo/Shutterstock.com

Do you know the difference between a dust mask and a respirator?

PERSONAL HYGIENE PRACTICES

The ingestion of chemicals or biological particulate is often the result of poor hygiene (e.g., hand hygiene). Individuals who handle agents without wearing proper protective gear, such as gloves, are at risk of food contamination. In other instances, chemicals that are not adequately removed at the workplace can be transferred to the worker's home. To ensure that this and similar incidents do not occur, individuals who handle toxic substances must adhere to the following:

- Remove outer protective clothing, and clean hands, arms, face, and nails before entering rest areas or lunchrooms.
- Avoid touching lips, nose, and eyes with contaminated hands.
- Wash hands before eating, drinking, or smoking, and eat, drink, and smoke only in designated areas.
- Remove work clothes and wash or shower before leaving work.

// SUMMARY

This chapter has focused on the types, characteristics, measurement, and control of chemical and biological agents. All workers who are exposed to these agents should be knowledgeable about their potential health effects as well as trained in their proper use and handling. Chemical agents and, to a lesser extent, biological agents are the major causes of occupational diseases. Much of the required knowledge is highly technical, and there is a lot of terminology to understand. HR practitioners should be sensitive to the potential effects of a broad array of health-related effects that can occur. Most important, the focus of an OH&S program should be on the appropriate management of exposure to these agents.

KEY TERMS

aerosols 138
agents 135 — biological + chemical
alveoli 141
biohazards 134
boiling point 143
chain of infection 136
chemical agent 134
dermatitis 143
mode of transmission 136
portal of entry 136
portal of exit 136
reservoir 136
surfactant layer 142
susceptible host 137
target organs 142
toxicity 137
turbinates 140

DISCUSSION QUESTIONS

1. This chapter lists the types of contaminants found in industrial workplaces. Consider the typical office setting; to what types of chemical hazards might office workers be exposed?

2. Explain the concept of a "synergistic effect" as used in this chapter.

3. What are the major ways of controlling the potential adverse effects of exposure to chemical and biological agents?

4. What is the Globally Harmonized System and what is its goal?

USING THE INTERNET

1. Research reports detailing the flu season in Canadian cities during 2016. Examine how this season compared to previous years. What procedures or measures did workplaces and individuals (e.g., hospitals) implement to minimize exposure or reaction to this biological hazard?

2. Cases of environmental illness or environmental sensitivity seem to be becoming more common. Search out contemporary cases in which employees have been exposed to chemical or biological agents with long-term consequences. Could these exposures have been prevented? Could the workers have been protected?

EXERCISE

1. As your workplace approaches cold and flu season, the healthy workplace committee has decided to take a number of proactive measures to prevent and minimize infection rates. Discuss the steps that HR can and should take to prevent the spread of cold and flu among employees. In other words, what tasks, measures, information, or programs should be developed that will help to break the chain of infection? Outline these precautions in terms of the level of responsibility associated with them (e.g., frontline employee, manager, supervisor).

OH&S IN ACTION

When it comes to biohazards, some individuals may be more sensitive to some exposures than others. For example, pregnant women may be more at risk when exposed to certain viruses or bacteria (e.g., measles, chickenpox) than other employees. Unfortunately, when humans and animals are reservoirs or carriers of infectious agents, they may be unaware and show no symptoms, and, as a result, may not take precautions to minimize the spread (e.g., through hand washing, wearing PPE). Your organization has a number of female staff, some of whom will be going out on maternity leave over the next few months. Create an employee information pamphlet that demonstrates the vulnerability of some populations of people, illustrates the chain of infection in simple terms, and outlines the various ways in which this chain can be broken.

CASE STUDY 1   FIREFIGHTERS AND CANCER

Sabrina is a firefighter for her town's fire service and she has seen a significant difference in the way houses and buildings are burning due to the use of new building materials that are not only lighter but also treated with chemicals designed to resist mould and insects. Furthermore, the new furniture in many homes and buildings is now made of lighter and manufactured materials that create a very acrid and toxic smoke when burned. Sabrina and her colleagues have been reading and researching that the incidence and types of cancers afflicting career firefighters is increasing dramatically. Sabrina and her colleagues have raised their concerns to their chief who has contacted you for help in responding to their concerns. As a health and safety professional, how would you handle this situation? What would you do to ensure your town's firefighters feel educated and protected from the new chemical hazards they are being exposed to?

CASE STUDY 2   UNEXPECTED GAS

A man was killed by an explosion when another worker attempted to cut through the top of one of two old steel drums using a handheld grinder. Both barrels had contained a fruit concentrate but were never cleaned. The sparks generated by the grinder ignited hydrogen gas that had been generated from the contents' residue after standing for many years. Because there was a defective sterile coating separating the walls of the drum from the concentrate, the acid in the fruit concentrate reacted with the metal of the drum and formed hydrogen gas. The gas accumulated and the pressure caused the drum ends to bulge. This deformation made it impossible to open the drum with the drum opener, and a hole was punched into the top of each drum. One worker was attempting to add water to one drum in order to displace the remaining gas, while another worker attempted to open the other drum with a grinder. Sparks ignited the hydrogen gas, causing an explosion and a fire. The fire was extinguished, but one worker lost his life. The defective drums had been recalled years before by the supplier, and only three remained unaccounted for before the accident.

What steps would you take to ensure that this event was never repeated?

// NOTES

1. Centers for Disease Control, "Chain of Infection." Found at http://www.cdc.gov/ophss/csels/dsepd/ss1978/lesson1/section10.html (accessed April 20, 2106).
2. Health and Safety Executive, "Hairdressing." Found at http://www.hse.gov.uk/hairdressing/index.htm (accessed April 20, 2016).

3. Peel District School Board, "Take One Step: Wellness at Work," (January 20, 2013). Found at http://www.takeonestep.org/pages/yoursafety/safenotsorry/chemicalhazards.aspx (accessed May 31, 2016).

4. P.L. Williams and J.L. Burson, eds., *Industrial Toxicology—Safety and Health Applications in the Workplace* (New York: Van Nostrand Reinhold, 1985).

5. C.W. Pilger, "Toxic Solvents," 23rd Intensive Workshop in Industrial Hygiene, Toronto, 1994.

6. Canadian Centre for Occupational Health and Safety, OHS Answers, "WHMIS, Safety Data Sheets." Found at http://www.ccohs.ca/oshanswers/chemicals/whmis_ghs/sds.html (accessed April 15, 2016).

PSYCHOSOCIAL HAZARDS

CHAPTER LEARNING OBJECTIVES

AFTER READING THIS CHAPTER, YOU SHOULD BE ABLE TO:

- describe and distinguish among the concepts of stressor, stress, and strain
- explain the transactional model of stress and its implications
- identify major sources of stress in the workplace
- discuss the psychological, physical, behavioural, and organizational consequences of stress
- discuss ways to recognize, assess, and manage psychosocial hazards at work
- describe and distinguish among primary, secondary, and tertiary stress interventions
- describe injustice, technology, and work–life conflict as prevalent workplace stressors

In 1990, the United States' National Institute of Occupational Safety and Health (NIOSH) declared occupational stress to be one of the 10 leading causes of workplace death, and it is now common to speak of occupational stress as an epidemic.[1] Estimates suggest that workplace stress costs the Canadian economy anywhere from $12 to 33 billion annually. In the United States this figure rises to a staggering $300 billion.[2] Mental illness is prevalent. Each year, one in five Canadians will experience a mental health problem. The associated cost to the economy exceeds $50 billion per year. Specific to workplace productivity, mental health problems cost organizations $6 billion annually in absenteeism and presenteeism.[3] Some estimates of the total costs to workplaces are closer to $20 billion annually.[4]

Though we recognize that estimates of the cost of work stress involve considerable guesswork, it is clear that workplace stress is a large and growing problem with considerable consequences for individuals and organizations. The workplace is replete with factors that contribute to stress, and many Canadian workers experience the reality of stress. The results of the 2010 General Social Survey on Time Use show that 27% of Canadian workers report being quite a bit or extremely stressed in their daily lives. Among those highly stressed workers, 60% identify work as their major source of stress.[5] A survey of employed Nova Scotians found that a large percentage of them experienced such stressors as high workloads (60%), conflicting demands (70%), and conflicts between work and family responsibilities (50%). Furthermore, about 20% of the sample reported health-related symptoms that commonly manifest themselves after the experience of stress.[6]

There are several reasons for organizations to address issues of mental health at work. From the statistics presented above, the economic drivers are clear. Further, given the prevalence of workplace stressors and the number of employees affected, one might also consider a moral incentive for workplaces to focus on creating psychologically healthy work. Beyond these reasons, there are legal motivations for Canadian employers to focus on creating psychologically healthy workplaces.[7] For instance, Canadian human rights tribunals are explicating the responsibility to accommodate mental illness at work. Workers' compensation boards are increasingly addressing claims related to mental stress. Occupational health and safety acts are recognizing that psychological safety is part of a safe workplace. And cases across jurisdictions show that managers are being held accountable to understand how their actions affect others.

Reflecting this increased focus on mental health at work, the Canadian Standards Association, with the support of the Mental Health Commission of Canada, published a voluntary workplace standard, CSA-Z1003-13, for a **psychologically healthy and safe workplace**. This standard provides guidance for employers on developing a psychological health and safety management system in the workplace.[8] A psychologically healthy and safe workplace "promotes workers' psychological well-being and actively works to prevent harm to worker psychological health including in negligent, reckless, or intentional ways."[9] Although voluntary, the standard is a way for employers to demonstrate due diligence when it comes to issues of psychological health at work.

One predominant assumption about workplace mental health is that organizations are concerned with this issue largely to address the costs associated with stress and mental health problems. Thus, the assumption is that firms are largely concerned with reducing absenteeism or disability leave or are focused on increasing productivity. Discussion of the effectiveness of workplace health programs often focuses on the "return on investment" that one might obtain from such programs.[10]

Recently, the Mental Health Commission of Canada commissioned a case study project in which researchers examined the experiences of 40 Canadian organizations that were in the process of implementing CSA Z1003. One surprising finding that emerged from was why companies were interested in improving health and safety.[11] For the most part, firms were not primarily concerned with financial returns. Rather, they expressed the view that improving mental health for employees was the "right" thing to do—companies felt a moral obligation to do work in this area. Alternately, many firms described their initiative as being "mission-critical"—the focus on mental health was closely related to their strategic goals and focus as an organization. For example, unions are focused on improving working conditions for employees, and initiatives around mental health clearly fall within their scope. Health care organizations are focused on health and well-being and mental health is a natural extension of that focus. These results don't suggest that financial returns aren't important, but they do suggest that financial motives are not the main drivers for organizations to become involved in workplace mental health.

So, what exactly is stress? One way to discuss stress is in terms of the **psychosocial model of health**. The term "psychosocial" highlights the importance of both the social environment and the psychological or individual factors that affect a person's health and well-being. Social factors that influence a person's health include family circumstances, exposure to violence, and workplace policies. Psychological factors that affect a person's health include levels of self-esteem and anxiety, as well as the ability to cope with pressure.

In everyday conversation, we use the term "stress" in several different ways. We talk about feeling stress and about stress as something we're exposed to. Even the scientific literature demonstrates considerable confusion over the precise meanings of stress-related terms.[12] Most researchers now agree on a general stress model that distinguishes among three closely related terms: stressors, stress, and strain.

psychologically healthy and safe workplace
a workplace that promotes workers' psychological well-being and actively works to prevent harm to workers' psychological health including in negligent, reckless, or intentional ways

psychosocial model of health
approach to the study of health that highlights the importance of both the social environment and psychological factors

// STRESSORS

A **stressor** is an objectively verifiable event in the environment that has the potential to cause stress. For example, congested traffic is a stressor. Stressors, then, exist outside the individual and reflect some of the social factors that affect a person's health. Stressors vary along several dimensions, including frequency of occurrence, intensity, duration, and predictability (time of onset).[13] These dimensions have led researchers to distinguish among four categories of stressors: acute, chronic, daily, and catastrophic (see **Table 7.1**).

Acute stressors have a specific time onset (i.e., you know exactly when it began), are typically of short duration and high intensity, and have a low frequency. For example, a traffic accident is an acute stressor. In terms of the work environment, a performance review meeting or a conflict with a supervisor may be an acute stressor. In contrast, a *chronic* stressor has no specific time onset, may be of short or long duration, repeats frequently, and may be of low or high intensity. Many individuals today are experiencing job insecurity as a chronic stressor. Most cannot point to a specific event or time that triggered the insecurity, but the nagging worry that their job is at risk is always with them.

Daily stressors have a specific onset, are of short duration, are low in intensity, and are typically infrequent. Dealing with a broken piece of office equipment may be a daily stressor for some employees. Finally, we need to recognize the existence of *catastrophic* stressors or disasters. Much like acute stressors, catastrophic stressors have a specific onset, occur infrequently, have a high intensity, and may be of long or short duration. The main distinction between acute and catastrophic stressors relates to the intensity of the stressor. Catastrophic stressors typically involve a direct threat to life, loss of life, or major property damage. Again, the complexities involved in categorizing stressors are indicated by the observation that catastrophic stressors can become chronic over time. For example, the events of September 11, 2001, constituted a catastrophic stressor for those directly involved, but also have had long-term consequences for those individuals who live with the fear of terrorism.

stressor
an objectively verifiable event that occurs outside the individual that has the potential to cause stress

Stoyan Yotov/Shutterstock.com

Some jobs, such as air traffic control, are inherently stressful because of the demands placed on individuals.

TABLE 7.1

CATEGORIES OF STRESSORS

TYPE	FREQUENCY	DURATION	INTENSITY	TIME OF ONSET
Acute	Rare	Short	High	Specific
Chronic	Frequent	Short or long	Low or high	Nonspecific
Daily	Infrequent	Short	Low	Specific
Catastrophic	Very rare	Short or long	Extremely high	Specific

STRESSORS IN THE WORKPLACE

The above categorization (as shown in Table 7.1) provides a general overview of stressors. Other researchers have focused on the content or sources of workplace stressors.[14] The NIOSH model identifies the following major categories of workplace stressors:

- *Workload and work pace.* This refers to the amount of work that must be completed and the speed at which employees must work to complete their tasks.

- *Role stressors* (conflict, ambiguity, inter-role conflict). Role conflict exists when individuals face incompatible demands from two or more sources. Role ambiguity reflects the uncertainty that employees experience about what is expected from them in their work; the opposite of role ambiguity is role clarity. Inter-role conflict exists when employees face incompatible demands from two or more roles. The most common form of inter-role conflict is work–family conflict, in which the demands of work conflict with the role of parent or spouse. We'll learn more about work–family conflict later in this chapter.

- *Career concerns.* This includes worries about job security, fear of job obsolescence, underpromotion and overpromotion, and, more generally, concerns about career progression.

- *Work scheduling.* Working rotating shifts or permanent night shifts results in a disruption of physiological circadian rhythms, as well as a disruption of social activities.

- *Interpersonal relations.* Poor interpersonal relations in the workplace are consistently identified as a source of stress. Poor interpersonal relationships can range from experiencing rude treatment to a variety of more intense experiences such as bullying or violence. Chapter 8 focuses exclusively on workplace violence as a psychosocial hazard in the workplace. Having well-established sources of social support (i.e., receiving support from coworkers and supervisors) may reduce the effects of other workplace stressors.

- *Job content and control.* Jobs that are highly repetitive, or that do not make use of a variety of workers' skills or give workers a measure of control over how and when they complete their tasks, can be a source of stress.

The Canadian standard for psychological health and safety at work (CSA-Z1003-13) identifies 13 organizational factors that affect psychological health at work. All these factors are in the control of the organization and, when met, provide sources of psychological safety for employees. However, when not met, the factors identified in this inventory represent workplace stressors. Managing these factors effectively should contribute to positive experiences and mental health for workers. The factors, along with their desired state, identified in the standard are:[15]

- *Organizational culture.* The culture reflects trust, respect, civility, and fairness.

- *Psychological and social support.* Workers experience supportive social interactions with coworkers and supervisors.

- *Clear leadership and expectations.* Leadership communicates clear expectations to employees about their work roles and organizational change.

- *Civility and respect*. Workers are respectful and considerate of each other and with clients.
- *Psychological demands*. The psychological demands of the job are recognized and assessed with respect to their potential impact on worker well-being.
- *Growth and development*. Employees are supported to develop skills.
- *Recognition and reward*. Workers' efforts are acknowledged and appreciated.
- *Involvement and influence*. Workers are able to influence the work process and important work decisions.
- *Workload management*. Tasks can be accomplished within the available timeframe.
- *Engagement*. Workers feel motivated and connected to their work.
- *Balance*. The workplace accepts that there needs to be balance between personal, family, and work aspects of life.
- *Psychological protection*. Workers feel they can ask questions, report mistakes, or propose ideas without fear of reprisal.
- *Protection of physical safety*. Workers are protected from risks in the physical environment.

For more information on the standard, see **OH&S Today 7.1**.

OH&S TODAY 7.1

MENTAL HEALTH AT WORK: CALMING THE PERFECT STORM

As a result of a number of circumstances, organizations have become more focused on issues related to workplace mental health. Examples of agencies promoting workplace mental health include the Mental Health Commission of Canada's promotion of workplace mental health, the publication of CSA Z1003, and the success of Bell's "Let's Talk" campaign. More pragmatically, organizations also recognize their legal obligations with respect to workplace conditions and the rising cost of long-term and short-term disability claims. A common estimate is that 30 to 40% of these claims relate to mental health issues.

It seems clear that mental health problems can negatively affect work. However, perhaps ironically, work itself can increase the risk of depression and other mental health concerns. Many workplace stressors are associated with depressive symptoms. For instance, those who work shift work, particularly evening and night shifts, are more likely to be depressed than others. Also, those who report being exposed to many workplace stressors most days on the job are at increased risk for depression. Employee stressors such as work role conflict, workload, and work–life conflict appear to be on the rise.

The Mental Health Commission of Canada recently sponsored "the case study project"—a detailed study of 40 Canadian organizations that have agreed to implement CSA Z1003. The results of the study are still unfolding; however, interim data have led to the identification of both success factors and barriers to implementing the standard. Perhaps most importantly, results of the case study indicate that it is feasible to implement the standard in a wide variety of organizations from very small private sector operations to large-scale public employers and even unions. Implementing the standard appears to be a practical way for most organizations to address issues of mental health in the workplace.

Sources: Ipsos, Great West Life Centre for Mental Health in the Workplace, "Mental Health in the Workplace Research" (August 2012). Found at: http://www.workplacestrategiesformentalhealth.com/pdf/GWLReleaseDeckDepressionintheWorkplace.pdf (accessed February 8, 2013).

// STRESS

Stressors are objective events. However, the individual's response to or evaluation of these events also plays an important role. Researchers in occupational health psychology (see **OH&S Notebook 7.1**) have typically referred to this response or evaluation as **stress**. Stress is an internal response to stressors and is often characterized by negative feelings of arousal. Stress, then, reflects some of the psychological factors that affect a person's health. In contrast to the objective stressors we have discussed, stress is an internal event that is subjectively defined. Stress is a consequence of any action, situation, or event that places special demands on a person. The stress response is an adaptive reaction to these demands and is influenced by differences between people.

Stress is an adaptive response. The stress response is our way of mobilizing resources to deal with stressors in the environment. Viewed in an evolutionary context, stress is the product of millions of years of evolution. The **general adaptation syndrome** (stress response) is the body's way of gearing up for fight or flight (i.e., to confront or run away from a predator).[16] Some of the physiological changes that occur as the body prepares for fight or flight include increased blood supply to the brain and major muscle groups, decreased blood supply to the digestive system and skin, increased heart rate and breathing, and increased activity in the stomach, bowels, and bladder. If the stress reaction is prolonged, the resulting symptoms include headaches, dry mouth, skin rashes, heartburn, hypertension, stomach ulcers, and asthma.

OH&S NOTEBOOK   7.1

OCCUPATIONAL HEALTH PSYCHOLOGY

Occupational health psychology applies psychology to questions of occupational stress, illness, and injury. Having developed throughout the 1990s, this field has brought considerable attention to psychosocial risk factors for workplace injury and illness.

Occupational health psychology aims to improve quality of work life and protect and promote the safety, health, and well-being of workers. Occupational health psychologists consider both organizational and individual factors in occupational health. They believe that the transformation of the work environment can carry positive effects for employee health.

Researchers and practitioners of occupational health psychology rely on a four-component strategy to reduce work-related psychosocial disorders:

1. *A focus on organizational change.* Organizational change is possible and is at times necessary to reduce psychosocial hazards in the workplace.

2. *A focus on information.* Workers should be provided with information, education, and training regarding psychosocial hazards and psychological health at work.

3. *A focus on psychological health services.* Enriched services for the promotion of psychological well-being and the treatment of psychological symptoms (e.g., employee assistance programs, inclusion of preventive services in benefits plans) should be provided to employees.

4. *A focus on surveillance.* The surveillance and monitoring of psychosocial risk factors and psychological disorders should be routine in organizations.

Sources: CDC, "Occupational Health Psychology." Found at: http://www.cdc.gov/niosh/topics/ohp (accessed May 5, 2016); S.L. Sauter, L.R. Murphy, and J.J. Hurrell, "Prevention of Work-Related Psychological Disorders: A National Strategy Proposed by the National Institute for Occupational Safety and Health (NIOSH)," *American Psychologist*, Vol. 45 (1990): 1146–58; L.E. Tetrick and J.C. Quick, "Prevention at Work: Public Health in Occupational Settings," in Quick and Tetrick, eds., *Handbook of Occupational Health Psychology* (Washington: APA, 2003), pp. 3–17.

Stress is moderated by individual differences. Psychologists have recognized for many years that our responses to events in the environment are determined largely by our interpretations of those events. Some people are less vulnerable to stressors in their environment than others. In fact, one of the most popular models of stress, the transactional model, is based on the notion that individuals may perceive and respond differently to the same stressors.[17] According to this model, people appraise the stressors in their environment and assess their ability to manage them. For example, a person may determine that though work demands are heavy, he or she can manage the workload by setting up a comprehensive "to do" list and by delegating some of the tasks to coworkers. Stress occurs when an individual realizes that a pertinent stressor is present and that he or she does not have the resources or ability to manage that stressor. Thus it is clear that stress does not always follow exposure to a stressor; rather, it results when an appraisal process indicates that the stressor is indeed an unmanageable threat to the person's well-being.

Researchers often talk about stressors as events that have the potential to cause change, harm, or loss, or to pose a threat or a challenge. Even events that are viewed as positive can be stressors. For instance, a promotion can be a stressor because it involves considerable change (e.g., in job duties), challenge (e.g., increased job responsibilities), and threat (e.g., the potential to fail in the new job). Stress is the body's way of coping with the environment, and the response is the same whether these demands are positive or negative.

STRESS MODERATORS

Many factors affect people's evaluations of stressors as well as how they react to them (i.e., degree of stress experienced). We often call these factors **moderators**. A moderator is a variable that changes the relationship between two other variables. Some moderators aggravate or increase the effects of stressors. These types of moderators are called **risk factors** for stress. Other moderators can protect an individual from the adverse effects of stressors. Because of their role in breaking the chain of response, these moderators are sometimes referred to as stress **buffers**.

Two well-accepted general classes of moderators in the stress process are the enduring properties of the individual (i.e., personality characteristics) and the social context (i.e., social support, individual relationships). We will consider each type of moderator.

THE INDIVIDUAL—PERSONALITY

A considerable amount of research has examined the role that personality plays in stress. Personality is the relatively stable set of characteristics, responses, thoughts, and behaviours of a given individual.[18] Two personality characteristics of particular relevance in considerations of stress are the **Type A behaviour** pattern and **negative affectivity**.

TYPE A BEHAVIOUR Type A individuals try to achieve increasingly more in increasingly less time. Their struggle is chronic and, if necessary, is carried out against the will of others.[19] Individuals who exhibit Type A behaviour are hard driving, competitive, and time urgent. There are two components of Type A behaviour: achievement striving and

moderator
a variable that changes the relationship between two other variables

risk factor
a variable that increases the negative effects of stress

buffer
a variable that protects people from the negative effects of stress

Type A behaviour
action–emotion complex that can be observed in any person who is aggressively involved in a chronic, incessant struggle to achieve increasingly more in increasingly less time

negative affectivity
a dispositional dimension reflecting persistent individual differences in the experience of negative emotion

impatience/irritability.[20] Someone who is high on achievement striving is typically very goal directed and action oriented. Individuals high on impatience/irritability are typically very time conscious, hostile, impatient, and irritable. In general, achievement striving is associated with performance outcomes but not health outcomes. That is, those high on achievement striving perform well, but this aspect of themselves is not related to their health. Conversely, impatience/irritability is associated with health outcomes. Those high on impatience/irritability experience more stress and have poorer health, but this is not related to their work performance.[21]

NEGATIVE AFFECTIVITY Negative affectivity is a mood factor that reflects persistent individual differences in the experience of negative emotion. More simply—perhaps too simply—some people are optimists and others are pessimists. Pessimists demonstrate negative affectivity across situations; that is, they seem predisposed to see the negative side of everything. These individuals may react negatively or adversely to *all* stressors, and in this sense, negative affectivity may be a risk factor for stress.

THE SOCIAL CONTEXT—SOCIAL SUPPORT

Social relationships are another important moderator of stress. Having sources of support can reduce a person's vulnerability to stressors.[22] In other words, people who provide support are a buffer against stress. For example, in an environment filled with challenging stressors (e.g., workload and time pressure), a high degree of organizational support can improve a person's performance at work.[23] Alternatively, a lack of social support can intensify the impact of stressors and may be a potential risk factor for stress.

Support can come from a number of sources, including supervisors, coworkers, and family members. Support can be offered in a number of ways. For instance, a coworker may provide *tangible* support by giving a new employee needed information about a job task. This same coworker may also show *emotional* support by offering positive feedback and encouragement to the new hire.

// STRAIN

strain
the result of stress; it is classified into four categories of reactions: psychological, physical, behavioural, and organizational

The result of stress is **strain**. When people encounter a stressor and experience persistent stress, ultimately strain will result. We will discuss four categories of strain reactions: psychological, physical, behavioural, and organizational.

PSYCHOLOGICAL STRAIN

Psychological strain reactions typically include either a disturbance in affect (e.g., mood) or a disturbance in cognition (e.g., concentration). Feeling irritable, anxious, overwhelmed, moody, depressed, and angry are all common affective strain reactions. Indeed, we often describe these moods as "feeling stressed out." Disturbances in mood resulting from stress range from short-lived periods of feeling blue, down, or irritable to longer-term and more serious diagnoses of psychological disorders such as depression and anxiety.[24] Similarly, we often hear people colloquially talking about being "burnt out."

More formally speaking, burnout has three dimensions: emotional exhaustion, cynicism about one's work, and a sense of inefficacy about one's contributions. People who are burnt out may feel exhausted owing to prolonged exposure to stress, have negative perceptions about the value of their work, and feel incompetent or unproductive.[25]

Most people recognize the affective or emotional reactions to stress; cognitive reactions often go unnoticed. Typical strain-related cognitive disturbances include difficulty making up your mind (often on trivial matters), difficulty concentrating and staying with one task, being unable to remember people's names even though you know them quite well, and other small mistakes. These small mistakes are generally not very important, but they can be devastating for an individual under considerable strain. For instance, even small mistakes in the workplace can sometimes have negative consequences for employee safety and performance.[26]

PHYSICAL STRAIN

Some physical symptoms of strain (e.g., stomach upsets, headaches) may seem quite trivial, but considerable evidence now suggests that stress is implicated in more serious physical conditions. Most prominently, coronary heart disease (CHD) has been consistently linked to increased stress; so has high blood pressure (hypertension), strokes, ulcers, asthma, and even some forms of cancer.[27]

The mechanisms through which strain manifests itself physically are not yet clearly understood, though it has long been known that changes in hormone and enzyme secretion occur under stress. Moreover, stress may play a dual role as a cause of serious physical illness. First, individuals exposed to a stressor may experience stress and ultimately develop a physical strain response—illness (e.g., being under constant pressure to meet deadlines and make clients happy may result in hypertension). Second, increased strain may lower the body's resistance by impairing the immune system, thereby opening the door to physical illness.[28] Indeed, evidence suggests that work-related stress is a risk factor for the common cold, such that those experiencing heavy psychological job demands have reported increased incidence of colds.[29]

BEHAVIOURAL STRAIN

Behavioural strain reactions take a variety of forms. Individuals under increased stress may develop nervous habits (e.g., nail biting or nervous tics). Other behavioural strain reactions include avoidance of certain situations, or a reduction in individual involvement, either because of a lack of interest or as a means of reducing time demands. Individuals may also engage in aggressive or violent behaviour stemming from stress. Evidence also suggests that individuals may increase their smoking, consumption of alcohol, or reliance on psychotherapeutic drugs under periods of increased stress.[30] Given the known health outcomes associated with smoking, excessive alcohol consumption, and overmedication, these are very dangerous ways of coping with increased stress.

ORGANIZATIONAL STRAIN

Stress researchers interested in organizations have identified increased absenteeism, decreased performance, disturbances of interpersonal relationships at work, and an increased likelihood of looking for alternative employment as some of the most common organizational outcomes of stress.[31] Consistent evidence suggests that high levels of stress are also associated with an increased risk of workplace accidents.[32] This increased risk may be a consequence of other strain reactions (e.g., increased cognitive failures, impaired ability to concentrate). Note also that the causal direction of this relationship is not certain. Though accidents and increased stress are certainly correlated, it may be that working in a dangerous or risky environment is in itself a stressor.

// RECOGNIZING, ASSESSING, AND MANAGING PSYCHOSOCIAL HAZARDS

It is clear that work-related stressors, stress, and strain have substantial negative consequences for both employees and organizations. Organizations must learn to recognize and control psychological hazards in the workplace. Certainly, the new Canadian Standard for psychological health and safety in the workplace (CSA-Z1003-13) not only sets the expectation that Canadian organizations will strive for psychologically healthy work environments, but also helps identify strategies to promote and sustain psychological health at work.

There are several means to identify psychosocial hazards:

- *Learn to identify stressors.* The NIOSH model identifies some stressors that can be recognized in job design. For example, any job that involves shift work places workers at risk for this psychosocial hazard. Air traffic control is widely recognized as a career that involves high cognitive demands and the associated stress. Transit operators are known to be targets of aggression from the public they serve. HR managers and OH&S professionals should acquaint themselves with the particular psychosocial risk factors that exist among the working population they serve.

- *Survey the employees.* Checking in with employees to gain their sense of the prevalent workplace stressors is a useful way to identify psychosocial hazards at work. An employee survey that asks employees about common stressors such as work overload, work–family conflict, and interpersonal conflict can identify problem areas in the workplace.

- *Look for telltale signs of stress.* As described earlier, there are organizational manifestations of strain. For example, if organizations are experiencing rates of absenteeism and turnover that are higher than the industry standard, this may be a warning sign for high levels of stress.

- *Be attuned to individual employees.* Changes in employee behaviour may reflect work stress. If a person who has always submitted things on time and had an excellent attendance record is suddenly handing things in late and missing lots of work, that person may be under strain. A manager who has a good relationship with this employee may be able to inquire tactfully about the person's well-being or encourage the person to use organizational resources such as an Employee and Family Assistance Program.

Fortunately, individual employees and organizational management can work together to offset or avoid negative outcomes by taking an approach known as **preventive stress management**. The basic principle of preventive stress management is that the

preventive stress management
an approach to managing stress in the workplace that emphasizes that the health of an organization and its employees are interdependent; encourages the reduction of stressors in the workplace as well as the recognition and management of occupational stress and strain

health of an organization and the health of its employees are interdependent.[33] In other words, organizations whose employees are in good health are more likely to succeed. Alternatively, employees who work for organizations that provide pleasant working conditions are more likely to be healthy, productive individuals.

The Canadian standard on psychological health and safety at work (CSA-Z1003-13) outlines how organizations can develop a psychological health and safety management system.[34] The recommended structure notes the importance of organizational commitment, leadership support, and employee involvement. It also outlines the value of careful planning of program implementation that involves the identification and prioritization of hazards and risks that is informed by organizational data. Once implemented, the psychological health and safety management system needs sustained and appropriate resources to engage in programs such as education, investigations, and critical event preparedness. Finally, the system should be the focus of management review and continual improvement.

Ideally, stress management programs will include both organizational and individual interventions designed to reduce exposure to stressors, reduce the experience of stress when stressors are unavoidable, and swiftly provide treatment options to those individuals who are experiencing the negative consequences of stress. In the following paragraphs, we describe three categories of interventions (primary, secondary, tertiary), providing illustrative examples for organizational and individual efforts to manage workplace stress.

PRIMARY INTERVENTIONS

Primary interventions involve reducing or removing the actual stressors and are highly effective in reducing work-related stress and strain.[35] The idea is that the removal of sources of stress from the workplace should reduce employee stress and strain. Despite the supporting evidence, primary prevention strategies have not been broadly implemented in Canadian organizations, presumably because organizational decision makers believe that the costs and logistics of primary preventive strategies would be excessive, so they prefer to focus on interventions that target the employees' ability to cope with existing stressors.[36] However, the costs associated with primary preventive efforts can be reasonable and, given the resulting reduction in employee stress, worth the effort involved to implement them. **Tables 7.2** and **7.3** provide examples of primary stress prevention strategies at the individual and organizational levels.

bikeriderlondon/Shutterstock.com

Individual practices such as mediation or yoga are secondary interventions that allow individuals to recover from stress.

primary interventions
stress interventions that involve the reduction or removal of actual stressors

CHAPTER 7 Psychosocial Hazards

TABLE 7.2

STRESS INTERVENTION STRATEGIES: INDIVIDUAL LEVEL	
LEVEL OF INTERVENTION	**EXAMPLES**
Primary	Avoid taking on an overload of work Take adequate leisure time Try to reduce Type A behaviour
Secondary	Talk with friends and coworkers Make time to exercise Use relaxation techniques
Tertiary	Seek medical treatment Participate in psychological counselling

TABLE 7.3

STRESS INTERVENTION STRATEGIES: ORGANIZATIONAL LEVEL	
LEVEL OF INTERVENTION	**EXAMPLES**
Primary	Redesign particularly demanding jobs Respect employees' opinions in management decision-making processes Provide flexible working conditions
Secondary	Provide comprehensive benefits programs that include provisions for options such as employee and family assistance programs (EFAPs), personal leave, massage therapy Offer on-site fitness centres Ensure balanced nutrition on the cafeteria menu
Tertiary	Offer benefits packages with sick days and leave options Provide counselling services following major stressors, such as a violent episode at work or a major act of terrorism Support employee efforts to find appropriate medical or psychological care

SECONDARY INTERVENTIONS

secondary interventions
stress intervention techniques that focus on minimizing negative consequences once a person is feeling stress

Secondary interventions focus on minimizing negative outcomes once a person is feeling stress. Techniques such as stress management and relaxation training help people identify the negative health effects of stress. This often involves teaching effective coping strategies, the premise being that appropriate strategies for managing stress can lessen the negative effects of stress on health.[37] Common interventions include relaxation training, stress management training and counselling, and programs in nutrition and physical fitness. We will explore some of these interventions in more detail in Chapter 14. Secondary interventions are more widely used than primary ones.

However, secondary strategies are less desirable than primary ones because they target stress only after it has developed. See Tables 7.2 and 7.3 for examples of ways that organizations and individuals can engage in secondary stress interventions.

TERTIARY INTERVENTIONS

Tertiary interventions include psychological therapy and medical attention—strategies, in other words, that are applied after the fact to help those individuals who have not been able to manage workplace stress effectively and who are now experiencing symptoms of strain.[38] In the "best of all organizations, primary and secondary prevention would be enough to manage the demands of work life."[39] However, in the event that stressors and stress are not adequately dealt with via primary and secondary efforts, it is important to consider tertiary intervention strategies that organizations and individuals could use to treat employees' symptoms of strain. At the tertiary level it is important that individuals experiencing strain be aware that the symptoms pose a real threat to their overall health and well-being, and seek treatment. The organization can facilitate tertiary interventions by providing education about strain-related illnesses for employees. Tables 7.2 and 7.3 outline the individual and organizational strategies that contribute to successful tertiary stress interventions.

> **tertiary interventions**
> stress intervention techniques that are used to help those individuals who have not been able to manage workplace stress effectively and who are now experiencing symptoms of strain

// SPOTLIGHT ON A STRESSOR: INJUSTICE AT WORK

Recent studies show that employees who experience unfairness in the workplace report higher levels of strain.[40] Indeed, research now shows that exposure to injustice at work is associated with increased risk of death from a cardiac event as well as with increased insomnia.[41] Researchers have long known that unfairness negatively affects employee attitudes, including their commitment to the organization. However, investigations of the relationship between the experience of unfairness at work and employee health are relatively new.

In organizational justice research, "fairness" is not treated as a one-dimensional construct. Researchers in this area focus on three separate categories of fairness judgments that a person can make: (1) the fairness of outcomes, or **distributive justice**, (2) the fairness of processes, or **procedural justice**, and (3) the fairness of interpersonal treatment, or **interactional justice**.[42] All three types of injustice have been associated with increased work stress and strain. Perceived injustice has been associated with increased risk of psychiatric symptoms, high blood pressure, and sickness-related absences from work.[43]

Employees are likely to judge an outcome as unfair when they do not receive a reward or the recognition they feel they deserve. For example, Joe, an employee who has recently put in many extra hours on a project at work, may feel that he deserves a bonus in recognition of his extra effort. If he does not receive it, he may feel that he has been the victim of a *distributive* injustice.

With respect to *procedural* injustice, people arrive at perceptions of fairness by examining several aspects of the process. Procedures that allow employee input; that are consistently implemented across conditions; that are unbiased, accurate, and ethical; that are subject to appeals on the part of those involved; and that are representative of all relevant parties, are viewed as more fair than those that are not.[44] For instance, Ellen would have

> **distributive justice**
> the perceived fairness of outcomes
>
> **procedural justice**
> the perceived fairness of decision-making processes
>
> **interactional justice**
> the perceived fairness of interpersonal treatment

Technology is increasingly blurring the line between "work" and "non-work."

judged the decision to change her work hours from 8 a.m. to 4 p.m. to 9 a.m. to 5 p.m. as more fair had she been told beforehand the reason for the decision and had she been permitted to give her opinion about the potential change.

In terms of *interactional* fairness, individuals judge the fairness of the interpersonal treatment they receive on several levels. For instance, they examine the extent to which their supervisors treat them with kindness and consideration, provide adequate explanations for decisions, and give useful and timely feedback. As an example, Tom is likely to have a better reaction to a negative performance review if his boss delivers that information in a sensitive manner and makes constructive suggestions on how he can improve his performance before the next performance appraisal.

CREATING A FAIR WORKPLACE

Organizations can engage in primary stress interventions by working to reduce occurrences of injustice at work. Organizational leaders should be given training on the importance of fairness at work. Leadership training programs that include a discussion of the value of fair treatment are likely to help leaders see the value of fairness and the damage associated with injustice. The provision of appropriate feedback in a kind and sincere manner can go a long way toward improving an employee's perceptions of interactional justice at work and may have a positive impact on that individual's health.

Organizations can also try to follow decision-making processes that are procedurally fair. For example, they might consider allowing employee representation on committees or decision-making bodies for important organizational procedures. For instance, if an HR manager is considering changing the employee review process, striking a committee that includes representatives from the various stakeholder groups may increase the perceived fairness of the new evaluation process and ultimately the well-being of the employees who undergo the performance review.

// SPOTLIGHT ON A STRESSOR: TECHNOLOGY

Innovations in computer hardware and software have profoundly changed the workplace, including how people do their work and interact with other employees (see **OH&S Today 7.2**).[45] Researchers in occupational health and safety recognize the health risks involved in the increasing presence of technology in the workplace. For instance, increased reliance on computers in the modern work environment has been associated with increased risk for physical health problems. The repetitive movements involved in keyboarding and cursor control place people at risk for musculoskeletal injuries. Carpal tunnel syndrome is an example of a common work-related musculoskeletal disorder that may stem from computer use. (In carpal tunnel syndrome, the median nerve of the arm and hand is compressed.)[46]

Musculoskeletal injuries are a prevalent and costly problem. Individuals with these injuries are sometimes in such chronic pain that they are forced to seek disability leave or early retirement.[47] Workers' compensation claims relating to musculoskeletal disorders can place heavy financial demands on companies and government compensation systems.

TOO MUCH MAIL?

The advent of electronic mail was first hailed as a revolutionary tool that would save time and streamline organizational communication. Few could have predicted just how popular email would become. Daily, worldwide email traffic is now at 141 billion messages. Some estimate that as much of 17% of each workday is spent dealing with emails.

The interruptions and information overload that come with large amounts of email can leave people exhausted and reduce their productivity. Pressures to respond quickly to email can lead to breaches of etiquette such as checking email during meetings or while in face-to-face conversation. One survey found that a majority of individuals have committed email "blunders" (i.e., sending confidential information to the whole company)—perhaps as a result of trying to respond too quickly.

Some companies are trying to combat the proliferation of email. Jon Coleman of Pfizer Canada has requested that staff in his department substantially reduce the number of emails they send over a one-year period. Email at work is bad enough but a growing trend is to receive and reply to emails after work hours, thereby extending the work day for employees and interfering with their home lives.

Pfizer has also introduced a program called Freedom Six to Six, banning email messages between 6 p.m. and 6 a.m. and on weekends. Volkswagon actually blocks its servers from sending email to some employees after work hours. The idea is to allow employees to really disengage from their work and to promote work–life balance—the idea being that employees will thus become more productive while at work.

Sources: CNN, "E-mails Hurt IQ More Than Pot." Found at: http://www.cnn.com/2005/WORLD/europe/04/22/text.iq (accessed May 2, 2013); Robert Half, "Business Etiquette in a Digital Age." Found at https://www.roberthalf.com/sites/default/files/Media_Root/Images/RH-PDFs/RH_BusEtiquette_SEC.pdf (accessed May 2, 2016); BBC, "Volkswagen Turns Off Blackberry Email After Work Hours." Found at http://www.bbc.com/news/technology-16314901 (accessed May 2, 2016).

Preventive solutions are available to employers. A field of study called ergonomics emphasizes the importance of creating workstation arrangements that fit the needs of workers. For instance, computer keyboards and cursor controls are being redesigned with the aim of reducing the likelihood of musculoskeletal strain. Other, more psychological, hazards are discussed in **OH&S Notebook 7.2**.

OH&S NOTEBOOK   7.2

TECHNOLOGY-RELATED STRESSORS

The increasing role of technology in the workplace affects the psychological as well as the physical well-being of workers. Several technology-related factors have been implicated as psychosocial stressors:

- *Malfunctions.* We have all likely experienced the frustration of an ill-timed computer crash. In these types of situations, our increasing reliance on technology to help us complete our work tasks can, in fact, be associated with reduced control at work. When our control over our work environment is reduced, increased stress and strain can result.

- *Isolation.* Our increasing reliance on technology has been associated with increased isolation in

(continued)

the workplace, reducing the incidence of positive social interactions among workers. For instance, employees who rely on computers are often "tied to their desks" to complete their work and thus are available for fewer social interactions with their coworkers.

- *Privacy.* The advanced state of technology in today's workplaces provides new means of employee surveillance and monitoring. Increasingly, organizations are turning to watchdog systems to keep track of things such as the amount of time an employee spends on the phone or email, the number of keystrokes a worker makes at the keyboard in a given amount of time, and the extent to which people use office technology (e.g., the Internet) for non-work-related tasks. In some cases these systems are used for performance monitoring.

- *Increased job demands.* The increasing role of technology in the workplace can also increase the demands associated with a job. (Recall that workload and work pace can be potent psychosocial stressors.) With respect to work pace, technological advances have increased the pace of many jobs. For example, the prevalence of technologies such as email and fax has shortened the expected turnaround times for work-related communications. Also, the need to keep pace with quickly advancing technology increases the workload of some employees.

- *Increased expectations for continuous learning.* Rapid changes in technology may require employees to learn new software, attend additional training, or change their work processes to incorporate new technology on a frequent basis. These changes may be particularly frustrating if employees are still mastering current systems.

Sources: Based on M.D. Coovert and L.F. Thompson, "Technology and Workplace Health," in J.C. Quick and L.E. Tetrick, eds., *Handbook of Occupational Health Psychology* (Washington: APA, 2003), pp. 223–48; A.L. Day, N. Scott, and E.K. Kelloway, "Information and Communication Technology: Implications for Job Stress and Employee Well-Being," in P.L. Perrewe and D.C. Ganster, eds., *New Developments in Theoretical and Conceptual Approaches to Job Stress: Research in Occupational Stress and Well Being*, Vol. 8 (Bingley, U.K.: Emerald, 2010).

// SPOTLIGHT ON A STRESSOR: WORK–FAMILY CONFLICT

For many people, work and family are life's central elements. Recent demographic shifts, such as those outlined in **OH&S Today 7.3**, have increased the extent to which responsibilities to work and those to family interfere with each other. For instance, more and more workers are facing childcare demands, and more and more families are dual-income, and these two circumstances together mean that working parents will sometimes be torn between work demands and childcare responsibilities. For example, a child who is home sick from school may prompt a working parent to miss work to care for the child. Studies suggest that work–family conflict is prevalent among Canadian workers.[48] For example, in one study of the Nova Scotia workforce, half the respondents reported high work–family conflict.[49] Researchers are interested in the factors that contribute to work– family conflict, the outcomes of this type of conflict, and how organizations can help employees meet their multiple work and family roles.

Organizational experts define work–family conflict as a form of inter-role conflict. That is, it is a type of conflict in which the responsibilities of two separate roles are incompatible in some respects. In other words, pressures experienced in the work and family domains are in opposition.[50] Participation in one role is made more difficult by virtue of participation in the other.

WORK–LIFE BALANCE: SOME CANADIAN STATISTICS

Balancing multiple commitments, including work and family, is a reality for Canadians. Here are some Canadian statistics on family, work, and well-being. In a study of more than 25,000 Canadian employees from 71 organizations:

- The typical employee worked just over 50 hours/ week with more than half of the respondents reporting taking work home with them

- 57% of those surveyed reported a high level of stress

- 40% of respondents report high levels of role overload with women reporting more overload than men

- Respondents were twice as likely to let work interfere with family than to let family interfere with work.

- Work family conflict was associated with increased presenteeism and absenteeism

- Women continue to work a "double shift" – doing the same work as men at work but also bearing a disproportionate share of household and child care responsibilities

- Caregiving now includes both child care and caring for sick or disabled relatives

Other important work–family facts include:

- The number of women in the workforce has increased. Women now account for 46% of the workforce, compared with 37% in 1976. In fact, in 1999, 61% of Canadian women with a child under the age of three worked (relative to only 28% in 1976).

- Both men and women in the Canadian labour force have childcare demands. Statistics from the mid-1990s suggest that nearly half of working Canadians have children living in the home. Furthermore, 15% of these individuals also care for elderly family members.

- Almost half of all Canadian children between the ages of one and five are in nonparental care.

- Family-friendly workplace policies are on the rise in Canadian organizations. A survey of Canadian employers found that 88% offer flextime, 50% make provisions for telework, and 63% offer family responsibility leave. However, other data suggest that there is limited access to flexible work arrangements even in organizations that offer this benefit and that the provision of childcare benefits in Canadian workplaces is low, with only 15% of companies indicating they provide on-site or near-site daycares.

Sources: L. Duxbury and C. Higgins, "Revisiting Work-Life Issues in Canada: The 2012 National Study on Balancing Work and Caregiving in Canada." Found at: http://newsroom.carleton.ca/wp-content/files/2012-National-Work-Long-Summary.pdf (accessed May 2, 2016); C. Higgins, L. Duxbury, and S. Lyons, "Reducing Work–Life Conflict: What Works? What Doesn't?" (2008). Found at: http://www.hc-sc.gc.ca/ewh-semt/pubs/occup-travail/balancing-equilibre/index-eng.php (accessed May 2, 2016); K.L. Johnson, D.S. Lero, and J.A. Rooney, *Work-Life Compendium 2001: 150 Canadian Statistics on Work, Family and Well-Being* (Guelph: Centre for Families, Work, and Well-Being, 2001).

Some experts in this area distinguish two categories of work–family conflict.[51] They note that work–family conflict is bi-directional: work may interfere with a person's ability to meet family demands, and family responsibilities may interfere with an individual's ability to keep pace with work demands. These two categories have been labelled **work-to-family conflict** and **family-to-work conflict**, respectively. Work-to-family conflict is a real problem for Canadian families. As indicated in **OH&S Today 7.3**, one in four respondents to a recent national survey reported that their work seriously interferes with their family responsibilities. Another 40% reported that work interferes with their family role to a moderate degree.[52]

work-to-family conflict a form of work–family conflict in which work demands interfere with the fulfillment of family responsibilities

family-to-work conflict a form of work–family conflict in which family demands interfere with the fulfillment of work responsibilities

When people experience two roles at the same time (e.g., employee and parent) then this creates the potential for work–family conflict.

CAUSES OF WORK–FAMILY CONFLICT

Several elements of work and family roles contribute to work–family conflict. One is the amount of time a person spends in each role, or **behavioural involvement** in the role. Generally, more time dedicated to one role means less time available to spend in the other role. Certainly, increased time devoted to work is associated with increased incidence of work-to-family conflict. Similarly, the more time a person spends on family pursuits and responsibilities in the home, the more likely that individual is to experience family-to-work conflict.[53]

A person's **psychological involvement** in work and family roles has also been implicated as a predictor of work–family conflict. Psychological involvement reflects the degree to which a person identifies with a particular role and sees the role as central to his or her self-concept. For example, a woman who considers her status as a mother to be the defining feature in her life has a high degree of psychological involvement in her mother role. A high degree of involvement in one role can cause it to conflict with other responsibilities.

Stress in either the work or the family role is also associated with work–family conflict. In particular, the experience of family-related stress, such as many family demands or dissatisfaction with family life, is associated with family-to-work conflict. Similarly, the experience of work-related stress, such as many work demands or job dissatisfaction, is associated with work-to-family conflict.[54]

behavioural involvement
the amount of time a person spends in a particular role

psychological involvement
the degree to which a person identifies with a particular role and sees the role as a central component of his or her self-concept

OUTCOMES OF WORK–FAMILY CONFLICT

Both work-to-family and family-to-work conflict are associated with negative consequences. Interestingly, the outcomes tend to be in the opposite domain from the cause of the conflict. That is, work-to-family conflict tends to affect family-related outcomes, and family-to-work conflict affects work-related outcomes. For instance, family-to-work conflict is linked with decreased work performance and absenteeism from work. Conversely, work-to-family conflict is associated with reduced performance in the family role and absences from family events.[55]

Although many individuals experience conflict between their work and family roles, it should also be noted that individuals also experience work–family facilitation whereby the skills and feelings experienced in one role improve functioning in another role.[56] For example, a supervisor who has children may be better able to understand the caregiving demands of her employees. People experiencing traumatic events in their personal lives (e.g., the death of a loved one) often report that coming to work allows them to "take their mind off" their grief.

// SUMMARY

In this chapter, we have distinguished among the concepts of stressors in the work environment, the experience of stress, and the possible strain consequences. Whether or not someone perceives an event as stressful, or as a stressor, is individual. Not everyone will react to the same situation in the same way. People must perceive the event to be demanding in some way (e.g., a threat or a challenge) for it to be deemed stressful. As we've discussed, stress is an adaptive and individualistic response to the demands of the objective environment (i.e., stressors). We have also demonstrated that these demands take a variety of forms (acute, daily, chronic, catastrophic).

Stress can have serious consequences. Individuals exposed to continued or high levels of stress develop strain reactions that may be psychological, physical, behavioural, or organizational. In turn, these forms of strain reactions can affect the organization and people's lives. The human and the monetary costs of occupational stress warrant our attention.

Organizationally and individually driven interventions are important to reduce the extent to which stressors exist in the workplace, as well as to minimize the damage caused by unavoidable stressors. Such programs involve primary (preventive) techniques, secondary interventions (to help people avoid the negative consequences of stress), and tertiary programs (to help people find the appropriate treatment when they are experiencing strain). The most successful stress management initiatives involve both the individual employee and the organization as a whole. The organizational responsibility to promote psychologically healthy workplaces is increasingly recognized. For instance, the first Canadian standard on psychological health and safety at work (CSA-Z1003-13) was published in 2013. This standard defines a psychologically healthy workplace and articulates guidelines for management systems to promote and sustain psychological health at work.

Injustice, technology, and work–life conflict are relevant workplace stressors. When reflecting on these stressors, we highlight the individual nature of stress. Not all employees reach the same conclusions about the fairness of a given situation, some employees are not bothered by the increasing technological demands of modern workplaces, and some individuals do not experience high levels of work–life conflict. For others, though, one or more of these stressors present potential health and safety issues in the workplace.

KEY TERMS

behavioural involvement 178
buffer 167
distributive justice 173
family-to-work conflict 177
general adaptation syndrome 166
interactional justice 173
moderator 167
negative affectivity 167
preventive stress management 170
primary interventions 171
procedural justice 173

psychological involvement 178
psychologically healthy and safe workplace 162
psychosocial model of health 162
risk factor 167
secondary interventions 172
strain 168
stress 166
stressor 163
tertiary interventions 173
Type A behaviour 167
work-to-family conflict 177

DISCUSSION QUESTIONS

1. Think of five stressors you have experienced in the past 12 months. Using the guidelines presented in this chapter, categorize the stressors as daily, acute, chronic, or catastrophic. Which, if any, seemed to lead to strain?

2. If only one individual in a workplace is experiencing strain, are the causes of that strain likely to be in the workplace? Why or why not?

3. What are the major stressors in modern workplaces?

4. How does stress manifest itself in behaviour? In organizational functioning?

5. What are some actions that individuals can take to help manage stress? What can organizations do to help employees avoid or manage stress?

6. What are some of the ways in which evolving technology contributes to the experience of workplace stress? What are some interventions that employees and employers might attempt in order to avoid or manage the stress associated with technology?

7. Discuss some emerging stressors in the workplace. How might companies help employees deal with the changing demands of work?

USING THE INTERNET

1. Psychological symptoms have been identified as a health-related outcome of stress. Individuals who feel prolonged stress may experience symptoms such as depression and anxiety. Many employees indicate that they would be uncomfortable telling their boss or coworkers that they are experiencing these types of psychological symptoms because of the associated stigma. Using the website resources of the Canadian Mental Health Association (http://www.cmha.ca), the Canadian Psychiatric Association (http://www.cpa-apc.org), the Canadian Psychological Association (http://www.cpa.ca), the Canadian Centre for Occupational Health and Safety (http://www.ccohs.ca), the Mental Health Commission of Canada (www.mentalhealthcommission.ca), and other websites, design an awareness program that might help reduce the stigma associated with stress-related mental health issues in the workplace.

2. Use Internet resources to find out what you can about CSA-Z1003-13, the Canadian standard for psychological health and safety in the workplace. Some angles you might

consider are the media's response to and coverage of the standard, the response by professional associations (e.g., HR, psychological, or safety associations), and the ways in which particular organizations are implementing the standard.

3. The "sandwich generation" is particularly exposed to issues of work–family conflict. Using Internet resources, define the sandwich generation. Why are they vulnerable to work–family conflict?

EXERCISES

1. Think about your current or most recent job. What are/were some of the pertinent stressors? What actions do/did you take to cope with them? How does/did the organization help you deal with the stress? Talk to some of your friends or members of your family about the stressors they encounter at work and the strategies they and their employers use to manage workplace stress.

2. Returning to work after a stress-related leave can be difficult for both the individuals coming back to work and their coworkers. Create and enact two role-plays in which you and your classmates are employees at an organization. In one of the scenarios, one of the employees is returning to work after a leave due to a stress-related mental health problem. In the second scenario, one of the coworkers is returning to work following a leave due to a car accident. Following the role-plays, discuss each scenario. How did the returning employee feel? What were the responses of the coworkers? Was there a greater sense of discomfort in discussing the well-being of the person who had been on stress leave relative to the person who was in the car accident? Do you think there are taboos about discussing mental health problems in the workplace? In your follow-up discussion, generate ways that organizations and individual employees might make the transition easier for the person returning to work from a stress-related leave.

3. Imagine you are the human resources director for a large organization. You have been given the job of designing and implementing a new performance review system. You know that the employees may find the shift to a new system stressful and that employees often think that performance review instruments are unfair. You are also aware that perceived injustice in the workplace is a stressor, and you would like to minimize the extent to which your employees are exposed to work stress. What might you do to maximize the perceived distributive, procedural, and interactional fairness of the performance review process?

4. Contact the human resources department of an organization. Interview the HR manager about psychosocial hazards in the workplace. Some of the things you should ask about are:

   a. the extent to which he or she considers workplace stress to be a problem in that organization

   b. the types of stressors experienced by the employees in that organization

   c. the types of strain reported by employees

   d. the organizational outcomes of employee stress that the company experiences (e.g., turnover, absenteeism)

   e. the types of interventions the company has to help employees reduce or manage stress

5. Issues of work–family conflict are highly prevalent for parents of young children. To find out more about the experience of work–family conflict, interview a working individual who also has responsibility for childcare. Some questions you might ask include the following:

   a. How many hours per week does the individual spend on paid work?

   b. How many hours per week does the individual spend on childcare activities?

   c. How many hours per week does the individual spend on nonpaid household chores and errands?

   d. If the individual has a spouse, in what ways does the spouse manage the multiple responsibilities of work and family commitments?

   e. What are some of the special challenges the individual encounters in balancing work and family life?

   f. What are some of the strategies the individual uses to meet all of his or her work and family demands?

   g. What efforts does the individual's employer make to help him or her manage work and family demands?

OH&S IN ACTION

As a OHS manager you are responsible for developing programs to improve employee health and well-being. The HR department reports that absenteeism rates are increasing and that the number of long-term disability claims related to mental health has nearly doubled this last year. What would you recommend that the organization do to address these concerns?

CASE STUDY 1   A STRESSFUL JOB

Joan is an emergency room nurse at a busy city hospital. She has always enjoyed the hustle of working in the ER and the challenges of dealing with the unexpected. However, lately, Joan has been worried about her own well-being. She has been very abrupt with her coworkers on several occasions and has had difficulty concentrating on her job. Though there have been no problems to date, Joan is worried that her deteriorating performance might cause a problem, given the critical nature of her work. Her doctor suggested that she take an extended leave because of her "nerves." As the HR representative, what do you think is going on here? Are Joan's concerns likely to be a result of stress? What stressors are present in the environment? If there are 20 employees in ER and Joan is the only one complaining, does this mean that her complaints are not real?

CASE STUDY 2   TECHNOLOGY AT WORK

SmithCorp is a quickly growing organization specializing in pharmaceuticals. The management prides itself on being on the cutting edge. Accordingly, it ensures that all its employees are provided with the latest advances in technology. Employees have laptops, wireless Internet access, BlackBerrys, and cellphones. SmithCorp also often upgrades its software and network systems. Many of the employees rely heavily on this technology and these programs in their daily work. Many of SmithCorp's staff work in sales and product management. They are often on the road visiting client sites and making sales calls. As such, much of the communication among coworkers and between coworkers and managers is technologically mediated. What are some of the potential psychosocial hazards that employees at SmithCorp might face? As an HR manager at Smith-Corp's head office, what types of programs could you implement to help employees manage the stress and strain that may result from exposure to these psychosocial hazards?

CASE STUDY 3   A TOXIC WORKPLACE

Tyrell is a sergeant with a regional police force. He's recently been given the commanding post at a large urban branch. Tyrell has 15 years' experience in the police services with many of those years in management roles. However, the situation he finds at this branch surprises and baffles him. Morale among the officers is extremely low. Several officers are off on long-term stress leave. Serving a high crime area, the officers in this branch often face challenging calls that also receive substantial press coverage. However, Tyrell senses that the problems run deeper than work overload or negative media attention. He notices that some of the male officers are noticeably disrespectful of their female colleagues. He also senses a good deal of animosity among some officers. Two in particular won't even work on the same shift. With some digging around, he finds that one of the two officers in question has alleged harassment from another officer. Tyrell knows that the sergeant who previously had command of the branch took an autocratic approach to leadership and didn't get involved with interpersonal aspects of the workplace. Tyrell sees that his employees are suffering and wants to reach out to them and help improve the situation. He and his wife hosted a potluck for all the officers and staff at their home, but only a few showed up. Tyrell is not sure what to do. Imagine you work in the central office of the force as the HR officer with responsibility for implementing psychologically healthy workplace programs. What advice would you give to Tyrell?

// NOTES

1. S.L. Sauter, L.R. Murphy, and J.J. Hurrell, "Prevention of Work-Related Psychological Disorders: A National Strategy Proposed by the National Institute for Occupational Safety and Health (NIOSH)," *American Psychologist* 45 (1990): 1146–58.

2. American Institute of Stress, *Job Stress* (New York: 2002).

3. Mental Health Commission of Canada, "Mental Health Strategy for Canada" (April 24, 2012). Found at http://www.fcmhs.ca/news/MHCC%20 Strategy%20-%20FINAL%20-%20april%2024%20FINAL%20PDF.pdf (accessed February 8, 2013); and P. Smetanin, D. Stiff, C. Briante, C. Adair, S. Ahmad, and M. Khan, "The Life and Economic Impact of Major Mental Illnesses in Canada: 2011 to 2041," RiskAnalytica, on behalf of the Mental Health Commission of Canada, 2011.

4. E. Anderssen, "Ottawa to Fund Mental-Health Strategy: First-Ever Canadian-wide Standards to Tackle Problem Estimated to Cost $20-Billion a Year in Workplace Losses Alone," *The Globe and Mail* (June 17, 2011).

5. S. Crompton, "What's Stressing the Stressed? Main Sources of Stress Among Workers" Statistics Canada (October 13, 2011). Found at: http://www.statcan.gc.ca/pub/11-008-x/2011002/article/11562-eng.pdf (accessed June 2, 2016).

6. E.K. Kelloway and L. Francis, "Stress and Strain in Nova Scotia Organizations: Results of a Recent Province-Wide Study," paper presented at the Nova Scotia Psychologically Healthy Workplace Conference, Halifax, February 2006.

7. M. Shain, "Tracking the Perfect Legal Storm. Converging Systems Create Mounting Pressure to Create the Psychologically Healthy Workplace, 2010, Calgary, AB. Mental Health Commission of Canada. Found at: http://www.mentalhealthcommission.ca/English/Pages/Mentalhealthintheworkplace.aspx (accessed February 11, 2013).

8. CSA Group, "CAN/CSA-Z1003-13 Psychological Health and Safety in the Workplace–Prevention, Promotion, and Guidance to Staged Implementation" (January 2013).

9. Ibid., p. 4.

10. J.K. Dimoff, E.K. Kelloway, and A.S. MacLellan. "Health and Performance: Science or Advocacy?" *Journal of Organizational Effectiveness: People and Performance*, 1 (2014): 316–34.

11. E.K. Kelloway, "Motivations for Addressing Psychological Health and Safety." Paper presented at the annual convention of the Canadian Psychological Association, Victoria, BC (2016).

12. L.I. Pratt and J. Barling, "Differentiating Between Daily Events, Acute and Chronic Stressors: A Framework and Its Implications," in J.J. Hurrell, L.R. Murphy, S.L. Sauter, and C.L. Cooper, eds., *Occupational Stress: Issues and Development in Research* (London: Taylor and Francis, 1988), 41–53.

13. Ibid.

14. Sauter et al., "Prevention of Work-Related Psychological Disorders."

15. CSA Group, "CAN/CSA-Z1003-13 Psychological Health and Safety in the Workplace–Prevention, Promotion, and Guidance to Staged Implementation" (January 2013).

16. H. Selye, "The General Adaptation Syndrome and Diseases of Adaptation," *Journal of Clinical Endocrinology* 6 (1946): 117; T. Theorell, "To Be Able to Exert Control Over One's Situation: A Necessary Condition for Coping with Stressors," in J.C. Quick and L.E. Tetrick, eds., *Handbook of Occupational Health Psychology* (Washington: American Psychological Association, 2003), 201–20.

17. R.S. Lazarus and S. Folkman, *Stress, Appraisal, and Coping* (New York: Springer, 1984).

18. M.S. Gazzaniga and T.F. Heatherton, *Psychological Science* (New York: Norton, 2003).

19. M. Friedman and R. Rosenman, *Type A Behavior and Your Heart* (New York: Knopf, 1974).

20. R.L. Helmreich, J.T. Spence, and R.S. Pred, "Making It Without Losing It: Type A, Achievement Motivation, and Scientific Attainment Revisited," *Personality and Social Psychology Bulletin* 14 (1988): 495–504.

21. P.A. Landsbergis, P.L. Schnall, K.L. Belkic, D. Baker, J.E. Schwartz, and T.G. Pickering, "Workplace and Cardiovascular Disease: The Relevance and Potential Role for Occupational Health Psychology," in Quick and Tetrick, *Handbook of Occupational Health Psychology*, 2nd ed. (Washington: American Psychological Association, 2011) 243–64; S.D. Bluen, J. Barling, and W. Burns, "Predicting Sales Performance, Job Satisfaction, and Depression Using the Achievement Striving and Impatience-Irritability Dimensions of Type A Behavior," *Journal of Applied Psychology* 75 (1990): 212–16.

22. C.D. Speilberger, P.R. Vagg, and C.F. Wasala, "Occupational Stress: Job Pressures and Lack of Support," in Quick and Tetrick, *Handbook of Occupational Health Psychology*, 185–200.

23. J.C. Wallace, B.D. Edwards, T. Arnold, M.L. Frazier, and D.M. Finch, "Work Stressors, Role-Based Performance, and the Moderating Influence of Organizational Support," *Journal of Applied Psychology* 94 (2009): 254–62.

24. Sauter et al., "Prevention of Work-Related Psychological Disorders."

25. C. Rubino, A. Luksyte, S.J. Perry, and S.D. Volpone, "How Do Stressors Lead to Burnout? The Mediating Role of Motivation," *Journal of Occupational Health Psychology* 14 (2009): 289–304.

26. J.C. Wallace and S.J. Vodanovich, "Can Accidents and Industrial Accidents Be Predicted? Further Investigation into the Relationship Between Cognitive Failures and Reports of Accidents," *Journal of Business and Psychology* 17 (2003): 503–14.

27. T.S. Kristensen, "Job Stress and Cardiovascular Disease: A Theoretical Critical Review," *Journal of Occupational Health Psychology* 3 (1996): 246–60; N. Wager, G. Fieldman, and T. Hussey, "The Effect on Ambulatory Blood Pressure of Working Under Favourably and Unfavourably Perceived Supervisors," *Occupational and Environmental Medicine* 60 (2003): 468–74.

28. S.C. Segerstrom and G.E. Miller, "Psychological Stress and the Human Immune System: A Meta-Analytic Study of 30 Years of Inquiry," *Psychological Bulletin* 130 (2004): 601–30.

29. C.L. Mohren, G.M.H. Swaen, P.J.A. Borm, A. Bast, and J.M.D. Galama, "Psychological Job Demands as a Risk Factor for Common Cold in a Dutch Working Population," *Journal of Psychosomatic Research* 50 (2001): 21–27.

30. M.R. Frone, M.L. Cooper, and M. Russell, "Stressful Life Events, Gender, and Substance Use: An Application of Tobit Regression," *Psychology of Addictive Behaviors* 8 (1984): 59–69; and S. Liu, M. Wang, Y. Zhan, and J. Shi, "Daily Work Stress and Alcohol Use: Testing the Cross-Level Moderation Effects of Neuroticism and Job Involvement," *Personnel Psychology* 62 (2009): 575–97.

31. W. Darr and G. Johns, "Work Strain, Health, and Absenteeism: A Meta-Analysis," *Journal of Occupational Health Psychology* 13 (2008): 293–318; and S. Sonnentag and M. Frese, "Stress in Organizations," in W.C. Borman, D.R. Ilgen, and R.J. Klimoski, eds., *Handbook of Psychology*, vol. 12: *Industrial Organizational Psychology* (New York: Wiley, 2003), 453–91.

32. J.C. Cullen and L.B. Hammer, "Developing and Testing a Theoretical Model Linking Work–Family Conflict to Employee Safety," *Journal of Occupational Health Psychology* 12 (2007): 266–78; and T.M. Probst, "Layoffs and Tradeoffs: Production, Quality, and Safety Demands Under the Threat of Job Loss," *Journal of Occupational Health Psychology* 7 (2002): 211–20.

33. J.C. Quick, J.D. Quick, D.L. Nelson, and J.J. Hurrell, Jr., *Preventive Stress Management in Organizations* (Washington: APA, 1997).

34. CSA Group. "CAN/CSA-Z1003-13 Psychological Health and Safety in the Workplace–Prevention, Promotion, and Guidance to Staged Implementation," January 2013.

35. R.J. Burke, "Organizational-Level Interventions to Reduce Occupational Stressors," *Work and Stress* 7 (1993): 77–87; C.G. Hepburn, C.A. Loughlin, and J. Barling, "Coping with Chronic Work Stress," in B.H. Gottleib, ed., *Coping with Chronic Stress* (New York: Plenum, 1997).

36. C.G. Hepburn, C.A. Loughlin, and J. Barling, "Coping with Chronic Work Stress," in B.H. Gottleib, ed., *Coping with Chronic Stress* (New York: Plenum, 1997).

37. Ibid.

38. Ibid.

39. Quick et al., *Preventive Stress Management in Organizations*.

40. M. Elovainio, M. Kivimäki, and K. Helkama, "Organizational Justice Evaluations, Job Control, and Occupational Strain," *Journal of Applied Psychology* 86 (2001): 418–24; L. Francis and J. Barling, "Organizational Injustice and Psychological Strain," *Canadian Journal of Behavioural Science* 37 (2005): 250–61; B.J. Tepper, "Health Consequences of Organizational Injustice: Tests of Main and Interactive Effects," *Organizational Behavior and Human Decision Processes* 86 (2001): 197–215.

41. M. Elovainio, P. Leino-Arjas, J. Vahtera, and M. Kivimäki, "Justice at Work and Cardiovascular Mortality: A Prospective Cohort Study," *Journal of Psychosomatic Research* 61 (2006): 271–74; J. Greenberg, "Losing Sleep over Organizational Injustice: Attenuating Insomniac Reactions to Underpayment Inequity with Supervisory Training in Interactional Justice," *Journal of Applied Psychology* 91 (2006): 58–69.

42. R. Cropanzano and J. Greenberg, "Progress in Organizational Justice: Tunneling Through the Maze," in C.L. Cooper and I.T. Robertson, eds., *International Review of Industrial and Organizational Psychology*, vol. 12 (London: Wiley, 1997), 317–72.

43. J.E. Ferrie, J. Head, M.J. Shipley, J. Vahtera, M.G. Marmot, and M. Kivimäki, "Injustice at Work and Incidence of Psychiatric Morbidity: The Whitehall II Study," *Occupational and Environmental Medicine* 63 (2006): 443–50; M. Kivimäki, M. Elovainio, J. Vahtera, and J.E. Ferrie, "Organizational Justice and the Health of Employees: Prospective Cohort Study," *Occupational and Environmental Medicine* 60 (2003): 27–34; N. Wager, G. Fieldman, and T. Hussey, "The Effect on Ambulatory Blood Pressure of Working Under Favourably and Unfavourably Perceived Supervisors," *Occupational and Environmental Medicine* 60 (2003): 468–74.

44. G.S. Leventhal, J. Karuza, and W.R. Fry, "Beyond Fairness: A Theory of Allocation Preferences," in G. Mikula, ed., *Justice and Social Interaction* (New York: Springer, 1980), 167–218; J. Thibaut and L. Walker, *Procedural Justice: A Psychological Analysis* (Hillsdale: Erlbaum, 1975).

45. M.D. Coovert and L.F. Thompson, "Technology and Workplace Health," in Quick and Tetrick, *Handbook of Occupational Health Psychology*, 221–41.

46. Ibid.

47. H. Brenner and W. Ahern, "Sickness Absence and Early Retirement on Health Grounds in the Construction Industry in Ireland," *Occupational and Environmental Medicine* 57 (2000): 615–20.

48. L. Duxbury and C. Higgins, "Work–Life Conflict in Canada in the New Millennium: A Status Report (Final Report)," Public Health Agency of Canada (2003). Found at http://www.phac-aspc.gc.ca/-publicat/work-travail/index.html (accessed February 16, 2007).

49. Kelloway and Francis, "Stress and Strain."

50. M.R. Frone, "Work–Family Balance," in Quick and Tetrick, *Handbook of Occupational Health Psychology*, 143–62.

51. M.R. Frone, J.K. Yardley, and K. Markel, "Developing and Testing an Integrative Model of Work–Family Interface," *Journal of Vocational Behavior* 54 (1997): 145–67.

52. Duxbury and Higgins, "Work–Life Conflict in Canada."

53. Frone, "Work–Family Balance."

54. Frone et al., "Developing and Testing an Integrative Model of Work–Family Interface."

55. Frone, "Work–Family Balance."

56. J.H. Wayne, J.G. Grzywacz, D.S. Carlson, and K.M. Kacmar, "Work–Family Facilitation: A Theoretical Explanation of Primary Antecedents and Consequences. *Human Resource Management Review*, 17 (2007): 63–76.

CHAPTER

8

WORKPLACE VIOLENCE, AGGRESSION, AND HARASSMENT

CHAPTER LEARNING OBJECTIVES

AFTER READING THIS CHAPTER, YOU SHOULD BE ABLE TO:

- define and distinguish among violence, aggression, and harassment
- identify the risk factors for workplace violence
- explain the idea of imminent risk
- describe ways to reduce the risk of workplace violence
- define sexual harassment
- describe what organizations should do to reduce the incidence of workplace sexual harassment

WORKPLACE HARASSMENT

At least three Canadian institutions have been rocked by accusations of workplace harassment. Linda Davidson, one of only nine women to rise to the rank of inspector in the RCMP, is the lead plaintiff in a suit alleging that she, and others, were subject to repeated sexual harassment and bullying throughout her career. Similarly, there have been repeated complaints about sexual harassment in the Canadian Armed Forces, leading to charges against individuals; investigations; and new, more stringent, policies.

Most recently, the Canadian Olympic Committee has introduced new policies in the wake of repeated complaints that senior managers engaged in both harassment and bullying behaviours in the workplace.

These cases tell us at least two things about harassment and aggression in Canadian workplaces. First, harassment is widespread and is experienced by a large number of individuals regardless of their status within the organization. Second, behaviours that may once have been considered "normal" or "part of the culture" are no longer tolerated. Indeed, Canadian jurisdictions have increasingly passed legislation giving employees legal recourse when they are subject to workplace harassment.

Increasingly we recognize that hostile interactions (e.g., yelling) in the workplace may constitute harassment or bullying.

Source: CBC News, "Canadian Forces Investigates 8 Sexual Misconduct complaints." Found at: http://www.cbc.ca/news/politics/progress-report-sexual-misconduct-investigations-1.3428532 (accessed May 2, 2016); *National Post*, "RCMP Dogged by Second Class-Action Lawsuit Alleging Rampant Sexual Harassment." Found at: http://news.nationalpost.com/news/canada/rcmp-dogged-by-second-class-action-lawsuit-alleging-rampant-sexual-harassment (accessed May 2, 2016); CBC, "Canadian Olympic Committee Hopes Latest Reforms Quiet Critics." Found at: http://www.cbc.ca/sports/olympics/canadian-olympic-committee-changes-1.3542952 (accessed May 2, 2016).

The postal shootings of the mid-1990s and the resulting popularization of the phrase "going postal" to describe an enraged state were, arguably, the defining moments that focused organizational and research attention on the notion of workplace violence and aggression.[1] However, the postal shootings were not the last highly publicized incidents of workplace violence. In Canada, tragic incidents such as the OCTranspo shootings (in which an employee of OCTranspo killed four coworkers and injured two others), the murders at Concordia (in which a faculty member killed four colleagues), and the shootings at the L'École Polytechnique (in which 28 people were shot and 14 women died) served to focus public and media attention on the phenomenon of workplace violence.

Though such tragic acts are extremely serious and call for action to understand their causes and prevent their occurrence, the available evidence suggests that they are actually quite rare. While there are approximately 14 workplace homicides each year in Canada, other acts of physical violence and workplace aggression are considerably more prevalent.[2] Not surprisingly, many jurisdictions have enacted health and safety legislation requiring employers to deal with issues of workplace violence and aggression.

// DEFINING WORKPLACE AGGRESSION AND VIOLENCE

Legislative approaches differ in how broadly they define workplace **violence** and **aggression**. Nova Scotia, for example, has adopted a very narrow definition that focuses solely on acts or threats of physical assault. Thus, Nova Scotia's legislation focuses solely on workplace violence.[3] Other jurisdictions, such as Quebec and Ontario, focus more broadly on acts of workplace aggression. Schat and Kelloway have defined workplace aggression as "behaviour by an individual or individuals within or outside an organization that is intended to physically or psychologically harm a worker or workers and occurs in a work-related context".[4] Accordingly, all violent behaviours are, by definition, aggressive, whereas not all aggressive behaviours are violent. In Canada, legislation enacted in Quebec, Ontario, and the federal jurisdiction uses the term **harassment**, which is another term for aggression. In Ontario, for example, harassment is defined as vexatious (i.e., annoying or embarrassing) conduct that is unwelcome.

A host of other terms are commonly used to describe some aspects of workplace aggression.[5] For example, articles in the popular press often refer to workplace bullying and the similar constructs of workplace abuse as **emotional abuse**, mistreatment, victimization, and **mobbing** (a term used in Europe to describe bullying). Though there are slight variations in the definitions of these terms, Keashly suggests that they generally refer to "interactions between organizational members that are characterized by repeated hostile verbal and nonverbal, often non-physical behaviours directed at a person(s) such that the target's sense of him/herself as a competent worker and person is negatively affected".[6] Thus, **bullying** and these other constructs are defined as repeated behaviours that are explicitly nonphysical, are perpetrated solely by organizational members, and occur over a prolonged period of time (e.g., six months).[7]

Workplace **incivility** is another construct that is conceptually related to workplace aggression. It is defined as "low-intensity deviant behaviour with ambiguous intent to harm the target, in violation of workplace norms for mutual respect. Uncivil behaviours are characteristically rude and discourteous, displaying a lack of regard for others".[8] Incivility can be a precursor to more serious forms of aggression.[9] This suggests that if aggressive behaviour is classified along a continuum of severity or intensity, incivility would represent the low end of this continuum.

Recently, a number of researchers have included sexual harassment behaviours in their definitions and operationalizations of workplace violence and aggression.[10] Workplace **sexual harassment**—which consists of **gender harassment**, **unwanted sexual attention**, and **sexual coercion**[11]—is a unique form of workplace aggression characterized by sexualized or sex-related behaviour. Though we include workplace sexual harassment in this chapter, much of the existing literature and legislation has emerged separately from that on workplace aggression. Therefore, we consider harassment on its own at the end of this chapter.

// THE PREVALENCE OF WORKPLACE AGGRESSION

Until recently, estimates of the prevalence of workplace aggression varied widely and were of dubious credibility. Accurate surveillance of the forms and frequency of workplace violence requires representative sampling procedures and standardized definitions,

---

violence
an actual physical assault or threat of an assault

aggression
behaviour by an individual or individuals within or outside an organization that is intended to physically or psychologically harm a worker or workers and that occurs in a work-related context

harassment
engaging in annoying or embarrassing conduct against a worker in a workplace—conduct that is known or ought reasonably to be known to be unwelcome

emotional abuse
another term for bullying

mobbing
a term used mainly in Europe to refer to bullying

bullying
aggressive, nonphysical behaviours perpetrated by organizational members over a prolonged period of time

incivility
rude or discourteous behaviour

sexual harassment
intentional, persistent, and unwelcome sexual conduct or remarks that occur despite resistance from the victim

gender harassment
comments or actions seen as creating a hostile environment based on gender

unwanted sexual attention
persistent and unwelcome sexual comments or attention

---

measures, and reporting mechanisms.[12] The most accurate estimates of the prevalence of workplace violence will be derived from large samples constructed so as to represent a known population. Data from three such surveys (one American and two Canadian) are available that provide some evidence for prevalence rates. Although these studies are becoming dated, they still represent the best available data about the prevalence of workplace violence and aggression.

U.S. PREVALENCE DATA

Schat, Frone, and Kelloway reported a detailed analysis of a large, nationally representative sample of workers in the United States.[13] They asked a series of questions about the experience of both workplace violence and workplace aggression. Their operational definition of workplace violence focused solely on physical assaults (i.e., excluding threats). Respondents were asked to indicate how frequently somebody at work had "(a) Pushed you, grabbed you, or slapped you in anger; (b) Kicked you, bit you, or hit you with a fist; (c) Hit you with an object, tried to hit you with an object, or threw an object at you in anger; and (d) Attacked you with a knife, gun, or another weapon."

Overall, they reported that 6% of the sample—corresponding to just under 7 million American workers—experienced these forms of workplace violence in the course of year.[14] Turning to the four specific physically aggressive behaviours examined in the survey, assault with an object was the most common, being reported by 4.2% of respondents. Being pushed, grabbed, or slapped in anger was reported by 3.9% of respondents; being kicked, hit, or bitten was reported by 3%; and being attacked with a knife, gun, or other weapon was reported by 0.7%.

Schat and colleagues also reported on workplace aggression, which they termed "psychological abuse."[15] Their measure included items such as "Shouted obscenities at you or screamed at you in anger; Insulted you or called you names in front of other people; Made an indirect or hidden threat, such as saying that 'something bad' would happen to you; Threatened to hit you or throw something at you; and Threatened you with a knife, gun, or another weapon." They found that 41% of their sample (representing 47 million workers) reported experiencing workplace aggression as measured by these items. About 35% reported being screamed at, and 24.4% being insulted. Fewer respondents reported being the victim of a hidden threat (12.2%), a threat of violence (7.6%), or a threat of an attack with a weapon (1.9%).

CANADIAN DATA

Though there are no comparable national studies of workplace violence in Canada, Francis and Kelloway conducted a large study of 1400 Nova Scotian workers.[16] The sample was drawn to match population parameters in terms of gender and geographic distribution within the province. The researchers defined violence in accordance with Nova Scotian legislation, which includes both physical assault and the threat of physical assault. Just under 21% of the respondents reported experiencing some form of physical violence:

- 9% reported being hit, kicked, punched, or shoved.
- 12% had objects thrown at them.

- 12.6% had been threatened with physical assault.
- 2.7% had been threatened with a weapon.

Francis and Kelloway also examined a wide variety of aggressive but nonviolent behaviours.[17] The results were strikingly different from those for violence—79.2% of the sample reported experiencing some form of aggressive behaviour in the workplace. Among their participants, they found that:

- 60.7% reported being glared at.
- 43.5% reported being given the silent treatment.
- 36.4% reported being the target of false accusations.
- 27.1% reported being the target of obscene gestures.
- 26.8% reported being refused needed resources.
- 27.6% reported being made fun of.
- 56.3% reported having their sense of judgment questioned.
- 25.2% reported being assigned meaningless tasks.
- 51.6% reported having their opinions dismissed.
- 37.5% reported having bad things said about them.
- 15.0% reported being told they were incompetent.
- 36.7% reported being teased.
- 44.9% reported being treated with disrespect.
- 30.9% reported someone taking credit for their ideas.

> **Type I violence**
> violence committed by someone with no legitimate relationship to the organization, often while committing another criminal act
>
> **Type II violence**
> violence committed by clients or customers of the organization
>
> **Type III violence**
> violence committed by coworkers (e.g., other employees of the organization)

Clearly, there appears to be more violence and aggression in Canadian workplaces than in American workplaces. Though the Nova Scotian results may not generalize to the rest of Canada, there are at least two sources of converging evidence. First, Statistics Canada's study of criminal victimization in Canadian workplaces also reported that 17% of all violent victimizations happened in workplaces.[18] This represents approximately 356 000 incidents of workplace violence in a 12-month period in Canada. Of these, 71% were physical (i.e., nonsexual) assaults. Second, in a study of Canadian public sector employees, 69% responded that they had experienced some form of verbal workplace aggression.[19]

Type 1 violence occurs from members of the public—often during the commission of a crime such as robbery.

SOURCES OF WORKPLACE VIOLENCE

A common approach to categorizing workplace violence focuses on the relationship between the assailant and the victim (see **Table 8.1**).[20] Here, various "types" of violence are considered based on who the perpetrator is.

Type I violence is associated with criminal activity; an assault or homicide that occurs in the context of a robbery is an example of Type I violence. Type II violence is also committed by a non-organizational member but is not typically associated with other forms of criminal activity. It is sometimes referred to as "client-perpetrated violence." An example would be a patient who assaults a health care worker. Type III violence is violence perpetrated by

TABLE 8.1

THE CAL/OSHA FRAMEWORK	
TYPE	**RELATIONSHIP OF ASSAILANT TO THE ORGANIZATION**
Type 1	Member of the public with no legitimate relationship to the organization, usually committing a criminal act
Type 2	Member of the public who receives legitimate service from the organization (e.g., client, patient)
Type 3	An employee or former employee of the organization
Type 4	The spouse or partner of an employee

Source: State of California, "Cal/OSHA Guidelines for Workplace Security," (1995). Found at: http://www.dir.ca.gov/dosh/dosh_publications/worksecurity.html.

OH&S NOTEBOOK   8.1

INTIMATE PARTNER VIOLENCE

For many individuals, work is a "social address." That is, partners or family members know where the person works and, often, his or her schedule. Lifetime prevalence rates of partner violence have been estimated at 25% for women and 8% for men.[21] Intimate partners are identified as the perpetrator in 1% to 3% of all workplace violence incidents.[22] Also, women are five times more likely than men to be attacked at work by a current or former intimate partner.[23]

There are several ways that intimate partner violence plays out in the workplace. First, because work is a social address, acts of intimate partner violence can occur in the workplace when one partner shows up there and assaults the other. Second, a partner may stalk the other person, including by sending emails and text messages to the workplace and by waiting outside for the partner. A third form of intimate partner violence is sabotaging the other's ability to get to, or do, work. Denying access to a home computer or hiding the car keys are frequently noted ways of sabotaging a partner. Fourth and finally, even when events do not occur in the workplace, individuals victimized by a partner are unlikely to be able to perform their work to their full potential as a result of the ongoing strain involved.

organizational "insiders"; examples include coworker assaults as well as tragedies such as the post office murders of the 1990s. Finally, Type IV violence is committed by the spouse or partner of the victim and is more properly seen as family/spousal or intimate partner violence that happens to occur in the workplace (see **OH&S Notebook 8.1**).

The CAL/OSHA framework excludes violence that occurs during a labour dispute, which is in several respects a unique form of workplace violence.[24] Picket line violence has been defined as the "non-privileged physical interference with the person or property of another, or the threat, express or implied of such interference" (p. 14).[25] Labour disputes tend to involve two broad categories of violent acts: confrontational and purposeful. Confrontational violence breaks out at the spur of the moment during a conflict. For instance, following a trade of verbal insults, a group

> **Type IV violence** violence committed by the spouse or partner of the victim

of picketers may throw rocks at line crossers. In contrast, purposeful violence is planned and deliberate.[26] Both forms tend to result in interpersonal attacks. Picket line violence is thought to occur most often when individuals (e.g., management or replacement workers) are trying to cross a picket line during a strike. Violence during labour disputes seems to have diminished over time, with a sharp decrease since 1995.[27] However, violence remains a real possibility during a labour dispute. Indeed, there is some speculation that picket line violence is "legitimated" by labour legislation and/or court rulings that do not discipline the participants in violent confrontations.[28]

PREVALENCE BY SOURCE

Though researchers have tried to estimate the prevalence of workplace violence by source, the most common distinction is between violence perpetrated by coworkers (Type III) and violence perpetrated by members of the public (Types I and II). The results of these analyses uniformly suggest that workplace violence is overwhelmingly perpetrated by members of the public. Respondents to the Canadian Public Service Employment Survey reported that violence was most likely from clients, residents, or other members of the public (approximately 71% of those reporting workplace violence) rather than from coworkers (approximately 34% of those reporting workplace violence).[29]

Analyses of American prevalence data suggest that an individual is four times more likely to be assaulted by a member of the public than by a coworker.[30] Results by source from the Nova Scotia Stress Survey are shown in **Figure 8.1**.[31] All four forms of physical violence were more likely to be experienced at the hands of members of the public.

FIGURE 8.1

PREVALENCE OF WORKPLACE VIOLENCE BY SOURCE OF PERPETRATOR

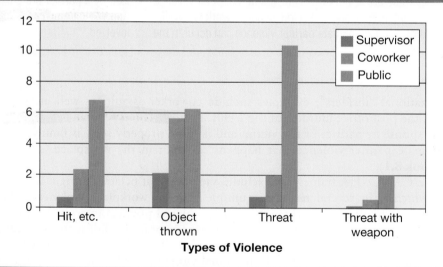

Source: L. Francis and E.K. Kelloway, "The Nova Scotia Workplace Stress Survey," (Halifax: Saint Mary's University, 2007).

// RISK FACTORS FOR WORKPLACE AGGRESSION

Most workplace homicides in the United States are perpetrated by members of the public during the commission of a robbery or similar crime.[32] Employees in the retail (e.g., convenience stores), service (e.g., restaurants), security (protective agencies), and transportation (e.g., taxi) sectors are at highest risk.[33]

Robbery is the primary risk factor for occupational homicide. It is not, however, the primary risk factor for nonfatal assaults—providing service, care, advice, or education can place employees at increased risk for assault, especially if clients, customers, inmates, or patients are experiencing frustration, insecurity, or stress.[34] Industries reporting high rates of nonfatal assaults include health care, education, social services, and law enforcement.[35]

SAV-T(1) AND SAV-T(2): THE RISK OF VIOLENCE

Since violence and aggression tend to be perpetrated by members of the public, the first overall risk factor is working with the general public. The acronym SAV-T has been suggested as a way of understanding the more specific risks associated with situations or occupations. With respect to situational risk, SAV-T[36] (refers to the increased risk of workplace violence associated with Scheduling, Authority, Valuables, and Taking Care of Others).

SCHEDULING

Individuals who work alone or at night and on weekends are at increased risk for violence. Taxi drivers, for example, often work at night and almost always work alone. They have long been identified as among those at greatest risk for workplace violence.

AUTHORITY

Individuals who have authority over others, who are in a position to deny services or requests, who supervise or discipline others, or who make decisions that influence others' lives are at increased risk for workplace violence. A social worker who decides whether a client gets benefits, an emergency room nurse who controls access to treatment, and wait staff at a bar who have to "cut off" a patron who has had too much to drink are all at increased risk because of their authority.

VALUABLES

Individuals who work around valuable products or objects are at increased risk of violence largely because the risk of criminal activity is greater. Valuables include objects as diverse as prescription medications, cigarettes, alcohol, weapons, and, of course, money.

Taxi drivers are at high risk of violence because they work alone, at night, often around people who might be intoxicated, and they carry money.

Providing physical or emotional care for others, especially if such care is outside a traditional workplace (e.g., home-based health care), puts individuals at increased risk for workplace violence and aggression. For example, nurses who provide both physical and emotional care are at very high risk of violence.

IMMINENT RISK

It is useful to understand which tasks increase the risk of workplace aggression; even so, there are limits to this analytical approach. For example, a nurse who provides care for patients is at increased risk, *but* (a) most of the time these risks do not translate into workplace violence, and (b) the nurse cannot stop providing care in order to manage the risk. In occupations that are inherently risky (e.g., working in psychiatric or correctional facilities), the focus has turned to the prediction of "imminent risk."[37]

> **imminent risk**
> the short-term risk of violence occurring in the current situation
>
> **assault cycle**
> a model suggesting that violence occurs only after a period of escalation

The assessment of imminent risk is conceptually grounded in the assault cycle, a model that identifies the escalation of violence from aggression to physical attack (see **Figure 8.2**).[38] Models based on the assault cycle typically point to the escalation of violence interactions from a triggering event through an escalation phase to a crisis or assault. The assault cycle tells us that (a) that aggression can escalate into violence, and (b) violence does not "come out of nowhere"–rather, there are clear signs that individuals

FIGURE 8.2

THE ASSAULT CYCLE

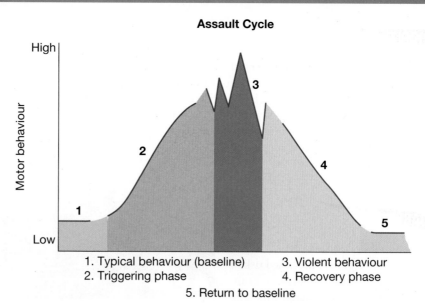

Assault Cycle

Motor behaviour (High / Low)

1. Typical behaviour (baseline)
2. Triggering phase
3. Violent behaviour
4. Recovery phase
5. Return to baseline

Source: Harold Hall, Pacific Institute for the Study of Conflict and Aggression, 2011.

are increasingly likely to become violent. By recognizing these signs, employees may be alerted to the increased risk.

The SAV-T acronym has also been used as a means of identifying the imminent risk of workplace violence (Swearing, Agitation, Volume, Threat) based on the assault cycle.[39] During the escalation phase of the assault cycle, individuals are more likely to use profane or obscene language, to show physical signs of agitation (e.g., getting red in the face, fidgeting or pacing, clenching fists, unable to keep still), and to begin shouting or talking loudly (see **OH&S Notebook 8.2**). Employees are advised to recognize these signs and to respond by establishing clear boundaries (e.g., pointing out that profane language or shouting is unacceptable, asking individuals to calm themselves), engaging in defusing, and alerting supervisors or coworkers to the situation. The more critical behaviours (swearing, agitation, shouting) present, the more employees should be concerned about the potential for violence.

Almost all acts of violence are preceded by a direct threat, and the articulation of that threat calls for the immediate cessation of the interaction. Employees should immediately escape from the situation and/or alert security personnel where appropriate. Employees should not try to defuse or reason with an individual who has uttered a threat—at this point, the time for managing the interaction has passed and employees should take immediate action to protect themselves. Though many threats may be uttered in the "heat of the moment" and not be serious, every threat should be interpreted as the onset of a violent interaction.

OH&S NOTEBOOK   8.2

MANAGING IMMINENT RISK

During the escalation phase of a conflict, individuals typically engage in swearing, are agitated, and increase the volume of their voice. As these behaviours occur, employees can respond in the following ways:

- Practise empathic listening.
  Avoid being judgmental.
  Give your undivided attention.
  Focus on feelings.
  Use silence.
  Use restatement.

- Set limits.
  Explain which behaviour is inappropriate.
  Explain why the behaviour is inappropriate.
  Give reasonable choices and consequences.
  Allow time to choose.
  Enforce consequences.

- Defuse.
  Get the individual to say "yes."
  Remain calm.
  Help the individual save face.
  Use humour.
  Use distraction/make requests.
  Provide a nonviolent and productive course of action.
  Go from "light" to "heavy" interventions.

If the situation continues to escalate even when these responses have been tried, a supervisor and/or security personnel should be summoned. If the individual utters a threat or if at any time the employee feels threatened, the interaction should be brought to an immediate end.

// PREVENTION

TYPE I VIOLENCE

Because most workplace homicides occur during the commission of a robbery, actions aimed at preventing robberies will likely reduce the number of workplace homicides.[40] Robbery reduction strategies typically focus on increasing the risks, reducing the rewards, and increasing the effort associated with robbery.[41] Because risk factors for robbery differ among workplaces, no single strategy is appropriate for all organizations and prevention strategies must be customized to worksites. That being said, three principles—increasing visibility, reducing rewards, and hardening targets—underlie most robbery reduction strategies.[42]

INCREASING VISIBILITY

Increasing visibility is thought to increase the perceived risks for potential criminals, thereby deterring crime. For example, for taxi drivers, means of increasing visibility include external emergency lights; global positioning system (GPS) that allows the location of a driver in distress to be pinpointed; and in-car surveillance cameras that make it possible to identify perpetrators. Data from Australia and Canada confirm the effectiveness of surveillance cameras in taxis as a means of reducing assaults on taxi drivers. Crimes against taxi drivers have been reduced by more than 50% since the implementation of a bylaw in Toronto, Ontario, requiring taxi owners to install either security cameras or GPS in their cars.[43]

In retail establishments, increasing visibility has meant increasing the chances of someone witnessing a crime. Most crimes occur late at night when there are few potential witnesses. Keeping windows clear of signs (e.g., advertisements) to allow passersby to see inside, and locating the cash register in a location that can be seen from the outside (e.g., in the centre of the store) are means of increasing visibility. Closed circuit televisions and video cameras may also deter criminal behaviour by increasing would-be robbers' perceptions of risk.[44] Clerk behaviour can also communicate visibility. Common recommendations are that clerks make eye contact with customers and greet them as they enter the store, thereby making would-be robbers feel conspicuous.[45]

A recommendation that remains contentious is that all retail outlets be required to employ two clerks during evening and night shifts to reduce the incidence of robberies. Industry associations and individual store owners resist this suggestion, pointing out (a) that there is limited empirical evidence supporting the utility of the two-clerk provision, (b) that hiring two clerks is expensive, and (c) that employing more than one clerk increases the number of workers exposed to robbery-related violence.[46] A more effective recommendation may be to ensure that commercial establishments have implemented work-alone procedures designed to ensure the safety of employees. For example, under regulations being

© Patti McConville/Alamy Stock Photo

Type 1 violence is countered by increasing visibility including the use of surveillance cameras.

implemented in British Columbia, late-night retail establishments are required to (a) have two employees working in the store at night, or (b) have the employee separated from the public by a locked barrier or door. The comparable legislation in Nova Scotia does not dictate a particular solution but mandates that employers take steps to mitigate the risk of working alone.

TARGET HARDENING

Target hardening strategies focus on physical designs that make it difficult to assault employees. For example, protective screens have been found to reduce the number of assaults experienced by taxi drivers. Opinions on screens remain mixed, however.[47] Many taxi drivers and customers do not like them because they can restrict air circulation, leave little leg room, and limit communication between drivers and passengers.

In retail environments, strategies that make flight difficult may deter robbers.[48] Potential strategies to make retail stores less attractive targets include blocking off laneways and using speed bumps in parking lots. Revolving doors and longer rather than shorter distances between the cash register and the exit may also help deter crime.

Besides preventing robberies, some target hardening strategies may reduce the likelihood that employees will be hurt during the commission of a robbery. Installing high and wide counters, with raised floors on the employee side, to prevent robbers from jumping over counters to assault employees, is an effective means of protecting workers. So is installing a bullet-resistant barrier.

Employee training is another form of target hardening. Such training typically focuses on general safety precautions and on behaviour during a robbery or threatened assault. Having instructions on how to behave may give employees a sense of control of the situation and lessen the possibility that they will be injured. Employee training should stress cooperation with robbers, since there is ample evidence that employees who do cooperate sustain fewer injuries.[49] Workers should also be told not to make any sudden moves during a robbery, to keep their hands in plain sight at all times, and to inform the robbers of what they are doing when they are doing it. Staff should also be told to activate the silent alarm only when it is safe to do so. Employees should also be aware that it is not constructive to confront shoplifters.

TYPE II VIOLENCE

Service providers—health care workers, teachers, social service workers, prison guards, and police officers—are among the most common victims of nonfatal workplace violence. In the United States in 2000, 48% of all nonfatal assaults occurred in the health care and social service industries.[50]

There are three general approaches to preventing or dealing with Type II violence: environmental, organizational and administrative, and behavioural. Several factors increase risk for care or service providers. For example, staff may be at risk when they attempt to set limits on behaviour (e.g., tobacco use), especially if the employee's actions are perceived as unfair or unreasonable. Violence can also occur when a client is involuntarily admitted to the hospital, or confined. Long waits for service may result in frustration and increase the propensity for patients and visitors to become aggressive.

Surveillance systems may also be used in hospitals and other public buildings where there is increased risk of violence.

ENVIRONMENTAL STRATEGIES

Security devices that may reduce employee risk include metal detectors, surveillance cameras, and bullet-resistant glass surrounding reception areas and nursing stations. Other suggestions include effective lighting both inside and outside hospitals, and curved mirrors at hallway intersections. The presence of security personnel may be effective at preventing assaults. Card-controlled entrances and security checks for identification can be used to limit public access to restricted areas.[51]

Given long waiting times, hospitals should provide patients and their families with comfortable waiting rooms designed to minimize stress (e.g., soothing colours on walls; toys for children to play with; reading materials). Waiting areas and patient care rooms should be designed with safety in mind: furniture should be lightweight, have few sharp edges, and be laid out to ensure that staff cannot be trapped in rooms. Rooms and waiting areas should be sparsely decorated (e.g., few pictures on the walls or vases on the tables) to limit the number of possible weapons that can be used against staff. Patient care rooms should have two exits and be equipped with phones and panic buttons.[52]

ORGANIZATIONAL/ADMINISTRATIVE STRATEGIES

Organizations should establish policies and practices to prevent aggression. A written policy should outline what constitutes unacceptable behaviour in the workplace, and clients, visitors, and employees should be aware of the document. Policies that encourage the reporting of violence are also necessary, and management should stress to employees the importance of reporting acts of aggression. Management should take all reports of aggression seriously and ensure that employees are aware of the organization's

BEST PRACTICES IN MANAGING WORKPLACE VIOLENCE

As a result of both legislative changes and concern for employee well-being, many Canadian organizations have implemented some form of policy for dealing with workplace violence and aggression. Organizations are required to comply with legislative requirements. Beyond that, an effective approach to dealing with workplace violence and aggression would include the following:

- A *policy statement* that clearly identifies violent and aggressive behaviour as unacceptable in the workplace. The statement should be clearly posted in the workplace and should apply both to employees and to members of the public.

- A *risk assessment* that considers the organization's history of violence and aggression, the nature of tasks performed in the workplace, and any special circumstances that may temporarily or permanently change these risks.

- *Risk mitigation* strategies specifically designed to reduce or mitigate the risks identified in the risk assessment.

- *Training for both employees and managers* in recognizing and managing risks and in applying the policy.

- An *emergency response plan* that deals with violent incidents in progress and also their aftermath. The plan should include provisions for escape/evacuation, for calling security/police forces, for treating physical injuries, and so on.

- *Follow-up procedures* to ensure that victims receive appropriate physical and psychological treatment, that risks are reassessed following an incident, that all incidents are documented and reported to appropriate authorities, and that all aspects of the workplace violence management plan are current and effective.

---

commitment to safety. It is not uncommon for employees to express concerns about reporting incidents of violence, because they fear their employers will assume that they provoked the incident. Organizations also need to have detailed plans for dealing with violent attacks when they occur and should develop procedures to ensure the sharing of information about violent or potentially violent clients (see **OH&S Notebook 8.3**).

When service providers, such as health care workers, work inside patients' homes, access to protections of the sort available to employees who work in traditional organizational settings is delayed or limited at best.[53] Therefore organizations need to establish policies and procedures for home health care providers. For example, home care workers could be required to keep a designated colleague informed of their whereabouts throughout their work shift. Workers should be accompanied to a patient's home by a coworker or a police escort if their personal safety may be threatened. In a similar vein, employees should be prohibited from working alone in emergency areas or walk-in clinics, especially during late night and early morning shifts. Policies and practices should be in place to restrict public (e.g., patients, visitors) movement in hospitals.[54]

BEHAVIOURAL/INTERPERSONAL STRATEGIES

Besides providing staff with necessary knowledge and skills, training may give employees the confidence to deal with potentially dangerous situations. One study found that hospital workers who received training targeting workplace violence reported higher levels of perceived control compared to workers who did not receive training. In that study, perceptions of control were positively correlated with employee emotional well-being and negatively associated with employee fear of future violence.[55]

Staff should be taught customer service skills, how to resolve conflicts, how to recognize escalating agitation, and how to manage and respond to aggressive behaviour.[56] Since violence is related to wait times, staff should provide patients and their families with sufficient information when there are going to be long delays for service (e.g., explain how long the delay will be and why there is a long delay). Employees who have direct patient contact (e.g., security guards, nurses, orderlies) should also be trained how and when to physically restrain patients.

TYPE III VIOLENCE

Though violence and aggression committed by coworkers is uncommon compared to that committed by organizational outsiders, it can happen, so a comprehensive workplace violence program needs to address the potential for coworker aggression and violence. Reviews generally point to the fact that coworkers do not act aggressively; rather, they react to certain situations in an aggressive way.[57] Triggers for workplace aggression include unfair treatment, abusive supervision, role stress, and job insecurity. Efforts at prevention focus on eliminating or managing these triggering events. This can be accomplished by eliminating triggering events, by creating a transparent and nonthreatening environment, and by preventing aggressive acts.[58]

A focus on improving interpersonal relationships in the workplace often eliminates some of the triggers to workplace violence and aggression. For example, organizational justice (see Chapter 7) should be explicitly considered when decisions are being made; this can greatly reduce employees' perceptions of unfair treatment. Leadership training activities may result in a decrease in abusive supervision and an increase in organizational justice. Similarly, explicit attempts to reduce role (and other) stress may help control those events with the potential to trigger workplace violence and aggression.

Creating an open and transparent environment includes developing specific procedures for employees to resolve conflicts and discuss grievances. Training in conflict resolution and the creation of confidential and effective complaint procedures ensures that inappropriate behaviour is identified and dealt with before it leads to workplace violence and aggression.

Finally, an organizational policy that clearly labels violent and aggressive acts as inappropriate is key to violence prevention programs. Indeed, some organizations have gone beyond these prohibitions to implement "respectful workplace" policies. Such policies go beyond simply banning violent or aggressive behaviour—they establish the expectation that all organizational members are to be treated with respect and courtesy at all times. In their broadest sense, respectful workplace policies try to limit or exclude rude behaviours that can trigger more serious aggression or violence.

TYPE IV VIOLENCE

Intimate partner violence almost always is perpetrated by someone (e.g., a spouse) who is not a member of the organization. Some forms of this behaviour are not overtly violent (e.g., waiting outside the workplace) and fall into a "grey area" where it is unclear whether the authorities should be called. Preventing or managing intimate partner violence requires a comprehensive and open approach.

First, managers and organizational decision makers need to be educated about the forms that intimate partner violence can take. Second, organizations should be aware of the resources that are available (e.g., through the Employee Assistance Program) to employees experiencing intimate partner violence. Third, organizational policies should allow for temporary accommodation during times of crisis. For example, some organizations have provided additional security or escorts to/from the parking lot for employees experiencing intimate partner violence (these often turn out to be services that other employees value as well). Others have allowed employees to work offsite or to take a period of leave until the situation is resolved. Perhaps most importantly, organizations need to recognize the potential for intimate partner violence to be expressed in the workplace and to take action to protect employees.

ORGANIZATIONAL POLICIES AND PROGRAMS

There are a variety of guidelines and tools available to help organizations manage the risks of workplace violence. One of the most comprehensive tailored to a Canadian environment is the Developing Workplace Violence and Harassment Policies and Programs manual available through the Occupational Health and Safety Council of Ontario (OHSCO; available at http://www.iapa.ca/main/documents/2010_april _violence_toolkit.pdf). As with the management of other forms of occupational hazards, the management of workplace violence follows the sequence of recognition, assessment, and control of hazards.

RECOGNITION

In the OHSCO framework, organizations should conduct regular assessments of the risks for workplace violence. These assessments should occur at three levels: assessment of the general physical environment, identification of risk factors, and assessments for specific risks. OHSCO provides tools for each of these assessments.

In assessing the general physical environment, one would want to consider aspects of the environment that might affect the risks for workplace violence. OHSCO suggests specifically reviewing the outside and parking lot, entry systems to the buildings, reception and waiting areas, public counters, elevators and washrooms, the location of cash and other valuables, and many other areas—in short, do a comprehensive security review of the physical environment.

Beyond the general environment, OHSCO recommends identifying the specific risk factors applicable to the organization or occupation. Specific assessments are provided for (a) direct contact with clients, (b) handling cash, (c) working with unstable or volatile clients, (d) working alone, (e) working in a community-based setting, (f) the mobile workforce, (g) working in high crime areas, (h) securing or protecting valuable goods, and (i) transporting people or goods. While not all of these risk factors are applicable in each organization, the idea is to identify the ones applicable to the particular context and conduct the appropriate assessment.

ASSESSMENT

Based on these risk assessments, one can rank the level of risk applicable to specific jobs. Although this a subjective process, OHSCO suggests that high risk would be when one or more risk factors regularly (i.e., as part of the normal routine) place an employee at severe risk. "Severe" in this context means that there is a potential for fatal or critical injury. Moderate risk is when the risk factors occasionally (i.e., a recognized part of work that occurs on an infrequent basis) place employees at moderately severe (i.e., potential for lost-time injury or injury requiring medical aid). Finally, low risk occurs when risk factors occur rarely and the risk is minimal (potential for first aid). Based on this analysis, organizations can choose to prioritize the most severe risk factors to develop solutions. Of course, a comprehensive approach to dealing with workplace violence would deal with all of the risk factors, not just the high priority ones.

CONTROL

OHSCO also provides guidelines and audit tools for the creation and monitoring of workplace violence programs and policies. In general, the formulation of a comprehensive workplace violence program would include the following:

1. creation of a workplace violence policy that conforms to the relevant legislation (note that these requirements vary by jurisdiction)
2. creation of a violence prevention program that includes:

   a. mechanisms for assessment
   b. procedures for obtaining immediate assistance for victims
   c. procedures for reporting actual and potential violence
   d. procedures for investigating such reports
   e. procedures for dealing with incidents, complaints, and threats

3. creation of an emergency response plan
4. inclusion of workplace violence in work refusal policies
5. procedures for recognizing and dealing with incidents of domestic violence that may occur in the workplace
6. training procedures to ensure that all employees are aware of the policies, procedures, and risks related to workplace violence

After establishing the program, employers also need to institute ongoing monitoring and compliance to ensure that the program is operating as it should. The entire program should be reviewed on a regular basis to ensure that policies and procedures are current.

// HARASSMENT AND BULLYING IN THE WORKPLACE

Although much of our discussion to date has focused on physical violence, there is growing recognition of the harm experienced by individuals exposed to less physical forms of abuse.[59] Perhaps most frequently these are discussed under the labels "harassment" and "bullying" (see definitions earlier in this chapter). Legislatively, bullying is often included as a form of harassment (e.g., Ontario's Bill 168); however, conceptually the two can be quite different. Harassment can occur, for example, as a single act whereas bullying is typically a sustained pattern of harassing behaviours over time.

Because of the extended pattern of behaviours, bullying can be quite subtle and, therefore, very difficult to deal with in an organization. For example, if an employee has been harassing another employee over a period of years then even innocuous behaviours can be experienced as bullying. After years of harassment, for example, simply looking at an individual as he or she enters a meeting can be intimidating and a form of bullying. In the absence of other complaints or a documented history of harassment, most organizations would have difficulty in dealing with an employee complaint based on "he looked at me."

Harassing behaviours, although non-physical, can run a gamut of behaviours from simple rudeness (e.g., slamming a door in someone's face) to more hostile acts (e.g., graffiti in the workplace or acts of sabotage). Correspondingly, some complaints of harassment can be difficult to deal with in the sense that it can be difficult to distinguish whether someone was harassing another or is simply inattentive or rude. Most organizations would know that they have an obligation to respond to hurtful graffiti in the workplace, for example, but might be less sure about how to handle a complaint that an employee let the elevator close in another employee's face.

Perhaps because of the difficulty in defining some acts of harassment and bullying, legislation addressing such actions imposes a lesser obligation on employers than does legislation addressing workplace violence. For example, under Ontario's Bill 168 employers are required to have a policy about harassment in the workplace but are not required to conduct risk assessments for harassment (but employers are required to conduct such assessments for workplace violence). Moreover, harassment does not constitute a grounds for a work refusal under the legislation (although violence might).

Reflecting a broader concern in society, employers have become increasingly sensitive to the use of email and other forms of digital media as a means of aggression. Often termed "cyber-aggression" or "cyber-bullying", such activities can involve both traditional and new forms of aggressive behaviour.[60] Thus, for example, one can blind copy an aggressive email to others (thereby escalating conflict in the organization) or distribute material about individuals to others in the workplace without the knowledge of the target. These would both be forms of cyberaggression. Emails that don't use a subject line, don't include a greeting, or are written in all capital letters may be seen as uncivil or harassing.[61]

Other forms of social media may be used to harass or bully other workers. Although most of the research in this area has focused on email, the use of platforms such as Twitter or Facebook is particularly concerning. In this case, the harassment can occur outside the workplace even though it is directly linked to workplace behaviour. Thus, teachers now report that students post inappropriate material about them on social media sites. Sites such as RateMyProfessor.com or RateMyMD.com are intended to provide consumer protection by providing public ratings of these professionals; however, just as often, the comments posted on these sites could easily constitute harassment or bullying behaviour even though they may be posted outside the work environment.

Organizational efforts to deal with harassment and bullying typically take one of two forms. First, organizations have an obligation to investigate and respond to specific complaints about harassment and bullying. Second, organizations have attempted to promote a more respectful workplace in an attempt to reduce the amount of harassment and bullying in the workplace.

// INVESTIGATION OF SPECIFIC INCIDENTS

A workplace harassment policy should include provision for the investigation and resolution of specific incidents. Recommended investigation policies typically include:

a. Provision to individuals to file a complaint
b. The conduct of an investigation by a neutral third party as soon as possible after the complaint has been filed
c. Consultation with each of the parties involved (i.e., the victim and the alleged perpetrator)
d. Evidence gathering (including interviewing witnesses, etc.) and decision making
e. Communicating the decision to the parties with a proposed resolution
f. Documenting the process and maintaining records[62]

Any such investigation procedure should accommodate the possibility of appeals. Although the exact procedures may vary from company to company, the general principle is that the investigation and appeals procedure should follow principles of natural justice—ensuring that all parties get to tell their side of the story, having investigators and decision makers who are neutral and unbiased, and ensuring that the process is both fair and seen to be fair by all the parties involved.

// RESPECTFUL WORKPLACES

There is no shortage of respectful workplace or anti-bullying programs being developed for implementation in organizations. For the most part, such programs take a training approach—teaching individuals about what constitutes bullying, harassment, and aggression, and working with staff to develop a norm of respectful interactions. Although these programs are well intended there is still very limited research examining whether they actually work

One of the few evaluated intervention programs that does exist for addressing workplace abuse is the civility, respect, and engagement (CREW) process.[63] The objectives of CREW are that "participants become more sensitive to the impact of their social behavior on others," "participants develop effective strategies for responding to incivility and disrespect at work" and "participants develop a deeper repertoire of supportive interactions with colleagues".[64] The program goes beyond simple training by involving employees in creating the definitions of respectful and disrespectful behaviour and establishing norms for how employees would treat each other in the workplace.

An evaluation of the CREW program found that this six-month civility intervention did help reduce incivility in the workplace. This intervention also positively affected health care workers' reports of burnout, job attitudes, management trust, and absences. In a subsequent study, the same authors showed that the positive changes from this civility intervention could be sustained over a one-year period. Specifically, when measured one year after intervention, improvements in civility, incivility, workplace distress, and job attitudes were sustained.[65] The findings demonstrate that incivility interventions have the potential to create long-lasting results.

Although successful, the CREW intervention is both time and resource intensive and these concerns prompted the development of other forms of respectful workplace training. Respect in the Workplace is a program that was developed in partnership with Canadian Red Cross and the RespectED organization, a division of the Red Cross. It is a 90-minute interactive program available in both French and English and delivered via computer. The Respect Group was responsible for developing the program, whose cofounders are Sheldon Kennedy and Wayne McNeil. While their Respect programs were initially developed for sports and schools, they have most recently expanded the scope and applicability of respect training for the workplace. The training consists of instructional slides, animated scenarios, expert clips, and interactive questions and answers. Participants are able to complete the training at a time that is convenient for them and do not have to complete the whole training in one sitting.

From an organizational perspective, the Respect in the Workplace program is an intervention that is both inexpensive and does not require a lot of resources (e.g., time, logistic arrangements). A recent evaluation of the program suggested that there were some positive effects associated with participating in the program. Relative to a control group that did not receive training, participants in the Respect in the Workplace program reported a small increase in workplace civility.[66] These evaluation studies show that respectful workplace programs do have a positive effect by reducing uncivil and increasing civil behaviour in the workplace.

// SEXUAL HARASSMENT

Several studies have identified sexual harassment as a workplace stressor of increasing importance. Most forms of sexual harassment involve unwelcome, intrusive sexual attention and verbal comments. A recent estimate, based on numerous research studies, is that 58% of women have experienced behaviours that are potentially harassing and that 24% of American women agree that they have experienced sexual harassment in the workplace.[67] Data collected in Canada suggest similar exposure rates: 56% of working women who responded to a large survey on sexual harassment indicated that they had experienced sexually harassing behaviour in the previous year.[68] The most commonly reported behaviours in the Canadian survey were insulting jokes and staring. Physically violent actions such as rape do occur in the workplace, but rarely.[69]

Section 247.1 of the Canada Labour Code prohibits sexual harassment and defines sexual harassment as any conduct, comment, gesture, or contact of a sexual nature

(a) that is likely to cause offence or humiliation to any employee; or

(b) that might, on reasonable grounds, be perceived by the employee as placing a condition of a sexual nature on employment or on any opportunity for training or promotion.[70]

Sexual harassment, then, is any intentional, persistent (i.e., repeated), and unwelcome sexual conduct or remark that occurs despite resistance from the victim (see **OH&S Today 8.1**). Note that in cases of severe misconduct (e.g., sexual assault), a single incident meets the definition and constitutes sexual harassment. The act or conduct must be deliberate and intentional. In other words, the offender must be aware that the behaviour is offensive. To alleviate the potential loophole of offenders claiming during a sexual harassment hearing that they were unaware their behaviour was offensive, tribunals use what they call the "reasonable person" test. Basically, this test determines whether a reasonable person would be aware that the behaviour is offensive.

PROTOTYPICAL CASES OF SEXUAL HARASSMENT: NOT WHAT YOU EXPECT?

You'd likely agree that prototypical stories of workplace sexual harassment call to mind an attractive young woman being pursued by an older man in a relative position of power. In the face of persistent, unwanted advances from the man, the woman ultimately makes an accusation of sexual harassment.

Recent research conducted by Dr. Jennifer Berdahl from the Rotman School of Business at the University of Toronto has found that such assumptions about sexual harassment are in fact wrong. The most frequent targets of sexual harassment are not meek, young, attractive women dealing with sexually coercive actions from men. Dr. Berdahl found that outspoken women who do not comply with gender stereotypes and who work in male-dominated jobs are the most frequent victims of sexual harassment. In essence, these women are more likely to experience hostile work environments in which they are the recipients of rude remarks, are made fun of, and face obstacles to their career progression.

Dr. Berdahl suggests that her research has implications for organizational interventions relating to sexual harassment. Policies that rely on things such as dress codes and rules about dating do not address the realities of sexual harassment in today's workplaces. She suggests that workplaces should instead focus on achieving a work environment where skilled men and women are viewed as equals.

Sources: J. Berdahl, "The Evolution of Harassment in the Workplace," *Rotman Magazine* (Winter 2007): 48–51; C. Goar, "True Face of Sexual Harassment," *Toronto Star* (January 24, 2007). Found at: http://www.thestar.com/article/174064 (accessed February 10, 2007).

The Labour Code definition seems to point to two different types of sexual harassment:[71]

1. *Sexual coercion* (or "quid pro quo" harassment) is an attempt to extort sexual cooperation. This extortion can take the form of subtle or explicit job-related threats (e.g., job loss, loss of promotion), or the promise of job-related rewards (e.g., promotions, raises). The Ontario Human Rights Code specifically prohibits both job-related rewards in exchange for sexual favours by a person in authority, and job-related punishment for not providing those favours.

2. *Hostile environment* is sexual harassment that occurs without any coercion or extortion; it does, however, create a hostile, intimidating, and discriminating environment. Sexually harassing behaviours of this nature can range from insulting, misplaced comments, through pervasive sex-related verbal or physical conduct, to life threats or physical attacks. According to most research on sexual harassment, "hostile environment" sexual harassment is the most prevalent type.

SEXUAL HARASSMENT AS A HEALTH AND SAFETY ISSUE

Sexual harassment becomes a health and safety issue for two primary reasons. First, studies show that being the victim of sexual harassment is associated with several organizational strains, including increased job dissatisfaction, decreased loyalty to the organization, and increased intent to leave the organization. Some women who have reported being a victim of sexual harassment to their organization have experienced the formal process as unjust—indeed, some report that they have been fired after making a sexual harassment claim. There are also personal consequences of sexual harassment, with victims significantly more likely to experience dissatisfaction with life in general and to experience psychosomatic disorders (e.g., respiratory, stomach, and sleep problems; headaches and migraines; weight loss or gain). Thus, exposure to sexual harassment is associated with impaired employee well-being and becomes a health and safety issue.

Second, the courts have increasingly viewed workplace sexual harassment as the responsibility of the employer. Before 1981, sexual harassment on the job was not prohibited by any human rights statute in Canada. A ground-breaking step occurred in 1989, when the Supreme Court of Canada concluded that sexual harassment is a form of sex discrimination and is therefore prohibited in employment. Sex discrimination had been prohibited by human rights statutes for some time in Canada, but sexual harassment was not initially recognized in those statutes.[72] This was an important progression from simply acknowledging that sexual harassment was a serious problem to taking steps to prevent it.

Another major change occurred when the Supreme Court of Canada stated that an employer is liable for the discriminatory acts of its employees. This decision had significant implications, for employers now had a legal motive to prohibit sexual harassment in their companies. Legal liability translates into a strong financial incentive to prevent illegal acts from occurring. For example, in one of the largest lawsuits of its type, Mitsubishi Motors in the United States paid $34 million to settle allegations of sexual harassment filed by the Equal Employment Opportunities Commission on behalf of 300 female employees. Essentially, the allegations were that the women had been subjected to sexual comments, innuendo, and unwanted groping, and that plant managers knew of these problems but did nothing to correct them.

The ruling that employers are liable for discriminatory acts, including harassment, has a number of implications for organizations:[73]

1. Employers are responsible for the due care and protection of their employees' human rights in the workplace.

2. Employers are liable for the discriminatory conduct of and sexual harassment by their agents and supervisory personnel.

3. Sexual harassment by a supervisor is automatically attributed to the employer when such harassment results in a tangible job-related disadvantage to the employee.

4. Explicit company policy forbidding sexual harassment and the presence of procedures for reporting misconduct may or may not be sufficient to offset liability.

5. Employers will be pressured to take a more active role in maintaining a harassment-free work environment.

6. Employers will feel greater discomfort with intimate relationships that develop between supervisors and their subordinates because of the legal implications, and this may motivate employers to discourage such office relationships.

7. Employers' intentions to have effective sexual harassment policies are insufficient. To avoid liability, the policies must be functional and must work as well in practice as they do in theory.[74]

Clearly, the Supreme Court has made employers responsible for any sexual harassment in the organization. As a result, employers are more likely to launch interventions to eliminate or at least reduce the occurrence of sexual harassment in their workplaces.

// SUMMARY

The scope of OH&S practice continues to expand and now incorporates the need for organizations to deal with issues of workplace violence, aggression, and harassment. Understanding these terms and how they occur in the workplace was a primary goal of this chapter. Addressing these issues requires understanding the situational and imminent risk factors in the workplace and devising ways of addressing these risks.

KEY TERMS

aggression 190
assault cycle 196
bullying 190
emotional abuse 190
gender harassment 190
harassment 190
imminent risk 196
incivility 190
mobbing 190
sexual coercion 190
sexual harassment 190
Type I violence 192
Type II violence 192
Type III violence 192
Type IV violence 193
unwanted sexual attention 190
violence 190

DISCUSSION QUESTIONS

1. How far can legislation go? Workplace violence legislation can focus very narrowly on physical assaults or more broadly on behaviours that make employees feel uncomfortable. Can we realistically enforce legislation that prohibits rudeness or teasing? At what point can legislation be effective?

2. Many of the behaviours reviewed in this chapter are illegal (e.g., sexual assault, physical assault). Do we need special workplace legislation to address these issues? What is the value of specific legislation around issues of violence and harassment?

3. Some legislation defines harassment or aggression, in part, by focusing on either the intent of the perpetrator (e.g., behaviour that is intended to annoy or embarrass) or the reaction of the victim (e.g., behaviour that is unwelcome). Does this pose a problem for regulation? How can we know the intent of the perpetrator or the anticipated reaction of the victim?

4. Managers often do not know when to get involved in workplace conflicts. How does one distinguish between a situation that constitutes "violence" or "aggression" and one that is just "normal" workplace violence? When does a manager need to intervene in a situation between coworkers or between a coworker and a customer?

5. We've all heard the expression "the customer is always right." Does this have any implications for the management of workplace violence and aggression?

USING THE INTERNET

1. Choose an occupation you know well and conduct a violence risk assessment for that job (Hint: Many provinces make sample risk assessments available online.)

2. Many people who experience workplace bullying simply don't know what to do about it. Using resources found on the Web, prepare a short (one-page) guide for victims of workplace bullying.

3. Imagine you are tasked with creating an organizational policy on cyber-aggression. Using material found on numerous websites, outline what should be included in such a policy.

EXERCISES

1. Many students work, or have worked, in retail environments. Find at least 10 students with this experience. Using the definitions in this chapter, ask them if they have ever experienced an act of workplace violence (i.e., a physical assault or threat of physical assault). What were the circumstances? What led up to the confrontation? Who was the perpetrator?

2. Over a period of time, collect articles from your local paper that report on incidents of workplace violence. What types of violence are reported? Does the reporting reflect research data suggesting that workplace violence is almost always perpetrated by people who are not members of the organization? Why might there be a difference between media reports and research findings?

OH&S IN ACTION

You are the OHS manager for a long-term care facility. Recently there has been a great deal of attention paid to the issue of violence in nursing homes. The focus of media attention has been on residents attacking other residents. However, in reviewing your incident reports you have noticed a dramatic increase in the number of staff being assaulted by residents. Although the facility has a non-aggression policy, many of the residents are experiencing some form of dementia and cannot be asked to leave the facility. What do you recommend be done to ensure that staff experience a safe work environment?

CASE STUDY 1   AGGRESSION POLICY

Valerie is the occupational health and safety manager for a Canadian university. She is responsible for ensuring that the OHS program is implemented in the university. Part of her job involves reviewing incident reports and compiling incident statistics for her monthly reports to the JOHSC committee. In getting ready for the next JOHSC meeting she has noticed that 50% of the incidents reported this month involved incidents of aggression or violence. This prompted her to review the past six months of reports and she notices that 30–50% of incidents each month deal with aggression and violence. The university has a no-aggression policy but has not paid much attention to this issue to date. If you were Valerie, what would you do?

CASE STUDY 2　　ADDRESSING INAPPROPRIATE EMAIL

Duygu is a manager in a large financial services firm. Like most workers in a busy office, she spends most of her time on the computer and gets hundreds of emails each day. Occasionally she is copied on messages that were not intended for her or she receives messages in error. Recently she has become increasingly disturbed by some of the emails she has seen. In the past couple of weeks she has received several "jokes" that seemed to be sexist or racist—making fun of women or a particular racial group. This morning she received an email that included a picture of two naked people. As a manager, Duygu thinks that she needs to speak to the people who sent these messages but is also wondering whether she needs to something more; should the company have a policy or training on the use of email? If so what would that look like?

CASE STUDY 3　　OFFSITE HARASSMENT

Hari is the human resources manager for a large engineering company. The company has well-developed programs and policies governing behaviour in the workplace (e.g., anti-harassment, anti-violence, and sexual harassment guidelines) but the company has always focused on behaviour in the workplace. Today Hari received a complaint from an employee that she is being "stalked and harassed" by another employee. Most of the offending behaviour seems to occur on Facebook and other social media sites and there is no evidence that this is occurring at work. Hari has to decide whether or not he should get involved in this issue. What do you think?

// NOTES

1. United States Postal Service Commission on a Safe and Secure Workplace, *Report* (New York: National Center on Addiction and Substance Abuse at Columbia University, 2000).

2. S. deLesulec, "Criminal Victimization in the Workplace 2004," Cat. no. 85F0033MIE–013 (Ottawa: Canadian Centre for Justice Statistics, 2007).

3. A.C.H. Schat and E.K. Kelloway, "Workplace Aggression," in J. Barling, E.K. Kelloway, and M.R. Frone, eds., *Handbook of Work Stress* (Thousand Oaks: Sage, 2005), 189–218.

4. Ibid.

5. J. Barling, K. Dupre, and E.K. Kelloway, "Predicting Workplace Violence and Aggression," *Annual Review of Psychology* 60 (2009): 671–92.

6. L. Keashly, "Interpersonal and Systemic Aspects of Emotional Abuse at Work: The Target's Perspective," *Violence and Victims* 16 (2001): 233–68.

7. H. Hoel, C. Rayner, and C.L. Cooper, "Workplace Bullying," in C.L. Cooper and I.T. Robertson, eds., *International Review of Industrial and Organizational Psychology*, vol. 14 (Chichester: Wiley, 1999), 195–230.

8. L.M. Andersson and C.M. Pearson, "Tit-for-Tat? The Spiralling Effect of Incivility in the Workplace," *Academy of Management Review* 24 (1999): 452–71.

9. Ibid; J. Barling, G. Rogers, and E.K. Kelloway, "Behind Closed Doors: In-Home Workers' Experience of Sexual Harassment and Workplace Violence," *Journal of Occupational Health Psychology* 6 (2001): 255–69.

10. M. Fendrich, P. Woodward, and J.A. Richman, "The Structure of Harassment and Abuse in the Workplace: A Factorial Comparison of Two Measures," *Violence and Victims* 17 (2002): 491–505.

11. M.J. Gelfand, L.F. Fitzgerald, and F. Drasgow, "The Structure of Sexual Harassment: A Confirmatory Analysis Across Cultures and Settings," *Journal of Vocational Behaviour* 47 (1995): 164–77.

12. A.C.H. Schat, M.R. Frone, and E.K. Kelloway, "Prevalence of Workplace Aggression in the U.S. Workforce: Findings from a National Study," in E.K. Kelloway, J. Barling, and J.J. Hurrell, eds., *Handbook of Workplace Violence* (Thousand Oaks: Sage, 2006), 47–89.

13. Ibid.

14. Ibid.

15. Ibid; L. Francis and E.K. Kelloway, "The Nova Scotia Workplace Stress Survey," (Halifax: Saint Mary's University, 2007).

16. L. Francis and E.K. Kelloway, "The Nova Scotia Workplace Stress Survey," (Halifax: Saint Mary's University, 2007).

17. Ibid.

18. deLesulec, "Criminal Victimization in the Workplace 2004."

19. A. Pizzino, "Dealing with Violence in the Workplace: The Experience of Canada Unions," in M. Gill, B. Fisher, and V. Bowie, eds., *Violence at Work: Causes, Patterns, and Prevention* (Cullompton, UK: Willan, 2002), 165–79.

20. State of California, "Cal/OSHA Guidelines for Workplace Security" (1995). Found at: http://www.dir.ca.gov/dosh/dosh_publications/worksecurity.html (accessed June 3, 2016).

21. P. Tjaden and N. Thoennes, *Extent, Nature, and Consequences of Intimate Partner Violence* (Washington: U.S. Department of Justice, National Institute of Justice, 2000).

22. Ibid.

23. Ibid.

24. L. Francis, J.E. Cameron, and E.K. Kelloway, "Crossing the Line: Violence on the Picket Line," in E.K. Kelloway, J. Barling, and J.J. Hurrell, eds., *Handbook of Workplace Violence* (Thousand Oaks: Sage, 2006).

25. A.J. Thieblot and T.R. Haggard, "Union Violence: The Record and the Response by the Courts, Legislatures, and the NLRB," (Philadelphia: Industrial Research Unit, Wharton School, 1983).

26. A.J. Thieblot, T.R. Haggard, and H.R. Northrup, *Union Violence: The Record and the Response by the Courts, Legislatures, and the NLRB*, rev. ed. (Fairfax, VA: John M. Olin Institute of Employment Practice and Policy, George Mason University, 1999).

27. Francis et al., "Crossing the Line."

28. Ibid.

29. M. Teed, E.K. Kelloway, and J. Barling, "Incidents and Predictors of Workplace Violence and Aggression," paper presented at the biannual conference of the European Academy for Occupational Health Psychology, Valencia, 2008.

30. Schat et al., "Prevalence of Workplace Aggression in the U.S. Workforce."

31. Francis and Kelloway, The Nova Scotia Workplace Stress Survey.

32. Bureau of Labour Statistics, "National Census of Fatal Occupational Injuries 1997," USDL 98-336 (Washington: Department of Labour, 1998).

33. C. Casteel, and C. Peek-Asa, "Effectiveness of Crime Prevention Through Environmental Design (CPTED) in Reducing Robberies," *American Journal of Preventive Medicine* 18 (2000): 99–115.

34. D.N. Castillo and E.L. Jenkins, "Industries and Occupations at High Risk for Work-Related Homicide," *Journal of Occupational Medicine* 36 (1994): 125–32.

35. C. Peek-Asa, C.W. Runyan, and C. Zwerling, "The Role of Surveillance and Evaluation Research in the Reduction of Violence Against Workers," *American Journal of Preventive Medicine* 20 (2001): 141–48; M.M. LeBlanc and E.K. Kelloway, "Predictors and Outcomes of Workplace Violence," *Journal of Applied Psychology* 87 (2002): 444–53.

36. K. Calnan, E.K. Kelloway, and K. Dupre, "Managing Workplace Violence: A Comprehensive Guide," SAV-T First: Managing Workplace Violence, R. Hughes, A. Kinder, and C.L. Cooper (Eds), *International Handbook of Workplace Trauma Support* (Chichester: Wiley-Blackwell, 2012): 105–20.

37. R. Almvik, P. Woods, and K. Rasmussen, "Assessing Risk for Imminent Violence in the Elderly: The Broset Violence Checklist," *International Journal of Geriatric Psychology* 22 (2007): 862–67.

38. G.M. Breakwell, *Coping with Aggressive Behaviour: Personal and Professional Development* (Leicester: British Psychological Society, 1997).

39. K. Calnan, E.K. Kelloway, and K. Dupre, "Managing Workplace Violence: A Comprehensive Guide," SAV-T First: Managing Workplace Violence, R. Hughes, A. Kinder, and C.L. Cooper (Eds), *International Handbook of Workplace Trauma Support* (Chichester: Wiley-Blackwell, 2012): 105–20.

40. H.E. Amandus, D. Zahm, R. Friedmann, R.B. Ruback, C. Block, J. Weiss, D. Rogan, W. Holmes, T. Bynum, D. Hoffman, R. McManus, J. Malcan, C. Wellford, and D. Kessler, "Employee Injuries and Convenience Store Robberies in Selected Metropolitan Areas," *Journal of Occupational and Environmental Medicine* 38 (1996): 714–20.

41. Occupational Safety and Health Administration, "Recommendations for Workplace Violence Prevention Programs in Late-Night Retail Establishments" (1998). Found at: http://www.osha.gov/Publications/osha3153.pdf (accessed March 5, 2004).

42. C. Mayhew, *Violence in the Workplace—Preventing Armed Robbery: A Practical Handbook*, Research and Public Policy series no. 33 (Canberra: Australian Institute of Criminology, 2000).

43. F. Calleja, "Cab Hold-Ups on Web" (2002). Found at http://www.taxi-library .org/camera04.htm (accessed May 29, 2010).

44. P.P. Purpura, *Retail Security and Shrinkage Protection* (Stoneham: Butterworth-Heinemann, 1993).

45. F.J. Desroches, *Force and Fear: Robbery in Canada* (Toronto: Nelson, 1995).

46. T. Gabor and A. Normandeau, "Preventing Armed Robbery Through Opportunity Reduction: A Critical Analysis," *Journal of Security Administration* 12 (1989): 3–18.

47. Idem, "Preventing Assaults on Taxi Drivers in Australia," *Trends and Issues in Crime and Criminal Justice* 179 (2000): 1–6.

48. M. Gill, *Commercial Robbery* (London: Blackstone, 2000).

49. K.A. Faulkner, D.P. Landsittel, and S.A. Hendricks, "Robbery Characteristics and Employee Injuries in Convenience Stores," *American Journal of Industrial Medicine* 40 (2000): 703–09.

50. Occupational Safety and Health Administration, "Guidelines for Preventing Workplace Violence for Health Care and Social Service Workers." Found at http://www.osha.gov/Publications/osha3148.pdf (accessed June 3, 2016).

51. National Institute for Occupational Safety and Health, *Violence: Occupational Hazards in Hospitals*, DHHS Publication no. 2002–101 (April 2002). Found at: http://www.cdc.gov/niosh/docs/2002-101 (accessed June 3, 2016).

52. P.F. Levin, J. Hewitt, and T.S. Misner, "Insights of Nurses About Assault in Hospital-Based Emergency Departments," *Image–The Journal of Nursing Scholarship* 30 (1998): 249–54.

53. Barling et al., "Behind Closed Doors."

54. NIOSH, *Violence: Occupational Hazards in Hospitals*.

55. A. Schat and E.K. Kelloway, "Reducing the Adverse Consequences of Workplace Aggression and Violence: The Buffering Effects of Organizational Support," *Journal of Occupational Health Psychology* 8 (2003): 110–22.

56. J.C. DelBel, "De-escalating Workplace Aggression," *Nursing Management* 34 (2003): 30–34.

57. S.M. Herschovis and J. Barling, "Preventing Insider-Initiated Violence," in E.K. Kelloway, J. Barling, and J.J. Hurrell, Jr., eds., *Handbook of Workplace Violence* (Thousand Oaks: Sage, 2006).

58. A.O. Manier, E.K. Kelloway, and L. Francis (in press). "Damaging the Workplace: Consequences for People and Organizations," in N.A. Bowling and M.S. Hershcovis, M.S. (eds.), *Research and Theory on Workplace Aggression* (Cambridge, UK: Cambridge University Press).

59. T. Weatherbee and E.K. Kelloway, "Cyber-aggression," in E.K. Kelloway, J. Barling, and J.J. Hurrell (eds), *Handbook of Workplace Violence* (Thousand Oaks, CA: Sage, 2006); C. Privitera and C.A. Campbell, "Cyberbullying: The New Face of Workplace Bullying?" *CyberPsychology & Behavior*. 12(4) (2009): 395–400. doi:10.1089/cpb.2009.0025.

60. Weatherbee and Kelloway "Cyberaggression."

61. L. Francis, C. Holmvall, and L. O'Brien, "The Influence of Workload and Civility of Treatment on the Perpetration of Email Incivility," *Computers in Human Behavior,* 46 (2015): 191–201.

62. WorkSafe BC, "Investigations Guide: Workplace Bullying and Harassment." Found at: http://www2.worksafebc.com/pdfs/bullying/bullyingharassment investigationsguide.pdf (accessed June 3, 2016); Ontario Safety Association for Community and Healthcare, "Bullying in the Workplace: A handbook for the Workplace." Found at: http://www.osach.ca/products/resrcdoc/rvioe528.pdf (accessed June 3, 2016).

63. M.P. Leiter, H. Laschinger, A. Day, and D. Oore, "The Impact of Civility Interventions on Employee Social Behavior, Distress, and Attitudes," *Journal of Applied Psychology*, 96(6) (2011), 1258–1274. doi:10.1037/a0024442.

64. K. Osatuke, S.C. Moore, C. Ward, S.R. Dyrenforth, and L. Belton, "Civility, Respect, Engagement in the Workforce (CREW): Nationwide Organization Development Intervention at Veterans Health Administration," *Journal of Applied Behavioral Science*, 45(3)(2009): 384–410. doi:10.1177/0021886309335067.

65. Leiter et al. "The Impact of Civility Interventions on Employee Social Behavior, Distress, and Attitudes"; M.P.Leiter, A. Day, D. Gilin-Oore, and H.S. Laschinger, "Getting Better and Staying Better: Assessing Civility, Incivility, Distress, and Job Attitudes One Year After a Civility Intervention," *Journal of Occupational Health Psychology*, 17 (2012): 425–34.

66. S. Smith and E.K. Kelloway (2016). Respect in the Workplace: Evaluation of a Short, Online Intervention Program. Manuscript submitted for publication.

67. R. Ilies, N. Hauserman, S. Schwaohau, and J. Stibal, "Reported Incidence Rates of Work-related Sexual Harassment in the United States: Using Meta-Analysis to Explain Reported Rate Disparities," *Personnel Psychology* 56 (2003): 607–31.

68. D. Crocker and V. Kalemba, "The Incidence and Impact of Women's Experiences of Sexual Harassment in Canadian Workplaces," *Canadian Review of Sociology and Anthropology* 46 (1999): 541–58.

69. L.F. Fitzgerald, "Sexual Harassment: Violence Against Women in the Workplace," *American Psychologist* 48 (1993): 1070–76.

70. A.P. Aggarwal, *Sexual Harassment in the Workplace* (Toronto: Butterworths Canada, 1992).

71. Ibid.

72. Ibid.

73. Ibid.

74. Ibid.

TRAINING

CHAPTER LEARNING OBJECTIVES

- discuss the importance of occupational health and safety training
- identify the components of a training program
- explain the role of a needs analysis when designing a training program
- discuss issues that arise in training design and delivery
- describe various options for the delivery of health and safety training programs
- discuss the role of evaluation in any training program
- evaluate the measurement concerns surrounding organizational measures of occupational safety training effectiveness
- describe some common health and safety training initiatives including safety orientation, first-aid training, and WHMIS

THE NEED FOR TRAINING

What do the following incidents have in common? In Nova Scotia there has been a dramatic increase in workers' compensation claims related to workplace violence among long-term care employees; in a packaging plant in Wisconsin, a worker had three fingers amputated by machinery; in British Columbia a fire in the segregation unit of the Fraser Regional Correction Centre resulted in 19 corrections workers suffering smoke inhalation. Although these incidents happened in different places and different industries, in each case a lack of employee training was identified as one factor that led to these incidents. Employees who are not trained in safe working procedures or who are not trained to deal with the specific hazards associated with their job are at greater risk of injury.

Not surprisingly, establishing an effective training program is an integral part of any safety programming. Training ranges from courses required by legislation (e.g.,

WHMIS, first aid) to training in safe work practices and hazards specific in a workplace. Recently, the Canadian Standards Association issued CSA Z1001—a standard for occupational health and safety training that specifies how training programs should be developed and evaluated in organizations.

Sources: OHS Canada, "Injuries Among Nova Scotia Nursing-Home Workers Caused by Residents Rising: Board." Found at: http://www.thecanadianpress.com/english/online/OnlineFullStory.aspx?filename=DOR-MNNCP.b3fa2561550a4e8b993f05e32f3e923b.CPKEY2008111310&newsitemid=37291749&languageid=1 (accessed May 2, 2016); OH&S, "OSHA Cites Packaging Company in Amputation Case." Found at: https://ohsonline.com/articles/2016/05/05/lack-of-safety-procedures-led-to-amputation-of-finger-tips.aspx?admgarea=news (accessed June 6, 2016); OHS Canada, "B.C. Prison Accused of Safety Violations During an Arson Incident." Found at: http://www.ohscanada.com/health-safety/b-c-prison-accused-safety-violations-arson-incident-2/1003349979 (accessed June 6, 2016).

Classroom training remains one of the most common forms of instruction.

The cases cited above illustrate the type of injuries that can occur when appropriate health and safety training is not delivered in a workplace. Workplace dangers are a reality for *all* workers. Workers of all ages, experience levels, and job types can and do experience safety incidents at work. A recent review of the occupational health and safety training research literature demonstrates that training in OH&S has a positive effect on worker practices and behaviour.[1] However, many workers in Canada have not received adequate safety training. A recent study of nearly 60 000 Canadian workers reported that only 12% of women and 16% of men had received workplace safety training in the previous year.[2] Though employees who were new to their jobs were more likely to receive training, the proportion who did remains disappointingly low, at only 20%.[3] Even though young workers and those in physically demanding jobs are at higher risk for injury, neither group was more likely to receive training.

In this chapter we explore the topic of health and safety training. Recent Canadian statistics on access to all types of employer-supported training suggest that vulnerable workers—who include the less educated, low-wage earners, and non-union members—face greater barriers to training access in the workplace than other groups. This discrepancy is particularly notable if the worker who falls into one of these groups is a woman.[4] Though these trends are not specific to health and safety training, they do raise a possible red flag about access to safety training for vulnerable workers.

The type of employment may also make workers vulnerable. Contingent workers (i.e., those who work on short-term contracts) might not be given the training required to ensure safe work performance. Employers may not wish to pay for training for these short-term employees. Perhaps more frequently, companies may subcontract work (e.g., hiring subcontractors to do specific tasks) and it may be difficult to ensure that the employees of subcontractors, who themselves might be contingent workers, receive proper training.

In this chapter, we apply a basic model of training in organizations to the specific concern of training workers in occupational health and safety. In particular, we consider the processes of designing, implementing, and evaluating health and safety training programs in organizations. The model we present is the same model that underpins CSA Z1001 and ensures that both individual courses and the training program as a whole is administered through a process of continual improvement. In this context, continual improvement means that training needs are regularly assessed and training programs are evaluated and, if required, adjusted to meet the needs of employees and the organization.

// THE ROLE OF OCCUPATIONAL HEALTH AND SAFETY TRAINING

All workers have several rights pertaining to their health and safety while at work. Three basic rights apply to all Canadian employees:

1. *The right to know.* Workers have a right to be informed about dangerous or unsafe materials and machinery in the workplace.

2. *The right to participate.* Workers have a right to take part actively in the protection of their own health and safety. This participation generally involves reporting unsafe work practices and conditions.

3. *The right to refuse unsafe work.* Workers have a right to withhold their services if they are asked to perform a task that they deem to be unsafe or are asked to use equipment that is not in good repair.

One goal of occupational health and safety programs is to ensure that workers are aware of their rights (see **OH&S Today 9.1** for an example of such a program).

Passport to Safety is a Canadian not-for-profit enterprise that describes itself as a "catalyst for change." Its vision is "a country where workplace safety is assured and Canadians return home healthy at the end of each day." Passport of Safety focuses much of its activity on young workers, who it believes have the ability to "influence the evolution of safe workplace cultures." Many youth who are injured at work report they were not aware of the life-threatening hazards in the workplace or basic safety rules that would have helped them avoid injury. Passport to Safety strives to increase risk awareness. The program is a creative one that focuses on a series of tests that young workers, or others soon to enter the workforce, can take to challenge their understanding of workplace safety. Following successful completion of a test, members receive transcripts to attach to their résumés.

Passport to Safety also partners with workers' compensation boards, teachers, and employers to promote workplace safety. The website contains numerous educational resources, such as videos. In provinces such as Ontario, New Brunswick, Newfoundland and Labrador, and Nova Scotia, some students and teachers can access the Passport testing program for free. For employers, the Passport program is designed to supplement rather than replace job- and organization-specific training. For example, supervisors can use a provided assessment test to gauge employees' knowledge.

Source: Passport to Safety. Found at: https://passporttosafety.parachutecanada.org (accessed June 6, 2016).

It is easy to see the vital role of training for the fulfillment of these basic rights. First, employees—especially new employees—must be advised of these rights. The communication of these basic rights can take place in a safety orientation when a person starts a new job.

Once employees are aware of their basic rights regarding health and safety at work, safety-related training is needed to help individuals ensure that these rights are being upheld. For instance, with respect to the right to know, employees must receive training on their workplace's potential dangers. Similarly, regarding the right to refuse unsafe work, effective health and safety training will help individuals judge accurately which tasks are indeed unsafe. As such, health and safety training plays a vital role in the protection of an employee's basic rights, and its provision is mandated in OH&S acts across the country. CSA Z1001 is a management standard that sets out how companies should develop and maintain their health and safety training.[5]

The importance of health and safety training is recognized internationally as well. For example, in the United States, training is prominently placed as one of five essential elements of OH&S programs, along with employer commitment, hazard surveillance, hazard control and prevention, and program evaluation.[6]

Of course, it is also important to ask when organizations should not use training as an OH&S intervention. As you'll see in the following sections, training interventions are helpful when they address knowledge or skills needs or gaps. If a skill or knowledge gap has not been identified, training is likely not the appropriate intervention.

That said, there are also cases where even though employees may not have a certain skill set, training would still not be the best answer. Throughout this book, we have stressed that *engineering* interventions, which focus on changing the physical environment to reduce hazard exposure and risk should be the first line of intervention and defence when it comes to worker safety. Generally speaking, if an engineering-based solution is available, it should be used before administrative or behavioural interventions. For instance, one would not recommend training workers to use a machine with a broken guard. Similarly, there are safety-related tasks for which highly specialized skills and equipment are required. In these cases, one would not train in-house workers to perform these jobs. For instance, carpenters who work for a contractor specializing in home renovations would likely not be trained for a task such as asbestos abatement. In that case, an external company, specializing in hazardous substance removal would be contracted to perform that kind of work.

Given the importance of effectively communicating health and safety information in today's workplaces, the question of how to develop and implement effective health and safety training programs is vital. There are two concerns, which are interrelated. One of these is how we can best design and implement specific courses as part of an occupational health and safety program. We know, for example, that employees need WHMIS training or may need first aid training. We might also want to develop training around specific hazards in the workplace. The second concern is how we develop a training program; that is an integrated series of courses designed to meet the training needs of the organization.

Although the focus of individual courses is typically on individual learning, from a training program perspective it is important to document (1) how the training was developed, (2) what training was actually delivered, (3) how the training was delivered and (4) which employees completed the training (and when they completed the training). The organization should also document training evaluations and how the continual improvement principle is applied to training. Depending on the circumstances, the organization might also keep records of what certifications were awarded as a result of training, the details of external training providers, and any need for recertification.

Maintenance of these records is important for two purposes. First, organizations have a responsibility to manage the training process. They need to ensure that the training being delivered is effective and current. They also need to ensure that employees get the training they need and that any certifications are kept current. In this sense, recordkeeping is just good management, ensuring that the training program is working as it should. Second, in the event of an accident or incident investigation, a labour officer who suspects that workers were not properly trained will frequently issue an order for the company to produce all of the documentation and records associated with the training program. Having a program that is well documented with complete records of employee training is a form of due diligence through which the company can demonstrate that it is meeting its obligations to run a comprehensive and effective occupational health and safety training program.

// HEALTH AND SAFETY TRAINING PROGRAMS

As our starting point we take the instructional systems design (ISD) model of training[7] and apply it specifically to occupational health and safety. The ISD model of training has three parts: (1) needs analysis, (2) training design and delivery, and (3) training evaluation. This is also the model that underpins CSA Z1001. The model is depicted in **Figure 9.1**. Each stage of this model is described and discussed in the sections that follow.

> **instructional systems design (ISD) model of training**
> a general model of the training process that incorporates needs analysis, training design and delivery, and training evaluation and that notes the interdependencies among the three major components of the training process

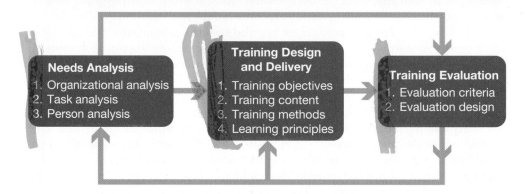

NEEDS ANALYSIS

needs analysis
the initial stage of the training development process, intended to identify employee and organizational deficiencies that can be addressed with training and to recognize potential obstacles to the success of a training program

The training and development process begins when a need or concern arises. With respect to health and safety, that concern might be the occurrence of a number of safety incidents or injuries in the workplace. Following such incidents, company officials may opt to develop a training program to improve workplace safety. Also, a large number of workplace safety incidents in a particular company may draw attention from various OH&S governing bodies. These groups may determine that safety training is required and mandate training within a particular organization. Alternatively, the move toward safety training could be prompted by new legislation requiring that a particular type of health and safety training be offered to workers in a particular industry. Whatever the case, a health and safety training process begins with a **needs analysis**.

Needs analysis is the recommended starting point in many models of organizational training because it helps determine the nature of the problems at hand. Needs analysis is a way to determine whether there is a gap between current and desired reality.[8] Needs analysis can also be used to identify potential obstacles to the effectiveness of a training program so that they can be dealt with early in the training and development process. Such an analysis ideally includes assessing the organization, the task or job at hand, and the employee(s) in question. The inclusion of all three levels in the initial analysis will help answer questions about what groundwork must be done before training begins, what the content of the training program should be, who should receive training, and how the program should be delivered (for a discussion of digital training delivery see **OH&S Today 9.2**). Let's consider the pertinent issues when assessing the needs of the organization, the task or job, and the employee.

organizational analysis
an analysis of the entire organization designed to examine its resources, strategy, and environment in order to assess the organization's support for training

ORGANIZATIONAL ANALYSIS

A needs analysis at the organizational level should be the starting point in any training intervention.[9] An **organizational analysis** should involve a study of the whole organization, considering areas such as the resources and strategy of the organization and the

DIGITAL SAFETY

If you read recent articles about organizations aiming to reduce their OH&S incident rates or increase worker safety, or reports from OH&S investigations, you'll see an increased focus on safety training. For example, the Workplace Safety and Prevention Services (WSPS) in Ontario offers a series of industry-specific safety courses Some of the training sessions are classroom-based, others involve self-guided study, and still others are offered online. Topics covered include ladder safety, incident investigation, ergonomic assessments, and confined-space safety.

Increasingly, online training is used by organizations—especially smaller businesses that cannot afford to develop and deliver their own custom training courses. For example, the Ontario Ministry of Labour has an online course focusing on the occupational health and safety act in that province. The course is designed so employers can access the training for free (the course is available at http://www.labour.gov.on.ca/english/hs/training/workers.php). A variety of providers, including government agencies, community colleges and private providers, have developed online WHMIS training courses that are available

at a modest cost to organizations or individuals (a free course is available at http://aixsafety.com/free-whmis-training-and-free-whmis-test-and-certification). Although such courses are convenient and easy to access for most employees, recall that there is a need for companies to also maintain a complete set of training records so companies should to keep track of what training has been completed by which workers and when the training was completed.

Although digital training may be simply an online lecture (maybe with some embedded testing), digital media also offers the potential to engage in more interactive simulations. Indeed, the emergence of virtual reality devices such as Oculus Rift have a potential application in safety training. Such programs may be more expensive to develop than traditional classroom training but are typically cheaper and easier to deliver because they don't require a class of participants in one place and at one time. Moreover, simulations and immersive technologies may offer a more intensive and realistic training experience and thereby foster learning and transfer to the workplace.

Sources: Workplace Safety and Prevention Services. Found at: http://www.healthandsafetyontario.ca/WSPS/Home.aspx (accessed June 6, 2016); OHS Canada, "Back to the Future." Found at: http://www.ohscanada.com/features/back-to-the-future (accessed June 6, 2016).

industry in which it operates. Organizational analysis can identify the health and safety areas that need knowledge and skills improvement and that may be targets for a training program. This analysis should also highlight any constraints that may limit the success of a training program before training is designed and delivered.

Successful training initiatives tend to be in line with the organization's overall strategy. Similarly, it is important to consider the resources the organization can dedicate to the training process, as the extent of the available resources can influence the nature of the training program. For example, if the organization has training facilities on-site, this may influence decisions about how the training is delivered. The budget available for training should also be considered, as financial constraints will influence decisions later in the training development process. Similarly, it is important to consider the industry and environmental factors that may affect the training program. For instance, if the organization is unionized, one must consider the role of the union in training program development.

Another major goal of the organizational analysis should be to establish organizational support for a training intervention. This can be done by developing a relationship with management. Support from the organization is vital to the success of any training program. An organization that truly values training will provide the necessary resources to make the program a success and get behind the training effort by encouraging employees to take part actively.

With respect to health and safety training, it is important that the individual conducting the organizational needs analysis determine not only the degree of organizational support for training and learning, but also the support for health and safety initiatives in general. The effectiveness of any health and safety efforts "will be a function of the organization's overall commitment to providing a safe work environment and the employee's perception and recognition of that commitment."[10] Certainly, studies show that organizational support plays a vital role in the success of health and safety training initiatives. In one examination of the effectiveness of hazard awareness training among individuals in construction trades, improvements in attitudes toward fall safety were associated with the organization's support for safety.[11] Investigations of the impact of management attitudes toward health and safety training generally illustrate the importance of managerial support for sustaining the positive outcomes associated with such training.

Examination of the organization's safety climate is one way to determine the extent of organizational support for a health and safety training program. That term relates to perceptions about safety-related policies, procedures, and practices that are shared by all stakeholders in the organization.[12] An organization that has explicitly enacted policies on safety, that encourages safety-related training, and that promotes safety may be said to have a strong safety climate. A company that has a strong safety climate is likely to enable and support initiatives relating to health and safety training. These organizations will invest the necessary money and time to make the training program a success, and employees are likely to be responsive to the effort.

In this regard, consider an organization that does not place a high value on safety—that is, a company that does not have a strong safety climate. This type of operation may be hesitant to provide the support necessary to make health and safety training a successful endeavour. Similarly, employees of such an organization may be suspicious of the training program, wondering why the company suddenly seems concerned about their health and well-being. If analysis reveals that the organization's safety climate is not currently conducive to safety training, the next logical step may be to emphasize to organizational management the need for increased organizational attention to safety as well as the need to communicate to employees the intended move toward a health and safety focus. These efforts, if launched early in training development, will lay important groundwork for a health and safety training effort and ultimately contribute to the success of the training program.

One situation that may arise when conducting an organizational analysis regarding health and safety training needs involves an organization that does not generally focus on employee health and safety and that does not have a strong safety climate, but that is required by law to offer safety training. There is no easy answer for how to deal with such a situation. However, we suggest that individuals involved in a training needs analysis with such an organization emphasize the importance of a supportive organizational environment for successful training. Managers in this type of organization may respond to a bottom-line approach—an argument based on the return on investment of training dollars. If management can be convinced that its support will result in increased training effectiveness and tangible long-term benefits, they will be more likely to provide a supportive training environment.

safety climate
employees' shared perceptions of the importance of safety in the workplace

JOB/TASK ANALYSIS

The second step is to conduct a **job/task analysis**. The starting point here involves identifying the jobs to be targeted for training. Some forms of training, such as a basic safety orientation or a seminar on the role of health and safety committees, will apply to employees in many positions within the organization. Other types of training will be far more specific in terms of jobs being targeted. For example, training on the safe operation of a particular piece of machinery will apply only to those individuals whose jobs bring them into contact with that machinery.

Once the target job has been identified, one should obtain a detailed job description that outlines the tasks, duties, and responsibilities of individuals who hold that position. By working with a group of job incumbents and subject matter experts, one can rate the required tasks for their importance and frequency in the job. With respect to health and safety-related training, incumbents and subject matter experts should be surveyed on the health and safety risks involved in each task and their perceived competence to perform those tasks in a safe manner. The person developing the training program may want to observe several people performing the tasks in question to identify potential health and safety concerns that were not mentioned by the subject matter experts. The information can then be analyzed and interpreted.

The evaluation of the job in question and the inclusion of people with experience performing the job can greatly inform the training program that will ultimately be offered. The task analysis can help determine the exact nature of the problem to be solved. To consider a health and safety example, the survey component of the task analysis might reveal that though employees are vigilant about wearing their protective equipment, they tend to use it incorrectly. In that case, the training program should focus more on the proper use of the equipment rather than on convincing people to wear it. This point might have been missed were it not for the completion of a task analysis.

> **job/task analysis**
> a component of the training needs analysis process during which the jobs and specific job tasks that are in need of training are identified and studied

PERSON ANALYSIS

Finally, the assessment needs to investigate the training needs of individual employees. Individual employees' behaviour is considered to see whether performance meets desired standards. The ultimate goal in the **person analysis** is to determine who needs training. Such a decision can be made by comparing a person's current performance with a desired standard or level of performance. Which individuals will be included at this stage of the analysis will be largely determined by the organization's needs. In some cases the consultant or training director may be asked to assess those individuals who have demonstrated poor or unsafe performance in the past. In other organizations, employees included in the person analysis may be chosen randomly.

The next step in the individual assessment is to identify the method of assessment. Common needs assessment techniques include observation, work samples, and tests.[13] From here, the relationship between the desired standard for performance and the actual performance can be measured and the potential reason for performance gaps can be determined. The data gathered during this stage of the process inform the next steps in developing a training program. In some cases the person analysis may reveal that training will not be able to address the barriers to effective performance. For instance, one might discover that certain safety concerns are the result of worn equipment that is continually in a state of ill repair. In this case, the maintenance or replacement of

> **person analysis**
> a component of the training needs analysis process during which individual employees' behaviour is studied to identify gaps in performance

Simulators provide immersive experiences that can facilitate skill acquisition and allow for learners to fail and make mistakes safely.

equipment, rather than a training program, would be the next logical step. In other situations, training will be a viable or preferred option for addressing the problems uncovered in the needs analysis.

The type of training offered will depend on the nature of the problem. For example, if the person analysis reveals that safety concerns stem from the fact that individuals are not well versed in the operation of dangerous equipment, the training program to follow should focus on delivering knowledge about the proper operation of the machinery. Again, consider a case where the person analysis reveals that though individuals are aware of safety regulations in the operation of equipment and are capable of complying with those protocols, they choose to ignore them. In this situation, the training would best focus on safety-related attitudes in the workplace.

TRAINING DESIGN AND DELIVERY

Following the needs analysis, an informed decision can be made about the potential effectiveness of training as an option for addressing health and safety concerns. If training has a role to play in the solution to a health and safety problem, several decisions must now be made. These decisions involve translating what was learned from the needs assessment into the actual training initiative. Some of the pertinent decisions include the following:

1. What are the objectives for training?
2. Will the training program be designed or purchased?
3. What is the appropriate content for the training?

4. Who will receive the training?
5. Who will deliver the training?
6. Where will the training take place?

TRAINING CONTENT

Let's consider some of these questions as they apply to OH&S training. The first pressing question involves the objectives for training. In other words, what do you hope the trainees will take away from the program? Generally speaking, the training objectives will touch on the knowledge, skills, and behavioural changes that will be acquired through training. Objectives serve a number of important functions; for example, they set the groundwork for the needed training content, and they provide a starting point for tools for evaluating the effectiveness of the training program.

A second question is whether to purchase an existing training package or design an original program. In many cases, the purchase of an existing prepackaged program is more economical and fully meets the organization's needs. When it comes to health and safety, many training programs are readily available for purchase. For instance, St. John Ambulance sells first aid and CPR programs, both generic and custom. For an organization that wants to institute a first aid training program for individuals in particular high-risk jobs, it would make financial sense to choose a proven, prepackaged program from a reputable provider.

In other cases the organization will decide to design a custom health and safety training program, either in-house or with the help of a consultant. When the program's content is highly specific to the organization, custom program design may be necessary. For instance, a company wanting to offer a health and safety orientation for new hires would need to incorporate information that is unique to itself; such a program would be difficult to purchase in a prepackaged form. Also, training in the safe use of particular equipment or in the performance of particular tasks may require a training program that is not readily available for purchase; therefore, a customized program may be the only option.

With respect to training content, it is important that the program matches the needs identified in the needs analysis and ensures trainees achieve the training objectives. Even when the training program is purchased, there is likely some flexibility in the material that will be presented. One way to ensure that the training content is appropriate is to consult subject matter experts in the area in question. For instance, in a training program on the safe handling of hazardous materials, individuals with expertise in industrial hygiene may be consulted and asked for their input on the needed components of the training program.

TRAINING LOGISTICS

Who will receive the training is another important question during this phase of curriculum development. In some cases the answer will be obvious. If the law requires that all operators of a particular type of machinery have training in the operation of that machinery, the job of selecting who receives training is as simple as identifying the operators. Similarly, if the training program is a health and safety orientation for all new employees, each employee will complete the program on joining the organization. In other cases, decisions about who receives training will not be as obvious. For instance, provincial and territorial legislation requires that organizations have a certain number of trained first aid providers on-site. Only a small number of employees will need to

training objectives
statements regarding the knowledge, skills, and behavioural changes that trainees should acquire in the training program

CHAPTER 9 Training

complete this training. The decision of who enters the program is one that will have to be dealt with case by case.

A related issue is *how many* people will be trained at the same time. The accumulated research on training in general and on health and safety training in particular reveals that smaller groups make for more effective learning.[14] Also, individuals in the same training group should have similar jobs characterized by common risk exposure.[15] This contributes to the success of health and safety training initiatives.

Yet another issue is who will deliver the training (see, for example, **OH&S Notebook 9.1**). An effective trainer is vital to a successful training program. The trainer should be knowledgeable about the material as well as an effective communicator. For instance, a recent study showed the effectiveness of occupational therapists providing workplace training on musculoskeletal disorders.[16] In some cases the trainer will require certification in a particular area—for instance, the person who delivers first aid training will need certification as an instructor.

Another effective approach is a train the trainer program. In these initiatives, a subject matter expert with the appropriate content skills is provided with coaching in areas such as program delivery and communication. For example, an individual who is a member of an organization's health and safety committee may be trained to deliver the health and safety orientation for new employees. Worker-trainers may also contribute to the evaluation of training effectiveness, further increasing a sense of worker empowerment and ownership over the training process.[17]

The research literature has examined the effectiveness of subject matter experts who have undergone train the trainer programs. Generally, it appears that trainees respond well to subject matter experts as OH&S trainers and that such an approach can result in improved safety performance in the workplace.[18]

The final question we consider here is *where* the training takes place. This has long been a question of on-the-job versus off-the-job training. On-the-job training takes place while individuals are at work performing their regular job tasks. In other words, the training is incorporated into the performance of the task. For example, on-the-job training in the safe operation of a particular tool may have subject matter experts demonstrate the safe use of the tool while a new hire observes the process. The new hire can then use the tool under the guidance of the subject matter expert.

train the trainer
programs designed to offer subject matter experts in various content areas skills in program delivery and communication

OH&S NOTEBOOK 9.1

HOW TO SELECT TRAINING PROVIDERS

Once a decision has been made that health and safety training is an appropriate intervention, organizations are in a position to decide who will deliver that training program. If skilled trainers are not available in-house, the organization will turn to an external, professional trainer. What steps can the organization take to ensure that it hires a good training provider? The following are some qualities that organizations will want to ensure their training provider possesses:

- knowledge of training models
- experience in training
- OH&S expertise and experience
- industry experience
- willingness to customize the training to meet organizational needs good references

Source: B. Broadbent, "Training Providers: How to Pick a Winner," OHS Canada. Found at: http://www.ohscanada.com/training/howtopickawinner.aspx (accessed January 5, 2013).

Off-the-job training takes place away from the area where the work is conducted. It may be in a room on-site or in a different facility. The nature of the room will depend on the nature of the training. Some forms of training require little more than a boardroom and PowerPoint slides. Other forms may require simulators or particular equipment. **OH&S Notebook 9.2** reviews the training delivery method options for on- and off-the-job training.

OH&S NOTEBOOK 9.2

TRAINING DELIVERY METHODS

Another decision in the design of a training program is what training delivery methods will be used. There are numerous training methods to choose from. Of course, training can be delivered on-the-job or off-the-job. In either case, the training may or may not involve technology. The training method one chooses might depend on where the training is being offered, the content of the training, or the people being trained. Here are some training delivery options to consider.

On-the-Job Training

Job instruction: A structured approach to training job skills that involves a trainer developing a training plan and demonstrating tasks to a trainee, which the trainee then performs with the trainer's guidance and receives feedback on.

Performance aid: Devices such as visual aids are used to help trainees perform tasks. For example, a sign with visual cues that help employees follow the lockout procedure on a piece of equipment.

Job rotation: Trainees learn various tasks by completing different jobs/tasks within the organization.

Apprenticeships: Trainees receive on-the-job experience combined with classroom instruction.

Coaching: An experienced employee works closely with a new employee to help develop skills and provide feedback.

Mentoring: A senior employee is personally invested in helping a junior employee's development.

Off-the-Job Training

Lecture: The trainer presents the content orally to the trainees.

Discussion: The trainer and trainees have a verbal exchange about the material.

Audiovisual methods: Media are used to illustrate points and ideas.

Case incident or study: Trainees analyze a real-life problem or situation.

Behaviour modelling: Trainees attempt to imitate the actions of a model who is performing a task.

Role-play: Trainees practise skills within the training environment.

Games: Competition-based activities are employed to help develop skills.

Simulations: Trainees engage in physical or social events that are designed to re-create real situations. These may involve technology in terms of simulating devices or equipment.

Technology-based Training

Web-based: Trainees engage in training materials that are provided via the Internet. One example would be a webinar in which a presentation is delivered via the Web.

Video/television: Trainees watch video-based or televised material relevant to the topic on which they are being trained.

CD/DVD: Training materials are provided to trainees via a CD or DVD.

Teleconference: Trainees at various locations take part in audio or audiovisual exchange of information with a trainer using technology such as conference calls or Skype.

Source: From SAKS/HACCOUN. *Managing Performance Through Training And Development.* © 2004 Nelson Education Ltd.

WHMIS
Workplace Hazardous Materials Information System; a legislated training program in the handling of potentially hazardous chemicals in the workplace that ensures Canadian workers recognize hazardous materials and are knowledge-able in emergency procedures following a chemical spill

More recently, a third dimension has been added to the question of where health and safety training will be conducted. Some health and safety training programs are now being offered on the Web. For example, courses in the Workplace Hazardous Materials Information System (WHMIS), a legislated program in the safe handling of hazardous materials, are now being offered online. Web-based training in programs such as WHMIS may prove useful to a company that often has new hires who are computer savvy. However, it may not be as appealing or effective when the individuals who require training do not have access to nor a high degree of comfort with computers and the Internet. That said, some studies have found that computer-based instruction can be effective for some types of health and safety training. For example, in a study of agricultural workers with low levels of education and little computer experience, a computer-delivered training program on ladder safety saw an increase in safe ladder practices up to two months post training.[19] An online computer-based simulation emphasizing situation awareness proved effective among licensed pilots.[20] Ultimately, the program delivery choice will depend on the unique needs of the organization and employees.

Regardless of the location, research on the effectiveness of various health and safety training initiatives emphasizes the importance of active approaches to learning.[21] As you might conclude from a review of the training delivery options outlined in **OH&S Notebook 9.2**, training delivery methods vary substantially in their potential to engage trainees and are based on different theories about how individuals learn (see **OH&S Notebook 9.3**). For instance, a lecture is a passive and typically less engaging

OH&S NOTEBOOK 9.3

LEARNING THEORY AND TRAINING DELIVERY

Training in occupational health and safety can be associated with positive safety outcomes, such as safer worker behaviour and a reduction in safety incidents. However, training experts sometimes point out that potential contributions from general theories of learning are not reflected in health and safety training programs. Thus, the training programs may not be maximally effective.[i]

The ultimate goal of OH&S training programs is that the knowledge and skills gained in the training environment be transferred effectively to the workplace. Principles determined from extensive psychological research on learning can help create such a training environment. Three major approaches to the study of learning are the behaviourist perspective, social learning, and experiential learning. How might these learning approaches influence the design of health and safety training programs?

Behaviourist Perspective

The behaviourist approach characterizes learning in terms of observable stimuli and responses, without reference to any activity that occurs inside the individual.[ii]

Behaviourists state that learning results when a person associates particular behaviours with certain immediate consequences or rewards. Certainly, this notion applies to the training context; the experience gained during training should influence later job performance. Thus, according to behaviourists, training can increase the performance of desired behaviours by following those actions with rewards. The behaviourist approach suggests that health and safety training should target specific actions.[iii]

Several basic learning principles may be effective in helping increase the transfer of the knowledge, skills, and abilities acquired during training to the jobsite.[iv] These include using identical elements, such that the stimuli in the training environment are identical to those in the transfer environment. For instance, in a safety training program on the proper use of protective equipment, the very same brand and type of safety gear used at the jobsite should also be used in the training program. Furthermore, transfer of training may be improved when trainees are taught not only applicable skills, but also general principles that underlie the training content. For example, a training

(continued)

program on the safe operation of a piece of heavy equipment should also stress underlying principles regarding the widespread importance of safe behaviour in the workplace and the basic workings of the machinery itself. Also, multiple examples of a concept will provide the *stimulus variability* necessary to promote transfer of training to the worksite. For instance, in an emergency preparedness training program the trainers should provide examples from several types of emergency scenarios.

Social Learning

Social learning theory reflects a cognitive approach to learning. Its premise is that people learn by observing others. Observing others can help us learn various motor skills or styles of behaving. For instance, observing more experienced people can help a new employee learn how to use safety equipment at work. The people we observe during social learning are called *models.* The influential proponent of the social learning approach is Canadian Albert Bandura, who proposed that four mental processes facilitate social learning:[v]

1. *Attention.* Learners must notice the behavioural models and find them interesting. For instance, new employees who are looking for models will likely look to experienced employees who attract their attention and seem willing to help.

2. *Memory.* Learners must remember what they have observed. New employees who are observing senior employees operate a particular piece of machinery must remember all of the actions taken by the senior employees as they complete the task.

3. *Motor control.* Learners must use their observations to guide their own actions. For instance, if new employees are modelling a work task that involves heavy lifting, they must be capable of lifting that weight.

4. *Motivation.* The learner must have some reason to perform the modelled actions. For instance, OH&S trainees must be motivated to perform the job in a safe manner.

In the training environment, the trainer is the model, who must capture the attention of the trainee and appear interesting. This person should be perceived as an expert in the relevant field and be credible and appealing to the trainees. The information should be presented in such a manner that the trainees store it in memory and draw from this information to guide their future performance (i.e., when they are back on the job).

Experiential Learning

Experiential learning is a process aimed at developing knowledge and skills. Proponents of experiential learning contend that learning is maximized when knowledge is acquired via direct participation, when new insights are applied to realistic situations, and when trainees reflect on prior and new experiences.[vi] This type of learning can be accomplished by numerous methods, including problem-based learning, role-playing, and simulations. From a health and safety perspective, experiential learning approaches mean that trainees should engage in active learning environments that incorporate the training content into their experiences. Also, trainees should be encouraged to reflect on what they are learning and how it relates to their work setting.[vii] For example, a stress management program that follows an experiential learning approach might explore how individuals currently manage stress, have trainees actively incorporate new coping techniques in role-plays and their daily lives, and ask trainees to keep a diary in which they reflect on how the new techniques are working and help them manage their stress responses.

Sources: (i) M. Burke, D. Holman, and K. Birdi, "A Walk on the Safe Side: The Implications of Learning Theory for Developing Effective Safety and Health Training," *The International Review of Industrial and Organizational Psychology*, Vol. 21 (2006): 1–44; M. Colligan and A. Cohen, "The Role of Training in Promoting Workplace Safety and Health," in J. Barling and M. Frone, eds., *Handbook of Workplace Safety* (Washington: APA, 2004), pp. 223–48. (ii) M.S. Gazzaniga and T.F. Heatherton, *Psychological Science: Mind, Brain, and Behavior*, 2nd ed. (New York: Norton, 2006). (iii) M. Burke, D. Holman, and K. Birdi, "A Walk on the Safe Side: The Implications of Learning Theory for Developing Effective Safety and Health Training," *The International Review of Industrial and Organizational Psychology*, Vol. 21 (2006): 1–44. (iv) T.T. Baldwin, J.K. Ford, and B.D. Blume, "Transfer of Training 1988–2008: An Updated Review and Agenda for Future Research," *International Review of Industrial and Organizational Psychology*, Vol. 24 (1990): 41–70. (v) A. Bandura, *Social Functions of Thought and Action: A Social Cognitive Theory* (Englewood Cliffs: Prentice Hall, 1986). (vi) M. Burke, D. Holman, and K. Birdi, "A Walk on the Safe Side: The Implications of Learning Theory for Developing Effective Safety and Health Training," *The International Review of Industrial and Organizational Psychology*, Vol. 21 (2006): 1–44. (vii) M. Burke, D. Holman, and K. Birdi, "A Walk on the Safe Side: The Implications of Learning Theory for Developing Effective Safety and Health Training," *The International Review of Industrial and Organizational Psychology*, Vol. 21 (2006): 1–44.

training method. On the other hand, training methods that use simulations of real events are an active and typically more engaging approach to training. Training efforts predominantly relying on less engaging methods such as posters or videos can result in initial improvements in safety behaviour, but the results may be short-lived. More active forms of training—such as hands-on or interactive—seem to have a stronger and more durable effect on behaviour. Training efforts that involve behavioural modelling (such as simulations) and multiway feedback are recognized as particularly engaging for trainees.[22] Dialogue and storytelling have also been identified as training tools that engage trainees' attention and encourage them to think about the material being presented.[23]

A recent review of the safety training literature noted that highly engaging training methods are particularly important when the risk associated with the hazards in question is high.[24] When hazard severity was high, highly engaging training methods were associated with better safety knowledge and safety performance than were less engaging methods. The training method did not appear to influence safety knowledge or performance gained in training when hazard severity was low. The authors of the study proposed that this effect is due to "the dread factor." When OH&S training involves a high-risk hazard—for instance, use of explosives—active and engaging training helps trainees realize the true degree of severity and experience dread for the potential outcomes associated with exposure. This dread is a motivating factor to prompt the trainees to learn how to avoid the risks associated with the hazard in question.

Even when safety training programs have demonstrated a positive impact on safety-related actions in the workplace, continual upgrading of skills may be important if employees are to maintain the knowledge and skills they gained in training. Consider the case of employees who are designated first aid providers in their workplaces. These individuals may well experience long periods during which they are not called on to use their first aid skills. Yet in the event of an emergency, it is imperative that they correctly recall what they learned in training. Periodic refresher courses that reinforce what employees learned in their initial training program will go a long way toward ensuring that first aid providers correctly and quickly recall their treatment skills when called on to do so.[25] In fact, retraining, upgrading, and refresher courses are valuable in *all* areas of safety training. The more often employees are reminded of safety-related issues in the workplace, the more likely they are to properly enact safety behaviour.

TRAINING EVALUATION

Evaluation efforts following training programs consider the extent to which the training program has added value to the organization and the individual employees. Information gathered during training evaluation can be useful for identifying strengths and weaknesses in the training program and thus guide further curriculum development. Evaluation results can also be used to estimate the economic value of a training program. In a safety training endeavour, an economic factor that can be measured is the number of safety incidents or injuries. A training program that reduces injury rates will save the company money in days lost and compensation claims.

What type of information should be considered when a health and safety training program is being evaluated? Kirkpatrick's hierarchical model—a frequently used training

training evaluation a component of the ISD training model designed to assess the value added for individuals and organizations following the implementation of a training program evaluation model—suggests that there are four important measures that provide insight into the effectiveness of a training program, as follow:[26]

1. Did the trainees have positive reactions to the training?
2. Did the trainees learn the material covered in the training?
3. Did the trainees apply what they learned in training and realize a change in their work *behaviour*?
4. Did the organization see positive *organizational* results following training?

According to Kirkpatrick, these four form a hierarchy, with succeeding levels providing increasingly important information regarding the value of the training program. Training programs in which trainees report positive reactions, learn the material, apply that learning to their workplace behaviour, and contribute to positive organizational outcomes (e.g., increased productivity, fewer lost-time injuries) are considered effective.

INDIVIDUAL EVALUATION

How might a training evaluator go about gathering information on these four levels of training outcomes? The HR manager or training consultant has several measurement options open to him or her. Individual reactions to the training program might be assessed using tools such as surveys, interviews, or focus groups. Questions should be designed to assess all aspects of the program—including overall reactions as well as attitudes toward particular aspects of the training schedule. For instance, a training evaluation questionnaire for a workplace safety orientation might ask trainees to share their perceptions of the presentation by the health and safety committee chairperson; to indicate whether they thought the safety walkabout—where the trainees tour various parts of the building to discuss the safety issues at each site—was informative; to report their degree of satisfaction with the overall curriculum; and to rate the effectiveness of the orientation facilitator. Clearly, both affective reactions and utility-based reactions can be garnered at this stage of the evaluation. Affective reactions involve whether the trainees enjoyed the program; utility reactions incorporate the trainees' perceptions of the usefulness of the program.[27] Positive affective and utility reactions are important in training programs. If employees do not enjoy the training program or do not feel it is useful, they may be less likely to give it their full attention and will be less likely to take away the important messages delivered by the program. Some frameworks for training evaluation suggest that it is also important to assess the strength of the trainee's attitudes about training.[28] For instance, did the trainees have intense or extreme affective responses to a particular aspect of the training program?

Efforts to measure learning must assess trainees' mastery of the information presented. Evaluators may be interested in how well the trainees recall the information and in the extent to which they are able to incorporate the information into actions. For instance, in a health and safety training program designed to teach safe operating procedures for heavy machinery, the evaluator would be interested in the trainee's ability to recall the points on the safety inspection checklist for a particular piece of equipment. There are a number of ways to assess this knowledge. An evaluation could measure a trainee's ability to recognize the material covered in training using multiple-choice tests. The mastery of skills introduced in the training program could also be assessed using longer, written tests. To continue the example given above, a trainee might be asked to list all the steps included in the safety inspection for a particular piece of equipment.

Obviously, a successful training program is one that results in considerable knowledge and skill acquisition on the part of trainees.

Recently, there has been a shift in the types of cognitive outcomes that training evaluators hope to capture. The traditional focus on straight recall of verbal knowledge is increasingly shifting toward a focus on "procedural understanding" of the material presented, including questions about *why* things work in particular ways.[29] Keeping with our example of safe operating procedures for heavy machinery, procedural knowledge would involve *why* the safety practices are important and *why* they follow in a particular order.

Behavioural outcomes can be assessed *during* the training or *after* training back in the workplace. When task simulation is incorporated into training, evaluators can assess trainees' performance during the training program. Similarly, evaluators can assess trainees' motivation to incorporate new skills or knowledge by asking questions about their performance goals and their confidence in their ability.[30]

On-the-job behaviour can be assessed using self-report inventories in which trainees rate their own behaviour or by having supervisors complete a report on trainees' actions when performing the task in question. Similarly, the training evaluator may observe the employees' on-the-job performance. For example, following the training program on the safe operation of heavy machinery introduced above, a supervisor might observe an employee performing a safety inspection on the piece of equipment and rate his or her performance. The evaluator might then use objective indices of performance to assess behavioural change. For instance, after a training program on the importance and use of safety equipment such as earplugs for loud environments, a behavioural assessment might include observing employees at work to see whether they have a high rate of compliance in using their earplugs and other safety equipment.

ORGANIZATIONAL EVALUATION

Organizational results following training initiatives can also be assessed. Usually, the assessment of organizational outcomes involves analyzing organizational records. With respect to health and safety training initiatives, a number of organizational outcomes may be especially relevant:

1. *Incident, injury, and fatality rates.* Safety training programs designed to increase safe behaviour should contribute to reduced incident rates and, ultimately, reduced injury and death rates.

2. *Incidence of close calls.* **Close calls** or near misses occur when incidents or injuries are narrowly avoided. Effective safety training programs should reduce the number of near misses.

3. *Incidence of lost-time injuries.* Lost-time injuries are those in which the employee involved misses some work time because of the injury in the days following the incident. Successful safety training programs should see a reduction in lost-time injuries.

4. *Absenteeism.* This objective factor may be of particular importance in evaluating health-related training programs designed to reduce stress.

5. *Workers' compensation claims and costs.* Ultimately, health and safety training programs should result in decreased resort to workers' compensation programs, as successful training programs should decrease incident and injury rates.

close call
a series of events that could have led to a safety incident but did not

6. *Employee benefit costs.* Effective safety training can contribute to reduced use of programs such as physiotherapy and occupational therapy.

7. *Safety inspection reports.* If an organization is subject to internal or external safety inspections, improved performance on these inspections should be seen in areas that have been the subject of health and safety training.

The training evaluator will want to compare the organization's performance *after* the training program with its performance *before* training. Access to pre-training *and* post-training information will allow the evaluator to reach conclusions about improvements in organizational outcomes that are a result of training.

However, training evaluators will want to take great care to ensure that their measurements of pre-training and post-training variables are accurate. The training evaluator must consider a number of factors when assessing organizational indices of health and safety. As noted earlier, incident, injury, and fatality rates are indicators of safe or unsafe behaviour in the workplace. Most discussions about occupational safety, whether in the academic literature or in workplaces themselves, focus on actual safety incidents or fatalities. As a result, the focus is often on the number of incidents, the amount of lost time, whether the incident resulted in a claim for workers' compensation, and occasionally the number of workplace fatalities. The focus on such variables is understandable, given their visibility and the social and economic interest they attract.

Several factors, however, limit the reliability and utility of incident and fatality measures for organizational research and practice. First, major incidents with injuries and especially fatalities are relatively rare. As such, the distribution of major incidents and fatalities is skewed, rather than normally distributed, and this introduces challenges for statistical analyses of such data. Second, there is no clear agreement across jurisdictions as to what constitutes an occupational injury. For example, what one province or territory accepts as evidence of a back injury requiring time off work another might refuse, which renders any comparisons of injury rates across jurisdictions limited at best. Third, there is considerable concern that organizations' databases on incidents and fatalities may misrepresent the actual prevalence of problems.

Logs of lost-time injuries maintained by government agencies actually underrepresent the magnitude of these incidents.[31] In particular, initial episodes of lost-time injury may be accurately reported, but lost time due to reinjury or the persistence of problems following return to work are underreported. Organizations' in-house recordkeeping processes may contribute to this problem.[32] To offset the statistical imbalance, researchers have begun to ask how incident reports can be improved. For example, the inclusion of close calls may provide a useful supplement to incident reports, because they occur with greater frequency than do safety incidents. Also, the difference between a close call and an incident may be no more than luck. Therefore, including close calls in incident reporting is important for a more complete picture of safety-related events.

Self-reported measures of occupational events and injuries may provide a more valid indication than compulsory reports by the organization to government agencies, as there appears to be little incentive for workers to misreport safety incidents and injury experiences in a deliberate way.[33] Though there could be legitimate errors as a result of memory lapses, these would occur randomly across people and organizations and therefore would not bias the reporting of injuries or safety incidents in any way. A potential solution is to use multiple sources or records in identifying the "real" rates of incidents and injuries.[34]

CHAPTER 9 Training

// COMMON SAFETY TRAINING INITIATIVES

The health and safety training needs of any particular organization will be largely determined by factors unique to that organization—its size and the industry in question being two factors that contribute heavily to safety training needs. That said, several common safety training initiatives are applicable to organizations of all sizes and sectors. Next we review three of these: safety orientation, first aid training, and WHMIS training.

SAFETY ORIENTATION

Organizations with successful safety programs and safety records often begin to emphasize health and safety through an orientation program at the time employees are first hired. Integrating health and safety into the employee orientation program ensures that all employees are provided with a base level of health and safety training; it also reinforces the development of a safety climate in the workplace. Though the details will vary with the needs of specific workplaces, a general orientation to health and safety should include a review and introduction to:

- fire and emergency safety procedures
- incident policies (e.g., reporting, procedures for obtaining first aid)
- hazards unique to the workplace (e.g., material hazards, chemical hazards, physical hazards)
- protective personal equipment (e.g., how to obtain, how to use)
- WHMIS training
- the role of the joint occupational health and safety committee
- the roles and responsibilities of individual employees
- job-specific safety procedures (e.g., proper lifting technique, decontamination, lockout procedures)
- housekeeping and safety awareness

Cardio-pulmonary resuscitation and first aid training often involve active, experiential learning to practise specific skills.

FIRST AID TRAINING

Many Canadian employers are required under OH&S acts to provide first aid training to employees. The number of employees requiring certification in first aid in any given organization depends on several factors. Provincial or territorial health and safety laws determine first aid requirements based on factors such as the number of workers per shift, the distance from fixed medical services, and the hazard level of the workplace. Larger, isolated, higher hazard worksites require more trained first aid providers. The exact number of first aid certificates and the level of certification required vary among the provinces and territories.

Organizations such as St. John Ambulance provide first aid training programs that help employers meet or exceed the requirements set forth in provincial and territorial OH&S acts. In fact, St. John Ambulance provides full services in the provision and management of workplace first aid training programs. For instance, via its key account program, St. John Ambulance tracks the training and certificates of employees in an organization and notifies the organization when recertification is required.

WHMIS TRAINING

WHMIS has been discussed throughout this book. It is the standard for communicating information about hazards in Canada. Under WHMIS, hazardous or controlled products are labelled in a standardized manner and information regarding the safe handling of these products is provided via material safety data sheets (MSDSs) and worker training programs. The federal, provincial, and territorial health and safety jurisdictions all incorporate WHMIS. Employers are required to properly store and dispose of hazardous materials and to ensure that workers receive training in handling and using controlled products.

// SUMMARY

Canadian employees have the right to be informed about the hazards they may encounter in the workplace, and OH&S acts require the provision of health and safety training. Even so, many Canadians report that they have never received any safety training at work. Recent legislation means that employers who fail to provide a safe workplace may face charges of criminal negligence.

OH&S training can be described under a general training model. The ISD model, applied to the issue of health and safety, emphasizes the importance of a complete needs analysis before training is designed and offered. Needs analysis includes a consideration of the organization, the job, and the person. Key to health and safety training is ensuring that the organization is supportive of the initiative. If a company is not supportive of health and safety issues in general, the training effort is likely to encounter roadblocks.

Several factors must be considered in the design and delivery of OH&S training, including the content of the training, who will receive training, and who will do the training. Organizations must make certain that the training programs they offer comply with the standards set out in their jurisdiction's occupational health and safety act.

Health and safety training efforts should be evaluated to consider whether the trainees had positive reactions to them and learned the material. Evaluations should also consider the extent to which employee behaviours and organizational outcomes were influenced by the training. Health and safety training programs should be evaluated for their impact on safety-related outcomes in the workplace, such as incident, injury, and fatality rates and the incidence of close calls. Safety training programs designed to increase safe behaviour should reduce incident rates and ultimately reduce injury and death rates, besides reducing the number of near misses and lost-time injuries.

KEY TERMS

close call 234
instructional systems design (ISD) model of training 221
job/task analysis 225
needs analysis 222
organizational analysis 222
person analysis 225
safety climate 224
train the trainer 228
training evaluation 232
training objectives 227
WHMIS 230

DISCUSSION QUESTIONS

1. Canadian statistics suggest that many Canadians are not receiving appropriate safety training in the workplace. What are some of the reasons organizational managers might give for not providing safety training for their employees? Imagine that you are a health and safety consultant trying to convince the top management of a negligent organization to provide a health and safety orientation for new employees. What are some arguments you might use to convince the organization to support the training program?

2. Why is organizational support for a health and safety training initiative so important for the success of the training program?

3. What are some important organizational outcomes that can be used to evaluate the value that a training program has added to an organization?

4. What are some of the advantages and disadvantages associated with the use of Web-based health and safety training programs for individual employees? for organizations?

USING THE INTERNET

1. Each provincial and territorial government has its own health and safety legislation. Each refers to the importance and role of health and safety training. Using the Internet, look up the health and safety legislation in your province or territory. Note the ways in which training can help organizations and employees adhere to the law.

2. Using various Web resources, find out more about young workers' safety. Along with your classmates, brainstorm ways to build health and safety knowledge among young Canadians entering the workforce. How might we educate parents and employers about the health and safety risks associated with young workers?

3. Visit the websites of some large organizations in various industries, and look for information about their health and safety policies. What portion of the sites you visited contained information about health and safety training? Did the

attention given to training or the type of training described vary by industry or organizational size?

4. Search your school's website to investigate the health and safety training programs offered in your institution.

EXERCISES

1. Young workers are at considerable risk for safety incidents and injury in the workplace. Perform a person analysis by interviewing a young person who has recently entered the workforce. Based on what you have learned about occupational health and safety in this course, try to get an idea of that individual's awareness of health and safety in the workplace and the extent to which he or she is worried about his or her own safety at work. If you are unable to interview a new worker, have a classmate think back to his or her very first job and try to recall his or her health and safety-related attitudes upon entering the workforce. You will want to find out some information about the tasks this person performed at work and identify some of the potential hazards that were associated with the job.

2. Think back to various jobs that you have held. What types of health and safety training did you receive? Were the training programs effective? Compare your experiences with those of your classmates.

3. To find out more about health and safety training, contact a human resource professional and ask about health and safety training programs in his or her organization. You might use some of the following questions to guide your discussion.

   a. Does your organization have a health and safety orientation program? If so, what types of information does it cover?

   b. How many trained first aid providers are required per shift in your organization?

   c. What are some of the safety hazards and concerns employees in your organization encounter? Do you think that training is a useful option to help employees manage their exposure to these risks? Why or why not?

   d. Under what conditions does your organization rely on purchased, pre-existing health and safety programs? When might the company opt for custom-designed health and safety training programs? What factors influence this decision?

   e. What is the general attitude toward occupational health and safety training among employees in your organization? among management?

4. Bill C-45, the "Westray Bill," went into effect on March 31, 2004. Research this legislation. How many charges could you find? How many convictions? What impact do you think this legislation will have on Canadian employees' access to health and safety training? Do you think it will influence Canadian employers' attitudes toward health and safety training? Debate these issues with your classmates.

5. Imagine that you are a health and safety training consultant who has been working with an international courier company to offer training for its on-the-ground delivery staff regarding proper lifting procedures and safe driving. When thinking about how to evaluate the effectiveness of the training programs, what specific measures would you include?

As the OHS manager for a small manufacturing firm (28 employees) you need to design and deliver an occupational health and safety training program. Outline how you would go about designing such a program. What barriers and challenges do you foresee and how do you plan to overcome these challenges?

CASE STUDY 1 THE NEW HR MANAGER AT A1 MANUFACTURING

Sabine is the new HR manager at A1 Manufacturing. When she began her new position, she quickly realized that A1 did not pay much attention to issues of occupational health and safety. In fact, she determined that this company was in violation of a number of legislated health and safety requirements. She approached members of upper management with her concerns. At first they seemed unruffled by her warnings about health and safety violations throughout the company. Only when she reminded the upper management that the organization could face fines and that some executive-level individuals could face criminal charges if there was a safety-related incident did they sit up and listen. Sabine was given the job of fixing the problem.

She has determined that the organization needs to provide more health and safety training programs. She has contacted you, a training consultant, to help her design and implement new programs. What steps do you take in helping Sabine determine her training needs and implement training programs? Is there anything about the organization or Sabine's conclusion that training is the answer that concerns you? What are some potential obstacles to a potential training effort?

CASE STUDY 2 A YOUNG WORKER'S QUANDARY

Eighteen-year-old Gurjit has just started his very first job, working at a lumber yard. On his first day, Gurjit was given a hardhat and told he should purchase steel-toed boots. A more senior employee gave him some basic instruction about how to operate the forklift and told him to be careful. After his first shift, Gurjit has a feeling he can't shake. His new job feels dangerous, yet the company managers and his fellow employees do not appear particularly concerned about training him on safe work procedures. He doesn't want to let down the boss, who has given him his first job, by complaining. He doesn't want to disappoint his family, who are proud that he is working, by quitting—and besides, he needs the money. What options does Gurjit have? Whom can he contact about his health and safety concerns?

// NOTES

1. L.S. Robson, C.M. Stephenson, P.A. Schulte, B.C. Amick III, E.L. Irvin, D.E. Eggerth, S. Chan, A.R. Bielecky A.M. Wang, T.L. Heidotting, R.H., Peters, J.A. Clarke, K. Cullen, C.J. Rotunda, and P.L. Grubb. "A Systematic Review of the Effectiveness of Occupational Health and Safety Training," *Scandinavian Journal of Work, Environment, and Health* 38 (2012): 193–208.

2. P. Smith and C. Mustard, "How Many Employees Receive Safety Training During Their First Year of a New Job?" *Injury Prevention* 13 (2007): 37–41.

3. Ibid.

4. G.B. Cooke, I.U. Zeytinoglu, and J. Chowhan, "Barriers to Training Access," *Perspectives*, July 2009: 14–25, Cat. No. 75-001-X. Found at: http://www.statcan.gc.ca/pub/75-001-x/2009107/pdf/10907-eng.pdf (accessed June 6, 2016).

5. Canadian Standards Association (2014). *Occupational Health and Safety Training*. Mississauga, ON: CSA Group.

6. M.J. Colligan and A. Cohen, "The Role of Training in Promoting Workplace Safety and Health," in J. Barling and M. Frone, eds., *Handbook of Workplace Safety* (Washington: APA, 2004), 223–48.

7. A.M. Saks and R.R. Haccoun, *Managing Performance Through Training and Development*, 5th ed. (Toronto: Nelson Canada, 2010).

8. I.L. Goldstein and J.K. Ford, *Training in Organizations: Needs Assessment, Development, and Evaluation*, 4th ed. (Belmont: Wadsworth, 2002); Saks and Haccoun, *Managing Performance*.

9. Goldstein and Ford, *Training in Organizations*; Saks and Haccoun, *Managing Performance*.

10. M.J. Colligan and A. Cohen, "The Role of Training in Promoting Workplace Safety and Health," in J. Barling and M. Frone, eds., *Handbook of Workplace Safety* (Washington: American Psychological Association, 2004), 223–48.

11. R.K. Sokas, E. Jorgensen, L. Nickels, W. Gao, and J.L. Gittleman, "An Intervention Effectiveness Study of Hazard Awareness Training in the Construction Building Trades," *Public Health Reports* 124 (2009): 161–68.

12. D. Zohar, "Safety Climate in Industrial Organizations: Theoretical and Applied Implications," *Journal of Applied Psychology* 65 (198): 96–102; D. Zohar and G.A. Luria, "A Multilevel Model of Safety Climate: Cross-Level Relationships Between Organization and Group-Level Climates," *Journal of Applied Psychology* 90 (2005): 616–28.

13. Goldstein and Ford, *Training in Organizations*.

14. Colligan and A. Cohen, "The Role of Training"; K.R. Saarela, "An Intervention Program Utilizing Small Groups: A Comparative Study," *Journal of Safety Research* 21 (1990): 149–56.

15. Colligan and A. Cohen, "The Role of Training."

16. T.F. Fisher, B. Brodzinski-Andriae, and S. Zook. "Effectiveness of Work Injury Prevention Education and Safety Training by an Occupational Therapist," *The British Journal of Occupational Therapy* 72 (2009): 450–57.

17. J.A. Daltuva, V. Williams, L. Vazquez, T.G. Robins, and J.A. Fernandez, "Worker-Trainers as Evaluators: A Case Study of a Union-based Health and Safety Program," *Health Promotion Practice* 5 (2004): 191–98.

18. Colligan and A. Cohen, "The Role of Training." For a specific example of a successful program see Q. Williams, Jr., M. Ochsner, E. Marshall, L. Kimmel, and C. Martino. "The Impact of a Peer-Led Participatory Health and Safety Training for Latino Day Labourers in Construction," *Journal of Safety Research* 41 (2010): 253–61.

19. W.K. Anger, J. Stupel, T. Ammerman, A. Tamulinas, T. Bodner, and D.S. Rohlman, "The Suitability of Computer-Based Training for Workers with Limited Formal Education: A Case Study from the US Agricultural Sector," *International Journal of Training and Development* 10 (2006): 269–84.

20. S. Kearns, "Online Single-Pilot Resource Management: Assessing the Feasibility of Computer-Based Safety Training," The *International Journal of Aviation Psychology* 21 (2011): 175–90.

21. Colligan and A. Cohen, "The Role of Training."

22. M.J. Burke, S.A. Sarpy, K. Smith-Crowe, S. Chan-Serafin, O.S. Rommel, and G. Islam, "Relative Effectiveness of Worker Safety and Health and Training Methods," *American Journal of Public Health* 96 (2006): 315–24.

23. M.J. Burke, M.L. Scheuer, and R.J. Meredith, "A Dialogical Approach to Skill Development: The Case of Safety Skills," *Human Resource Management Review* 17 (2007): 235–50; E.T. Cullen, "Tell Me a Story," *Professional Safety*, July 2008, 20–27.

24. M.J. Burke, R.O. Salvador, K. Smith-Crowe, S. Chan-Serafin, A. Smith, and S. Sonesh. "The Dread Factor: How Hazards and Safety Training Influence Learning and Performance," *Journal of Applied Psychology* 96 (2011): 46–70.

25. D. Arnold, "A Matter of Life and Death," *Occupational Health* 55 (2003): 21–23.

26. D.L. Kirkpatrick, "Evaluating Training Programs: The Four Levels (San Francisco: Berrett-Koehler, 1994); Saks and Haccoun, *Managing Performance*.

27. Saks and Haccoun, *Managing Performance*.

28. J.K. Ford, K. Kraiger, and S.M. Merritt, "An Updated Review of the Multidimensionality of Training Outcomes: New Directions for Training Evaluation Research," in S.W.J. Kozlowski and E. Salas, eds., *Learning, Training, and Development in Organizations* (New York: Routledge/Taylor and Francis Group, 2010).

29. Ibid.

30. Ibid.

31. B. Evanoff, S. Abedin, D. Grayson, A.M. Dale, L. Wolfe, and P. Bohr, "Is Disability Underreported Following Work Injury?" *Journal of Occupational Rehabilitation* 12 (2002): 139–50.

32. H. Conway and J. Svenson, "Occupational Injury and Illness Rates, 1992–1996: Why They Fell," *Monthly Labor Review* 121, no. 11 (1998): 36–58.

33. L. Grunberg, S. Moore, and E. Greenberg, "The Relationship of Employee Ownership and Participation to Workplace Safety," *Economic and Industrial Democracy* 17 (1996): 221–41.

34. Conway and Svenson, "Occupational Injury and Illness Rates."

MOTIVATION AND SAFETY MANAGEMENT SYSTEMS

CHAPTER LEARNING OBJECTIVES

AFTER READING THIS CHAPTER, YOU SHOULD BE ABLE TO:

- discuss the importance of safety behaviour in the workplace
- identify the categories of safety behaviour
- explain the importance of individual motivation in safety behaviour
- describe behaviour modification approaches to motivating safety
- articulate how goal setting and feedback influence safety behaviour
- understand the facets of self-determination theory of motivation and how they relate to safety motivation
- evaluate the role of organizational support for safety in contributing to safety behaviour
- discuss the role of the safety climate in the performance of safety behaviours
- understand the role that safety leadership plays in creating a safe work environment
- describe OH&S management systems, such as CSA-Z1000-14, and appreciate how they help organizations promote workplace safety

The Vancouver Airport Authority operates by four values: Safety, Teamwork, Accountability, and Innovation. You'll notice that safety comes first. In his corporate blog, Craig's Corner, President and CEO Craig Richmond wrote that "Safety is paramount at YVR. It's embedded in all our decision making and is our core corporate value which we live every day ..."

The Vancouver Airport Authority operates Vancouver International Airport (YVR). In 2015, the busy airport saw more than 20 million passengers, 287 000 aircraft take-offs and landings, and $484.7 million in revenue. In early 2016 Vancouver International Airport was recognized as the Best Airport in North America, a position it has now held for seven straight years. The Best Airport designation is based on passenger airport experiences in things such as check-in experiences, comfort, efficiency, and friendliness. YVR achieves all this success on the foundation of safety as its first value.

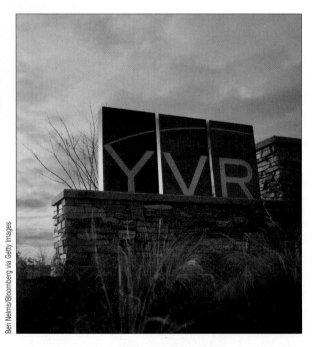

Vancouver International Airport (YVR) places safety as the foundation of its values and operations. In 2015 it was awarded the distinction of Canada's Best Occupational Health + Safety Culture.

Another distinction for Vancouver International Airport is safety related. In late 2015, the Vancouver Airport Authority was awarded "Canada's Best Health + Safety Culture," the top prize in the Canada's Safest Employers Awards Program. The airport authority has integrated health and safety into its culture and operations. In this workplace, all meetings start with a safety discussion, all departments set safety goals, employees work actively to protect themselves and each other, and employees have a voice and role in developing and fostering the safety programs. There is a President's Award for Safety Excellence for departments that develop innovative safety measures. The framework for safety for the Vancouver Airport Authority comes from its Safety, Security, and Environment Policy. This policy is the foundation of its occupational health and safety management system, which reflects the OHSAS 18001 Standard. The occupational health and safety committee plays an important role in the organization. But, in addition, the airport authority's view is that health and safety applies in every part of the organization. The efforts have positive safety outcomes. For example, in 2015 the organization had zero health and safety non-compliances. You can read about the organization's programs, practices, and successes in "YVR Connects: 2015 Sustainability Report," which is available on the YVR website.

Sources: Vancouver Airport Authority, "YVR Connects: 2015 Sustainability Report." Found at: http://www.yvr.ca/en/about-yvr/leadership-and -accountability/sustainability-report(accessed May 7, 2016); Craig Richmond, "Craig's Corner. Safety First" (April 29, 2015). Found at: http:// www.yvr.ca/en/blog/craigs-corner-safety-first (accessed June 6, 2016); Vancouver Airport, "YVR Breaks Record: Named #1 Airport in North America for Seven Years in a Row" (March 16, 2016). Found at: http:// www.yvr.ca/en/media/news-releases/yvr-named-number-one-airport -in-north-america-for-seven-years-in-a-row (accessed June 6, 2016); Vancouver Airport, "YVR Wins Prestigious Safety Awards" (November 4, 2015). Found at: http://www.yvr.ca/en/blog/yvr-wins-prestigious-safety -awards (accessed June 6, 2016); Workplace Safety and Prevention Services, "Inside the Vancouver Airport Authority's Award-winning H&S Culture" (January 12, 2016). Found at: http://www.wsps.ca/Information -Resources/Articles/Inside-Vancouver-Airport-Authority-s-award -winning.aspx (accessed June 6, 2016); Workplace Safety and Prevention Services, "Vancouver Airport Authority Wins Inaugural "Canada's Best Health + Safety Culture Award" (November 9, 2015). Found at: http://www.wsps.ca/Information-Resources/Articles/ Vancouver-Airport-Authority-wins-H-S-Culture-Award.aspx (accessed June 6, 2016).

In the previous chapter we considered the importance of health and safety training in the workplace. In this chapter we consider the equally important issue of how employees are motivated to utilize their knowledge and skills, perhaps those gained during training, to consistently perform their work duties in a safe manner. We explore this issue by considering safety behaviour, theories of motivation, and organizational factors (e.g., safety leadership and climate) that support employee safety efforts. The issues we consider here focus on preventing incidents and injuries at work rather than simply responding to workplace incidents. We further examine how these motivational and organizational factors of leadership and climate play important roles in occupational health and safety management systems. However, as a starting point for our discussion, we first need to consider the qualities of workplace safety behaviour to illustrate the value of employee behaviour in incident and injury prevention in the workplace.

// SAFETY BEHAVIOUR

There are several ways to categorize health and safety programs. One is in terms of *engineering* interventions, *administrative* interventions, and *behavioural* interventions.[1] Engineering interventions typically focus on changing the physical environment to reduce exposure to hazards. Administrative interventions modify workplace procedures, policies, and exposure in the work environment. Finally, behavioural interventions focus on changing employee attitudes, knowledge, or behaviour regarding occupational health and safety. All three types of intervention have been at least somewhat successful in improving health and safety at work. A review of the empirical research on comprehensive OH&S management systems—those encompassing multiple intervention categories—reports mostly favourable results for these programs on outcomes such as safety climate, injury rates, and economic factors like insurance rates.[2] However, additional research is needed to help address some of the methodological limitations noted in the research literature.

All things being equal, it is preferable to remove or eliminate the hazard via an engineering solution than to rely on other types of health and safety programming. However, such engineering controls are not always possible.[3] Therefore, much of the psychological research in the area of occupational safety has focused on behavioural interventions, in particular those designed to increase safety-related behaviours. There is a relationship between safety behaviours and injury rates[4] and targeting employee behaviour is an effective injury prevention strategy.[5]

> **safety behaviours** behaviours leading to safe performance of a particular job

At least eight general categories of behaviour contribute to safe working performance:[6]

- proper use of hazard control systems in the workplace
- development of safe work habits
- increased awareness and recognition of workplace hazards
- acceptance and use of personal protective equipment (PPE)
- maintenance of housekeeping and maintenance standards
- maintenance of accepted hygiene practices
- proper responses to emergency situations
- self-monitoring and recognition of symptoms of hazardous exposure

Health and safety programs have been aimed largely at encouraging one or more of these general classes of behaviour. Some of these categories will be familiar to

CHAPTER 10 Motivation and Safety Management Systems

MyLoupe/UIG via Getty Images

Proper use of PPE is an aspect of workplace safety behaviour.

you as the targets of the health and safety training efforts we described in Chapter 9. For example, training programs might teach proper lifting techniques to develop safe work habits and WHMIS training enhances the worker's ability to recognize chemical hazards. However, workplace safety promotion encompasses more than ability-based training.

When considering safety behaviour a distinction is often made between safety compliance and safety participation.[7] Safety compliance is achieved when employees follow core safety-related rules and generally work in a safe manner. Certainly, safety compliance helps reduce injuries and safety incidents.[8] Safety participation refers to employee behaviours that go beyond simply working within safety standards and safety compliance. It involves employees behaving proactively and voluntarily to improve safety levels in the working environment.[9] For example, proactive employees engage in behaviours such as volunteering to participate in safety audits, attending safety meetings, and encouraging their supervisor to take actions to improve safety. Both safety compliance and safety participation are components of safety behaviour.

Generally, for individuals to work safely at least three conditions are necessary. First, workers must have the *ability* to work safely—that is, they must possess the knowledge and skills to perform their jobs in a safe manner. This requirement is generally addressed through the provision of OH&S training. Second, workers must be *motivated* to work safely—that is, they must intend to use their knowledge and skills to enhance safe working performance. Finally, workers must have the *opportunity* to work safely—that is, the environment or organization must support and encourage safe work.

These three factors combine in a multiplicative rather than an additive fashion (see **Figure 10.1**). Thus,

$$\text{Safety performance} = \text{Ability} \times \text{Motivation} \times \text{Opportunity}$$

safety compliance
the extent to which employees follow safety rules and procedures

safety participation
the extent to which employees go beyond compliance and engage proactively and voluntarily to actively improve safety

FIGURE 10.1

ABILITY, MOTIVATION, OPPORTUNITY

Safety performance relies on ability, motivation, and opportunity. This figure presents safety behaviour as a full circle. You can see that if any one of these important components is missing, the full circle of safety behaviour will not be achieved and thus safety performance in the workplace will not be realized.

An important implication of this multiplicative equation is that the model of safety performance is noncompensatory. A high level of motivation and many opportunities do not compensate for a lack of ability. Similarly, a high level of ability and motivation cannot make up for a work environment that does not provide opportunities and support for safe working. Safety performance relies on ability, motivation, and opportunity together. If any one of these components is missing, safety performance in the workplace will not be realized. The question for health and safety programs is, How do we use this model to increase safe work behaviours?

The basic premise of the multiplicative model of safety performance is that safety can be enhanced by increasing an employee's abilities, motivation, and opportunities to work safely. Having said this, it is important to note that all three components of the model must be implemented for safety performance to be enhanced. For example, training (i.e., increasing ability) alone is insufficient to change safety behaviours over the long term.[10] However, safety training coupled with motivational programs appears to be an effective combination in changing safety behaviours. After the great deal of attention paid in Chapter 9 to increasing employees' ability to perform safety behaviours, this chapter focuses on motivation and opportunity. We will consider these facets of safety performance in turn.

// MOTIVATING SAFETY BEHAVIOUR

Safety motivation reflects an "individual's willingness to exert effort to enact safety behaviour and the valence associated with those behaviours."[11] Higher levels of safety motivation are associated with improved safety behaviour in workplace.[12] Thus, one way to facilitate workplace safety is to increase safety motivation. Let's consider three major theoretical explanations of motivation: reinforcement theory (or behaviour modification), goal-setting theory, and self-determination theory as they relate to health and safety at work.

> **safety motivation**
> an individual's willingness to exert effort to enact safety behaviour and the valence associated with those behaviours

REINFORCEMENT THEORY

Reinforcement theory, which focuses on how consequences shape motivation, is the foundation for workplace behaviour modification programs. Because a behaviour is more likely to be repeated when it is followed by reinforcement, organizations rely on rewards and incentives to influence positive workplace behaviours. For example, a financial bonus is given as a reward if an employee meets a sales target. Or an employee is given a public praise for becoming actively involved in the workplace's safety program.

Using behaviour modification approaches to increase workplace safety behaviours in the workplace has been largely successful and adaptable across various types of workplaces.[13] Evidence shows that behavioural programs promote safety behaviours and are associated with reductions in incident and injury rates[14] across a wide range of work environments, including mining,[15] bus driving,[16] and construction.[17]

Behavioural programming in the workplace relies on the ABC model of behaviour.[18] Simply stated, the ABC model holds that any behaviour occurs because of events that trigger the behaviour (the antecedents) and the results that follow the behaviour (the consequences). Thus, any behaviour can be represented as

Antecedent → Behaviour → Consequence

To change a specific behaviour, we have to change either the antecedent or the consequence of the behaviour. Behaviour modification focuses on changing the consequences of behaviour. If we want to understand why workers perform unsafe acts or fail to engage in safe practices, a good place to begin is by considering the consequences of both safe and unsafe behaviours.[19] Such consequences can be characterized along three dimensions: positive or negative, immediate or delayed, and certain or uncertain. Generally, behaviour that is followed by immediate, positive, and certain consequences is more likely to occur again.[20] Conversely, consequences that are delayed, negative, or uncertain have either a minimal or an adverse effect on safety behaviour.

Unfortunately, the consequences of safe behaviour are typically delayed, negative, or uncertain. It is rare for coworkers to praise for using a proper lifting technique, and it is more likely to go unnoticed by supervisors. Sometimes safe actions such donning PPE takes extra time or are uncomfortable, both of which are often perceived as negative consequences. Even when there are positive consequences for behaviour, they are often delayed or uncertain. For example, a safety award may be given to an individual based on behaviours that occurred a year or more ago, irrespective of the recent behaviours used by that worker.

On the flip side, unsafe behaviours often have positive, immediate, and certain rewards. For example, not wearing protective equipment may increase comfort and speed of work. Any negative consequences that could follow, such as disciplinary warnings or injuries, are typically rare and often delayed. Individuals may go months and even years not wearing safety goggles and never experience an injury as the result. Even this simplistic consideration suggests that the decision to wear the protective clothing is unlikely to be based on the consequences associated with not wearing the clothing.

Behavioural programs attempt to institute positive, immediate, and certain consequences for safe working procedures. Simple feedback is a popular type of consequence in such programs; individuals are typically observed performing their job and given immediate feedback on the safety of their actions. Incentives such as free lunches or lottery tickets are second in popularity. You can learn about the elements of behaviour-based safety programs in **OH&S Notebook 10.1**. **OH&S Today 10.1** considers the

ELEMENTS OF A BEHAVIOUR-BASED SAFETY PROGRAM

The content of a behaviour-based safety initiative will vary with the context in which it is offered (e.g., organization, type of job), but several basic elements are common across behaviour-based safety programs:

1. Identifying observable behaviours that affect safety-related outcomes

2. Outlining precise measurement of the identified behaviours

3. Providing feedback on how to perform the behaviour more safely

4. Highlighting the consequences of the behaviour to motivate employees

5. Rewarding safe performance of the targeted behaviour

Several factors that support the success of a behaviour-based program have been suggested. These include ensuring that the workplace is ready for a behaviour-based safety intervention, customizing the program to the needs of the organization, receiving support from all levels of organizational leadership, and reflecting on the value added by the program as it is implemented. Factors that likely hinder program success include forcing people to be involved, using the data collected to launch employee discipline, and focusing only on behaviour without also considering the work environment that supports it.

Sources: Adapted from E.S. Geller, "Behavior-Based Safety in Industry: Realizing the Large-Scale Potential of Psychology to Promote Human Welfare," *Applied and Preventive Psychology*, Vol. 10 (2010): 87–105; B. Sulzer-Azaroff and J. Austin, "Does BBS Work? Behavior-Based Safety and Injury Reduction: A Survey of the Evidence," *Professional Safety*, (July 2010): 19–24; S.M. Galloway. "What It Takes to Make Behavior-based Safety Work," *Occupational Health & Safety* (September 1, 2015). Found at: https://ohsonline.com/Articles/2015/09/01/What-It-Takes-to-Make-Behavior-Based -Safety-Work.aspx (accessed May 7, 2016); S.M. Galloway. "The Contributing Factors of Behavior-based Safety Failures," *EHS Today* (March 1, 2011). Found at: http://ehstoday.com/safety/management/contributing-factors-behavior-based-safety-failures-0301 (accessed May 7, 2016).

A RISKY SIDE OF BEHAVIOUR-BASED SAFETY PROGRAMS?

Behaviour-based safety programs appear to succeed in reducing workplace incidents. However, some stakeholders are wary of this approach, even questioning whether it revives the notion of "accident proneness" as an explanation for why some workers are injured. Some workers' groups note the downsides of safety programs that focus exclusively on behavioural interventions. What are their concerns?

At some point safety incentives can be intimidating for employees. No one wants to be the person who costs coworkers a reward for achieving a reduction in injury rates. As such, some workers feel peer pressure not to report an actual injury and may even rely on their leave days rather than file a workers' compensation claim.

Other workers fear discipline if they are injured; thus, an employee who sustains an injury may fear reprisal from the organization and decide not to report the incident. Of course, the result in these cases is the underreporting of workplace injury and illness.

Sometimes the actions rewarded under behaviour-based programs are the avoidance of negatives that may be out of the individual's control (e.g., the reduction in lost-time injuries) rather than the achievement of positives that *are* under an individual's control (e.g., consistently wearing

(*continued*)

protective equipment, refusing unsafe work). Critics also note that a focus on employee behaviour as an avenue for injury reduction sometimes leaves real hazards unabated in the workplace, diverting attention from the core concern, which is to make the workplace safer. Additionally, these critics question whether such an approach is effective at reducing occupational illnesses.

How might an HR manager address these concerns about behaviour-based safety programs? Certainly, the use of engineering interventions whenever possible will reduce the burden placed on individual employees. Additionally, comprehensive safety programs incorporate administrative interventions in the health and safety management program. The organization should have a progressive health and safety policy, strive for a positive safety culture, and truly support employee safety initiatives. Employees need to have the opportunity to work as safely as possible. If value is placed on the well-being of every worker, rather than on the interpretation of injury or safety incident statistics alone, employees may feel less threatened by behavioural interventions at work.

When the decision is made to include incentives as part of a behaviour-based safety program, keep the following in mind:

a. Feedback alone may be a sufficient incentive.

b. Incentives should be tied to preventive behaviours under individual control (e.g., the proper use of a personal protective device) rather than to outcomes such as incidents or injuries that may be beyond an individual's control.

c. Focus on positive reinforcement for safe behaviour rather than using approaches that apply punishment.

Courtesy of MyHardHatStickers.com

Critics of behaviour-based safety programs point out that rewards and recognition based on factors outside the employee's control, such as injury rates, can be intimidating for employees. This hard hat sticker is an example of such a public recognition based on injury data. One can imagine that the owner of this sticker might not want to report an injury that would end a run of injury-free work. Best practice suggestions for behaviour-based safety programs suggest rewarding actions within the employee's control.

d. Incentive programs should not attempt to compensate for a lack of training, shoddy equipment, poor maintenance, or, more generally, other failures in the safety systems.

e. All employees should be eligible to earn and receive incentives.

f. Incentives should be meaningful.

Sources: Workers' Health and Safety Centre, "Behaviour-Based Safety: The Blame Game." Found at: https://www.whsc.on.ca/Files/Resources/Hazard-Resource-Lines/Hazard-Resource-Lines-Complete-Library/Behaviour-Based-Safety-WHSC-Resource-Line-en.aspx (accessed June 6, 2016); UFCW Canada, "Behaviour-based Safety." Found at: http://www.ufcw.ca/index.php?option=com_content&view=article&id=40&Itemid=125&lang=en (accessed June 6, 2016).

possible downsides of this approach and how to mitigate them. Research generally suggests that feedback alone, without the use of material incentives, is an effective means of behavioural change. For example, one study illustrated that increased feedback from supervisors regarding safety incidents and PPE increased hearing protection use, reduced injury, and improved perceptions of safety climate.[21]

GOAL SETTING

Goal-setting theories focus on how our internal intentions, the goals we want to achieve, influence behaviour.[22] Setting goals can have desirable behavioural effects[23] and it has been extensively applied in organizations. As a method for changing behaviour, goal setting concerns itself with the antecedents of behaviour–that is, the "A" of the ABC model described above. One interesting study examined how changing the antecedents of a behaviour can influence attendance at a health and safety training program. Researchers manipulated the type of mailing that the staff members received about the training program. Some received messages that stressed the importance of the content of the training program and invited them to take part in a session. Others received a mailing that asked them to commit to attending a particular session. Those who signed up for a session in advance had a higher rate of actual attendance at the training program than did those who received the message about the importance of the program.[24]

Setting a specific goal (e.g., wearing PPE 95% of the time) provides an antecedent for the behaviour by reminding the individual of what he or she is expected to do. Goals serve as antecedents to behaviour in four main ways:

1. They direct attention and action to the desired behaviour.
2. They mobilize effort toward actions to achieve the goal.
3. They increase persistence.
4. They motivate the search for effective strategies to help obtain them.

Several investigators have demonstrated that goal-setting techniques provide a valuable adjunct to feedback systems in motivating desired behaviours. It appears that five factors augment the effectiveness of goal setting:[25]

1. Goals must be *difficult and challenging* to result in improved performance. Goals that are a stretch for the individual have more of an impact on performance than easy goals or the absence of goals.
2. Goals must be *achievable* to lead to better performance. Goals that are too hard can quickly become demotivating.
3. Goals must be *specific*. The goal must identify specific behaviours, specify how many times they must be performed, and specify the performance standard. Nonspecific goals that are too broad are more like wishes or desires–not goals.
4. Individuals must be *committed* to the goals. Goals that aren't accepted aren't acted on. People tend to accept a goal when they see its importance, participate in setting the goal, trust the coach, or feel they can control the behaviour.
5. *Feedback* regarding goal progress is also helpful in goal achievement.

Goal setting is one component of the classic management by objectives approach introduced by Peter Drucker.[26] Management by objectives is an approach to management that focuses efforts on goal setting, employee participation in decision making, and feedback on one's efforts and progress. Research suggests that management by objectives interventions can positively influence employee productivity.[27] Management by objectives has been applied specifically to occupational health and safety initiatives.[28] As you'll see later in the chapter, occupational health and safety management systems draw on elements of the management by objectives approach including goal setting and employee involvement.

SELF-DETERMINATION THEORY

The self-determination approach recognizes that people are motivated by a variety of things and have varied reasons for acting.[29] Looking to various motivators for safety, we might presume that some people wear their PPE to avoid injury while others might wear it only to comply with their employer's behavioural safety program. People may volunteer for the JOHSC to garner favour with their boss or they may do so because they truly value safety.

Self-determination theory distinguishes amotivation from motivation. Amotivation reflects a complete lack of motivation.[30] Self-determination theory reflects multiple dimensions of motivation. At one level, self-determination theory differentiates between extrinsic and intrinsic motivation.[31] Intrinsic motivation or internal motivation happens when people engage in behaviour purely out of interest and because they find the experience satisfying. Extrinsic motivation happens when people act for more instrumental reasons, such as gaining a reward or avoiding a negative outcome. To use a broad example, Chung is taking a dance class for fun. Mike is taking the same dance class because he wants to make his wife happy.

It is easy to articulate extrinsically motivated examples of safety behaviour.[32] For instance, Angie attends the safety meetings at work because they are required for all employees. Sadek wears his fall protection while working at heights because his supervisor strictly enforces safety rules. Examples of true, instrinsically motivated safety behaviour are perhaps less common, but we can imagine individuals who become very interested in and enjoy aspects of workplace health and safety such as an OH&S officer who is nominating her employer for a safety award out of a true pleasure at sharing the company's safety accomplishments. That said, it is harder to imagine a person who wears earplugs, eye protection, and so on because they are so much fun to wear![33] But self-determination theory has a more nuanced view of extrinsic motivation that may have important implications in the realm of OH&S.

There are different types of extrinsic motivation, reflecting the extent to which the person experiences the extrinsic motivation as controlling or as autonomous.[34] Autonomous motivation is self-directed and happens when people act on their own will and choice. Controlled motivation happens when people act in response to pressure, like Sadek wearing his fall protection or Angie attending the safety meetings.

In particular, self-determination theory identifies four types of extrinsic motivation.[35] The most controlled form of motivation is *external regulation*, which occurs when pressures outside the individual—for example, a boss, a law, or a reward—prompt a person to behave in a particular way. Consider Evan, who works in a machine shop. He consistently uses PPE on a particular day because he knows a safety inspector is on-site and being caught without it may result in disciplinary action. Another type of controlled motivation, *introjected regulation*, happens when a person acts in a particular way because of pressure originating within him or herself. For instance, in the machine shop Gretchen uses PPE because she'd feel guilty if she didn't.

Extrinsic motivation can also stem from self-directed or autonomous reasons.[36] With *identified regulation*, people choose to act in a manner that is in line with their own goals. At the machine shop, Ricardo consistently performs all the appropriate lockout procedures because he wants to avoid injury and knows that the lockout procedures will help him achieve that goal. Finally, *integrated regulation*, the most autonomous form of extrinsic motivation, reflects engaging in actions that reflect one's sense of identity. Harry, machine shop supervisor, acts safely and encourages others to do so because he identifies himself as a safety-conscious person, whether it be in wearing PPE, following the OH&S

---

amotivation
complete lack of motivation

intrinsic motivation
motivation based on one's interest and enjoyment

extrinsic motivation
motivation rooted in instrumental reasons for acting

autonomous motivation
self-directed motivation reflecting an individual's free will

controlled motivation
motivation based in response to pressure

TABLE 10.1

A SUMMARY OF LEVELS AND TYPES OF MOTIVATION IN SELF-DETERMINATION THEORY					
SELF-DETERMINATION THEORY					
NO MOTIVATION	EXTRINSIC MOTIVATION				INTRINSIC MOTIVATION
Amotivation	External	Introjected	Identified	Integrated	Internal
	[__Controlled Motivation__]		[_____Autonomous Motivation_____]		

Source: Based on M. Gagné and E. L. Deci, "Self-Determination Theory and Work Motivation," *Journal of Organizational Behaviour*, Vol. 26 (2005): 331–62.

regulations, or driving the speed limit. **Table 10.1** summarizes the relationships among the different types and levels of motivation incorporated in self-determination theory.

Considering the ABC model described above, one can see that self-determination theory relates to both the antecedents and the consequences of behaviour. Like behavioural reinforcement models, controlled motivation focuses on the consequences of actions (e.g., reward, guilt). Alternatively, like goal-setting models, autonomous motivation focuses on the antecedents of behaviour (e.g., goals, self-identity).

Self-determination theory offers several important implications for OH&S research and practice.[37] For instance, the distinction between controlled and autonomous motivation might help us better understand people's safety compliance efforts versus their safety participation efforts. Self-determination theory also offers researchers and practitioners guidance for developing autonomous motivation among workers. Certain social conditions, particularly those that promote people's sense of autonomy, sense of competence, and sense of relatedness, promote self-directed, internalized motivation.[38] The development of interventions targeting workplace climate and leadership as organizational factors to foster these social conditions may be advantageous.

// INCREASING OPPORTUNITY FOR SAFETY BEHAVIOUR

Even when workers are well trained and highly motivated, they may not perform safely on the job. Workers also need to have an opportunity to perform safely through the provision of resources and organizational support. Consider PPE use as an example; management must make the equipment and training on its use available. Perhaps more importantly, management must demonstrate a commitment to health and safety and communicate it throughout the organization. Organizations with a commitment to safety can help and learn from each other as a means to improve safety across organizations, as illustrated by Ontario safety groups program, described in **OH&S Today 10.2**.

MANAGEMENT COMMITMENT TO OH&S

Management commitment to health and safety is a key requirement for improved workplace health and safety. A review of the empirical literature on health and safety training initiatives shows that a high level of management support for safety increases

PEER LEARNING AND SUPPORT TO CREATE SAFETY CHANGE: SAFETY GROUPS IN ONTARIO

The Workplace Safety and Insurance Board (WSIB) of Ontario offers safety group opportunities for companies that prioritize safety. Within the groups, organizations can learn from each others' experiences in implementing occupational health and safety programs. Working with a group sponsor who leads the group, the groups identify safety program elements to target and group members choose what one they want to focus on in their workplaces. The meetings allow for shared experiences, resources, and support. There are financial incentives to participate, as groups can receive WSIB premium rebates based on their safety activities. The program has been effective; group members report improved safety outcomes such as improved injury rates and have realized savings via the rebate incentive element. Group members also reported confidence in being able to transfer what they learned in the group back to their workplaces.

Sources: WSIB. "Safety Groups Program." Found at: http://www.wsib.on.ca (accessed May 7, 2016); S. Perruzza, Workplace Safety & Prevention Services, "The Importance of Incentives in the Safety Group Program: A Sponsor's Perspective" (November 30, 2012). Presented at International Symposium on the Challenges of Workplace Injury Prevention through Financial Incentives, Toronto. Found at: https://www.iwh.on.ca/prevention-incentives-2012/proceedings/perruzza (accessed June 6, 2016).

the impact of health and safety-related training in workplaces.[39] Certainly managers who are committed to health and safety can help create opportunities for employees to engage in safety behaviours. For instance, managers can encourage safety behaviours by not placing productivity-related goals ahead of employee safety.[40] Knowing that their safety comes first will allow employees the freedom to take the time to work safely, properly use protective equipment, and halt work operations if there is a risk to safety.

Though top management has an important role to play in the promotion of workplace health and safety, it is also apparent that that supervisors' attitudes play an important role in shaping risk perceptions. Similarly, coworker attitudes can influence individual perceptions of workplace hazards and encourage or inhibit self-protective behaviour. One study showed that workers' perceptions of risk were influenced more by their perceptions of management, supervisory, and coworker commitment to health and safety than by their personal experiences with incidents in the workplace.[41]

In short, management has a central role to play in improving safety performance. By sending a strong message about the importance of health and safety in the organization, by holding individuals responsible for their own and their subordinates' safety performance, and by taking safety concerns seriously, managers establish an orientation toward health and safety that allows individuals to perform their jobs safely. We suggest that there are two important vehicles by means of which management communicates the value they place on safety in their organization: the safety climate, and safety leadership.

IMPROVING SAFETY CLIMATE

You will recall from the previous chapter that an organization's *safety climate* reflects the shared perceptions among all employees and organizational stakeholders regarding the importance of safety in the workplace.[42] A positive safety climate is associated with a number of positive safety outcomes such as improved safety motivation, reduced injuries, and lower rates of underreporting for workplace injury.[43]

An organization can use several different strategies to promote a positive safety climate in several ways. In Chapter 9, we illustrated that supporting safety training is one such avenue. Another is to have explicit and enacted policies on safety. If employees are aware of the organizational safety policy and believe the organization stands behind that policy, they should feel secure in making safety a priority in their own actions. In this way, the policy will contribute to safe conduct. As you'll see below, an occupational health and safety management system can help integrate OH&S concerns across a company's operations.

An effective route to promoting a positive safety climate is to include safety-related information when communicating production-related goals. A managerial focus on achieving high productivity may inadvertently deter employee safety. To the extent that employees want to reach or exceed the organizational production expectations, they may become so focused on working quickly that they ignore safety protocols. Certainly, such a course of events is most likely in cases where following safety procedures slows the pace of work. Therefore, managers should be careful to stress that the achievement of production goals does not come before employee safety at work.

Another strategy organizations use to influence safety climate is rewarding safe behaviour. Individuals or groups with good safety records benefit from various bonuses or even job promotions. Other companies opt to withhold rewards from those who have a safety violation on their record. Still others promote their reputation as a safe organization by making their safety records—such as number of days without a lost-time injury—available to the public. The data are mixed as to the effectiveness of these approaches. As discussed in **OH&S Today 10.1**, there is a potential risk to behavioural-based programs.

Some have considered how organizations can improve safety performance by engaging strategies to improve a company's *safety culture*. Safety culture is a broader concept than safety climate and can be taken to reflect the qualities of the organizational culture that affect safety attitudes and behaviour.[44] In one study, an intervention to increase the quality and frequency of interactions of workers with safety committee members and among safety committee influenced indicators of safety culture and injury data.[45] Improving communication between workers and front line management appears to have positive influence on safety in workplaces.[46]

Perceived safety climate is a strong predictor of employees' safety performance.[47] One study of restaurant employees reported that positive safety climate perceptions were related to a reduction in safety-related events common in restaurants (e.g., knife slips, grease spatters, trips) and this decrease in safety events in turn contributed to a reduction in occupational injuries (e.g., cuts, burns, fractured bones).[48] A study of drivers in a motor vehicle fleet found that safety climate perceptions were associated with the safety of current work-related driving behaviour and of future driving intentions.[49]

SAFETY LEADERSHIP

Organizations can create opportunities for safety behaviour, and to achieve a positive safety climate, via safety leadership—that is, organizational leadership that focuses on and promotes safety. Substantial evidence suggests that when leaders actively promote safety, employees and organizations alike experience better safety records and more positive safety outcomes.[50] Employees' perceptions of managers' and supervisors' commitments to safety are strongly related to safety-related outcomes[51] and employees' perceptions of managerial receptiveness to safety issues predict individual willingness to raise safety concerns.[52] Additionally, employees' perceptions of supervisors' safety-related

safety leadership
organizational leadership that is actively focused on and promotes occupational health and safety

Courtesy of NIOSH

Leaders who take an active approach to safety contribute to positive safety outcomes. Be a champion for safety!

active transactional leadership
a form of leadership based on the foundation that leaders actively communicate to followers the tasks that are required to meet expectations

contingent reward
a form of active transactional leadership in which leaders reward employees who meet their communicated expectations

management by exception (active)
a form of active transactional leadership in which leaders monitor workers' actions and step in with corrective action when needed to prevent serious problems from occurring

transformational leadership
highly effective approach to leadership that emphasizes employee well-being and is characterized by idealized influence, inspirational motivation, intellectual stimulation, and individualized consideration

leadership are positively associated with safety consciousness; perceptions of the safety climate; and, through these intervening variables, safety events and actual injuries.[53]

Leaders need to enact active safety-focused behaviour to realize positive safety outcomes. Leaders taking a passive approach to safety predicts negative health and safety-related outcomes.[54] Leaders who ignore safety concerns and who "turn a blind eye" to safety-related issues may think they are not doing any harm, but they are sending a message to their employees that safety issues are not important. Furthermore, inconsistent safety leadership that jumps between active and passive approaches sends mixed messages to workers and can reduce the positive effects of safety leadership on safety outcomes.[55]

Two styles of active leadership discussed in the OH&S domain are active transactional leadership and transformational leadership.

ACTIVE TRANSACTIONAL LEADERSHIP Via transactional leadership, leaders articulate to workers the tasks that are required to meet leadership expectations.[56] Sometimes this is achieved in a passive manner, whereby leaders intervene only to correct problems that occur. More effectively, individuals can use active types of transactional leadership. One such active approach is contingent reward, in which leaders reward employees who meet their communicated expectations.[57] Sound familiar? Influencing safety behaviour by rewarding consequences is an aspect of behaviour-based safety programs. In the academic safety literature, safety-related contingent rewards have been associated with fewer injuries, as well as increased safety compliance and participation.[58] Certainly, one would imagine that being rewarded for adhering to articulated safety rules would lead to safety compliance behaviour.

Leaders might also invoke a type of active transactional leadership called management by exception (active) where leaders monitor workers' actions and step in with corrective action when needed to prevent serious problems from occurring.[59] The influence of management by exception (active) on safety behaviour is not fully clear. Some research has concluded that it is an intrusive and corrective form of leadership with negative effects on safety.[60] However, in the broader sense, management by exception (active) has been associated with positive outcomes such as perceived leader effectiveness.[61] Certainly, in safety-critical occupations, well-timed corrective actions can help avert disaster.[62] It may also draw attention to safety rules, thus promoting safety compliance.

A meta-analytic review of safety leadership found that active transactional leadership was directly associated with increased safety compliance, which in turn predicted reduced workplace injuries. Active transactional leadership also has a positive effect on safety climate. Safety climate was related to safety participation, which in turn predicted injuries.[63] The take-home message? Active transactional leadership can exert a positive influence on safety in workplaces.

TRANSFORMATIONAL LEADERSHIP Another active approach to safety leadership is **transformational leadership**. Transformational leadership can help leaders become champions of safety.

Transformational leaders are highly effective leaders who also show a substantial degree of concern for the well-being of their employees.[64] They exhibit four characteristics in their interactions with their employees: idealized influence, inspirational motivation, intellectual stimulation, and individualized consideration.[65] Transformational leaders provide idealized influence in that they are admired and trusted role models. Via inspirational motivation, transformational leaders communicate high expectations to their subordinates and provide a sense of meaning and challenge for followers. Transformational leaders intellectually stimulate their followers in that they encourage creativity and questioning of the status quo. Finally, transformational leaders provide individualized consideration in that they pay attention to each employee as an individual and act as a mentor or coach.

When these characteristics are directed toward safety-related concerns, improved safety behaviours tend to follow.[66] Transformational leadership is associated with increased safety compliance and participation.[67] For instance, a leader who communicates high expectations regarding the safe performance of work tasks, who motivates employees to behave safely and report safety concerns, who encourages employees to question the assumption that working safely equates to working slowly, and who individually discusses safety concerns with employees is engaging in safety-specific transformational leadership. Such a leader is likely to foster a highly safe work environment. A research example from the nuclear power industry shows that the promotion of open communication via empowering leadership is associated with improved safety participation.[68]

For an organization looking to improve its safety climate and provide an environment in which employees feel able to engage in safety behaviours, an increased focus on transformational leadership may be one option. Studies suggest that transformational leadership, including safety-specific transformational leadership, can be effectively trained.[69]

The accumulated evidence shows that transformational leadership has a direct and positive effect on safety participation behaviour and an indirect effect, via its influence on safety climate, on safety compliance. Contrast this to active transactional leadership, which has the opposite pattern directly affecting compliance, but only indirectly affecting participation.[70] What does this pattern mean? It might mean that different types of active leader behaviour differentially predict safety outcomes. That is, active transactional leadership on its own might promote and sustain safety compliance behaviour among employees, but promoting and sustaining safety participation may require the safety championing support of a transformational safety leader.

// ORGANIZATIONAL HEALTH AND SAFETY MANAGEMENT SYSTEMS

Throughout this chapter and the previous chapter on training, we have considered how to promote safe behaviour in the workplace. We have concluded that the utilization of safety behaviour requires that employees have the needed skills, be motivated to act in a safe manner, and have the opportunity to engage in safe behaviour while at work. We particularly looked at how organizational leaders can help promote a positive safety climate and build safety motivation among employees. We now consider how all of these come together in workplaces. One vital tool for organizations is an **occupational health and safety management system (OHSMS)**. These are also sometimes simply

> **occupational health and safety management system (OHSMS)**
> reflect an interactive collection of strategic organizational approaches and programs focused on identifying, achieving, and maintaining desired occupational health and safety targets

CHAPTER 10 Motivation and Safety Management Systems

called safety management systems. OHSMS can be "characterized as a set of institutionalized, interrelated and interacting strategic elements designed to establish and achieve OH&S goals and objectives."[71] In other words, OHSMS reflect an interactive collection of strategic organizational approaches and programs focused on identifying, achieving, and maintaining desired occupational health and safety targets. The role of organizational leadership in helping to build, implement, and sustain a successful OHSMS must be emphasized. Leaders from various areas and levels of an organization need to work jointly to prioritize workplace safety, integrate safety practices into all aspects of the organization's operations, and communicate the pivotal importance and value of safety to employees and other stakeholders. OHSMS interventions have become increasingly popular over the past two decades, with organizations implementing systems and various agencies—for instance, the Canadian Standards Association and the International Labour Organization—developing standards and auditing practices for their development and implementation.

Occupational health and safety management systems range in scope. An effective OHSMS places OH&S as an integrated concern across all aspects of an organization's business operations. For instance, all departments, such as human resources, purchasing, maintenance, finance, and sales should consider OH&S as a core concern. What might this look like in practice? An OHSMS might dictate that the purchasing department should routinely consider safety as a decision factor before deciding on new equipment to buy and install. The finance department should consider OH&S in its budgeting processes, and maintenance should keep in mind all the recommended upkeep procedures to ensure that equipment functions safely.

What separates an OHSMS from more traditional OH&S programs? Typically, OHSMS feature OH&S concerns in a more integrated and proactive light.[72] Although OHSMS approaches may differ across organizations, there are some common features. First and foremost in many OHSMS is a focus on organizational and leadership commitment to safety. Similarly, employee participation, the assurance of adequate resources to support OH&S activities, and safety goals and objectives are core features in these systems.[73] For more on these and other common OHSMS features, see **OH&S Notebook 10.2**. Read about one company's experience and success with OHSMS in **OH&S Today 10.3**.

OH&S NOTEBOOK 10.2

PRIMARY ELEMENTS OF OCCUPATIONAL HEALTH AND SAFETY MANAGEMENT SYSTEMS

There are several standards for occupational health and safety management systems available internationally. These various models have much in common and provide frameworks by which organizations can become more proactive about safety and integrate OH&S across their business operations. What are the core elements of an OHSMS? One team of researchers who were developing a performance measurement tool for OHSMSs compared a range of models. Choosing four highly comprehensive models, they identified 16 primary elements of OHSMSs to incorporate into their assessment tool. They are:

1. Management commitment and resources
2. Employee participation
3. OHS policy
4. Goals and objectives

(*continued*)

5. Performance measures

6. System planning and development

7. OHSMS manual and procedures

8. Training system

9. Hazard control system

10. Prevention and corrective action system

11. Procurement and contracting

12. Communication system

13. Evaluation system

14. Continual improvement

15. Integration

16. Management review

Other researchers have since compared the OHSMS components and found substantial overlap with the list above.

Sources: C.F. Redinger and S.P. Levine, "Development and Evaluation of the Michigan Occupational Health and Safety Management System Assessment Instrument: A Universal OHSMS Performance Measurement Tool," *American Industrial Hygiene Association Journal*, Vol. 59 (1998): 578; L.S. Robson, J.A. Clarke, K. Cullen, A. Bielecky, C. Severin, P.L. Bigelow, E. Irvin, A. Culyer, and Q. Mahood, "The Effectiveness of Occupational Health and Safety Management System Interventions: A Systematic Review," *Safety Science*, Vol. 45 (2007): 332; J.M. Haight, P. Yorio, K.A. Rost, and D.R. Willmer, "Safety Management Systems: Comparing Content & Impact," *Professional Safety*, 59, 5 (2014): 44–51.

OH&S TODAY 10.3

SETTING A GOAL FOR SAFETY: "NOBODY GETS HURT" AT IMPERIAL OIL

Imperial Oil is committed to a safe and productive workplace with the goal "Nobody Gets Hurt." The company is working toward this goal via the company-wide Operations Integrity Management System (OIMS), which is a comprehensive health and safety framework that focuses on 11 elements, with management leadership, commitment, and accountability viewed as core drivers of the system. Imperial Oil believes that its health and safety focus contributes to organizational performance and increases its competitive advantage.

Imperial Oil's commitment to health and safety is showing results. The company's 2014 numbers tell the tale. That year Imperial Oil logged more than 52 million hours worked, the company's highest ever. Its safety incident frequency rate was less than half the industry rate and more than 2500 people received multi-day safety fundamentals training. Other aspects of Imperial Oil's health and safety program include safety leadership training, office safety, driver safety, contractor safety, and a loss prevention program that involves employees in hazard identification and peer coaching.

Source: Imperial Oil. Found at: http://www.imperialoil.ca/Canada-English/community_safety_people.aspx (accessed June 7, 2016); Imperial Oil, *2014 Corporate Citizenship Summary Report*. Found at: http://www.imperialoil.ca/Canada-English/Files/Imperial_CCR_Report_2014.pdf (accessed June 7, 2016).

There are several standards available internationally by which to measure OHSMS. These include the International Labour Organization's ILO-OSH 2001, the British Standards Institute's OHSAS 18001, and the American National Standards Institute's ANSI Z10. The Canadian Standards Association published its standard for occupational health and safety management systems, CSA-Z1000-06, in 2006, and updated it in 2014. The various standards have much in common in guiding organizations toward effective occupational health and safety management systems. Let's consider the CSA-Z1000-06, and its 2014 update (CSA-Z1000-14) in more detail.

Like many other standards, the CSA-Z1000 is based on the Plan-Do-Check-Act continuous quality improvement model.[74] As illustrated in **Figure 10.2**, this cycle promotes OH&S in a strategic and continuous manner. Guided by OH&S policy, the Plan stage allows organizations to consider issues such as legal requirements pertaining to safety,

FIGURE 10.2

THE CSA-Z1000-06 PLAN-DO-CHECK-ACT MODEL FOR OCCUPATIONAL HEALTH AND SAFETY MANAGEMENT SYSTEMS

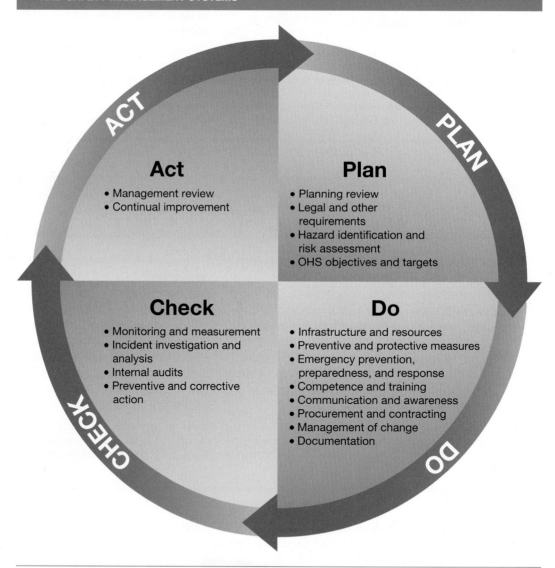

Act
- Management review
- Continual improvement

Plan
- Planning review
- Legal and other requirements
- Hazard identification and risk assessment
- OHS objectives and targets

Check
- Monitoring and measurement
- Incident investigation and analysis
- Internal audits
- Preventive and corrective action

Do
- Infrastructure and resources
- Preventive and protective measures
- Emergency prevention, preparedness, and response
- Competence and training
- Communication and awareness
- Procurement and contracting
- Management of change
- Documentation

Source: With the permission of the Canadian Standards Association, operating as CSA Group, material is reproduced from CSA Group standard, Z1000-14 entitled "Occupational Health and Safety Management," which is copyrighted by CSA Group, 178 Rexdale Blvd, Toronto, ON, Canada M9W 1R3. This material is not the complete and official position of CSA Group on the referenced subject, which is represented solely by the standard in its entirety. While use of the material has been authorized, CSA Group is not responsible for the manner in which the data is presented, nor for any interpretations thereof. For more information or to purchase standards from CSA Group, please visit http://shop.csa.ca/ or call 1-800-463-6727.

hazards and risk, and the setting of OH&S goals and objectives. At the Do stage organizations are engaged in ongoing safety activities such as emergency preparedness, safety training, and preventive measures. In the 2014 update, emphasis is provided on how to incorporate workers into workplace safety management activities and programming. The Check stage incorporates activities such as safety monitoring, incident investigation, and auditing. The Act stage involves managerial review and continuous improvement, an aspect strengthened in the 2014 update. The Plan-Do-Check-Act model is cyclical. For instance, a concern raised via managerial review would influence later planning and acting with respect to OH&S.[75]

The standard emphasizes that commitment, leadership, and participation are "crucial to the success of an OHSMS."[76] Its proscribed activities for senior management include establishing the OHSMS, ensuring appropriate resources for OH&S, developing OH&S policy, and encouraging worker participation. To encourage worker participation, an element emphasized in the recent revision, organizations need to do things such as remove barriers to participation, establish OH&S committees, and deliver appropriate health and safety training.

The CSA Standard also recognizes the core role of an OH&S policy in the effective delivery of an OHSMS.[77] The policy should be developed in consultation with employee groups. Once adopted, it should be widely publicized by means of meetings, newsletters, pamphlets, and so forth. The policy should be posted in management offices to serve as a constant reminder of the commitment and responsibility of the executive branch. The corporate health and safety policy is the most visible sign of management commitment to health and safety, so this commitment should be expressed clearly and unambiguously.

Individuals must understand their role in enacting the health and safety policy. Accountability for OH&S elements assigned to various positions should be articulated. Employees should be held responsible for safe work practices, including the reporting of all observed unsafe practices, procedures, and hazards to the appropriate supervisor. All employees should be required to participate in OH&S training and development programs. As part of the OHSMS, a timetable for the review and evaluation of the policy and regulations by the chief executive officer, president, or board should be outlined. For more information, see the tips for writing a health and safety policy outlined in **OH&S Notebook 10.3**.

OHSMS interventions are embedded within organizations and several contextual factors can influence the effectiveness of the system. Organizational and leader support is emphasized as a core aspect of program success. The energy and persistence of the individuals involved in delivering the elements of the OHSMS are drivers of success. Additionally, a workforce that is engaged in the program elements and feels empowered to enact safety behaviours, make safety relevant decisions, and create safety change is associated with program success. Programs elements that are designed to reflect the concerns and interests of the workers contribute to effectiveness.[78] Additionally, efforts need to ensure that the OHSMS is a visible part of the organization that is understood by employees.[79]

Elements of OHSMS can be used a motivator for firm-level and individual safety performance. One study examined administrative elements of OHSMS that focus on human performance. Researchers considered factors such as making hiring decisions with safety in mind, cooperation, safe work procedures, and employee involvement. Each had a positive influence on injury and illness rates in workplaces.[80]

Occupational health and safety management systems can be mandatory or voluntary. Some industries require safety management systems. For instance, Transport Canada requires them in the aviation industry.[81] Requirements can also vary depending

HEALTH AND SAFETY POLICY CHECKLIST

An organizational health and safety policy must be comprehensive and effective. The CCOHS provides useful information regarding policy development and evaluation on its website. Below are some example questions that a health and safety committee might ask when evaluating its own organization's policy. Responses to items like the ones here will help guide further development and refining of the policy:

- Is a clear commitment to health and safety evident in the policy statement?

- Is the senior officer responsible for implementing and reviewing the policy identified?

- Is the policy signed by the president or CEO?

- Have the views of all stakeholders (e.g., employees, managers, supervisors, safety representatives, and safety committees) been incorporated?

- Was the safe performance of work tasks discussed with employees? Is there a clear statement of how their performance will be assessed?

- Is the role of employees in health and safety matters stated (e.g., the positions on inspection teams and safety committees)?

- Are individual responsibilities for health and safety duties clearly allocated?

- Are the people responsible for functions such as safety incident reports, safety inspections, and first aid identified?

- Is health and safety given as great a priority as economic and marketing matters?

- Is the employer's duty to provide health and safety training to all employees stated in the policy?

- Does the policy ensure that health and safety issues will be considered when planning new methods or processes?

- Is the financing of health and safety programs detailed and ensured?

- Are all employees aware of the policy? Are copies of the policy available to all employees?

- Are there periodic revisions and updates of the safety policy? Are the procedures for and timing of such reviews clarified?

- Does the policy make clear that the ultimate responsibility for safety rests with senior management?

- Is safety and health performance included in employee performance reviews?

- Does the policy list arrangements for liaison with contractors?

- Does the policy help make individuals aware of their legal responsibilities?

Source: CCOHS, "Guide to Writing an OHS Policy Statement." Found at: http://www.ccohs.ca/oshanswers/hsprograms/osh_policy.html (accessed June 7, 2016).

on location. In some countries, it is mandatory for organizations to have an OHSMS in place. For example, via its regulations, Norway requires an OHSMS. In Canada, an OHSMS and compliance with CSA-Z1000-14 is voluntary for organizations. However, despite its voluntary nature, implementing an OHSMS that meets the CSA-Z1000-14 standards carries numerous benefits. An effective OHSMS can help improve an organization's OH&S performance. One study found that organizations that adopted an OHSMS had better safety performance on a variety of outcomes including employee safety training, articulation of safety goals, risk identification, and risk analysis.[82] Another study reported that improvements in existing OHSMSs were associated with improved safety outcomes including safety participation.[83]

Another benefit of adopting an OHSMS that complies with the CSA-Z1000-14 standard is that if a safety incident were to occur, compliance with the standard would help an organization establish due diligence. A common misconception exists that written programs, policies, and audits raise the liability of the corporation in terms of regulatory compliance or in the event of a safety incident. In fact, many courts are basing the severity of civil and criminal penalties in part on the employer's ability to prove that it was duly diligent in auditing and correcting deficiencies in its own operations. If the corporation does not have an OHSMS in place, how will it prove beyond a reasonable doubt that it has taken every reasonable precaution to ensure the health and safety of the workers and the environment as required under Canadian occupational health and safety legislation? Clearly, maintaining an OHSMS is increasingly important for Canadian employers.

// SUMMARY

A comprehensive approach to increasing health and safety in the workplace should emphasize employees' ability to act in a safe manner, their motivation to do so, and the provision of opportunities to perform their tasks safely. A number of approaches can be taken to increase employees' safety motivation, including the use of behaviour modification, goal setting, and a focus on autonomous motivation via self-determination theory. Also, the organizational context in which the employee is asked to perform his or her work should emphasize safety. We stressed the importance of a positive safety climate and active safety leadership in setting the stage for safety behaviours. We also considered the importance of occupational health and safety management systems, particularly those that comply with standards such as the CSA-Z1000-14 to help integrate OH&S with other organizational functions, to improve an organization's safety performance, and to demonstrate due diligence.

KEY TERMS

active transactional leadership 256
amotivation 252
autonomous motivation 252
contingent reward 256
controlled motivation 252
extrinsic motivation 252
intrinsic motivation 252
management by exception (active) 256
occupational health and safety management system (OHSMS) 257
safety behaviours 245
safety compliance 246
safety leadership 255
safety motivation 247
safety participation 246
transformational leadership 256

DISCUSSION QUESTIONS

1. Though considerable empirical data support their effectiveness, debate continues about the use of behaviourally based safety programs in industry. Employees and unions have often rejected such programs. Why do you think this is so? What can be done to enhance the acceptance of such programs?

2. Explain how focusing on behaviours rather than on safety incidents might be a better approach to improving occupational health and safety.

3. Why do you think setting goals can influence an employee's safety-related actions in the workplace?

4. How might organizations help employees create autonomous motivation for safety-related behaviours?

5. Describe the role of an organization's safety climate in the promotion of safety behaviours at work.

6. What role must organizational leaders play in creating a safety-focused workforce?

7. What are the main characteristics of occupational health and safety management systems?

8. What are the main benefits of OH&S management systems, like CSA-Z1000-14? What types of challenges might an organization face when trying to implement such a program?

USING THE INTERNET

1. Many organizations have their health and safety policies posted on their websites. With a group of classmates, examine these policies. Each of you should choose a different organization in a different market sector. How long are the policies? What information do they cover? Do they establish the unique responsibilities of management and employees? Do they refer to the organization's safety leadership? Compare your findings with those of your classmates.

2. Assess the safety culture of your school or workplace. The following weblink may give you some ideas about questions that assess factors related to safety culture: http://www.tc.gc.ca/eng/civilaviation/publications/tp13844-menu-275.htm.

3. Search social media sites such as Facebook and Twitter for organizations that are using these sites to promote occupational health and safety. What are some of the messages they are getting out? Who are they likely to reach? To what extent are they interactive? Do you think that social media are effective tools in communicating OH&S messages?

4. Organizations are increasingly adopting comprehensive OH&S management systems that aim to comply with the standards articulated by various agencies (e.g., CSA, ILO). Search the Internet for examples of the types of management systems companies are using. Compare the programs to the frameworks suggested by the standards' associations. Do you think they comply?

EXERCISES

1. In discussing health and safety management systems, we have emphasized the responsibilities and roles of management in establishing and enforcing safety

standards. What is the role of employees in these programs? To what extent should employees be responsible for taking the initiative to enhance health and safety in the workplace?

2. Imagine you are on a newly formed national committee that will be awarding safety awards to Canadian organizations. The mandate of this committee is to recognize excellence in the promotion of safety at work. What criteria do you think should be used to assess organizations' performance in this area? Create a draft of a rating form that the committee might use to evaluate nominated organizations.

3. Throughout this chapter we have emphasized the importance of managerial support for health and safety initiatives. In particular, we have noted the importance of a positive safety climate in the realization of safety-related goals. Imagine you are the newly hired human resource director in a manufacturing organization that currently does not place a high degree of value on health and safety—in other words, an organization with a negative safety climate. Top executives have indicated that they would like this situation to change, and they tell you that part of your job will be to improve safety performance in the organization. What are the first three initiatives you would launch to improve the safety climate of this organization?

4. With a small group of classmates, create a proposal for developing an effective OH&S management system for an organization that one of the team members has worked in (or is knowledgeable about). You will need to identify the health and safety concerns in that organization, suggest ways that these concerns could be addressed, and describe how you (as an HRM consulting team) would go about solving these problems. Here are some questions you will need to consider:

   a. What do you think the critical issues and real problems are, and why?

   b. What OH&S knowledge that you have gained in this course can be applied to the problems you have identified?

   c. What solutions do you propose, and why?

   d. How would you implement your plan? Why?

   Prepare a written proposal (eight to ten doubled-spaced pages) detailing the proposed system. Your proposal must include an executive summary of no more than one page. Then develop an audiovisual presentation based on that proposal and deliver it to the class. (Based on an exercise by Catherine Fitzgerald.)

OH&S IN ACTION

The team at your workplace is very excited. The CEO has won the City Business Association's Health & Safety Leader of the Year Award. You've been asked to draft a press release that you can share with the public relations department. You're in an ideal position to do this task, because you are not only on the JHSC, but also the company's healthy & wellness programs coordinator. In the press release you need to comment on the organization's health and safety programming and how Amelia, the CEO, has championed and promoted safety in your workplace. (You can decide the type of organization, the manner of programming, and nature of Amelia's actions. The important thing is to paint a picture of a positive safety climate championed by a senior executive who cares about safety).

CASE STUDY 1 · NONCOMPLIANCE WITH SAFETY STANDARDS

Pat Singh is confused. As plant manager at a manufacturing plant, he has tried to comply with all applicable legislation. Based on his experiences as a line employee, Pat is particularly keen on health and safety initiatives, and he has spent a considerable sum of money to purchase the best available protective gear (e.g., hearing protectors, safety glasses, hardhats). Yet today when he walked through the plant, he saw many employees with the hearing protectors draped around their necks, the safety glasses tucked into their shirt pockets, and the hardhats hung on convenient pegs. Pat does not understand why workers won't wear the equipment bought for their protection. Pat has turned to you as a recognized expert in health and safety programming to improve conditions at the plant. What should Pat do?

CASE STUDY 2 · SAFETY IN THE BAKERY

Su Mei Lawrence manages the bakery department in a large supermarket. She oversees 20 employees working three shifts (the store is open 24 hours a day). Most employees are part-time, working 20 hours a week or less. Many are high school and university students working their way through school. In the past three weeks, Su Mei has noticed a marked increase in the number of safety-related incidents in the department. Several employees have injured their backs lifting racks of bread into position, and product has been crushed by the careless use of a forklift in the rear storage area. Today, one employee was knocked to the floor when a stack of 15 trays of bread fell on him. Su Mei is convinced it is time to take action to improve the safety of working conditions in the department, but she needs your help in deciding exactly what to do.

CASE STUDY 3 · WORKING TO CHANGE SAFETY

Ali Al-Farsi has recently purchased a medium-sized sawmill. He recognizes that health and safety has been a problem at the mill in the past; just last year, one worker lost a limb in a safety incident. Ali and his new management team are serious about safety and want to improve the mill's safety performance. You are the health and safety consultant who has been contracted to help Ali and his team engineer a safety turnaround at the mill. Your primary task is to help design and implement an occupational health and safety management system. What are the vital components of a successful health and safety management system? What steps would you work through with the team? How might Ali convince skeptical employees that a safer workplace is truly a priority?

// NOTES

1. L.M. Goldenhar and P.A. Schulte, "Intervention Research in Occupational Health and Safety," *Journal of Occupational Medicine* 36 (1994): 763–75.

2. L.S. Robson, J.A. Clarke, K. Cullen, A. Bielecky, C. Severin, P.L. Bigelow, E. Irvin, A. Culyer, and Q. Mahood, "The Effectiveness of Occupational Health and Safety Management System Interventions: A Systematic Review," *Safety Science* 45 (2007): 329–53.

3. M.J. Colligan and A. Cohen, "The Role of Training in Promoting Workplace Safety and Health," in J. Barling and M. Frone, eds., *Handbook of Workplace Safety* (Washington: APA, 2004), 223–48.

4. S.E. Johnson, "Behavioral Safety Theory: Understanding the Theoretical Foundation," *Professional Safety* (October 2003): 39–44; B. Sulzer-Azaroff and A. Austin, "Does BBS Work? Behavior-Based Safety and Injury Reduction: A Survey of the Evidence," *Professional Safety* (July 2007): 19–24.

5. E.S. Geller, "Behavior-Based Safety in Industry: Realizing the Large-Scale Potential of Psychology to Promote Human Welfare," *Applied and Preventive Psychology* 10 (2001): 87–105; Sulzer-Azaroff and Austin, "Does BBS Work?"

6. A. Cohen and M.J. Colligan, "Accepting Occupational Health and Safety Regimens," in D.S. Gochman, ed., *Handbook of Health Behaviour Research II: Provider Determinants* (New York: Plenum, 1997), 379–94.

7. M.A. Griffin and A. Neal, "Perception of Safety at Work: A Framework for Linking Safety Climate to Safety Performance, Knowledge, and Motivation," *Journal of Occupational Health Psychology* 17 (2000): 347–58.

8. Ibid.

9. Ibid.

10. B. Sulzer-Azaroff, T.C. Harris, and K.B. McCann, "Beyond Training: Organizational Performance Management Techniques," in M.J. Colligan, ed., *Occupational Safety and Health Training* (Philadelphia: Hanley and Befus, 1994), 321–40.

11. A. Neal and M.A. Griffin," A Study of the Lagged Relationships Among Safety Climate, Safety Motivation, Safety Behaviour, and Accidents at the Individual and Group Levels," *Journal of Applied Psychology* 91(2006): 946–53.

12. M.S. Christian, J.C. Bradley, J.C. Wallace, and M.J. Burke, "Workplace Safety: A Meta-analysis of the Roles of Person and Situation Factors," *Journal of Applied Psychology* 94 (2009):1103–27.

13. Geller, "Behavior-Based Safety in Industry"; J. Saari, "When Does Behaviour Modification Prevent Accidents?" *Leadership and Organizational Development Journal* 15 (1994): 11–15.

14. T. Setenay, H. Lotlikar, S. Salen, and N. Daraiseh, "Effectiveness of Behaviour Based Safety Interventions to Reduce Accidents and Injuries in Workplaces: Critical Appraisal and Meta-analysis," *Theoretical Issues in Ergonomics Science* 7 (2006): 191–209.

15. J.S. Hickman and E.S. Geller, "A Safety Self-Management Intervention for Mining Operations," *Journal of Safety Research* 34 (2003): 299–308.

16. K.A. Hutton, C.G. Sibley, D.N. Harper, and M. Hunt, "Modifying Driver Behaviour with Passenger Feedback," *Transportation Research Part F: Traffic Psychology and Behaviour* 4 (2001): 257–69.

17. M.D. Cooper, R.A. Phillips, and I.T. Robertson, "Improving Safety on Construction Sites by Psychologically Based Techniques: Alternative Approaches to the Measurement of Safety Behaviour," *European Review of Applied Psychology* 43 (1993): 33–37.

18. L.M. Frederiksen, ed., *Handbook of Organizational Behaviour Management* (New York: Wiley, 1982); Geller, "Behavior-Based Safety in Industry."

19. J. Komaki, "Promoting Job Safety and Accident Prevention," in M.F. Cataldo and J. Coates, eds., *Health and Industry: A Behavioural Medicine Perspective* (New York: Wiley, 1986), 301–19.

20. A. Daniels. "Positive Reinforcement: The Best Way to Change Any Work Behavior," *Leadership Excellence*, 31(3) (2014): 9.

21. D. Zohar, "Modifying Supervisory Practices to Improve Subunit Safety: A Leadership-Based Intervention Model," *Journal of Applied Psychology* 87 (2002): 156–63.

22. M.L. Ambrose and C.T. Kulik, "Old Friends, New Faces: Motivation Research in the 1990s," *Journal of Management* 25 (1999): 231–92; E.A. Locke and G.P. Latham, "Building a Practically Useful Theory of Goal Setting and Task Motivation: A 35-Year Odyssey," *American Psychologist* 57 (2002): 705–17.

23. Locke and Latham, "Building a Practically Useful Theory."

24. P. Sheeran and M. Silverman, "Evaluation of Three Interventions to Promote Workplace Health and Safety: Evidence for the Utility of Implementation Intentions," *Social Science and Medicine* 56, no. 10 (2003): 2153–63.

25. Locke and Latham, "Building a Practically Useful Theory."

26. P.F. Drucker, "What Results Should You Expect: A User's Guide to MBO," *Public Administration Review* 36 (1976): 12–19.

27. R. Rodgers and J.E. Hunter, "Impact of Management by Objectives on Organizational Productivity," *Journal of Applied Psychology* 76 (1991): 322–36.

28. E. Rune, "Road Safety Management by Objectives: A Critical Analysis of the Norwegian Approach," *Accident Analysis and Prevention* 40(2008): 1115–22.

29. E.L. Deci and R.M. Ryan, *Handbook of Self-Determination Research* (Rochester, NY: The University of Rochester Press, 2002).

30. M. Gagné and E.L. Deci, "Self-determination Theory and Work Motivation," *Journal of Organizational Behaviour* 26 (2005): 331–62; and E.L. Deci and R.M. Ryan, *Handbook of Self-Determination Research.*

31. Ibid.

32. N. Scott, M. Fleming, and E.K. Kelloway, "Understanding Why Employees Behave Safely from a Self-Determination Theory Perspective," in M. Gagné, ed., *The Oxford Handbook of Work Engagement, Motivation, and Self-Determination Theory* (New York: Oxford University Press, 2014).

33. Ibid.

34. M. Gagné and E.L. Deci, "Self-determination Theory and Work Motivation."

35. M. Gagné and E.L. Deci, "Self-determination Theory and Work Motivation"; and E.L. Deci and R.M. Ryan, *Handbook of Self-Determination Research.*

36. Ibid.

37. N. Scott, M. Fleming, and E.K. Kelloway, "Understanding Why Employees Behave Safely from a Self-Determination Theory Perspective."

38. M. Gagné and E.L. Deci, "Self-determination Theory and Work Motivation."

39. Colligan and Cohen, "The Role of Training."

40. M.J. Smith, B.T. Karsh, P. Carayon, and F.T. Conway, "Controlling Occupational Safety and Health Hazards," in J.C. Quick and L.E. Tetrick, eds., *Handbook of Occupational Health Psychology* (Washington: APA, 2003), 35–68.

41. T. Cree and E.K. Kelloway, "Responses to Occupational Hazards: Exit and Participation," *Journal of Occupational Health Psychology* 2 (1997): 304–11.

42. D. Zohar, "Safety Climate in Industrial Organizations: Theoretical and Applied Implications," *Journal of Applied Psychology* 65 (1980): 96–102; idem, "The Effects of Leadership Dimensions, Safety Climate, and Assigned Priorities on Minor Injuries in Work Groups," *Journal of Organizational Behavior* 23 (2002): 75–92.

43. J. Barling, C. Loughlin, and E.K. Kelloway, "Development and Test of a Model Linking Safety-Specific Transformational Leadership and Occupational Safety," *Journal of Applied Psychology* 87 (2002): 488–96; A. Neal and M.A. Griffin, "A Study of the Lagged Relationships Among Safety Climate, Safety Motivation, Safety Behaviour, and Accidents at the Individual and Group Levels," *Journal of Applied Psychology* 91 (2006): 946–53; T.M. Probst, T.L. Brubaker, and A. Barsotti, "Organizational Injury Rate Underreporting: The Moderating Effect of Organizational Safety Climate," *Journal of Applied Psychology* 93 (2008): 1147–54.

44. K.J. Nielsen, "Improving Safety Culture Through the Health and Safety organization: A Case Study," *Journal of Safety Research*, 48 (2014): 7–17.

45. Ibid.

46. A.R. Hale, F.W. Guldenmund, P.L.C.H. Van Loenhout, and J.I.H. Oh, "Evaluating Safety Management and Culture Interventions to Improve Safety: Effective Intervention Strategies," *Safety Science*, *48*(8) (2010): 1026–1035.

47. M. Hemingway and C.S. Smith, "Organizational Climate and Occupational Stressors as Predictors of Withdrawal Behaviours and Injuries in Nurses," *Journal of Occupational and Organizational Psychology* 72 (1999): 285–99; D.A. Hofmann and A. Stetzer, "A Cross-Level Investigation of Factors Influencing Unsafe Behaviours and Accidents," *Personnel Psychology* 49 (1996): 307–39.

48. Barling et al., "Development and Test of a Model."

49. A. Wills, B. Watson, and H. Biggs, "An Exploratory Investigation into Safety Climate and Work-Related Driving," *Work: Journal of Prevention, Assessment, and Rehabilitation* 32 (2009): 81–94.

50. Barling et al., "Development and Test of a Model"; C.-S. Lu and C.-S. Yang, "Safety Leadership and Safety Behaviour in Container Terminal Operations," *Safety Science* 48 (2010): 123–34; J. Mullen, "Testing a Model of Employee Willingness to Raise Safety Issues," *Canadian Journal of Behavioural Science* 37, no. 4 (2005): 273–82; H.S. Shannon, J. Mayr, and T. Haines, "Overview of the Relationship Between Organizational and Workplace Factors and Injury Rates," *Safety Science* 26 (1997): 201–17.

51. Cree and Kelloway, "Responses to Occupational Hazards."

52. J. Mullen, "Testing a Model of Employee Willingness to Raise Safety Issues," *Canadian Journal of Behavioural Science* 37, no. 4 (2005): 273–82.

53. Barling et al., "Development and Test of a Model."

54. E.K. Kelloway, J. Mullen, and L. Francis, "The Divergent Effects of Transformational and Passive Leadership on Employee Safety," *Journal of Occupational Health Psychology* 11 (2006): 76–86.

55. J. Mullen, E.K. Kelloway, and M. Teed, "Inconsistent Style of Leadership as a Predictor of Safety Behaviour," *Work and Stress* 25 (2011): 41–54.

56. B.M. Bass, *Leadership and Performance Beyond Expectations* (New York: Free Press, 1985).

57. Ibid.

58. D. Zohar, "The Effects of Leadership Dimensions, Safety Climate, and Assigned Priorities on Minor Injuries in Work Groups," *Journal of Organizational Behavior* 23 (2002): 75–92; and E.A. Kapp, "The Influence of Supervisor Leadership Practices and Perceived Group Safety Climate on Employee Safety Performance," *Safety Science* 50 (2012): 1119–24.

59. B.M. Bass, *Leadership and Performance Beyond Expectations.*

60. D. Zohar, "The Effects of Leadership Dimensions, Safety Climate, and Assigned Priorities on Minor Injuries in Work Groups."

61. T.A. Judge and R.F Piccolo, "Transformational and Transactional Leadership: A Meta-analytic Test of Their Relative Validity," *Journal of Applied Psychology* 89 (2004): 755–68.

62. S. Clarke, "Safety Leadership: A Meta-analytic Review of Transformational and Transactional Leadership Styles as Antecedents of Safety Behaviour," *Journal of Occupational and Organizational Psychology*, 86(1) (2013), 22–49, doi: 10.1111/j.2044-8325.2012.02064.x.

63. Ibid.

64. B.M. Bass, *Leadership and Performance Beyond Expectations*; T.A. Judge and J.E. Bono, "Five-Factor Model of Personality and Transformational Leadership," *Journal of Applied Psychology* 85 (2000): 751–65.

65. Idem, "From Transactional to Transformational Leadership: Learning to Share the Vision," *Organizational Dynamics* 18, no. 3 (1990): 19–31.

66. Barling et al., "Development and Test of a Model."

67. E.A. Kapp, "The Influence of Supervisor Leadership Practices and Perceived Group Safety Climate on Employee Safety Performance."

68. M. Martínez-Córcoles, M. Schöbel, F.J. Gracia, I. Tomás, and J.M. Peiró, "Linking Empowering Leadership to Safety Participation in Nuclear Power Plants: A Structural Equation Model," *Journal of Safety Research* 43 (2012): 215–21.

69. J. Barling, T. Weber, and E.K. Kelloway, "Effects of Transformational Leadership Training on Attitudinal and Financial Outcomes: A Field Experiment," *Journal of Applied Psychology* 81 (1996): 827–32; J.E. Mullen and E.K. Kelloway, "Safety Leadership: A Longitudinal Study of the Effects of Transformational Leadership on Safety Outcomes," *Journal of Occupational and Organizational Psychology* 82 (2009): 253–72.

70. S. Clarke, "Safety Leadership: A Meta-Analytic Review of Transformational and Transactional Leadership Styles as Antecedents of Safety Behaviour."

71. P. Yorio, D.R. Willmer, and S.M. Moore, "Health and Safety Management Systems Through a Multilevel and Strategic Management Perspective: Theoretical and Empirical Considerations," *Safety Science* 72 (2015): 221–228.

72. L.S. Robson, J.A. Clarke, K. Cullen, A. Bielecky, C. Severin, P.L. Bigelow, E. Irvin, A. Culyer, and Q. Mahood, "The Effectiveness of Occupational Health and Safety Management System Interventions: A Systematic Review."

73. C.F. Redinger and S.P. Levine, "Development and Evaluation of the Michigan Occupational Health and Safety Management System Assessment Instrument: A Universal OHSMS Performance Measurement Tool," *American Industrial Hygiene Association Journal* 59 (1998): 572–81.

74. L.S. Robson, J.A. Clarke, K. Cullen, A. Bielecky, C. Severin, P.L. Bigelow, E. Irvin, A. Culyer, and Q. Mahood, "The Effectiveness of Occupational Health and Safety Management System Interventions: A Systematic Review"; Canadian Standards Association, CSA Standard Z1000-06–Occupational Health and Safety Management and International Labour Organization, OSH Management System: A Tool for Continual Improvement (2011).

75. Canadian Standards Association, CSA Standard Z1000-06: Occupational Health and Safety Management; CSA Group. "CAN/CSA-Z1000-14. Overview." Found at: http://shop.csa.ca/en/canada/occupational-health -and-safety-management/cancsa-z1000-14/invt/27024062014 (accessed June 7, 2016).

76. Canadian Standards Association, CSA Standard Z1000-06: Occupational Health and Safety Management.

77. Ibid.

78. A.R. Hale, F.W. Guldenmund, P.L.C.H. Van Loenhout, and J.I.H. Oh, "Evaluating Safety Management and Culture Interventions to Improve Safety: Effective Intervention Strategies."

79. P. Yorio, D.R. Willmer, and S.M. Moore, "Health and Safety Management Systems Through a Multilevel and Strategic Management Perspective: Theoretical and Empirical Considerations."

80. PL Yorio and J.K. Wachter, "The Impact of Human Performance Focused Safety and Health Management Practices on Injury and Illness Rates: Do Size and Industry Matter?" *Safety Science*, 62 (2014): 157–67.

81. Transport Canada. "Safety Management Systems." Found at: https://www .tc.gc.ca/eng/civilaviation/standards/sms-menu-618.htm (accessed June 7, 2016).

82. E. Bottani, L. Monica, and G. Vignali, "Safety Management Systems: Performance Differences Between Adopters and Non-adopters," *Safety Science* 47 (2009): 155–62.

83. S. Torp and B.E. Moen, "The Effects of Occupational Health and Safety Management on Work Environment and Health: A Prospective Study," *Applied Ergonomics*, 37 (2006): 776–83.

EMERGENCY PLANNING

CHAPTER LEARNING OBJECTIVES

AFTER READING THIS CHAPTER, YOU SHOULD BE ABLE TO:

- define an emergency
- list the key elements in emergency preparedness
- describe the concept of an emergency plan
- explain the necessity of having emergency and evacuation plans
- describe the principles of fire prevention and suppression

FORT McMURRAY

At the time of this writing, the largest wildfire in Alberta's history is raging in the area of Fort McMurray. Fort McMurray. The fire currently covers 10 000 hectares, has destroyed more than 1600 structures and resulted in the mass evacuation of Fort McMurray residents. Although the origins of the fire are unclear at present, a combination of climate conditions (i.e., a mild winter and a heat wave just before the fire) has resulted in an unprecedented event and the Province of Alberta has declared a state of emergency. There is no doubt that the fire will have long-term consequences directly related to organizations that operated in the Fort McMurray area.

Although the immediate concern has been on getting people to safety, the long-term concerns revolve around what the people will return to—are their houses still standing, are their workplaces still existing, is there still work for them? In many ways the fire in Albert has the classic hallmarks of an emergency; it demands an immediate response to ensure the safety of people but also has long-term consequences for individuals and the companies in which they work.

Source: Adapted from CBC, "Fort McMurray wildfire burning so hot only weather can stop it." Found at: http://www.cbc.ca/news/technology/alberta-wildfire-science-background-1.3565932 (Accessed May 2, 2016).

The Fort McMurray fire of 2016 was an unprecedented event requiring the evacuation of the entire town.

The widespread impact of the 1998 ice storm in Ontario and Quebec; the events of September 11, 2001; the subsequent rash of anthrax-related scares; the outbreak of severe acute respiratory syndrome (SARS) in Canadian cities; the predicted H1N1 pandemic of 2009; the devastation by Hurricane Juan in Nova Scotia in 2003; and, of course, the *Deepwater Horizon* oil spill of 2010, are all examples of emergencies. The fire in Fort McMurray and the 2014 shooting in the Canadian parliament are more recent examples of emergencies. What do these events have in common?

Emergencies are by definition catastrophic stressors (see Chapter 7). First, they are sudden. There is a defined starting point for each of these emergencies and the events are usually time-limited. Note that this is not to say that the events could not be anticipated or that it was not possible to have a planned response. Although we might not be sure when an emergency might happen there are many emergencies that require a response that we can anticipate in advance. Second, each of the events are severe—in many cases, they threatened the lives of affected individuals and, in some cases, resulted in the loss of life. Moreover, although emergencies are typically time-limited, the consequences of the event may linger for years. Thus, although the immediate focus in Alberta has been to evacuate individuals and ensure that they were safe, we can anticipate an extended recovery period during which the city will be rebuilt and things will slowly get back to "normal." Although the emergency is likely to be over within a period of weeks, the recovery process will most likely extend for years.

Aside from the immediate physical perils and the recovery process, organizations may also be judged by how they respond to emergencies. Indeed there are now firms that specializing in advising companies on how to respond to crises and emergencies. For example, the owners of Chapman Ice Cream in Markdale, Ontario, were lauded for their response to the fire that destroyed their factory. The owners committed to rebuilding their plant and to "taking care of " their 350 employees by keeping them on salary while the plant was being rebuilt. In doing so the company solidified its reputation as a good corporate citizen. Emergencies can also extend well beyond the company—the Lac Mégantic fire resulting from a railcar derailment killed 47 people in the town and resulted in the railway company being widely vilified for causing the tragedy. As these examples illustrate, the way that a company handles an emergency reflects on their image as a corporate citizen.

In Canada, emergency response is largely up to individuals and each individual is responsible for knowing what to do in an emergency. As events overwhelm an individual's capacity to respond, governments take action in a progressive manner. This might include involving organizations such as companies. For example, during a weather emergency such as a snowstorm, governments might ask employers to suspend work (i.e.,declare a snow day) in order to keep traffic off of the streets to allow for snow clearing operations.

First, local emergency organizations (e.g., municipal emergency services, emergency measures organizations) respond. At the next level, each province and territory has an emergency measures organization (EMO) that is tasked with managing large-scale emergencies and with supporting local organizations as required. Finally, the federal government and its agencies may become involved in emergency response efforts, depending on the nature of the disaster. For example, during Hurricane Juan in Nova Scotia, the Canadian Forces were deployed to assist in the cleanup efforts.

Organizations must consider the possibility of a disaster, in which the potential for loss is very high. No safety program is complete without a planned response to the threat of a disaster. Such plans comprise part of a company's due diligence on safety. In cases like the Deepwater Horizon, the company's liability for disasters may be increased by the failure to plan for emergencies that a reasonable person might anticipate. Many would suggest that there is also a moral responsibility (i.e., in addition to a legal responsibility) for companies to have emergency plans in place. This responsibility might be enhanced when companies engage in activities that are thought to pose a special risk to the environment or to workers.

In this chapter, we consider two central aspects of emergency planning in organizations. First, we consider issues related to emergency preparedness. Second, we address the organization's response to emergency. We finish the chapter with a specific consideration of fire and evacuation plans.

// EMERGENCY PREPAREDNESS

An **emergency** is any sudden set of circumstances demanding immediate action. For the most part, we are concerned with emergencies that either cause or threaten to cause the loss of, or damage to, life or property. Being a victim of a computer virus or having your computer crash is also an emergency (and one that business needs to be concerned with), but we will limit our consideration to health and safety–related emergencies.

> **emergency**
> a sudden, generally unexpected occurrence or set of circumstances demanding immediate action

Emergencies can be naturally occurring or caused by humans. Naturally occurring emergencies include disease epidemics (animal, human, plant) and weather conditions (e.g., blizzards, hail, hurricanes, earthquakes, storm surges, torrential rain). Some natural emergencies may be deceptive, in that their severity may not be immediately apparent. For example, at the beginning of the SARS outbreak, nobody recognized the seriousness of the impending crisis—indeed, the initial diagnosis was atypical pneumonia. It was a month after the initial reports from China that the World Health Organization issued a health alert.

Other emergencies are caused by humans. They can include explosions, accidents, fires, and chemical and oil spills. They can also include riots, civil disorder, terrorism, and acts of workplace violence. Riots and civil disorder have always been concerns of health and safety professionals; we now also recognize the need to anticipate and respond to terrorism and acts of violence.

The general probability of any of these emergencies actually happening may be low, but they *can* happen, and a company (or the home) is remiss if it does not institute an emergency plan. A disaster may be prevented or mitigated by an effective emergency plan.

Many organizations focus on how they will respond during an emergency; true emergency planning, though, begins long before the onset of any emergency and continues long afterward. Emergency planning involves anticipating and planning for emergencies, putting those plans into action as needed, and then getting back to work and refining plans in light of new learning.

One study describes a five-stage crisis management process that generates specific strategies at each stage.[1] The first step, *signal detection*, is targeted at prevention and begins with the recognition that an emergency is possible or imminent. The next step, *preparation*, involves senior management in the adoption of a crisis management mindset, the creation of a response plan, and the introduction of response training. The third stage, *damage containment*, consumes most of an organization's crisis management resources. The literature on organizational communication, organizational support, employee assistance programs (EAPs), and stress interventions focuses largely on activities at this stage. The fourth stage, recovery, involves developing short- and long-term plans to resume normal business.[2] The final stage is *learning*, where the focus is on assessing and reflecting on the incident with a view to improving operations and procedures.[3]

Emergencies often arise from natural events such as snowstorms.

Though the benefits of a proactive response to emergencies are well known,[4] many organizations resist this and do not do any systematic preparation for emergencies.[5] Management commitment to preparedness seems to be a critical determinant of how organizations prepare for emergencies. Response strategies typically begin with organizational leaders.[6] Moreover, organizational leaders are responsible for both minimizing risk and responding to events in an effort to aid recovery and readjustment after the events have occurred.[7]

With respect to workplace violence, organizations make a huge mistake when they "focus on systems, operations, infrastructures and public relations and ignore the people . . . [Employees] need to be assured of their safety and have their trust in leadership reinforced."[8] The importance of "people" issues was shown by a study in the aftermath of the Mount Allison University Norwalk outbreak (see **OH&S Today 11.1**).[9] Students' perceptions of how well the university administration handled the crisis were a better predictor of their fear of future contamination and resulting stress than students' own experiences with the virus. Clearly, given the importance of these issues, HR has a major role to play in developing and implementing emergency plans.[10]

As was the case with other forms of hazard control (see Chapter 4), an emergency plan needs to consider issues at the precontact, contact, and postcontact stages of any emergency. Issues at the precontact stage include assessing hazards and planning potential responses. Issues at the contact stage include evacuation, caring for the injured, and ensuring emergency response. Issues at the postcontact stage include dealing with the emotional trauma of an emergency and issues regarding the orderly return to work.

Emergency Plan (handwritten margin note)

PRECONTACT

The necessary elements in managing emergencies include an emergency plan, an emergency manager, a fire plan, an evacuation plan, and a medical attention plan.

AN EMERGENCY PLAN

The first thing required is a formal, workable, well-controlled, rapid-response emergency plan. Ensuring low levels of loss is dependent on a well-developed plan. The joint occupational health and safety committee, as well as the local government, should be involved in developing the plan.

An organization requires the following: hazard evaluation, an emergency response plan, an evacuation plan, a means to notify the authorities, supplies, and drills. *+ a manager*

HAZARD EVALUATION HR and safety professionals (and managers) must evaluate the hazards that could cause an emergency (e.g., storage of flammable solvents near static electricity or ignition sources), as well as the hazards with the greatest risk and loss potential. They must also understand how emergency plans could be aborted or sidetracked if an emergency were to occur; the extent of possible damage and injuries or fatalities; and the possibility of the loss (including financial) of the total plant, its individual departments, and critical equipment or processes.

An emergency is a rare occurrence; knowledge of these hazards can be augmented by consulting Public Safety Canada, provincial and territorial Emergency Measures Organizations (EMOs), and fire departments and insurance companies. Planning for disasters involves both knowing the hazards and having a plan to mitigate and recover from these hazards (See **OH&S Notebook 11.1**).

EMERGENCY RESPONSE PLAN A response plan for different types of emergencies must be developed (see, for example, **OH&S Today 11.2**). These plans should be written, published, and posted. There must be good alarm facilities with emergency communication devices, and everyone in the plant must be familiar with their locations and use.

OH&S NOTEBOOK   11.1

FUTUREPROOFING

Writing for the Canadian Centre for Emergency Preparedness, Geary Sikich uses the term "futureproofing" to denote an integrated approach to emergency preparedness. Futureproofing is based on the notion that organizations have to anticipate and assess the potential risk and consequences of a wide range of emergencies in order to be protected from unexpected events. This approach is based on "graceful degradation" and "agile restoration"—that is, on the ability of the organization to identify an event, determine its consequences, establish a minimal functionality, and begin to direct efforts toward restoration in a timely fashion.

Source: G. Sikich, *Futureproofing—The Process of Active Analysis.* Found at: http://www.continuitycentral.com/ActiveAnalysisFutureproofing.pdf (accessed June 8, 2016).

PANDEMIC PLANNING

Health experts generally agree that there is a real risk of a pandemic flu outbreak in the near future. Indeed, many commentators maintain that the outbreak of swine flu, or H1N1 virus, in 2009 was the pandemic that had been predicted for the past 10 years or so. Possibly as a result of mass immunization and a large-scale public health response, the predicted pandemic did not occur. However, the possibility of such an outbreak is still very real. Any such outbreak will present substantial challenges to businesses. Imagine, for example, how businesses will cope with absenteeism rates in the neighbourhood of 35% to 50%, disruptions in key supplies, and the loss of key customers—conditions that may last for six weeks or more. Health care organizations will be particularly hard hit, as they are expected to experience the same staff and material shortages while at the same time being overwhelmed by the sudden increase in demand for their services. Staff will experience exceptionally high levels of stress from workloads—and the predicted mounting death rate will also extract a toll on health care workers. To begin preparing for the potential outbreak, the federal government has launched a coordinating website (http://www.phac-aspc.gc.ca/influenza/plans-eng.php). As is the case for emergency planning in general, these plans attempt to forecast the likely effects of a pandemic and outline the necessary responses of various organizations.

A list should be published of the people in charge of every aspect of any emergency activity. Accompanying the list should be information on the actual event, security and protection for the workers, protection of what is left, documentation of damage and injuries, and liaison with bureaucrats, insurance firms, and the media.

EVACUATION PLAN Plans for evacuating employees and clients in the event of a major emergency or disaster are a key element in emergency preparedness (See **OH&S Notebook 11.2**). Every worker in the plant must know exactly where to congregate when the need arises and be aware of at least two evacuation routes. There should be well-marked, unobstructed evacuation paths with well-lit exits. Notices about exit procedures should be posted, along with instructions about notifying appropriate personnel of the emergency. Designated assembly areas and assigned assistance should be part of the plan.

A roll call (head count) should be done at the assembly site, and a list of missing employees should be given to the command centre. No one should be allowed to re-enter a building until all personnel are accounted for, debriefed, and emergency personnel have confirmed that it is safe to re-enter the building.

The following are some basic requirements of evacuation plans:

1. The site must be divided into small, related areas. The workers in each area must be identified and trained to recognize and remember workers who are not part of their section. This probably happens routinely during working hours, but the noted presence of these "outsiders" must become second nature. In case of a major emergency, all workers must be accounted for.

2. Outside the building and away from any roadways there should be assembly points that allow for the movement of emergency vehicles. The personnel from each work area noted above must be trained to quickly move to their respective assembly points and remain there until a head count is complete and missing workers are accounted for.

EVACUATION PLANS

As with all aspects of emergency planning, evacuation plans must consider the possibility of individuals who are uniquely vulnerable to some hazards. For example, evacuation plans should consider the need to evacuate employees who may have vision, hearing, mobility, or other physical problems that may impede them from using a particular evacuation route. In the case of a fire, for example, evacuees are typically told to use the stairs rather than the elevators. Such plans need to make special provision for individuals with limited vision who may need assistance in using the stairs or individuals with mobility issues that preclude the use of stairs.

Many types of organizations need well-developed evacuation plans that specify what should happen in case of an emergency such as a fire. Public institutions (e.g., schools, universities, hospitals, etc.) are examples of organizations that require specific evacuation plans. However, many workplaces are now located in high-rise towers that require specific planning for emergencies. The National Fire Protection Association offers information on high-rise evacuations at http://www.nfpa.org/safety-information/for-consumers/occupancies/high-rise-buildings/faqs-about-building-evacuation.

3. Once every employee has been accounted for and the extent of the emergency has been determined, and depending on the instructions of emergency personnel employees can be instructed to return to work or to go home and report when called.

4. Any critical equipment or process that may increase the overall risk of the emergency should be addressed. For example, the supply sources of flammable materials such as gas must be shut off. These tasks should be undertaken only by maintenance personnel who are highly trained in emergency procedures.

5. The end of the emergency can be called only by the senior person responsible for the operation's emergency procedures.

6. A post-evacuation assessment must be done to identify problems in the evacuation plan. Remedial measures can then be taken.

The Canadian Standards Association has developed a standard for emergency response plans (ERPs) that provides further information on evacuation requirements (CAN/CSA-Z731-03).Many organizations are now adopting two-stage alarm systems to alert building occupants to the possibility of an emergency and to provide instructions. In contrast to a one-stage alarm (e.g., in which a bell or horn sounds when the alarm is triggered and immediate evacuation is necessary), a two-stage alarm allows for different signals depending on the condition and locale. For example, at a university with many connected buildings, a fire in the Science building may trigger an evacuation alarm. Additionally, however, connected buildings might receive an alert telling them to gather their belongings and be ready but not necessarily to evacuate. Two-stage alarms allow for the programmed evacuation of a building or buildings—when coupled with a voice system the alarms may also provide specific instructions to building occupants. If conditions worsen, then occupants of the second building can also be evacuated. The capacity to deliver announcements makes the alarm system more adaptable to a wide variety of emergency situations beyond fires.

NOTIFICATION OF AUTHORITIES   Companies should be aware of any legislative requirements—such as the requirement to notify the Ministry of Labour, police, and so on—related to an emergency. In locations with the 911 emergency system, an industrial call for medical assistance will automatically bring police, ministry, and other associated specialists, along with medical assistance.

SUPPLIES Emergency first-line equipment such as fire extinguishers must be in well-defined, easily accessible locations. Designated workers must be trained in their use.

DRILLS Regular emergency drills, with the occasional unannounced drill to keep everyone current and knowledgeable, are a standard part of most plans. Rehearsals are an important part of training. Simulating disasters will help employees deal effectively with real emergencies. Fire drills are rehearsals that require employees to be aware of reporting requirements and the locations of exits and fire extinguishers. Drills test the response capability of the organization. The results (evacuation times, etc.) are monitored and reported to management. A full-scale dress rehearsal involves simulated injuries and provides a measure of an organization's ability to respond.

In planning and conducting training or emergency drills, companies need to be aware of the complete circumstances of their workforce. For example, if an organization works shifts it is important to conduct training and drills on all of the shifts, not just the day shift. Similarly, if the company uses temporary or contingent workers it is important to ensure that they are included in any training or drills.

EMERGENCY MANAGER

Any emergency plan must have a senior person—generally the plant manager—who will be in charge of all emergency activities. This individual should speak for the organization and must be committed to the plan. If the emergency manager works a regular day shift and the plant is on multiple shifts, there must be assistants on each of the other shifts with the authority and training to handle emergencies. The command centre, with a designated chain of command, is a critical component of the plan (see **OH&S Notebook 11.3**).

OH&S NOTEBOOK 11.3

EMERGENCY OPERATIONS CENTRES (EOCS)

Also called the command post or the command centre, an EOC is a geographic space dedicated to the strategic management of an emergency. An EOC is typically geographically separate from the actual emergency site. The role of the EOC is to designate the individual in charge of the emergency site, facilitate communications with the public, disseminate emergency public information, and initiate the recovery process.

The requirements for an EOC vary with circumstances but in general should include communications capabilities sufficient to allow coordination of efforts, and space for briefings and decision making. Basic supplies (e.g., office supplies) should also be available along with connectivity through networks, radios, and so on.

Source: Province of New Brunswick, *Planning Guide for the Emergency Operations Centre.* Found at: http://www2.gnb.ca/content/dam/gnb/Departments/ps-sp/pdf/emo/opscentre-e.pdf (accessed June 8, 2016).

CONTACT

FIRE PLAN ①

The fire plan will have the same characteristics as the main emergency plan, though some of the requirements dealing with major damage and fatalities may not be followed if the fire gets out of control and a full-blown emergency results. A group of workers must be trained in firefighting techniques and be part of the plant's fire brigade. In small to mid-sized businesses in which an in-house fire brigade is not economically feasible, workers should receive fire extinguisher training and participate in ongoing practice sessions.

The first goal in every emergency is to protect life; in the case of fire, an evacuation plan is a necessary part of preparation.

The local fire department is a good source of training for any in-house firefighting team that may be required. The fire department can also assist in fire hazard evaluations and regular inspections. Fire prevention and suppression is discussed next.

FIRE PREVENTION AND SUPPRESSION ②

A **fire** is a chemical process in which fuel, oxygen, and heat combine to create a disastrous condition. The products of fire are gases, flame, heat, and smoke.

The fire process can be graphically represented by means of the fire triangle (see **Figure 11.1**). The new model is the fire tetrahedron (see **Figure 11.2**). The triangular model shows that the three elements—fuel, oxygen, and heat—must come together for a fire to be sustained. The second model adds a fourth element: the chain reaction. Once a fire starts, it is perpetuated by the ongoing (or chain) reaction of the other three elements.

> **fire**
> a chemical process in which fuel, oxygen, and heat are combined

---

FIGURE 11.1

FIRE TRIANGLE

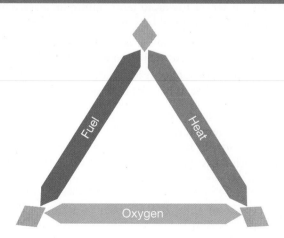

FIGURE 11.2

FIRE TETRAHEDRON

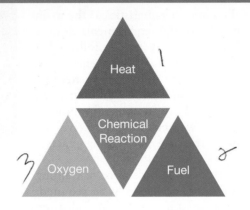

Fire has four stages:

incipient stage
a source of ignition and
fuel come together

1. The **incipient stage**. At this stage, a source of ignition (e.g., a cigarette butt or a hot electrical wire connection) and fuel (e.g., papers or wood) come together. This stage can continue for hours until the resultant heat from the initial reaction becomes great enough to cause combustion. The air is filled with molecule-sized products of combustion. The airborne particulate can be detected with an ionizing (smoke) detector. In the case of an explosion, this stage (and the next) is very short.

smouldering stage
fuel, oxygen, and heat are
present and are causing
the heat to rise through
limited chain reaction

2. The **smouldering stage**. The three elements are present and are causing the heat to rise through limited chain reaction. The area begins to fill with smoke, which increases in amount as the process continues. With visible airborne particulate (smoke) now present, a photoelectric detector is effective. This stage is short and can be measured in minutes.

free-burning stage
the stage at which
flames first appear

3. The **free-burning stage**. This is the stage at which flames first appear. The rate of energy release (heat) is increasing very rapidly, and the surrounding combustible materials are beginning to burn. The free-burning stage is very short and can be measured in minutes or less. A rate-of-rise detector can be effective at this stage because it senses the rapid temperature increase. This detector works well in conjunction with a sprinkler system.

uncontrolled fire stage
fire is out of control and
major property damage
is under way

4. The **uncontrolled fire stage**. The fire is out of control, and major property damage is under way. All personnel must be evacuated. This stage can be measured in seconds. The rate of reaction doubles every 10°C. No heat is lost during this reaction; rather, it becomes cumulative.

The fire triangle or tetrahedron (see Figures 11.1 and 11.2) can serve to illustrate the requirements for extinguishment. If any one of the parts of these models is removed, the fire cannot be sustained and will be put out. For instance, a carbon dioxide fire extinguisher blankets a fire with a gas that displaces the oxygen, thereby smothering the fire. Similarly, water sprayed on the fire reduces the heat, also resulting in extinguishment (see **Table 11.1**).

Hazardous byproducts of fires, besides heat and smoke, include carbon monoxide, carbon dioxide, hydrogen sulphide, sulphur dioxide, hydrogen cyanide, and

TABLE 11.1

CLASS	GROUP	MATERIAL	SYMBOL		COLOUR	EXTINGUISHER
CLASSES OF FIRE						
A	Combustible	Paper, wood	Triangle	△	Green	Water
B	Flammable liquid	Oil, grease, gas	Square	▱	Red	CO_2, dry chemical
C	Electrical	Wiring	Circle	◯	Blue	CO_2, halon
D	Metals	Flammable metals such as magnesium or titanium	Star	☆	Yellow	Powder
K	Grease	Cooking oil, fat	Frying pan or K		Black	Wet grease chemical

Notes: Though comparatively rare, Class D fires require metal/sand extinguishers that work by smothering the fire. The most common extinguishing agent in this class is sodium chloride, but powdered copper metal (for lithium fires) and other materials are used. Class K is a more recent designation of fires. Extinguishers of this class are specially designed to supplement the fire suppression systems found in commercial kitchens. They use a wet chemical agent such as potassium acetate.

hydrogen chloride. These toxic materials are produced when the burning materials (fuel) are broken down into their original chemicals under extreme heat and chain reactions. (See **OH&S Notebooks 11.4** and **11.5**)

When a fire prevention program is being developed, the following should be considered:

1. *Structural design.* Standards for the construction of buildings are detailed in the federal and provincial or territorial fire codes, as well as by the fire marshal and in building codes and regulations.

2. *Barriers.* Walls and floors can delay or prevent the spread of fire. Specially constructed fire barriers should be maintained.

3. *Detection and suppression.* Most buildings have a detection system that senses heat and smoke. When triggered, sprinklers are activated to suppress the fire.

4. *Storage.* Combustible materials should be rated and stored in separate or isolated areas. They should not be stored near exits, and reactive materials should not be stored near flammable materials.

reactive materials cause a violent, explosive reaction when they comes in contact with another material, such as acetylene with water, or bleach with chlorinated cleaner

OH&S NOTEBOOK   11.4

TOXIC FUMES

Although most of the dangers of fire seem self-evident, fires may also contain hidden dangers. Reduced oxygen levels and carbon monoxide are common hazards contained in the smoke from a fire but other forms of toxins are also present in smoke. For example, the use of synthetic materials in construction and furnishings means that toxic fumes can be produced by the fire and inhaled by building occupants and firefighters. The use of synthetic polymers may result in the production of hydrogen cyanide when set alight and create a risk of cyanide poisoning in individuals exposed to the smoke. The use of a self-contained breathing apparatus is one means of protecting firefighters from these toxins.

Source: Y. Alayrie, "Toxicity of Fire Smoke," *Critical Review of Toxicology*, 32 (2002): 259–89.

CHEMICAL SPILLS

A chemical spill is an uncontrolled release of gas, liquid, or solid chemical. Chemicals can, of course, be highly toxic, and emergency procedures must be oriented toward avoiding exposure to the chemical. Good procedures for a chemical spill include the following:

- Avoid coming into contact with the chemical and warn others in the area.

- Isolate the area around the spill.

- Assist those who are injured but do not risk exposing yourself to the chemical.

- Determine the level of response. If the spill is minor and trained personnel are available with the necessary protective gear and materials, the material should be cleaned up. Otherwise, the authorities should be contacted.

Source: University of Alberta, Environmental Health and Safety, "Chemical Spills." Found at: www.ehs.ualberta.ca/ManualsandDocuments/Guidelines -Chemicalspills (accessed May 2, 2016).

Many fires are triggered by unsafe acts (e.g., a person tries to weld a container holding flammable liquid residue without cleaning it first) and unsafe conditions (e.g., faulty or improper equipment is installed near a potentially flammable material).

FIRST AID AND MEDICAL ATTENTION

The various provincial and territorial regulations spell out in detail the requirements for first aid and medical aid facilities. Medical services run the gamut from a first aid kit in a small firm to a fully equipped hospital with doctors in very large firms. Degree of risk

Some emergencies, such as chemical skills, required specialized training and equipment.

can be an additional factor in determining the extent of medical services. An insurance office with a staff of 4000 would not likely need the same facilities as an automobile manufacturer with the same number of workers (see **OH&S Notebook 11.6**).

Beyond conforming to legal requirements, every company should arrange to have at least one trained first aid attendant present on each shift. All employees should be given the opportunity to take a cardiopulmonary resuscitation (CPR) course. A cost-benefit analysis may show that there would be advantages to contracting with a local occupational health clinic for medical aid services. These services might include pre-employment and post-employment medicals, exposure medical testing, and potential occupational illness identification. Complete first aid records must be kept and maintained.

POSTCONTACT

Postcontact efforts focus on two areas: helping individuals deal with the stresses associated with experiencing or witnessing an emergency situation, and getting back to normal operations.

STRESS

An emergency is an acute or catastrophic stressor (Chapter 7), and individuals may experience long-lasting consequences as a result. Acute stressors can be more psychologically devastating, and their effects more enduring, than chronic stressors, which suggests that their effects need to be understood. For example, individuals exposed to hurricanes and other traumatic stressors have reported ongoing impairments of psychological well-being, including symptoms of post-traumatic

Nuclear disasters, such as the one at Chernobyl, illustrate the potential for an emergency situation to have far reaching and long-lasting consequences.

stress that endure for much longer than the actual precipitating event.[11] Studies of a variety of traumatic stressors suggest several dimensions that may be important to understanding the impact of stressors on individuals.

Studies have highlighted the role of control perceptions when individuals are exposed to stressful situations, including acute stressors.[12] Natural disasters such as hurricanes or blizzards may involve an almost total lack of control, suggesting that their effects may be pronounced.[13]

The multivariate risk/resilience model has been developed to explain individual reactions to disasters.[14] The model incorporates situational factors such as the extent to which the individual receives social support on an ongoing basis, targeted social support, or social support in direct response to the disaster, as well as the individual's exposure to the disaster.[15]

One approach to crisis response has been referred to as **critical incident stress debriefing (CISD)**. The characteristics of CISDs vary; generally, though, they involve psychologists (or other trained personnel) providing assistance immediately following a traumatic event in order to prevent the development of serious or lasting negative consequences. Elements of CISDs include ensuring confidentiality; providing individuals with the opportunity to talk about their perspective on, thoughts about, and emotional reactions to the incident; assessing psychological and physical symptoms; and providing information about stress responses and coping strategies.[16] CISD interventions are popular among individuals who are regularly exposed to traumatic stressors. For example, almost every police, fire, and ambulance service in the country has some form of CISD intervention for its employees. The Canadian Forces uses CISD to debrief returning peacekeepers.

One study of the effectiveness of CISD compared the coping strategies and levels of anger of two groups of police officers who had experienced a traumatic event.[17] One group of officers received CISD, the other did not. The results suggested that the CISD group exhibited more adaptive coping strategies and lower levels of anger than did those in the non-CISD group. The lack of random assignment to conditions casts some doubt on the validity of these findings, though they do provide preliminary evidence of the efficacy of CISD following exposure to traumatic work-related events. If these results are replicable, it would be unethical to withhold such debriefings from employees who experience traumatic events.

Unfortunately, despite these promising results, the research literature also provides a basis on which to question the effectiveness of CISD. First, a review of 67 studies concluded that debriefing does not mitigate the effects of traumatic stress.[18] Second, based on a meta-analytic review, other authors found that single-session debriefing was less effective than other forms of intervention and less effective than no intervention in reducing the effects of traumatic stress.[19] Finally, growing lists of studies suggest that individuals receiving CISD interventions may experience exacerbated traumatic reactions and more adverse outcomes.[20] These findings violate the widely accepted maxim that psychological interventions should in the first instance do no harm. The inconsistent findings as to the effectiveness of CISDs suggest the need for more research in this area, to identify whether some elements of CISDs are helpful and should be retained and whether some are harmful and should be removed from such programs.

critical incident stress debriefing (CISD)
a post-trauma intervention focused on providing victims with an opportunity to discuss their experiences and reactions to a traumatic event

GETTING BACK TO NORMAL

Getting back to normal after an emergency is not as straightforward as a simple return to work. Depending on the circumstances, individuals may continue to experience stress reactions. They may also continue to live with the effects of the emergency (e.g., damaged

Even during an emergency, critical services must be continued. Some employers may have to continue operations during an emergency, and all employers will eventually have to return to normal operations. Business continuity planning is a proactive approach to ensuring that critical services and products continue during an emergency. Developing a business continuity plan will help ensure that employers recover data, assets, and facilities and have the necessary resources (including human resources) to continue business.

Source: Adapted from Public Safety Canada, *Keeping Canadians Safe: A Guide to Business Continuity Planning.* Found at: http://www.ps-sp.gc.ca/prg/em/gds/bcp-en.asp#4.

housing, loss of income, transportation) long after its acute phase has passed. For example, although the fire in Fort McMurray was over in a relatively short period of time, some people were displaced for over a month. Still others who might have to rebuild their house and replace lost possessions may be dealing with the aftermath of the fire for a year or more.

Given these potential reactions and experiences, it is unlikely that individuals will return to the workplace focused on the task at hand. Employers should display some tolerance for distractions and for employees' need to share their experiences. Adjusting to normal work may take some time (see **OH&S Notebook 11.7**).

Employers may inadvertently increase or decrease employee stress as a result of how they handle personnel decisions related to the emergency. In Fort MacMurray, for example, many of the oil-producing firms took special steps to help displaced employees. These steps included continuing to pay employees, offering employees interest-free loans and even offering employees lump sum payments.[21]

// SUMMARY

The goals of an emergency plan are to reduce injuries and property damage and to restore the organization to its normal operations. Emergency preparedness consists of preparing an emergency response plan, designating and training those responsible for its implementation, and communicating it to employees. Developing an evacuation plan, establishing a fire prevention and suppression program, and controlling fire hazards are other elements of emergency preparedness.

KEY TERMS

critical incident stress debriefing (CISD) 286
emergency 275
fire 281
free-burning stage 282

incipient stage 282
reactive materials 283
smouldering stage 282
uncontrolled fire stage 282

DISCUSSION QUESTIONS

1. Who should be involved in developing emergency response plans?

2. What types of emergencies should organizations in your area be prepared for?

3. Decide what type of fire extinguisher would be most effective in the following fire situations:

   a. a hair dryer engulfed in smoke

   b. grease burning in a frying pan

   c. rags smoking in the garage

   d. a log that has rolled from the fireplace onto the living room floor

   e. a coffee machine whose wires are shooting flames

4. Though this chapter has focused on health and safety implications, there are also public relations issues in an emergency. What principles would be appropriate for an organization to adopt in dealing with the media and public during an emergency?

USING THE INTERNET

1. Each province and territory has an Emergency Planning Organization (EMO) as does the Federal Jurisdiction. Find the website for the EMO in your jurisdiction. What information/resources are available? What is the structure and function of your EMO?

2. What emergencies have occurred in your local area in the past five years? How effective was the emergency response? (Hint: Local EMO sites often have debriefing reports on past emergency responses.)

3. What plans are being made for the predicted flu pandemic in your area? (Hint: What information is available from government agencies; what firms are publishing pandemic plans?)

EXERCISES

1. Determine whether your workplace or school has an emergency response plan. Compare this plan with the one outlined in this chapter.

2. Prepare a fire prevention and suppression plan for your own home or apartment.

3. What does it cost to create and maintain a comprehensive emergency plan for a specific organization? Choose a specific organization and try to estimate these costs. Consider the costs (e.g., time) associated with developing a plan, training employees in the plan, drills or practice (e.g., evacuation drills), and maintaining the plan to ensure currency.

// NOTES

1. C.M. Pearson, J.A. Clair, S.K. Misra, and I.I. Mitroff, "Managing the Unthinkable," *Organizational Dynamics* 26 (1997): 51–64.

2. B.T. Blythe, *Blindsided: A Manager's Guide to Catastrophic Incidents in the Workplace* (New York: Portfolio, 2002).

3. Pearson et al., "Managing the Unthinkable."

4. C.M. Pearson and J.A. Clair, "Reframing Crisis Management," *Academy of Management Review* 23, no. 1 (1998): 59–76.

5. I.I. Mitroff, C.M. Pearson, and L.K. Harrigan, *The Essential Guide to Managing Corporate Crises* (New York: Oxford University Press, 1996).

6. Blythe, *Blindsided*.

7. Pearson and Clair, "Reframing Crisis Management."

8. M. Braverman, "Managing the Human Impact of Crisis," *Risk Management* 50, no. 5 (2003): 10–14.

9. E.K. Kelloway, J. Mullen, and L. Francis, "The Stress (of an) Epidemic," *Stress and Health*, 29 (2012): 91–97.

10. N.R. Lockwood, "Crisis Management in Today's Business Environment: HR's Strategic Role," *HR Magazine* 50 (2005): 1–9.

11. F.H. Norris, C.M. Byrne, E. Diaz, and K. Kaniasty, "50,000 Disaster Victims Speak: An Empirical Review of the Empirical Literature, 1981–2001" (2001).

Found at: http://www.dhss.mo.gov/SpecialNeedsToolkit/General/disaster -impact.pdf (accessed May 29, 2010).

12. A.C.H. Schat and E.K. Kelloway, "Reducing the Adverse Consequences of Workplace Aggression and Violence: The Buffering Effects of Organizational Support," *Journal of Occupational Health Psychology* 8 (2003): 110–22.

13. A. Baum, R. Fleming, and L.M. Davidson, "Natural and Technological Catastrophe," *Environment and Behavior* 15 (1983): 333–54.

14. J.R. Freedy, M.E. Saladin, D.G. Kilpatrick, and H.S. Resnick, "Understanding Acute Psychological Distress Following Natural Disaster," *Journal of Traumatic Stress* 7, no. 2 (2004): 257–73.

15. K. Byron and S. Peterson, "The Impact of a Large-Scale Traumatic Event on Individual and Organizational Outcomes: Exploring Employee and Company Reactions to September 11," *Journal of Organizational Behavior* 23, no. 8 (2002): 895–910.

16. J. Mitchell and G. Bray, *Emergency Services Stress* (Englewood Cliffs: Prentice Hall, 1990).

17. R. Leonard and L. Alison, "Critical Incident Stress Debriefing and Its Effects on Coping Strategies and Anger in a Sample of Australian Police Officers Involved in Shooting Incidents," *Work and Stress* 13 (1989): 144–61.

18. M. Arendt and A. Elklit, "Effectiveness of Psychological Debriefing," *Acta Psychiatry Scandanavia* 104 (2001): 423–37.

19. A.A.P. Van Emmerik, J.H. Kamphuis, A.M. Hulsbosch, and P.M.G. Emmelkamp, "Single Session Debriefing After Psychological Trauma: A Meta-Analysis," *The Lancet* 340 (2002): 768–71.

20. I.V.E. Carlier, R.D. Lamberts, A.J. Van Uchelin, and B.P.R. Gersons, "Disaster-Related Posttraumatic Stress in Police Officers: A Field Study of the Impact of Debriefing," *Stress Medicine* 14 (1998): 143–48; R.A. Mayou, A. Ehler, and M. Hobbs, "Psychological Debriefing for Road Accident Victims: Three-Year Follow Up of Randomized Control Trial," *British Journal of Psychiatry* 176 (2000): 589–93; R. Small, J. Lumley, L. Donohue, A. Potter, and U. Waldenstroem, "Randomized Controlled Trial of Midwife Led Debriefing to Reduce Maternal Depression After Operative Childbirth," *British Medical Journal* 321 (2001): 1043–47.

21. C. Tait and K. Cryderman, "Oil Sands Producers Helping Workers Affected by Fort Mcmurray Wildfire," *The Globe and Mail* (May 15, 2016). Found at: http://www.theglobeandmail.com/report-on-business/industry-news/energy -and-resources/oil-sands-producers-helping-workers-affected-by-fort-mcmurray -wildfire/article30027628 (accessed June 29, 2016).

CHAPTER 2

INCIDENT INVESTIGATION

CHAPTER LEARNING OBJECTIVES

AFTER READING THIS CHAPTER, YOU SHOULD BE ABLE TO:

- describe the intent and steps of an incident investigation
- gather information to analyze the human, situational, and environmental factors contributing to incidents
- outline the legal requirements of incident investigation results
- explain the concept of a walkthrough survey
- list the steps to conducting interviews concerning an incident
- conduct a re-enactment
- complete the various types of incident and injury reports

Niklas Jay Kristen Taylor was killed on the job at Fountain Tire. He was unloading a truck full of tires when one fell on him. The tires were industrial tires—some of which stood over 2 metres high and weighed more than 800 kilograms. As with most incident investigations, the subsequent investigation noted that the fatality resulted from a number of causes:

a. This was not the employee's regular job; he was called in to replace another employee who was unavailable.

b. It was early in the morning and he was working alone

c. Although there was a forklift available, it was awkward to use with oversized tires.

d. The company did not have a written "safe work procedure" for this task.

Although the company was subsequently charged with not having a written work procedure and not doing a risk assessment for lone workers, it is likely that it was the combination of factors rather than one individual factor that resulted in the fatality. If the worker had used the forklift it might not have happened. If the regular employee was there, or another employee there to help, it might not have happened.

Investigations, particularly when conducted by the Department of Labour or as a result of a serious incident or fatality, often result in charges and orders being written. However, the real goal of incident investigation is not to blame individuals or find out who was at fault; rather, the goal is to identify the cause of incidents so that preventive actions can be taken to ensure that the incident is not repeated. In a very real sense, the focus of investigation is on prevention.

Source: C. Fortens, "Two Violations Noted in Workers' Death at Fountain Tire in 2015, Accidents News," *Kamloops This Week* (April 28, 2016). Found at: http://www.kamloopsthisweek.com/two-violations-noted-in-workers-death-at-fountain-tire-in-2015 (accessed May 2, 2016). Adapted with the permission of the publisher.

Photographee.eu/Shutterstock.com

When an incident occurs we often do not know why—or how to prevent it from happening again. This is the goal of incident investigation.

RAC program
a hazard recognition, assessment, and control program; a key element in most health and safety programs

The investigation of incidents is a vital component of an organization's health and safety program. This chapter describes the rationale for incident investigations, the critical factors in the investigative process, the types of information to be collected, and the investigative methods and tools for conducting an investigation. The importance of reporting and keeping records is also discussed.

// RATIONALE FOR INCIDENT INVESTIGATION

The investigation of incidents is an important component in a hazard recognition, assessment, and control (RAC) program, which in turn is an integral part of a health and safety program. One study identifies the benefits of incident investigation as follows:[1]

1. *Determines direct causes.* An investigation uncovers the direct causes of an incident, thereby allowing for the subsequent exploration of corrective measures.

2. *Identifies contributing causes.* Some incidents may be the result of many factors. For example, the direct cause of an incident may be inadequate safeguards on equipment, but there may also be contributing factors, such as loose clothing

on the employee and a lack of instruction in the proper procedures for equipment use.

3. *Prevents similar incidents.* Once the direct and contributing causes are identified, corrective measures such as training programs or equipment design improvements can be implemented to prevent similar incidents.

4. *Creates a permanent record.* The reports generated by an investigation can be used by HR and safety specialists to identify trends (e.g., sites of frequent incidents, inefficient layouts and designs, unsafe acts, improper operating procedures). Reports can also be valuable in the event of litigation or compensation claims. Actions taken to improve safety records can be cost efficient in the sense that money and time are being allocated to sites or equipment that generate the most frequent or most severe incidents and injuries.

5. *Determines cost.* The delineation of the exact situation may help the organization determine the actual costs accruing from an incident. All factors, even a worker's lost time, count more than once if there were multiple activities by this worker directly related to the event.

6. *Promotes safety awareness among employees.* When a thorough investigation is conducted, employees realize that management is serious about safety and interested in their well-being. This should motivate employees to show greater concern for safe practices.

// CRITICAL FACTORS IN THE INVESTIGATIVE PROCESS

Incident investigations are strongly influenced by timing, severity, and legal requirements.

TIMING

Timing is a critical factor in incident investigations. Time affects several types of information. Delays in an investigation may lead to partial or complete memory loss by the witnesses, changes at the incident site, and removal of important evidence. Furthermore, those directly involved in the incident, be they witnesses or late arrivals, tend to discuss the incident, and details may become distorted in the retelling.

Of course, the investigation should start only after any injured people have received medical attention and the incident site has been secured to prevent access, further injuries, and attempts by helpful observers to "fix" the hazard.

SEVERITY

Given that investigations are time consuming, companies tend to examine only those incidents that have the most serious consequences (see **OH&S Today 12.1**). Yet incidents that result in minor injuries often signal a hazard that may one day have more serious consequences.

One corporate director of health and safety recommends that the following types of incidents be investigated: those resulting in lost-time injuries beyond the day of the incident; those in which the injury was minor, but the employee was treated by a doctor

WHAT TO INVESTIGATE

A wide variety of safety-related events may be subject to investigation. OH&S legislation may mandate post-incident investigations in some cases, depending on the nature and severity of the incident. For example, when a workplace death occurs, it is clear that external agencies such as the police will become involved and assume the primary investigative role. When injury-causing incidents are severe or constantly recurring, provincial or territorial and federal health and safety agencies (such as the Labour Program of Human Resources and Social Development Canada) may appoint an investigator to inspect the workplace and may require the submission of a formal report. In B.C., for example, employers are required to investigate (1) any incident that requires reporting to the board (e.g., incidents resulting in serious injury or death, incidents involving major structural collapses, incidents involving release of a hazardous substance); (2) incidents resulting in an employee requiring medical treatment,

and (3) incidents that could have resulted in serious injury but did not. Standards for determining which incidents need to be investigated may also be set by the employer (note that the employer's standards must meet or exceed those required by legislation—the employer *can* investigate incidents that are not specified by legislation but *must* investigate any incident specified in legislation). The OH&S policy at Dalhousie University, for example, mandates the investigation of the following types of incidents:

1. all serious-injury incidents that result in hospitalization or absences for two or more days

2. all fires or explosions

3. all major spills or releases of chemicals

4. any incident or series of incidents that the environmental health and safety committee wants to have investigated

Sources: Dalhousie University, "Health and Safety Policy and Procedures." Found at: http://environmentalhealthandsafetyoffice.dal.ca/ radiatio_1536 .html (accessed June 13, 2016); WorkSafeBC, "Accident Investigations." Found at: http://www2.worksafebc.com/topics/accidentinvestigations/home .asp (accessed May 2, 2016); E.K. Kelloway, V. Stinson, and C. MacLean, "Can Eyewitness Research Improve Occupational Health and Safety? Towards a Research Agenda," *Law and Human Behavior*, Vol. 28 (2004): 115.

and there was potential for a serious injury; close calls; incidents without injuries but property damage in excess of $1000; and lost-time incidents resulting from aggravation of a previous injury.[2] Regardless of the system used to judge seriousness, organizations have a legal obligation to report injury-related incidents.

LEGAL REQUIREMENTS

Depending on the seriousness of the incident, the presence of an injury, and the jurisdiction in which the incident happened, employers have reporting requirements to fulfill. Certain types of events—those in which an injury requires medical aid or results in lost time, for instance—must be reported to a workers' compensation board, normally within three days. Forms are supplied by the board.

// TYPES OF INFORMATION COLLECTED

Most incidents are the result of many contributing factors. The Three Mile Island disaster (a nuclear plant disaster near Harrisburg, Pennsylvania, on March 28, 1979) was preceded by multiple contributing factors ranging from inadequate emergency training, through equipment failing to shut down, to fail-safe systems that failed to consider the human equation. Although no lives were lost in that incident, public trust in the nuclear-power industry plummeted.

The area supervisor should conduct the investigation, assisted by a human resource or occupational health and safety specialist. When investigating an incident, the human resource or occupational health and safety specialist should concentrate on three factors: human, situational, and environmental. These factors, while similar in name, are not the same as the sources of hazards described in Chapter 4 (see **OH&S Notebook 12.1**).

HUMAN FACTORS

Studying the worker as a source of incidents does not mean that the investigator is looking for a scapegoat. As emphasized throughout this text, the intent is to collect facts, not assign blame. The following questions could be asked when investigating human factors:

- What was the worker doing at the time of the incident? Was he or she performing a regular task or a different task, doing maintenance work, or helping a coworker?

OH&S NOTEBOOK 12.1

THE STEPS OF AN INCIDENT INVESTIGATION

To some extent, every incident investigator has his or her own "method" of conducting incident investigations. Legislative or policy requirements may mandate an investigation but often do not specify *how* the investigation is to be conducted. Although not available at the time of this writing, the Canadian Standards Association is currently developing a standard for incident investigation that is anticipated to be available in 2017.

There are few "hard and fast" rules; that said, a general approach to incident investigation would be to:

a. *Secure the scene.* The initial response to an incident should be to secure the scene—ensure that injuries are treated, that individuals are evacuated if necessary, and that immediate steps are taken to control hazards. The investigator will also need to ensure that the scene of the incident, and any relevant evidence, is protected until the investigation is concluded. The incident should be reported as soon as possible.

b. *Gather evidence.* After the scene is secured, the investigation should commence immediately. The investigator will want to gather evidence—including witness reports, pictures, and physical evidence—before too much time has elapsed or the scene of the incident is disturbed.

c. *Analyze the information.* Information must be collected in order to identify the probable cause(s) of the incident. Rarely will an incident have just one cause, and it is important to consider the contributions of human, situational, administrative, and environmental factors to the incident.

d. *Report the results of the incident investigation.* Reports must be made to the relevant authorities. Internally, this may be to a JHSC or to a health and safety coordinator; externally, this may be to the Department of Labour or the workers' compensation board.

e. *Make recommendations.* A primary reason for conducting an incident investigation is to prevent the recurrence of incidents. Every incident investigation should result in specific recommendations to ensure that similar incidents are not repeated.

f. *Follow up.* The process does not stop with making recommendations. The JHSC or its designate needs to follow up to ensure that the recommendations have been implemented and to assess whether they are achieving the desired effects.

CHAPTER 12 Incident Investigation

- Was the work being performed according to procedures? Were the tasks or procedures new?
- Was a supervisor present?
- What was the employment status of the worker—seasonal, part-time, or full-time?
- How much experience did the employee have with respect to this particular operation?
- What was the posture and location of the employee?
- Did some unsafe act contribute to the event?

SITUATIONAL FACTORS

An analysis of the unsafe conditions that led to the incident is a critical step in an incident investigation. The equipment and tools must be examined. The following questions could be asked when investigating situational factors (see **OH&S Notebook 12.2**):

- Was the machine operating in a satisfactory manner?
- Were all the control and display positions working and ergonomically sound?
- Were the safety measures satisfactory and functioning?
- Does an analysis of failed materials or equipment indicate how the incident happened? For instance, if a shaft broke, causing a machine part to fly off, an engineer can examine the break and determine the mode of failure. A failure of

OH&S NOTEBOOK 12.2

THE EYEWITNESS

Most incident investigations rely on eyewitness accounts and those of individuals involved in the incident. Yet there is good reason to suspect the accuracy of eyewitness statements. A review of the literature on eyewitness testimony indicated that "what we know about eye-witness memory comes from hundreds of studies . . . Overall, this body of research tells us that eyewitness testimony is not like a videotape recorder; memory is fragile, malleable, and susceptible to forgetting, even in optimal conditions." The authors cite an example of an airplane crash that killed nine people. Dozens of people witnessed the crash and at least one insisted at the inquest that the plane had nosedived into the ground. Photographic evidence proved that, in fact, the plane had coasted down and skidded for nearly 300 metres.

TV dramas portray eyewitness testimony as "proof positive" but in reality eyewitness accounts are fallible and subject to a number of distortions.

Source: E.K. Kelloway, V. Stinson, and C. MacLean, "Can Eyewitness Research Improve Occupational Health and Safety? Towards a Research Agenda," *Law and Human Behavior*, Vol. 28 (2004): 115.

metal through shear or bending will leave definite patterns at the failed ends. Once the mode is known, the cause is usually easily determined.

- What was the site or location of the incident?
- What tools, equipment, or objects were involved in the incident?
- Was the correct equipment available and being used to do the job?
- What personal protective equipment (gloves, goggles, etc.) was being worn?
- Were guards in place?
- What time of day did the incident occur?
- What shift was being worked?

ENVIRONMENTAL FACTORS

Environmental factors such as light and noise may increase the likelihood that an incident will occur. The setting sun may blind the driver of a delivery truck; the noise of a machine may mask the approach of a vehicle; the vibrations of a certain piece of equipment may dislodge another tool.

WHO INVESTIGATES?

Numerous individuals may be involved in incident investigations, including the following:

- *The supervisor.* The supervisor possesses a detailed knowledge of the work and the working conditions and is, therefore, well positioned to conduct the investigation. In most companies, supervisors assume principal responsibility for the investigation.
- *Technical advisers and specialists.* It may be appropriate to bring in technical advisers or specialists when incidents are serious and involve highly technical processes. Bringing in outside expertise may also enhance the objectivity of the investigation.
- *Safety and health officer.* The department or company health and safety officer can offer guidance in coordinating an incident investigation. The health and safety representative may be more aware of, and familiar with, health and safety issues than is the supervisor.
- *Safety and health committee or representative.* Where there is an established health and safety committee, that committee must take part in the investigation.
- *A safety team.* In the event of a serious incident—especially when it is difficult to determine the cause of an incident—a team approach is highly recommended. The team would include the supervisor, the health and safety officer, members of the health and safety committee, and, possibly, outside experts.

// INVESTIGATIVE METHODS

A variety of methods may be used in conducting the investigation (see **OH&S Notebook 12.3**).

A carpenter is making some tool holders and needs to trim about 0.5 cm off the length of a piece of 4 × 4 wood. The 4 × 4 is 121 cm long. The carpenter spends 15 minutes adjusting the table saw to remove the correct width of material. In the process, the carpenter also removes the legally required saw guard because it tends to interfere with cutting. The supervisor had been after the company to purchase a new and proper guard for the saw. The usual answer has been: "Why buy a new guard when one came with the machine?" The carpenter decides not to replace the guard for this cut because the last time this operation was performed, the wood snagged on the guard support and allowed the blade to burn the cut surface. This necessitated extra sanding to remove the stain. However, this time, even though the carpenter uses the proper hand pusher and guides, the saw hits a knot, causing the work piece to jump up from the spinning blade. Luckily, the carpenter receives only minor lacerations.

The unsafe acts in this incident are (1) the carpenter removing the guard and leaving it off during the operation, (2) the supervisor allowing the saw to be used with the poor guard and not insisting on replacing the defective guard, (3) the carpenter continuing to use a piece of unsafe equipment, and (4) the company purchasing the saw without specifying the correct type of guard.

The unsafe conditions are (1) having the improper guard on the machine, (2) providing a machine without a proper guard, and perhaps (3) the supervisor being unaware of the use of the improper guard.

In most provinces and territories, a company official such as the plant manager may be found liable if an identified unsafe act or condition is ignored. The carpenter displayed voluntary risk in that the saw was used even though it was known to have a defective guard.

OBSERVATIONS OR WALKTHROUGHS

walkthrough
inspection of the incident scene to get a picture of the total environment

At the beginning of an investigation, an overall picture of the total environment is achieved by means of a **walkthrough**. Observation of causal factors, physical conditions, and work habits will help the occupational health and safety specialist identify potential causes of the incident. Because the manager may not be totally familiar with the details of the operation, the specialist should turn to the supervisor for any necessary information.

INTERVIEWS

The following are some basic rules for conducting an interview:

1. Interview witnesses on the spot as soon as possible after the event, while their memories are still fresh. Inform each witness of the purpose of the interview and of what you hope to accomplish.

2. Interview witnesses separately and in a neutral location, such as the cafeteria. Do not use your office, since it could have an authority stigma associated with it. The witness should be permitted to have a worker representative present if he or she desires. Make sure the representative listens and says little or nothing.

3. Put the witness at ease. If the person witnessed a serious injury, he or she may well be shaken or upset. If the person witnessed a death, counselling may be

necessary before any discussion can take place. Reassure the witness that you are simply trying to gather information, not to lay blame.

4. Let the individual recall the event in his or her own way. Do not try to bias the account with questions that are pointed or directed. "Will you please tell me in your own words what you saw or heard?" is much better than, "Can you think what prompted John to do what he did?"

5. Ask necessary questions at appropriate times, without interrupting the speaker's train of thought. The questions should serve to clarify a point or fill in gaps, not to support conclusions you may be forming. "Can you explain again how you knew the machine was turned off?" is preferable to, "You commented that the table saw was not running–did you see the worker turn it off?"

6. Give the witness feedback. "Based on what you said, this is my understanding of what you saw. If there is something I missed or haven't got right, please add to or clarify it." By the time you have finished, both you and the witness should be able to agree that the statement is a factual representation of what was said.

7. Make sure that critical information–either from the witnesses or from your own observations–is recorded in a timely fashion. The longer the delay, the more bias will affect the results. Supplement your written record with visuals (e.g., sketches, photographs, videos).

8. End the interview on a positive note by thanking the witness for his or her valuable time and assistance. Encourage the witness to come to you with any further information that may emerge (see **OH&S Notebook 12.4**).

OH&S NOTEBOOK 12.4

COGNITIVE INTERVIEWING

Cognitive interviewing is a technique that was developed for police officers conducting forensic investigations. A great deal of research suggests that cognitive interviews are effective in retrieving accurate eyewitness testimony. Cognitive interviews result in more information and a higher accuracy rate than do "regular" investigative interviews. Some preliminary evidence shows that the cognitive interview elicits more accurate statements from incident witnesses. A typical cognitive interview follows this sequence:

1. *Introduction.* Develop rapport, communicate needs, encourage active participation.

2. *Open-ended narration.* Establish mental context, note mental images, develop plan for probing.

3. *Probing.* Use richest images to probe, ask questions related to images.

4. *Review.* Review information reported.

5. *Close.* Finish official business and encourage future contact.

Sources: C. MacLean, V. Stinson, and E.K. Kelloway, "Cognitive Interviewing of Incident Witnesses: An Initial Test," Paper presented at the annual meeting of the Canadian Psychological Association, St. John's, 2004; R.P. Fisher, "Interviewing Victims and Witnesses of Crime," *Psychology, Public Policy, and Law*, Vol. 1 (1995): 732–64; R.P. Fisher, R.E. Geiselman, and M. Amador, "Field Test of the Cognitive Interview: Enhancing the Recollection of Actual Victims and Witnesses of Crime," *Journal of Applied Psychology*, Vol. 74 (1995): 722–27; R.P. Fisher, M.R. McCauley, and R.E. Geiselman, "Improving Eyewitness Testimony with the Cognitive Interview," in D.F. Ross, J.D. Read, and M.P. Toglia, eds., *Adult Eyewitness Testimony: Current Trends and Developments* (New York: Cambridge University Press, 1994), pp. 245–72.

RE-ENACTMENTS

re-enactment
a simulation designed
to recreate the circum-
stances leading up to
an incident

Re-enactment is a powerful incident recall method that requires careful handling and planning. The most obvious problem is the danger that simulating an actual injury will produce another one.

Circumstances will dictate whether a re-enactment is essential to complete a thorough investigation. In one documented case, the occupational health and safety professional was on-site when a worker was impaled between the couplers of two boxcars in a company's rail-yard. That person filmed the car separation and the removal of the body. Then, while all the witnesses were present and all of the details were fresh—horribly so—in their minds, he had each witness walk through what he or she saw. The local coroner complimented the safety officer on the thoroughness of the evidence, and a re-enactment was obviously unnecessary.

The following are some guidelines for conducting a re-enactment:

1. *A qualified observer is necessary.* If none are available, the in-house specialist will have to do the job. If it appears that evidence is being gathered for an inquest or court hearing, every possible explanation—even suicide—must be considered.

2. *Do not show—tell.* The witnesses must relate *in their own words* what they observed. The analyst must know precisely what took place during the event. Their stories will provide that information. The company cannot afford any surprises that might lead to additional injury. Filming the witness can be very helpful, but if, and only if, the witness agrees.

3. *Shut down every energy source and lock them out.* Follow the lockout procedures discussed in Chapter 4. The professional who is conducting the re-enactment should control the major key for the lockout.

4. *Carefully act out the events.* The witness should describe what happened at each step (just as he or she did when verbally describing the events), and then, with the specialist's approval, will act out that step. For obvious reasons, the re-enactment will stop before the point of incident.

Photo by Ken Lubas/Los Angeles Times via Getty Images

Incident investigations often focus on trying to reconstruct the events leading up to the incident as in this traffic investigation.

// INVESTIGATIVE TOOLS

The walkthrough, the interview, and the re-enactment can be supplemented by the following:

- *Photographs.* Incident photography is helpful and even necessary for efficient incident investigation. When pictures are being taken, make sure they show the whole area, as well as every angle and every nook and cranny. Colour is best, though black and white can be useful. One advantage of black-and-white photographs is that they can be scanned and included in the incident report. Point-and-shoot cameras, including the cameras available on most smart phones, also require minimal operator skill. Digital video cameras are effective and preferred, since the film can be viewed immediately and the data can be entered into the computer.

- *Drawings.* After the interview, prepare a series of sketches or drawings of the incident scene. A good CAD program will facilitate the drawing process. If the in-house specialist does not have access to CAD software and the training to use it, then a scale pencil sketch is fine. All parts of the drawing should be well labelled.

- *Computers.* Incident recall involves gathering and recording large amounts of information. A computer with a user-friendly database is a necessity. Portable laptops can be taken directly to the scene of an incident. Any computer will facilitate the structured entry of data and facts into the safety files.

- *Other tools.* Depending on the circumstances of the event, other tools such as tape measures, clipboards, water-resistant pens, and flashlights will be of assistance to the investigator.

- *Record check.* Training records and maintenance or production schedules can offer the investigator some valuable insights. A careful review of training records can provide the answers to some questions: Was the worker properly instructed in the accepted and safe methods of doing the job or task? Was he or she aware of the rules of operation, and were they followed? Has the worker signed a training attendance sheet or examination form? Maintenance logs and records should provide information about potential hazards within the company and about what, if anything, was done to address them. Preventive maintenance data are particularly important, since they can be used to predict possible future failures in equipment.

// INCIDENT REPORTS

Once all the information from the investigation has been gathered, incident reports must be completed. These reports should provide some explanation of causal factors. Though the principal causes will be unsafe acts (e.g., not using a personal protective device) or unsafe conditions (e.g., a broken guard), there may be other explanatory factors. The factor most closely associated with the cause of an incident is referred to as the *agency.* The following are some examples of agents:

- animals (insects, dogs, raccoons, etc.)
- pressure vessels (boilers, piping)
- chemicals (solvents, explosives)
- materials-handling systems (conveyers, forklift trucks)
- dust, fumes, smoke, mists (silica, wood)

- electrical equipment (motors, fuses, wiring)
- elevating devices (elevators, vertical stop belts)
- tools (hammers, wrenches)
- lifting devices (hoists, cranes)
- machine tools (lathe, drill press)
- motive power sources (engines, vehicles)
- radiation (X-ray, ultraviolet)

The *agency* refers to the subgroup of the factors listed above. For example, a dog bite would be the agency part of the animal group.

Another consideration in reports is the *incident type*, which attempts to categorize the nature of the incident. Some examples:

- caught in or between (e.g., crushed between two moving machines)
- struck by (impact or blow to the body by an object)
- struck against (walking into a door)
- fall to the same level (tripping on a level walkway)
- fall to a lower level (falling off a ladder)
- fall to a higher level (tripping while walking up steps)
- abraded, scratched, or punctured (an injury such as hitting the face when falling)
- overexertion (sprains, strains, etc., caused by a greater-than-average effort)
- contact with an energy (mechanical, kinetic, electrical, chemical, thermal, gravity, or radiation)

Personal factors (e.g., lack of knowledge, fatigue, restricted vision) should also be included on the incident investigation form to assist in entry, recordkeeping, and analysis.

The actual report format will vary by company. (Samples of short and long reports are provided in the Appendix **Figures 12A.1** and **12A.2**, respectively.) Organization and layout should be straightforward. Accuracy and thoroughness are also important. Where information is unknown or is not applicable, the respondent should indicate "information unknown" or "not applicable." Abbreviations such as "n/a" for "not applicable" should not be used (it can mean "not available" as well). Do not leave the space blank!

Reports that must be submitted to outside parties such as OH&S agencies or WCBs should include basic information about the company (i.e., type of industry, number of employees, etc.).

A description of any injury that was sustained should be included. A separate physician's report (see Appendix **Figure 12A.3**) should also be provided, along with a witness report (see Appendix **Figure 12A.4**).

Completed reports are submitted to the senior managers, the JHSC, others directly involved, and possibly the Ministry of Labour if the incident involved serious injury. It is then up to the senior manager directly responsible for the operation in question to implement the recommendations contained in the report.

INCIDENT ANALYSIS

Once the data are collected, the next task is to analyze the information to identify the cause of the incident (See **OH&S Today 12.2**). A variety of analytic models and techniques are available for use in assessing the cause of an incident.

DOMINO THEORY

Every event—incident or disaster—comprises a series of happenings that result in some negative condition. The domino theory, developed by H.W. Heinrich, is based on a set of five dominos, labelled as follows:[3]

1. Social, environmental and behaviour: How a person was raised and educated.
2. Faults of the person either inherited or acquired
3. Personal and mechanical hazards that result from carelessness or improper maintenance
4. Accidents resulting from hazards
5. Injuries resulting from accidents

> **domino theory**
> the theory that every incident results from a series of events

Heinrich's model emphasizes that injuries and incidents result from a whole chain of actions and situational characteristics. However, it is clear that Heinrich's original formulation focused on the individual and was seen by many as blaming the victim. A more modern incorporation of the domino principle maintains the principle of sequential causation but broadens the focus so that the dominos are labelled:

1. *Background:* a lack of control over the management function (planning, organizing, leading, controlling)
2. *Personal defects:* personal factors such as physical or mental problems, and job factors such as normal wear and tear of equipment
3. *Unsafe acts and conditions:* (described earlier)
4. *Incident:* a series of undesired events with release of energies that can cause harm
5. *Injury:* the most undesired result (e.g., trauma or property damage)

Though there are other models, such as those dealing with the release of energy[4] and with the theory of multiple factors,[5] the domino model is the easiest to illustrate. The domino theory asserts that if any one of the domino categories does not happen, injury probably will not occur (see **Figure 12.1**). For example, if a worker is trying to make a production quota (background), is wearing loose clothing (personal defects or unsafe conditions), and is operating a machine at unsafe speeds (unsafe act), an incident or injury will be more likely to occur. However, if the worker is wearing well-fitting clothes or operating the machine at the proper speed (removal of domino number 2 or 3), the risk of an incident is greatly reduced.

FIGURE 12.1

HEINRICH'S DOMINO MODEL

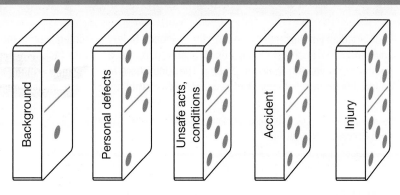

(a) Five factors in accident sequence

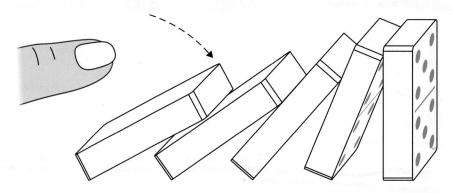

(b) Injury caused by action of preceding factors

(c) Removal of a factor may prevent the accident from occurring

THE SWISS CHEESE MODEL

J. Reason presented an updated version of the domino model that is often depicted as series of dominoes with holes in them.[6] In this view (often called the "Swiss cheese model"), an incident results when the holes line up (i.e., there are failures at multiple levels). Reason's model focuses on the series of events that must occur for an incident to occur. His model emphasizes that unsafe acts cannot be viewed in isolation; they are a product of the organizational culture, the level of supervision, and a variety of other contextual factors. It follows that incident analysis focuses on identifying these factors to "plug the holes" in the Swiss cheese.

Reason's incident causation model specifies four levels of defence:

1. organizational influences
2. local working conditions
3. unsafe acts
4. defences, barriers, and safeguards

For example, an organization with a poor safety culture may not have a high incident rate if it has well-developed safe working procedures or safety-conscious supervisors. Similarly, committing an unsafe act may not result in an incident if appropriate safeguards are in place. It is only when organizational influences and local working conditions allow for an unsafe act and there are no safeguards against such an act that an incident results.

BOW-TIE ANALYSIS

A more modern way of analyzing risks in the workforce is known as bow-tie analysis. It gets this name because the figure that results from the analysis resembles a bow-tie (see **Figure 12.2**). Essentially a bow-tie analysis combines a fault tree with an event tree. On the left of the diagram is a listing of potential hazards and the measures taken to control those hazards. On the right of the diagram are the measures taken to mitigate the consequences of an event and the resulting consequences. The "knot" in the bow-tie is the event or incident to be prevented. An overview of the bow-tie methodology can be found at http://www.bowtiepro.com/bowtie_uses.asp.

FIGURE 12.2

BOW-TIE ANALYSIS

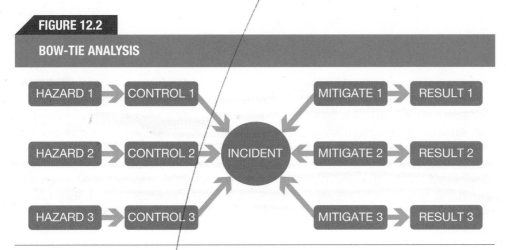

Source: Based on material found at http://www.bowtiepro.com/bowtie_uses.asp.

normal incidents
the theory that incidents are expected outcomes of interactive complexities

high-reliability organizations
organizations in hazardous industries that maintain a high safety record over time

The theory of normal incidents,[7] especially in high-reliability organizations (e.g., chemical plants, nuclear plants),[8] suggests that incidents result from the interactive complexities in the technological system. That is, no single event causes an incident, and the search for a single discrete cause, analogous to a single perpetrator, may well be fruitless in such an environment. The futility of the endeavour may be difficult to recognize, given the common tendency to make sense out of organizational events. As one researcher notes, "people who know the outcome of a complex prior history of tangled, indeterminate events remember that history as being much more determinant, leading 'inevitably' to the outcome they already knew."[9]

// THE PSYCHOLOGY OF INCIDENTS: COGNITIVE FAILURES

In many incident investigations, focus is placed on human error. As a result, we often end up concluding that highly trained and experienced workers simply "made a mistake" in the routine performance of their duties. In fact, the most common types of human errors responsible for fatalities and accidents are skill-based slips and lapse from inattention.

Psychologists refer to these slips or lapses as a "cognitive failure."[10] There seem to be at least three forms of cognitive failure; these relate to memory, focus, and physical skills. Forgetfulness is when you forget (even momentarily) things you ordinarily know (e.g., the name of your spouse or partner). Distractability is a failure in focus—finishing reading a page of text and realizing you have no idea what you just read is a common example of distractability. Finally, physical blunders include actions such as tripping over your own feet or bumping into things. Though much more research is required, we know that cognitive failures are often a sign of individuals under stress and that cognitive failures are related to the occurrence of both motor vehicle and work-related incidents.[11]

cognitive failure
a mistake or failure in the performance of an action that an individual is normally capable of performing

// SUMMARY

Incident investigation is a very important part of an OH&S program. The reasons for conducting an investigation are primarily to identify direct and contributing causes and to ensure that the incident does not recur. Timing and severity are the important variables in investigations. The types of information collected can be grouped under human factors, situational factors, and environmental factors. The investigative methods include observations or walkthroughs, interviews, and re-enactments, all of which are complemented by investigative tools such as cameras and computers. Records also supply information that may be important in determining causes. The reporting and analysis of the information collected is the last step in incident investigation.

KEY TERMS

cognitive failure 306
domino theory 303
high-reliability organizations 306
normal incidents 306
RAC program 292
re-enactment 300
walkthrough 298

DISCUSSION QUESTIONS

1. What are the three factors that should be considered as potential contributors to any incident?

2. Describe the methods that can be used in incident investigation.

3. What tools can assist the incident investigator?

4. What steps should be taken to properly re-enact an incident?

5. Give an example of how human, environmental, and situational factors can combine to result in an incident.

6. Given our focus on analyzing and understanding incident causation, it is worth noting that some occupational health and safety professionals now refuse to use the term "accident." They claim that doing so implies that incidents are random, unforeseeable events, whereas we know that most incidents result from a foreseeable series of events. What are the merits (pros and cons) of this position? Do "accidents happen," or are all incidents preventable?

7. Some safety professionals now talk about the notion of "system risk." In essence, they suggest that incidents do not result from single causes. Rather, they suggest that incidents are the result of multiple events working together. How might the factors identified in this chapter interact to result in an incident?

USING THE INTERNET

1. Search news media and online reports to find accounts of workplace incidents. For at least one such report, try to identify the human, situational, and environmental factors contributing to the incident.

2. Take the incident investigation training for supervisors presented at https://work.alberta.ca/elearning/Incident/Incident.htm.

EXERCISE

1. Many incident investigations, such as traffic and airline incident investigations, conclude that "human error" was the principal cause. We know that situational and environmental factors also play a role. Why do we emphasize the role of humans in incident causation? Does this result in an under-emphasis of these other factors?

In my small business we have had a lot of incidents and injuries. Even though I have only 10 employees we seem to always have somebody on the injured list. I think that my employees are just careless. What do you think I should do about this?

CASE STUDY 1   INCIDENT INVESTIGATION

You are the president and largest shareholder of an original equipment manufacturer (OEM) that employs 300 workers. You do not have a safety specialist on staff, but you do take a personal interest in incident prevention. Recently you assigned general responsibility for safety to the day shift superintendents as a minor part of their regular duties.

The plant has never been thoroughly analyzed for hazards, and you are aware that the operation is not as safe as it could be. Many of the operations require considerable ongoing maintenance by the workers to prevent incidents. Since for several years the business has been only breaking even, you have delayed making any improvements to the plant and equipment. You and the superintendents have concentrated your efforts on preventing unsafe acts by the employees. An elaborate system of worker reminders, such as posters and instruction by supervisors, has been used to make the workforce safety conscious.

For the past few years, your performance with respect to medical aid and lost-time injuries has been average for your WCB rate group. Your company has escaped any lost-time injuries for the past two years, including the current year to date. The continuation of that record has become an important goal. Signs in the plant indicate the number of days that have passed without a lost-time injury.

Today, at 15:30 hours, a container of nearly red-hot, upper-control-arm forgings was overturned. The hot forgings fell on a worker who was helping the drop forge machine operator. The worker suffered third degree burns over 20% of his body. Though he is expected to recover, the worker will lose most of his right arm, right ear, and sight in his right eye. Describe the investigative methods and tools you would use to investigate this incident.

CASE STUDY 2   OFFICE INCIDENT

Cathy Calvin is the newly appointed occupational health and safety specialist for the local school board. She has just been told of an incident experienced by an employee in the administrative office. It seems that two employees were trying to move a full filing cabinet from one corner of the office to another. The cabinet tipped, crushing the foot of one of the employees. The office staff applied first aid and rushed the injured employee to the hospital. The employee will be off work for at least two weeks. Board policy requires a full investigation of any lost-time injury. As a relative newcomer to the health and safety role, Cathy has never conducted an incident investigation before. Can you help Cathy design an appropriate strategy for approaching the investigation?

APPENDIX

INCIDENT REPORT FORMS

PE+E Supervisor's Accident/Incident Report

A. General Information

last name: first name: gender: [] male [] female

department: job title:

type: [] full time   [] part time   [] casual

date of injury: time of injury: [] am [] pm

date reported: time reported: [] am [] pm

incident category: [] illness   [] injury   [] first aid   [] medical aid

B. Accident Investigation

Nature and extent of injury: [] left   [] right

What job was the employee performing:

Was this part of regular duties: [] yes   [] no

Length of time employee performing this type of work:

Exact location of accident:

Describe sequence of events leading to accident. Name tools, machines, materials used.
Provide sketch on reverse if necessary.

Describe any unsafe mechanical or physical condition involved in accident:

Describe any unsafe act involved in accident:

Name and address of hospital or clinic: [] company doctor:

Doctor's name: Doctor's estimate of lost time:

Measures taken to prevent similar accidents:

(continued)

C. Diagrams

> *Diagrams or photographs may be placed here:*

Witness name: _____   Witness name: _____

Address: _____   Address: _____

Phone: Res: _____   Phone: Res: _____

      Bus: _____   Bus: _____

Supervisor's signature: _____   Date: _____

Employee's signature: _____   Date: _____

Please have this document processed and forwarded to   *Original to:*   *Manager, Safety and Environment*
                                                                Copies to: *Vice President, Manufacturing,*
                                                                                 Manager, Human Resources
                                                                                 Department

The information you provide on this document will enable PE+E to effectively manage claims. Thank you for taking as much time as possible.

Supervisor's Accident/Incident Report

To be completed by the supervisor with the employee immediately after an accident/incident

Please Print

last name _____ first name _____ gender _____

street _____ apt _____ city _____ prov _____

postal code _____ telephone _____ date of birth _____ marital status _____

date of employment _____ department _____ job title _____

[ ] full time   [ ] part time   [ ] casual   hrs/week _____

years' experience _____ social insurance number _____

accident/incident occurred: yyyy mm dd (   )   hhmm (   ) am/pm

reported to employer: yyyy mm dd (   )   hhmm (   ) am/pm

who was accident reported to _____

location of accident _____

supervisor's name (dept, machine, location of machine) _____

witness name(s) _____

Has this employee ever had a similar work-related injury or non-work-related injury? [ ] yes [ ] no

If yes, explain: _____

_____

List the employee's job description/task analysis at the time of the injury _____

(Include job title, duties, weights, sizes of equipment, tools, etc.) _____

_____

_____

_____

_____

_____

_____

What physical effort was involved? (List job function plus weights and sizes of materials used.)

_____

_____

_____

_____

_____

_____

_____

(*continued*)

Investigation of accident/incident (*who, what, why, where, how*)

Who was involved? _____

_____

Where did the accident/incident occur? _____

_____

What happened to cause the accident/incident? (explain—facts only) _____

_____

_____

_____

_____

Why did the accident/incident occur? (be objective, do not lay blame) _____

_____

_____

How did the accident/incident occur? (based on facts only) _____

_____

_____

Injury

[ ] lost time [ ] medical aid [ ] first aid [ ] information only or [ ] hazardous condition, no injury treatment memorandum sent [ ] yes [ ] no modified work form sent [ ] yes [ ] no

Causes

[ ] unsafe act [ ] unsafe condition [ ] information only or [ ] poor/damaged equipment [ ] no/poor training [ ] no/poor procedures [ ] other

Explain

_____

_____

_____

_____

_____

_____

_____

_____

(*continued*)

Accident type

[] overexertion/strain [] caught in/between [] slip/fall [] struck by/against [] exposed to

[] motor vehicle   [] contact with/by   [] other

Explain: _____

_____

_____

Injury type

[] bruise   [] burn (heat) [] burn (chemical)   [] cut   [] crush   [] strain

[] twist   [] lift   [] electric shock   [] inhalation [] occupational illness

[] rash   [] other

Explain: _____

_____

_____

Part of body injured   *[ ] left   [ ] right*

[] head   [] face   [] eye   [] ear   [] neck   [] chest

[] lungs   [] abdomen [] groin   [] back-upper [] back-middle   [] back-lower

[] buttock [] shoulder   [ ] arm   [] wrist   [] hand   [] finger:th 2 3 4 5

[] leg   [] knee   [] ankle   [] foot   [] toe:big 2 3 4 5 [] other

Explain: _____

_____

_____

Suggested corrective action

[] review procedures   [] protective equipment [] repair equipment

[] develop procedure [] re-instruction of staff

Explain: _____

_____

_____

_____

_____

(*continued*)

name & address of hospital or clinic _____

_____

_____

name of attending doctor   estimated time off work _____

name of family physician _____

address _____

date & hour last worked   Work hours: from   to _____

shift information: [ ] Day   [ ] Afternoon   [ ] Midnight

hours worked: from: to: days/week: _____

provide average gross earnings   [ ] hourly   [ ] daily

Additional information _____

_____

_____

_____

_____

_____

Diagram of accident

Employee's signature _____ Date _____

Supervisor's signature _____ Date _____

MAKE COPIES AND SEND TO:

[ ] Manager, Loss Control (original) [ ] Human Resources   [ ] Department

INJURY/ILLNESS ASSESSMENT FORM
to accompany employee to physician

For use in on-duty instances of sickness or injury to determine the rehabilitation duties to which an employee can return in the workplace as presented in Bill 162 of the Workers' Compensation Act.

To be completed by an Employee's Supervisor (please print)

A. Personal Data   Date:_____

Employee's Name: _____   Signature: _____

Job Title: _____   SIN: _____

Date of illness or injury on duty: _____   Date of birth: _____

Date absence commenced: _____   Health No.: _____

Nature of injury: _____

Supervisor's Name: _____   Department: _____   Telephone: _____

To be completed by Physician (please print)

B. Assessment of fitness to work

1. [ ] Employee is fit to return to regular work.

2. [ ] Employee is fit to return to modified work—with restrictions as indicated in C & D (reverse).

   Indicate number of hours to be worked and on what basis?

   [_____] hours   [ ] daily   [ ] weekly

   Estimate date of return to modified work: _____

3. [ ] Not fit for work at this time.

   Employee to return for medical reassessment on (yyyy mm dd) _____

See reverse side for Physical Evaluation to be completed by the Physician

Please return this completed form to the Manager, Loss Control via the Employee

(continued)

PHYSICIAN'S REPORT (*continued*)

To be completed by the treating Physician

C. Physical Evaluation

Step 1 *Location of problem*

(a) head: include vision, hearing, speech
(b) neck
(c) upper back, chest or upper abdomen
(d) lower back, lower abdomen or genitalia
(e) shoulder or upper arm
(f) elbow or lower arm
(g) wrist or hand
(h) hip or upper leg
(i) knee or lower leg
(j) ankle or foot
(k) systemic or internal organ

Right   Left

Step 2 *Please indicate restrictions for modified work*

1. Walking: [] only short distances   [] other
2. Standing, not more than: [] 15 minutes   [] 30 minutes [] other
3. Sitting, no more than: [] 30 minutes   [] 60 minutes [] 2 hours [] other
4. Bending and twisting, explain:
5. Lifting, floor to waist, not more than: [] 7 kg   [] 14 kg   [] 25 kg   [] other
6. Lifting, waist to head, not more than: [] 7 kg   [] 14 kg   [] 25 kg   [] other
7. Carrying, not more than: [] 7 kg   [] 14 kg   [] 25 kg   [] other
8. Climbing stairs: [] no stair climbing   [] 2 or 3 steps only [] only short flight
9. Climbing ladder: [] no climbing   [] 2 or 3 steps only [] 4 or 6 steps only
10. Manual dexterity, not able to: [] type   [] sort   [] other
11. Pushing and pulling trolley, not more than: [] 16 kg   [] 25 kg   [] other
12. Can operate motorized equipment: [] any vehicle [] forklifts [] not recommended
13. Vision, potential safety hazard   [] yes   [] no   [] other
14. Other comments (explain)

D. Treatment

1. Is the employee's prescribed treatment likely to impair performance or safety?   [] yes   [] no
2. Is the employee referred to: [] physiotherapy   Date commenced:_____
                                     [] occupational therapy   Duration: _____

Physician's Name: _____   Telephone: _____

Address: _____

Date: _____   Signature: _____

Accident/Incident Witness Statement

Injured employee: _____ Date of injury: _____

Witness name: _____

Does the witness have knowledge of the accident or injury? [ ] yes [ ] no

Did the witness see the injury happen?   [ ] yes   [ ] no

If yes to either of the above, please explain below:

Knowledge of injury: Explain what you know about the injury/accident (e.g.,what type of work was being done at the time of the injury/accident, what happened to cause the injury/ accident, how seriously was the injured employee hurt).

_____

_____

_____

_____

What witness actually saw: Please identify what you saw before the injury/accident, during the injury/accident, and immediately after the injury/accident.

_____

_____

_____

_____

Give your **opinion** as to how this injury/accident could have been prevented.

_____

_____

_____

_____

_____

Witness signature: _____ Date: _____

// NOTES

1. P. Laing, ed., *Incident Prevention Manual for Business and Industry: Administration and Programs*, 10th ed. (Washington: National Safety Council, 1992).

2. T. Ryan, "Incident Investigations: II Group Investigations," in F. Briggs, ed., *Guide to Health and Safety Management* (Toronto: Southam, 1991).

3. H.W. Heinrich, *Industrial Incident Prevention* (New York: McGraw-Hill, 1936).

4. W. Haddon, Jr., "The Changing Approach to Epidemiology, Prevention and Amelioration of Trauma: The Transition to Approaches Etiological Rather Than Descriptively Based," *American Journal of Public Health* 58 (1968): 8.

5. V.L. Gross, "System Safety in Rapid Rail Transit," *ASSE Journal*, August 1972.

6. J. Reason, *Human Error* (Cambridge: Cambridge University Press, 1990).

7. C. Perrow, Normal Incidents: Living with High-Risk Technologies (New York: Basic, 1984); idem, "Incidents in High-Risk Systems," *Technological Studies* 1 (1994): 1–20.

8. K. Roberts, "Some Characteristics of High-Reliability Organizations," Organization Science 2 (1989): 160–76; K.E. Weick, K.M. Sutcliffe, and D. Obstfeld, "Organizing for High Reliability: Processes of Collective Mindfulness," *Research in Organizational Behavior* 21 (1999): 81–123.

9. K. Weick, *Sensemaking in Organizations* (Thousand Oaks: Sage, 1995).

10. J.C. Wallace and S.J. Vodanovich, "Can Incidents and Industrial Mishaps Be Predicted? Further Investigation into the Relationships Between Cognitive Failure and Reports of Incidents," *Journal of Business and Psychology 17* (2003): 503–14.

11. Ibid.

DISABILITY MANAGEMENT AND RETURN TO WORK

CHAPTER LEARNING OBJECTIVES

AFTER READING THIS CHAPTER, YOU SHOULD BE ABLE TO:

- articulate the financial and legal motivations for disability management programs
- describe the goals and values of disability management programs
- discuss the important outcomes used to evaluate disability management efforts
- discuss the best practices in disability management programming
- consider the benefits of return-to-work planning
- describe the common methods and approaches used in workplace accommodation
- identify the stakeholders in disability management programs
- consider potential barriers to successful disability management

Anyone who follows professional sports knows that a team's success can hinge on its injury list. Fans of the National Hockey League's Montreal Canadiens, for instance, closely followed star goaltender Carey Price's status following a lower body injury that kept him out for the bulk of the 2015/2016 season. Many attribute the Canadiens' lackluster season and missed Stanley Club Playoffs to this crucial absence.

Perhaps the most talked about hockey injuries in recent years are the multiple concussions suffered by NHL superstar Sidney Crosby. Two on-ice hits to the head in January 2011 resulted in long-lasting, concussion-like symptoms that kept him largely out of the game for nearly two years—two prime playing years.

In looking at professional sports injuries, you can easily see some of the elements we'll consider in this chapter on disability management and return to work. Consider Sidney Crosby. He sustained a lost-time injury and during his initial recovery period he eased back to work; for example, with no-contact practices. He officially returned to the ice with the Penguins in late 2011, but less than a month later symptoms forced him off the ice once again for three additional months. In other words, his initial return to competitive play was not sustained. Now, Crosby is back strong. Carey Price? We're still waiting to see of his return in the coming hockey season.

There are other stories of elite athletes who return to high-level competition following injury or illness. WNBA star Jessica Breland beat cancer to return to competitive play. Italian race car driver Alex Zanardi, whose legs were severed in a horrific racing crash during the 2001 CART racing league's season, returned to professional racing in a race car adapted for hand controls.

In these stories we see evidence of determination and learn that it is possible to return in a meaningful way to one's work after experiencing serious injury or illness.

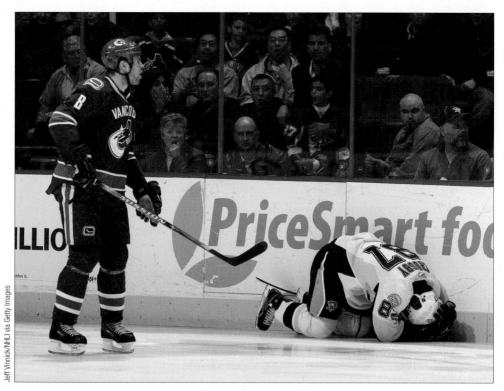

Jeff Vinnick/NHLI via Getty Images

Hockey superstar Sidney Crosby experienced a concussion that resulted in a lengthy absence before his successful return to play.

(*continued*)

These athletes dug deep into their inner strength and used specific strategies and equipment to rebuild their physical strength to return, perhaps gradually, to competition. In this chapter we explore how disability management programs can help injured or ill workers return successfully to the workplace.

Sources: P. Hickey, "Canadiens' Fortunes Clearly Revolve Around Carey Price," *Montreal Gazette* (April 15, 2016). Found at: http://montrealgazette.com/sports/hockey/nhl/montreal-canadiens/hickey-on-hockey-notes-canadiens-fortunes-clearly-revolve-around-carey-price (accessed June 13, 2016); CTV News, "Sidney Crosby Ready to Put Concussions Behind Him." Found at: http://www.ctvnews.ca/sports/sidney-crosby-ready-to-put-concussions-behind-him-1.1115158 (accessed June 13, 2016); Postmedia News, "Sidney Crosby Cleared for Practice with the Penguins." Found at: http://www.canada.com/Sidney+Crosby+cleared+practice+with+Penguins/5413600/story.html (accessed June 13, 2016); M. Isaacson, "The Miracle That Is Jessica Breland," Espn.com (June 18, 2014). Found at: http://espn.go.com/wnba/story/_/id/11100323/wnba-jessica-breland-playing-better-ever-chicago-sky (accessed June 13, 2016); The Independent, "Alex Zanardi: A Fierce Spirit Triumphs in Return to the Track." Found at: http://www.independent.co.uk/sport/motor-racing/alex-zanardi-a-fierce-spirit-triumphs-in-return-to-the-track-19383.html (accessed June 13, 2016).

As we saw in the opening vignette, workplace injuries and illness happen in all types of work environments. As a society we're used to following injured athletes on their roads to recovery, aspects of which are often made public in news releases and press conferences. However, we might be less familiar with disability management and return-to-work practices in other work environments. In this chapter we explore how organizations can use disability management approaches both to prevent injuries and illnesses and to facilitate successful return to work following an employee's recovery after injury or illness occurs. In contrast to Chapter 3, where we focused on workers' compensation as an insurance program for injured or ill workers, here we consider the active processes, strategies, and stakeholders involved in managing work-related disability during recovery and eventual resumption of work activities.

// MOTIVES FOR DISABILITY MANAGEMENT

FINANCIAL MOTIVES

Work-related injuries are prevalent and costly. Each year an estimated 317 million workplace incidents occur worldwide, with many leading to prolonged work absence. The International Labour Organization estimates the annual cost of these incidents is about 4% of global Gross Domestic Product.[1] Canadian estimates suggest that occupational injuries cost the Canadian economy $9.7 billion per year in direct costs (e.g., compensation benefits). This number jumps to $19 billion per year when indirect costs are also included.[2] In 2014, workers' compensations boards across Canada accepted 239 643 claims for lost-time injuries at Canadian workplaces.[3] In 2013, for every 100 employees who worked for employers covered under workers' compensation boards, there were 1.60 compensated lost-time injuries.[4] Looking at the costs of absenteeism in general, workplace absenteeism costs the Canadian economy more than $16 billion annually.[5] Furthermore, there is growing concern that the various costs of workplace injury and illness will continue to increase. The prevalence of chronic disorders among the workforce, due in part to demographic factors such as labour shortages and an aging population, may result in even more lost work time.[6] Thus, there are financial motivations for workplaces to reduce costs associated with injury and illness. Disability management programs can help achieve this goal. Learn more about the business case for disability management programs in **OH&S Notebook 13.1**.

THE BUSINESS CASE FOR DISABILITY MANAGEMENT

Organizations have an obligation to facilitate timely and safe return to work for injured employees. However, an effective disability management and return-to-work program also makes good business sense. There are numerous employer benefits of effective disability management and return-to-work programs. These include:

- minimizing the costs of disability
- a quicker return to previous productivity levels
- reduced work delays

- improved employee morale
- retaining skilled employees
- improvement in the company's reputation and image
- reduced training costs
- may help reduce insurance costs
- avoiding grievances or litigation for failure to accommodate

Sources: Work Safe NB, "Workplace Disability Management: A Guide to Establishing a Program in your Workplace." Found at: http://www.worksafenb .ca/docs/Workplac.pdf (accessed June 13, 2016); Canadian Society of Professionals in Disability Management, "Making a Business Case for Disability Management" (n.d.). Found at: http://www.cspdm.ca/dm-in-context/dm-programs-benefits/making-a-business-case-for-disability-management (accessed June 13, 2016).

MORAL AND SOCIAL MOTIVES

The human and social costs of workplace work-related injury and illness are intolerably high. OH&S professionals are motivated by ethical arguments in support of safety initiatives.[7] Certainly, injured individuals experience social costs over and above the financial costs that they and others (e.g., employers, public and private insurers, and the health care system) incur. There are emotional costs for injured workers, which include psychological symptoms such as depression, anxiety, and post-traumatic stress disorder.[8] Further, work is an important source of meaning, social support, and identity for individuals, and these factors may motivate injured and ill workers to return to work.[9]

LEGAL MOTIVES

In Canada, legislation protects the rights of disabled workers, including those who lose work time due to an injury or work-related illness. Under Canadian human rights legislation, employers have a **duty to accommodate** individuals as they return to work.[10] That is, employers are held to a high standard in their obligation to accommodate workers who are attempting to return to work following an injury or illness, in that they are required to implement changes in job tasks and or the work environment to enable workers with a temporary or permanent disability to perform work productively.[11] For example, a worker who has sustained a back injury may return to work on light duties that do not involve heavy lifting. Organizations are expected to engage in reasonable accommodations up to the point of **undue hardship**. Undue hardship is evaluated in the context of the organization in question; there is no precise legal definition of the concept.[12] However, it is generally interpreted to mean that employers must accommodate the needs of a disabled worker unless the necessary accommodation would lead to health

duty to accommodate legislated responsibility of employers to accommodate workers who are attempting to return to work following an injury or illness via changes in job tasks and/or the work environment to enable workers with a temporary or permanent disability to perform work productively

undue hardship aspect of human rights legislation that means that employers must accommodate the needs of a disabled worker unless the necessary modifications would lead to health and safety difficulties or present unsustainable economic or efficiency costs

and safety difficulties or present unsustainable economic or efficiency costs. For instance, a company would not be expected to accommodate an injured worker if the cost of the specialized equipment the worker required would result in bankruptcy or if the employee wished to return to a given job before the employer felt certain that the worker could perform the job safely. The duty to accommodate and the concept of undue hardship are outlined in more detail in **OH&S Today 13.1**. You can also learn more about the employer's obligations to re-employ ill or injured workers in **OH&S Notebook 13.2**.

OH&S TODAY 13.1

THE DUTY TO ACCOMMODATE AND UNDUE HARDSHIP

Canadian employers have a legal obligation to accommodate individuals and to be proactive in removing discriminatory workplace practices. When exploring accommodation options for returning workers, both employers and employees have responsibilities to fulfill. For example, employers need to ensure their workplaces are inclusive. They must also inform employees about their right to accommodation, and to accommodate workers to the point of undue hardship

Employees' roles and obligations include informing the employer that accommodation is needed and when it is no longer necessary. This will likely involve providing medical information outlining the nature of the accommodation required. Employees also need to cooperate to help find a suitable accommodation, which may require the employee to be flexible when considering possible accommodation solutions.

Employers report that they often face challenges in determining how to provide appropriate accommodations. For example, it is difficult to design suitable accommodation when there is very little or vague information from the health care providers involved. Without understanding the medical limitations for the returning worker, it is difficult to identify appropriate work arrangements. Having a proactive disability management system can help alleviate these challenges. A return-to-work coordinator or a disability management consultant can work with the current health care team or seek a third-party medical opinion.

Employers also report questions about what constitutes undue hardship. Such uncertainty reflects the fact that undue hardship is defined on a case-by-case basis. Furthermore, the wording of human rights legislation pertaining to undue hardship can differ across provinces. For example, the Ontario Human Rights code considers only the following three factors in evaluating undue hardship: cost, the possibility of outside funding assistance, and health and safety concerns. However, the PEI act is broader in the factors considered in assessing undue hardship, including financial pressure, health and safety concerns, employee morale, and collective agreement provisions. Exploration of case law decisions can help define the boundaries of undue hardship. An Alberta Human Rights tribunal found that a school division had discriminated against an injured caretaker due to its perfunctory attempts to find modified work before letting the employee go. A BC Human Rights tribunal concluded that a university did not have to create a new position to accommodate a research employee who had developed an allergy from working with mice.

Sources: Government of Canada, "The Fundamentals—Duty to Accommodate: Roles and Responsibilities" (2011). Found at: https://www.tbs-sct.gc.ca/psm-fpfm/ve/dee/dmi-igi/fun-fon/dta-oda-eng.asp#Toc297620654 (accessed June 13, 2016); L. Johnson, "Employers Face Challenges with Duty to Accommodate" (June 7, 2012), *Canadian Occupational Safety*. Found at: http://www.cos-mag.com/Legal/Legal-Stories/employers-face-challenges-with-duty-to-accommodate-lawyer.html (accessed June 13, 2016); Ontario Human Rights Commission, "Policy and Guidelines on Disability and the Duty to Accommodate (revised December 2009). Found at: http://www.ohrc.on.ca/en/policy-and-guidelines-disability-and-duty-accommodate (accessed June 13, 2016); Prince Edward Island Human Rights Commission, "Workplace Rights: A Guide to the PEI Human Rights Act for Employers and Employees" (2010). Found at: http://www.gov.pe.ca/forms/pdf/2756.pdf (accessed June 13, 2016); OHS Insider, "University Accommodated RA with Mice Allergy to Point of Undue Hardship" (November 3, 2014). Found at: https://ohsinsider.com/search-by-index/disabilities/university-accommodated-ra-mice-allergy-point-undue-hardship (accessed June 13, 2016); OHS Insider, "School District Didn't Accommodate Caretaker Injured on the Job" (March 16, 2015). Found at: https://ohsinsider.com/search-by-index/disabilities/school-district-didnt-accommodate-caretaker-injured-on-the-job (accessed June 13, 2016).

RE-EMPLOYMENT OBLIGATIONS

Under Canadian human rights legislation, Canadian employers have a duty to accommodate employees with disabilities to the point of undue hardship. That said, workers' compensation acts for various Canadian jurisdictions differ in their requirements pertaining to duty-to-accommodate and re-employment obligations. For example, in Manitoba employers with 25 or more employees are required to re-employ injured workers who worked for them for at least 12 continuous months prior to the injury. Moreover, the employers must accommodate those employees to the point of undue hardship. Several other jurisdictions have exemption policies for small employees; for instance, New Brunswick exempts employers with fewer than 10 employees. In some provinces, such as Alberta, the relevant acts are silent on the issue of re-employment obligations, though Canadian human rights legislation pertaining to the duty to accommodate workers with disabilities still applies.

The limits of re-employment also differ by jurisdiction. In Manitoba, for instance, the obligation to re-employ ends two years after the date of the injury, six months after the worker is medically able to perform his or her pre-injury job, or the normal retirement date of the worker, whichever comes first. Those working in the field of disability management should check the local requirements of their province or territory to ensure that they are upholding the relevant legislation.

Sources: Workers' Compensation Board of Manitoba, "Reemployment Obligations." Found at: http://www.wcb.mb.ca/sites/default/files/resources/2826%20WCB%20Re-Employment%20Brochure%20Web.pdf (accessed June 13, 2016); Association of Workers' Compensation Boards of Canada, "Rehabilitation/Return to Work." Found at: http://awcbc.org/wp-content/uploads/2013/12/rehab_return_to_work.pdf (accessed June 13, 2016).

At present, Canada does not have a federal law for the protection of persons with disabilities. Currently, the Charter of Rights and Freedoms is the mechanism by which protection against discrimination is offered. There is movement toward the development of a federal act in Canada, with the March 2016 federal budget allocating funding for consultations on the possible introduction of such an act. Some Canadian provinces have provincial accessibility legislation. Ontario was the first province to introduce legislation. The Accessibility for Ontarians with Disabilities Act (AODA) has been phased in since 2005 with a goal of a completely accessible Ontario by 2025. The AODA has implications for disability management and return-to-work practices for employers in Ontario. For instance, as of January 1, 2016, employers with 50 or more employees must have accommodation plans and return-to-work processes for disabled workers under the accessible employment standard. Other provinces have followed Ontario's lead. The Accessibility for Manitobans Act (AMA) became law in 2013 and some provinces have legislation or strategic plans in development, including Nova Scotia, which has committed to introducing legislation and BC, which has introduced the Accessibility 2024 initiative.[13]

// DISABILITY MANAGEMENT

Organizations can use disability management programs as an effective response to the motives described above. These programs outline strategies to prevent workplace injury and illness and to accommodate workers in a manner that facilitates early and safe return to work, thus addressing financial, moral, and legislative realities.

Disability management encompasses a set of proactive employer practices whose goals are to prevent or reduce workplace disability; to intervene early in the event of risk or injury; and to provide coordinated management and rehabilitation functions that promote workers' recovery and safe and timely return to work.[14] The goals of disability management programs include promotion of safe workplaces; coordinated programming in health, rehabilitation, and accommodation interventions; and representation of all stakeholders, including workers, unions, management, government, and insuring agencies.[15]

Disability management programs are most effective when developed and applied using a **systems approach**.[16] A systems approach to disability management emphasizes the work and organizational context—for instance, the type of work and the safety record of the organization—instead of focusing solely on individual employees. When disability management efforts are fully integrated into the workplace, the workplace culture reflects the overarching commitment to prevention and restoration. Senior managers and frontline employees alike appreciate the value of safety and support the goals of the disability management initiatives.

The research indicates that workplaces with a people-focused workplace culture, positive safety attitudes, and articulated policies on disability management tend to report shorter absences, lower disability costs, and less frequent absences arising from workplace injury.[17] The value of this type of support from the top makes sense; the most intense efforts of frontline supervisors to help injured employees return to work will be futile if organizational policy and practice do not support return-to-work practices, such as modified or light-duty work.

disability management
proactive employer practices with the goals of preventing or reducing workplace disability, intervening early in the face of risk or injury, and providing coordinated management and rehabilitation functions to promote workers' recovery and safe and timely return to work

systems approach
an approach to disability management that emphasizes the work and organizational context

ASSESSING DISABILITY MANAGEMENT PROGRAMS

Two primary values of disability management programs are (1) safe and productive employment for individuals, including those with disabilities; (2) and reduced *incidence* and *impact* of workplace injury and illness.[18] As we move deeper into our discussion of disability management programs, it is important to keep in mind the indicators of a successful intervention. In other words, how do we measure the success of a disability management program? As you work through the remainder of this chapter, keep the following financial and social indicators in mind:

1. *The rates of safety incidents and occupational illnesses.* Decreases in incidence of incidents and exposures can support the effectiveness of disability management programs.

2. *Duration of the work disability.* Duration of the disability is the most commonly used outcome in research in this area. It is often reported as the amount of time that a worker receives benefits.[19] Longer absences are more both more costly for the employer and may also be associated with negative emotional experiences for the individual workers.

3. *Associated costs.* Various associated costs, such as wage replacement, health care costs, and intervention costs, are used in evaluation.[20] Reducing the duration of the disability can help decrease associated costs.

4. *Sustained return to work.* Whether workers are able to sustain their return to the workplace provides important information about disability management efforts. A quick but unsustainable return to work might indicate problems with

the return-to-work planning. In fact, researchers are increasingly looking at the work attitudes and quality of work experiences for those who are returning, in addition to the timing and sustainability of return to work when evaluating disability management programs.[21]

5. *Quality of life.* Workers' quality-of-life indicators, such as symptom severity and general health, are important outcomes in disability management and return-to-work programs.[22] Programs are viewed as more successful when injured workers report exhibit fewer symptoms and improved health.

BEST PRACTICES IN DISABILITY MANAGEMENT

The severity of a worker's injury or illness and the physical demands of that worker's job are obviously important predictors of initial and sustained return to work.[23] For example, for a worker who has sustained a musculoskeletal injury, returning to a job that involves heavy physical labour or working in awkward positions may take longer, or require more substantial accommodations, than returning to a job that is more sedentary.[24] A more serious injury, such as losing a limb, will obviously require a longer recovery than a less serious injury, such as sustaining a deep cut that requires stitches.

However, the nature of the injury and the job are not the only important predictors of return-to-work and effective disability management. Research has identified several best practices that can reduce the incidence and impact of workplace disability. These are outlined below.

PEOPLE-FOCUSED CLIMATE

A disability management program can be most effective when it is embedded in an organizational system that values its human resources and is supportive of safety initiatives. Employees should have a voice in the development and delivery of disability management programs.[25] Furthermore, *all* employees should be educated on their company's safety values and disability management program, including their rights and responsibilities within that program. Injured workers need to feel that they are welcome to return to the workplace and that the organization values their contributions. Injured workers are empowered when they are given an active role in their rehabilitation and return-to-work plans, including any necessary workplace accommodation.[26]

PREVENTION FOCUS

A common theme in disability management is "prevention first."[27] Prevention efforts that reduce the incidence of illness and injury result in cost savings for organizations.[28] A good starting point when developing a disability management program is to examine the organization's safety record. Are there particular jobs or worksites where injuries are prevalent? Are there injuries that employees report frequently? Aiming prevention efforts at injuries that are frequent or particularly costly will increase the company's return on investment. For example, if an analysis reveals that carpal tunnel syndrome is a common experience among press operators in a particular company, that organization might engage in directed prevention efforts, such as training on proper techniques to operate the press and the provision of personal protective equipment such as wrist braces. Or, the organization might use benefits programs as a way to promote prevention. For instance, by regularly using such services as massage therapy, workers may avoid sustaining certain types of injuries.

EARLY INTERVENTION

Organizations with progressive disability management programs continually assess risk for injury or illness in workplaces and take swift and early steps to eliminate or reduce these risks. These organizations track and understand patterns in employee absenteeism and sick/disability leaves and engage efforts to prevent short-term absences from extending into longer-term leave.[29] They extend this model of early intervention to cases where an injury has occurred.

Having a supervisor reach out to make early and considerate contact with an injured employee is considered a best practice in disability management programs.

A core aspect of disability management is for employers to make "early and considerate" contact with injured workers and to begin rehabilitation efforts as soon as possible.[30] The exact timing of early contact from the employer depends on the worker's situation. However, within a week or two is a suggested guideline for the immediate supervisor to place a call to the employee.[31] The goal of this contact is to express that the employer cares about the worker and his or her well-being. Early referral to a disability management program can decrease the length of absences and result in net savings for companies.[32] One study showed that early contact with the worker predicted increased perceptions of fair treatment among injured workers, which in turn predicted higher commitment to their organizations and better mental health.[33]

EDUCATION

Supervisors are called upon to support the disability management, in its preventive and return-to-work senses. Thus, they need to be educated about disability management programming and factors that support return to work. For example, it is often the supervisor who makes early contact with an injured employee.[34] Supervisors can engage in various practices to show their support for returning employees. For instance, they can be inclusive of returning employees by doing things such as meeting them when they return to work, trying to make the first weeks back to work less stressful, and explaining any changes in work practices. Supervisors should also be careful to avoid negative actions such as losing patience or excessively questioning the returning employee.[35] The supervisor will also have to work with the return-to-work coordinator to ensure that work modifications for a returning employee address the needs of both the returning worker and the supervisors and coworkers. Coworkers or supervisors may be suspicious or resentful of a work modification that increases coworkers' workloads or that threatens the group's ability to meet production goals.[36]

RETURN-TO-WORK CASE MANAGEMENT

Health and social services provided to those who are injured, disabled, or ill should be coordinated so that services are appropriate, timely, and efficient. The goals of case management are to enhance the injured worker's quality of life and, if possible, reduce the costs associated with care. A *return-to-work coordinator* can be responsible for case management. Outcomes such as duration of absence and disability costs are improved when organizations have a **return-to-work coordinator**.[37] The coordinator ensures that there is ongoing communication among the stakeholders, including the worker, the supervisor, and those providing treatment such as a physician or an occupational therapist.[38] The coordinator works with these stakeholders to plan return to work. There is strong evidence that this type of contact reduces the duration of absences.[39]

INTEGRATED CLAIMS MANAGEMENT AND MONITORING SYSTEMS

When workers require a leave from work due to illness or injury, they submit compensation claims to a benefits program. The particular provider will vary. Depending on the type of job and industry, and various other eligibility criteria, injured or ill workers may apply for compensation through the public workers' compensation system or via a private insurer.[40] In an integrated claims management system these processes are facilitated within the disability management program, which ideally leads to a more timely resolution of the compensation claim, thus ameliorating a potentially adversarial aspect of workplace disability insurance claims. If claims are not processed in a timely and sensitive fashion, workers may become frustrated because they are without an income for a period of time or begin to develop doubts about rehabilitation and return to work.[41]

Integrated systems also allow ready tracking of where a worker is in the claims, recovery, and rehabilitation process, which is helpful in return-to-work planning.[42] It may also help organizations monitor their safety and disability management performance. For example, potential risks may be uncovered if certain injuries are commonly occurring, or weaknesses in the return-to-work offerings may be identified if patterns about the success of return-to-work experiences emerge. For instance, examining amalgamated data may permit a return-to-work coordinator to detect which worksites appear to have a good record of sustained return to work and others where the record is not as strong. Particular interventions can be developed on the basis of this information.

Employee databases can be a vital tool in an integrated disability management program. In-house databases that log employee information such as sick time, injury dates, and contacts with health care providers can help manage individual cases. They can also help track valuable statistics, like average days post-injury until first contact, or the average length of short-term leaves. In larger organizations, such databases might be Web-based and integrated across sites. **OH&S Today 13.2** describes PepsiCo's Canada integrated absence management system.

Another valuable resource in disability management programming are broad-based databases that provide resources to disability management specialists. For instance, the National Institute of Disability Management and Research (NIDMAR) provides free access to its REHADAT Canada database.[43] This database contains information on disability management practices, assistive devices, case studies, and current research. Clearly, such a tool could be useful to help create or improve disability management programming and rehabilitation efforts.

ABSENCE MANAGEMENT AT PEPSICO CANADA

PepsiCo Canada's corporate website proudly bears the logos of several "top employer" distinctions. For 2016 PepsiCo Canada is included among Canada's Top 100 Employers, Canada's Best Employers for Young People, Canada's Best Diversity Employers, and Greater Toronto's Top 100 Employers. The company is noted for its ownership culture, financial rewards, and flexible health, wellness, and family-friendly benefits. However, one particular distinction is of substantial relevance in this chapter. In October 2015, PepsiCo won the Benefits Canada Award for its Absence Management Programming.

Like many companies, PepsiCo Canada faced challenges in balancing operational efficiency needs with efforts to ensure regulatory compliance, support the health and safety of employees, and manage the accuracy in reporting and costs of its employee leave administration systems. PepsiCo Canada partnered with an external provider, Morneau Shepell, to implement a comprehensive and integrated absence and leave management system. In doing so the company has turned their challenges into successes.

PepsiCo now has a single leave management system for all types of leaves, from jury duty to parental leave to short-term disability, etc. It is easy for employees to access. A single phone call links to a centralized system that incorporates referrals to additional employee supports, such as the Employee Family Assistance Program, if needed. There is communication to other employee functions (e.g., payroll), which reduces the burden of paperwork and reporting. The system also includes return-to-work planning and support for employees returning from disability leaves. The program has been highly successful. Employees feel supported and understand why absences matter. Managers have access to the information they need. The company is saving money.

Sources: PepsiCo Canada. Found at: http://pepsico.ca/en/index.html (accessed June 13, 2016); R. Yerema and K. Leung, "PepsiCo Canada 2016 Winner," Mediacorp (November 8, 2015). Found at: http://content.eluta.ca/top-employer-pepsico-canada (accessed June 13, 2016); Morneau Shepell, "Case Study: Pepsico Canada" (2015). Found at: http://www.morneaushepell.com/permafiles/62690/case-study-pepsico-canada.pdf (accessed June 13, 2016); Benefits Canada, "Who Are the Winners of the 2015 Workplace Benefits Awards?" (October 8, 2015). Found at: http://www.benefitscanada.com/benefits/health-benefits/the-2015-workplace-benefits-awards-winners-are-72694 (accessed June 13, 2016).

// RETURN-TO-WORK PLANNING

An effective disability case management will involve individualized **return-to-work planning** for injured or ill workers. In return-to-work planning, workers, employers, case managers, and health care providers work together to identify the worker's return to work goals. These goals will consider the type of job the employee wishes to return to. This ideally is the pre-injury/illness job, but depending on the nature of the situation could involve modified work or retraining. It will also outline timeline targets, actions required by the employer and employee, and health care needs. As the recovery unfolds, the plan can be discussed and revised as necessary.[44] Research illustrates that return-to-work plans that consider the individual's capabilities and workplace demands, and have identified time frames are effective.[45]

> **return-to-work plan**
> a collaboratively developed individualized plan that identifies an injured or ill worker's return-to-work goals

WORK ACCOMMODATION

Workplace accommodation, also called offers of modified work arrangement, are a vital aspect of return to work planning. An offer of work modification is strongly associated with reduced disability duration and reduced disability costs for permanently and temporarily disabled workers.[46] Estimates based on a comprehensive literature review suggest

> **workplace accommodation**
> modifications to the arrangement of work that promote early and safe return to work for injured, ill, or disabled workers

CHAPTER 13 Disability Management and Return to Work   **329**

AP Photo/Fernando Bustamante

Work accommodations can involve modifications to the equipment provided for returning workers. A well-known situation involving adapted equipment is the modified race car that double-leg amputee Alex Zanardi drove. The modified steering wheel incorporated functions that would usually be controlled by foot pedals.

that injured workers who receive offers of work modifications return to work twice as often and that their absence durations are about half as long as for workers who are not given an accommodation offer.[47] There are several categories of modified work. What does modified work look like? Some common types of modified work arrangements include:[48]

LIGHT-DUTY WORK

<table>
<tr><td>

light-duty work
workplace accommodation where workers return to a job that is less demanding than their previous job

</td><td>

When injured workers are offered light-duty accommodations they return to work in a capacity that is less demanding than their regular job. This might involve adapting the tasks of the person's pre-injury job or placing the person in a different job in the organization. For example, a courier who has sustained a lower-back injury might return to her work but be assigned tasks that do not involve heavy lifting. Alternatively, a master mechanic with an upper-extremity musculoskeletal injury who can no longer sustain certain positions—such as reaching above his head for long periods of time—might return to modified work tasks that involve quick diagnostics of potential problems with vehicles, after which he passes the detailed repair off to another mechanic; or the modified task might involve more interfacing with clients of the service centre. These arrangements can be permanent or temporary, depending on the worker's condition and changing abilities.

</td></tr>
</table>

GRADUAL WORK EXPOSURE

gradual work exposure
a type of light-duty accommodation where job demands slowly increase until the workers are performing the full requirement of their pre-injury jobs

Gradual work exposure is a form of light-duty work in which a person's hours and expected duties slowly increase until the worker is able to perform his or her pre-injury job without any problems. This type of modification is also referred to as *work hardening*.

WORK TRIALS

Workers may return to work on a trial basis to evaluate whether they are able to withstand the demands of the workplace, given the current state of their recovery. The length of the trial may be at the discretion of the employer, the worker, or (possibly) the worker's physician.

work trials
a form of accommodation where workers return to work on a trial basis

SUPPORTED AND SHELTERED WORK

These types of modified work arrangements are designed to help those with permanent disabilities who have not succeeded in competitive work environments or who require substantial support to return to work. This type of accommodation may be offered in regular work environments (supported) or in special worksites offered via social services (sheltered). For example, an individual who sustained a traumatic head injury after a fall off a ladder while working in a large hardware store may require supervision from a job coach to return to supported work in a retail environment.

supported and sheltered work
modified work arrangements designed to help those with permanent disabilities who have either not been successful in competitive work environments or require substantial support to return to work

Note that any of the above categories of work accommodations could also involve modifications to the work equipment or work environment to facilitate a safe and early return to work. Consider the following examples. Amara's employer provided a new ergonomic computer mouse for her to use during her gradual return to work following surgery for a repetitive-use injury to her wrist. Awan's employer switched out the lights used in his lab after the usual lights triggered his post-concussion headaches during a work trial. Sometimes, the change in equipment will be permanent, as in the case of a lasting disability. For example, Milton's employer purchase a motorized wheelchair for him to access different parts of their large worksite after a hip injury left him with a permanent limp and difficulty walking long distances.

Work accommodations are among the most cost-saving strategies in disability management. Bringing employees back to work once they can perform at least some of their tasks can speed up recovery by giving an employee practical goals to achieve during rehabilitation. It can also serve a work-hardening function by gradually strengthening the employee's ability, thereby reducing the risk of re-injury. In many jurisdictions the early return to work via modified work is a formalized aspect of workers' compensation, and workers' compensation boards may offer programs designed to promote early and safe return to work.[49]

PHYSICAL DEMANDS ANALYSIS

Part of devising a return-to-work plan is to match the recovering worker's current and forecasted future capabilities with the demands involved in the job. This is commonly achieved by conducting **physical demands analyses** for the jobs in question and assessing the functional capabilities of the employee. A physical demands analysis (PDA) is a standardized evaluation of the physical and cognitive demands of a job.[50] A PDA should be completed by someone highly familiar with the job in question. It could be an employee who performs the job, a supervisor, or an external expert contracted by the employer. The PDA will involve identifying the types of activities involved in the job as well as the frequency and intensity for the activity. For example, the analysis might reveal that light lifting is frequently necessary in the job, but heavy lifting is needed only occasionally. Many movements and demands can be assessed from walking to neck

physical demands analysis
a standardized evaluation of the physical and cognitive demands of a job completed by a person familiar with the job

movement to vision requirements. Various WCBs across the county have PDA forms to guide an employer representative through the analysis.

PDA can be used to inform all aspects of the disability management process.[51] In a preventive sense it can help identify risk factors and heavy demands in various jobs that can result in changing the job design, equipment and PPE used, or training. It can also be used once an injury has occurred. For example, it can help medical care providers determine if the recovering worker is ready to resume the job. It can also help the stakeholders in the disability case management team determine what types of job modifications and accommodations would help the worker return to work.

FUNCTIONAL ABILITY ASSESSMENT

functional ability assessment
a standardized assessment of an injured or ill worker's ability to perform job tasks that is completed by a member of the health care team treating the injured worker

In the case of return-to-work planning, the PDA can be used in conjunction with a **functional ability assessment**. A functional ability assessment, sometimes called a functional capacity evaluation, is a standardized assessment of a person's abilities to perform work-related tasks.[52] This inventory would be completed by a member of the health care team treating the injured worker. When mapped onto the results of the PDA, the disability case management team can see what aspects of the existing job an injured worker can return to and what tasks are still barriers to return to work. This mapping can help identify the types of job modification and accommodations that would lead to a safe and early return to work.

// STAKEHOLDERS IN DISABILITY MANAGEMENT

Obviously, there are several important stakeholder groups in disability management and return to work, each with its own roles and responsibilities. You can learn more about becoming involved in the disability management field in **OH&S Today 13.3**, which

---

OH&S TODAY   13.3

CAREERS IN DISABILITY MANAGEMENT

Throughout this chapter we have referred to staff positions in disability management programs, such as return-to-work coordinator. What type of training prepares a person to work in disability management? Several institutions in Canada offer certificate or degree programs in disability management and return to work. For instance, Dalhousie University offers a certificate in disability management that is designed to supplement work experience in that field. McGill University offers a Master of Science, Applied, in occupational health for individuals with a background in disciplines related to occupational health and safety. Pacific Coast University, a new institution in BC, specializes in workplace health sciences. Professionals with sufficient experience working in disability management and with the appropriate education can write national exams to earn the Certified Return to Work Coordinator (CRTWC) or Certified Disability Management Professional (CDMP).

Sources: Dalhousie University, Certificate in Disability Management. Found at: http://www.dal.ca/faculty/healthprofessions/occupational-therapy/programs/disability-managementcertificate.html (accessed April 27, 2016); McGill University, Master of Science, Applied, Occupational Health. Found at: http://www.mcgill.ca/study/2016-2017/faculties/medicine/graduate/programs/master-science-applied-msca-occupational-health-resident-non-thesis (accessed June 14, 2016); Pacific Coast University. Found at: http://www.pcu-whs.ca (accessed June 14, 2016); NIDMAR, "Expanding Your Horizons: A Career Guide in Disability Management." Found at: http://www.nidmar.ca/career/career_horizons/horizons_contents.asp (accessed June 14, 2016).

explores careers in this field. Coordinated efforts on the part of all stakeholder groups can improve the return-to-work outcomes.[53] Each of these stakeholders has been referenced at various points in this chapter; let's bring them all together in a summary.

1. *Injured or ill workers.* Workers who have been injured or who have sustained an occupational illness are major stakeholders in disability management. Broadly speaking, workers should be empowered in disability management programs. They should have input into the development of related workplace policies and procedures, and they should be educated on their organization's disability management program.

   Injured or ill workers also have several responsibilities to uphold in the disability management process.[54] They must report their condition as soon as possible and take an active role in developing a return-to-work program. They need to comply with treatment recommendations, work to maintain and improve their health, and keep their employer up to date on their health status during the return-to-work process.

2. *Employers.* Employers need to foster a workplace that supports the goals of disability management. They should ensure that adequate resources are available to the program.[55]

   Supervisors of returning workers have particular responsibilities in return-to-work case management. They need to help identify options for work modifications and monitor the safety of returning employees. In doing so they should keep in close contact with the employees in question and their return-to-work case managers. Supervisors should also be available to coworkers who might have concerns about work modifications.[56]

   The disability management or return-to-work coordinator will work closely with returning employees and play a large role in return-to-work planning. That person will also assist the injured or ill employee in applying for financial benefits and seeking treatment. Besides working with the employees who are enrolled in the program, disability management coordinators will play a liaison role with other stakeholders and contribute to policy development and evaluation of the disability management program.[57]

3. *Unions.* Ideally, workplace unions will help develop the disability program, perhaps through a joint labour/management committee. Union officials need to support and promote disability management goals when negotiating collective agreements. They can also serve as advocates for employees with disabilities and communicate the benefits of disability management to their members.[58]

4. *Health care providers.* Working with injured, ill, or disabled workers and employers, health care providers need to review the job requirements so as to suggest possible job modifications that would facilitate return to work.[59] With the employee's permission, it can be beneficial for the health care provider to have direct contact with the employer.[60]

5. *Insurance providers.* Public and private insurers provide benefits to workers who are on leave. They may also be involved in identifying and facilitating return-to-work options and return-to-work readiness among injured, ill, or disabled employees. The exact services they provide differ somewhat from provider to provider. As an example, WorkplaceNL, the public insurer in Newfoundland and Labrador has released "Leadership in Prevention Through Collaboration: A Workplace Injury and Illness Prevention Plan for Newfoundland and Labrador,

2015–2017." This strategic plan outlines how all stakeholder groups can work together to create safer workplaces.[61]

6. *Governments.* Governments can develop legislation that supports the values of disability management—for example, the availability of rehabilitation options and disability programs for employees, and return-to-work clauses in collective agreements.[62]

7. *Disability management contractors.* Some private firms provide disability management services to organizations on a contract basis. These services may include case management and rehabilitation. We saw an example of this in **OH&S Today 10.2** with PepsiCo Canada and Morneau Shepell. Private firms should stay in close contact with the employees who are using their services and with the employer to facilitate early and safe return to work.

// BARRIERS TO RETURN TO WORK

Early and safe return to work has many benefits to employees and employers. However, there are potential barriers that can interfere with the goal of returning injured, ill, or disabled workers to the workplace. Problems or delays can stem from several stakeholder groups and can ultimately pose barriers to return to work. One study illustrated that seemingly mundane factors such as health care providers being too busy to quickly file paperwork, employers inaccurately reporting their ability or willingness to accommodate, an individual being referred to a retraining program that is not suitable, or injured workers not understanding formal letters issued by WCBs can interact to increase the length of absence from work.[63] Psychosocial factors, such as those we discussed in Chapter 7, can affect return to work. Low-quality jobs—for instance, those with high demands, job stress, or a lack of control—are associated with delayed return to work.[64] Fear of stigma is another barrier to return to work; you can read more about stigma in **OH&S Notebook 13.3**.

Workers who have "invisible" conditions may feel particularly vulnerable to stigma. For instance, for people with mental health conditions, fear of stigma is a barrier both to disclosing their condition and in seeking treatment. The fear of disclosure can hinder all aspects of the disability management process. If an employer is unaware that a person has a particular condition, the employer cannot provide support. Without support the condition may worsen, and ultimately result in a lengthy disability leave or unsustained return to work.

What Can an Organization Do?

Organizations and individuals can work to reduce stigma for returning workers. In Canada, human rights legislation places considerable onus on employers to work to eliminate sources of workplace discrimination. Therefore, employers must look for ways to manage the stigma and its negative outcomes. *Education* programs may help replace myths about injury and illness with accurate information. Promoting *contact* between injured and noninjured workers can also help alleviate stigma. Also, organizations can *diminish barriers* between workers by emphasizing similarities such as the fact that they are all employees of a single organization. On-site disability case managers have important roles to play in implementing these types of strategies. Organizations should also ensure that their safety values are not communicated in a way that devalues those who have experienced a near miss, a safety incident, or a lost-time injury. Publicly emphasizing the company's safety record—such as number of days without a lost-time injury—may add to the stigma experienced by a returning employee.

It is important that returning employees feel welcomed by their coworkers.

Therefore, organizations may be wise to emphasize the importance of employee well-being and safety in general, instead of safety in the narrower sense of reducing lost-time injuries or costs.

Sources: L. Francis, J. Cameron, E.K. Kelloway, V.M. Catano, A. Day, and C.G. Hepburn, "Working Wounded: Stigma and Return to Work," in P.Y. Chen and C.L. Cooper, eds., *Wellbeing in the Workplace: From Stress to Happiness* (pp. 339–356) (Oxford: Wiley-Blackwell, 2014); M. Ilic, J. Reinecke, G. Bohner, H.O. Röttgers, T. Beblo, M. Driessen, and P.W. Corrigan, "Belittled, Avoided, Ignored, Denied: Assessing Forms and Consequences of Stigma Experiences of People with Mental Illness," *Basic and Applied Social Psychology* 35, 1 (2013): 31–40; K.E. Toth, and C.S. Dewa, "Employee Decision-making about Disclosure of a Mental Disorder at Work," *Journal of Occupational Rehabilitation* 24, 4 (2014): 732–46; A.M. Santuzzi, P.R. Waltz, L. Finkelstein, and D.E. Rupp, "Invisible Disabilities: Unique Challenges for Employees and Organizations," *Industrial and Organizational Psychology* 7, 2 (2014): 204–19; J. M. Eakin, "The Discourse of Abuse in Return to Work: A Hidden Epidemic of Suffering," in C.L. Peterson and C. Mayhew, eds., *Occupational Health and Safety: International Influences and the "New" Epidemics* (Amityville: Baywood, 2005), pp. 159–74; K. Lippel, "Workers Describe the Effect of the Workers' Compensation Process on Their Health: A Québec Study," *International Journal of Law and Psychiatry*, Vol. 30 (2007): 427–43.

Without proper assurances, employees may resist return-to-work opportunities out of fear. They may think that taking a modified job means they won't get their regular job back. They may also fear re-injury or exacerbation of their condition, or they may simply feel unable to return to work.

Disability-related absence is often described as having three stages: acute (1–30 days), subacute (31–90 days), and chronic (91 + days).[65] Long absences can be a barrier to successful return to work. Estimates from private insurers suggest that the average length of a chronic disability is nearly three years.[66] Certainly the amount of time someone is away from work on a disability leave reflects heavily the severity of the injury or illness. That said, to the extent that early and safe return is possible, facilitating early return is important for all stakeholders.

What happens when an employee's return to the original workplace is not possible? Labour market re-entry programs can help an individual who cannot return to the original workplace owing to the nature of the injury or the former employer's limited ability to accommodate. During a labour market re-entry process, the injured, ill, or disabled worker's capabilities, experience, and training are reviewed. Additional skills training may be provided to help that worker find employment that provides earnings comparable to those in the previous job.

SUMMARY

Throughout this chapter we have explored the costs of workplace injury and the benefits that disability management programs bring to employees, employers, and society at large. In Canada, human rights legislation protects the rights of disabled workers, and employers have the duty to accommodate—to the point of undue hardship—injured, ill, or disabled workers. In general, disability management programs that focus on prevention and early intervention when injuries or illness do occur are associated with improved outcomes, including earlier return to work and sustained return to work. These disability management programs are most effective when fully integrated into a workplace system that is supportive of safety and return to work. Individualized return-to-work planning that considers the physical demands of the job, the functional abilities of the worker, and possibilities for modified work arrangements help achieve early and safe return to work. When the stakeholders in disability management, including employers, employees, unions, and health care providers, work together they can overcome the barriers to return to work and help employees achieve the psychosocial and financial benefits that come with full and active participation in the workforce.

KEY TERMS

disability management 325
duty to accommodate 322
functional ability assessment 332
gradual work exposure 330
light-duty work 330
physical demands analysis 331
return-to-work coordinator 328
return-to-work plan 329
supported and sheltered work 331
systems approach 325

undue hardship 322
work trials 331
workplace accommodation 329

DISCUSSION QUESTIONS

1. What are some ways to empower employees when developing and implementing a disability management program?

2. How can organizations create a climate/culture that supports a safe working environment?

3. Can the organization really prevent stigma from occurring? If so, how? How can we reduce injured or ill employees' fears about stigma?

4. Do you think any of the disability management best practices are more important than others? For example, do you think an organization focused solely on prevention will be equipped to handle injuries and compensation when they do occur?

5. Can you think of any reasons employees may be hesitant to use their disability management programs, particularly those offered in-house?

6. What are some concerns that people might raise about the use of an absence management program in their workplace? How could an occupational health and safety professional help alleviate those concerns?

USING THE INTERNET

1. Many organizations post their disability management policies online. Search out companies representing different sectors (e.g., manufacturing versus universities) and compare their programs.

2. Search for news articles related to compensation, injuries at work, and return-to-work claims. Determine what strategies were used by the employers.

3. Look up the WBC guidelines in your jurisdiction to seek its policies and practices on return-to-work programs. Compare them to those of another jurisdiction.

4. Compare Canadian human rights and disability management guidelines and practices in disability management and return to work to those of another country of your choosing.

5. Some organizations rely on external providers to provide their disability management services. Search out a company that specializes in providing external disability management services. What types of programs does it offer?

EXERCISES

1. Think of policies and practices that were in place in an organization where you have worked. What were the risks for injury? Could the organization do anything to prevent them? Were safeguards in place? Did the organization appear to support the overarching values of disability management?

2. Companies that use in-house disability management programs tend to employ nurses and other staff solely focused on health and safety and disability management. Other organizations contract out their disability management services. Contrast and compare the pros and cons of in-house and contracted disability management services.

3. What are the challenges faced by small organizations when facing accommodations, disability management, and return to work? How do these compare with the challenges faced by large organizations? Outline how an organization can play to its strengths when addressing disability management issues.

OH&S IN ACTION

You work as kinesiologist and have been consulted by a house painting firm to help one of their crew supervisors conduct a physical demands analysis for the job of interior painter (residential). Locate a PDA form (Hint: various WCBs across the country have online forms, as do health and safety associations) and fill it out to reflect the job duties of an interior house painter. Note that ideally you would be working directly with a painter to get details on the job. However, for this exercise, you could use online tools such as the National Occupational Classification (NOC) for information on the job tasks.

Zoë is a painter with this organization. She is returning to work following a knee injury sustained when she slipped on a scaffold. Her functional capacity evaluation shows that she is able to sustain most working postures, but cannot maintain a position involved bended knees. Additionally, although she is able to stand for periods of time, she needs to rest at least 10 minutes per hour and to perform a short series of knee flex exercises. Using the information you have, make three suggestions for ways you can modify the painting job to accommodate Zoë's injuries.

CASE STUDY 1   FORGOTTEN ORDERS: A CASE OF MEMORY IMPAIRMENT IN A RESTAURANT

Lan sustained a head injury following a slip-and-fall accident in her job as a waitress at a busy family restaurant. Lan has been off work on workers' compensation benefits for six weeks and is in the care of a physician and an occupational therapist. Since the fall, Lan has had some problems with her short-term memory. She loses track of tasks and has trouble focusing on what she's supposed to be doing. Otherwise she feels fine and would like to be working again. Lan, her boss, and her health care providers agree that unless her memory symptoms improve, Lan cannot perform her duties as a waitress. Lan's boss has suggested that she return to work in the kitchen, washing dishes. Lan is insulted by this suggestion. She has four years' experience as a successful waitress and is concerned that if she says yes, she'll never get her job back. Her physician and occupational therapist aren't particularly familiar with her workplace and aren't quite sure what to recommend. You are the workers' compensation case manager who has been assigned to Lan's case. What would you do to facilitate the interactions among Lan, her boss, and the health care providers? What suggestions might you have for a return-to-work plan for Lan?

You are a certified return-to-work case manager at WidgIT, a company that manufactures computer parts. WidgIT has a disability management program with a successful track record of achieving its goals of early intervention and sustained return to work. In fact, the company has been nationally recognized for its disability management program. Tyler, one of WidgIT's employees, sustained injuries to his back and leg after being pinned between two pieces of equipment. You intervened right away and have helped Tyler get immediate and sustained medical treatment and helped him navigate the necessary documents to file for compensation. He's now been off work for five weeks. Tyler has been completely out of touch for three weeks, ever since you indicated that you'd like to have contact with his physician. You have tried reaching him by phone and email, but he does not return your calls or messages. You are now worried that Tyler has become suspicious and has disengaged in the process. What do you do?

// NOTES

1. ILO. "Safety and Health at Work". Found at: http://www.ilo.org/global/topics/safety-and-health-at-work/lang--en/index.htm (accessed June 14, 2016).

2. J. Gilks and R. Logan, "Occupational Injuries and Illnesses in Canada, 1996–2008: Injury Rates and the Cost to the Economy" (July 2010), Human Resources and Skills Development Canada. Found at: http://publications.gc.ca/collections/collection_2011/rhdcc-hrsdc/HS21-4-2008-eng.pdf (accessed April 26, 2016).

3. Association of Workers' Compensation Boards of Canada, Detailed Key Statistical Measures Report 2014. Found at: https://aoc.awcbc.org/KsmReporting/KsmSubmissionReport/2, accessed April 26, 2016.

4. Association of Workers' Compensation Boards of Canada, Detailed Key Statistical Measures Report 2013. Found at: https://aoc.awcbc.org/KsmReporting/KsmSubmissionReport/2, (accessed April 26, 2016).

5. N. Stewart, *Missing in Action: Absenteeism Trends in Canadian Organizations* (Ottawa: The Conference Board of Canada, 2013).

6. World Economic Forum, *Working Towards Wellness: The Business Rationale* (Geneva: 2008).

7. P. Miller and C. Haslam (2009). "Why Employers Spend Money on Employee Health: Interviews with Occupational Health and Safety Professionals from British Industry," *Safety Science*, 47, 163–69.

8. J. Kim, "Depression as a Psychosocial Consequence of Occupational Injury in the US Working Population: Findings from the Medical Expenditure Panel Survey," *BMC Public Health*, *13* (2013): 303; K.H. Lin, N.W. Guo, S.C. Liao, C.Y. Kuo, P.Y. Hu, J.H. Hsu, et al., "Psychological Outcome of Injured Workers at 3 Months After Occupational Injury Requiring Hospitalization in Taiwan," *Journal of Occupational Health*, *54*(4) (2012): 289–98.

9. S.L. Saunders, and B. Nedelec, "What Work Means to People with Work Disability: A Scoping Review," *Journal of Occupational Rehabilitation, 24*(1) (2014): 100–10.

10. Canadian Human Rights Commission, "Duty to Accommodate," (2013). Found at: http://www.chrc-ccdp.ca/eng/content/duty-accommodate (accessed June 14, 2016).

11. Ibid.; National Institute of Disability Management and Research (NIDMAR), *Code of Practice for Disability Management* (Vancouver: 2000).

12. Canadian Human Rights Commission, "Duty to Accommodate."

13. Ontario, Accessibility for Ontarians with Disabilities Act, 2005, S.O. 2005, c. 11. Found at: https://www.ontario.ca/laws/statute/05a11 (accessed June 14, 2016); Ontario, "Accessibility Rules for Businesses and Non-profits." Found at: https://www.ontario.ca/page/accessibility-rules-businesses-and-non-profits (accessed June 14, 2016); Manitoba, "Introducing the Accessibility for Manitobans Act," Found at: http://www.gov.mb.ca/dio/pdf/introducing_accessibility_for_manitobans_act.pdf (accessed June 14, 2016); Council of Canadians with Disabilities. "Trudeau Government Headed in the Right Direction with Budget 2016" (March 23, 2016). Found at: http://www.ccdonline.ca/en/socialpolicy/access-inclusion/Budget-2016 (accessed June 14, 2016); Nova Scotia Government, "Accessibility Legislation." Found at: http://novascotia.ca/coms/accessibility (accessed June 14, 2016); British Columbia, "Accessibility 2024." Found at: http://www2.gov.bc.ca/gov/content/governments/about-the-bc-government/accessibility/accessibility-2024 (accessed June 14, 2016).

14. L. Chénier, *Creating an Effective Workplace Disability Management Program.* Ottawa: The Conference Board of Canada, 2013; NIDMAR, *Code of Practice for Disability Management.*

15. Ibid.

16. N. Buys and C. Randall, "Disability Management: A Global Response to Disability in the Workplace," in C.A. Marshall, E. Kendall, M.E. Banks, and R.M.S. Gover, eds., *Disabilities: Insights from Across Fields and Around the World* 3 (Santa Barbara: Praeger/ABC-CLIO, 2009), pp. 129–43.

17. B.C. Amick, III, R.V. Habeck, A. Hunt, A.H. Fossel, A. Chapin, R.B. Keller, and J.N. Katz, "Measuring the Impact of Organizational Behaviors on Work Disability Prevention and Management," *Journal of Occupational Rehabilitation* 10, no. 1 (2000): 21–38; T.H. Tveito, G. Sembajwe, L.I. Boden, J.T. Dennerlein, G.R. Wagner, C. Kenwood, et al., "Impact of Organizational Policies and Practices on Workplace Injuries in a Hospital Setting," *Journal of Occupational and Environmental Medicine, 56*(8) (2014): 802–08.

18. NIDMAR, Code of Practice for Disability Management.

19. R.L. Franche, K. Cullen, J. Clarke, E. Irvin, S. Sinclair, J. Frank, and Institute for Work and Health Workplace-Based RTW Intervention Literature Review Research Team, "Workplace-Based Return-to-Work Interventions: A Systematic Review of Quantitative Literature," *Journal of Occupational Rehabilitation* 15, no. 4 (2005): 607–31.

20. Ibid.

21. H.L. Hees, K. Nieuwenhuijsen, M.W.J. Koeter, U. Bültmann, and A.H. Schene, "Towards a New Definition of Return-to-Work Outcomes in Common Mental Disorders from a Multi-Stakeholder Perspective," *PLOS One* 7(2012): e39947; C.G. Hepburn, E.K. Kelloway, R.-L. Franche, "Early Employer Response to Workplace Injury: What Injured Workers Perceive As Fair and Why These Perceptions Matter," *Journal of Occupational Health Psychology* 15(2010): 409–20.

22. R.L. Franche, K. Cullen, J. Clarke, E. Irvin, S. Sinclair, J. Frank, and Institute for Work and Health Workplace-Based RTW Intervention Literature Review Research Team, "Workplace-Based Return-to-Work Interventions: A Systematic Review of Quantitative Literature," *Journal of Occupational Rehabilitation* 15, no. 4 (2005).

23. N. Krause and T. Lund, "Returning to Work After Occupational Injury," in J. Barling and M. Frone, eds., *The Psychology of Workplace Safety* (Washington: APA, 2004).

24. N. Krause, L. Dasinger, and A. Weigand, "Does Modified Work Facilitate Return to Work for Temporarily or Permanently Disabled Workers? Review of the Literature and Annotated Bibliography," unpublished report prepared for the Industrial Medical Council of the State of California and the California Commission on Health and Safety and Workers' Compensation, University of California, 1997.

25. NIDMAR, Code of Practice for Disability Management.

26. Buys and Randall, "Disability Management."

27. NIDMAR, Code of Practice for Disability Management.

28. Buys and Randall, "Disability Management."

29. Chénier, Louise. *Creating an Effective Workplace Disability Management Program* (Ottawa: The Conference Board of Canada, 2013).

30. Institute for Work and Health (IWH), "Seven 'Principles' for Successful Return to Work" (Toronto: March 2007).

31. IWH, "Seven 'Principles.'"

32. Franche et al., "Workplace-Based Return-to-Work Interventions."

33. C.G. Hepburn, E.K. Kelloway, and R.-L. Franche, "Early Employer Response to Workplace Injury: What Injured Workers Perceive As Fair and Why These Perceptions Matter," *Journal of Occupational Health Psychology* 15(2010): 409–20.

34. K. Thorpe and L. Chénier, *Disability Management: Opportunities for Employer Action* (Ottawa: The Conference Board of Canada, 2013).

35. F. Munir, J. Yarker, B. Hicks, and E. Donaldson-Fielder "Returning Employees Back to Work: Developing a Measure for Supervisors to Support Return to Work (SSRW)," *Journal of Occupational Rehabilitation* 22(2012): 196–208.

36. IWH, "Seven 'Principles.'"

37. Buys and Randall, "Disability Management."

38. IWH, "Seven 'Principles.'"

39. Franche et al., "Workplace-Based Return-to-Work Interventions"; S. Schandelmaier, S. Ebrahim, S.C. Burkhardt, W.E. de Boer, T. Zumbrunn, G.H. Guyatt, et al., "Return to Work Coordination Programmes for Work

Disability: A Meta-Analysis of Randomised Controlled Trials," *PloS one*, *7*(11) (2012): e49760.

40. NIDMAR, Code of Practice.

41. Buys and Randall, "Disability Management."

42. NIDMAR, *Code of Practice*; Williams and Westmorland, "Perspectives on Workplace Disability Management."

43. NIDMAR, REHADAT database. Found at: http://rehadat.nidmar.ca/db (accessed April 29, 2016).

44. WSIB Ontario. "Return to Work Plan Package" (n.d.). Found at: http://www .wsib.on.ca/WSIBPortal/faces/WSIBArticlePage?fGUID=835502100635000344 &_afrLoop=3845313468501919&_afrWindowMode=0&_afrWindowId=null#% 40%3F_afrWindowId%3Dnull% (accessed June 29, 2016).

45. M.V. Ntsiea, H.Van Aswegen, and S. Lord, "The Effect of a Workplace Intervention Programme on Return to Work After Stroke: a Randomised Controlled Trial," *Clinical Rehabilitation*, *29*(7) (2015): 663–73; N. Hoefsmit, I. Houkes, and F.J. Nijhuis, "Intervention Characteristics That Facilitate Return to Work After Sickness Absence: a Systematic Literature Review," *Journal of Occupational Rehabilitation, 22*(4) (2012): 462–77.

46. Franche et al., "Workplace-based Return-to-Work Interventions"; N. Krause, L.K. Dasinger, and F. Neuhauser, "Modified Work and Return to Work: A Review of the Literature," *Journal of Occupational Rehabilitation* 8, no. 2 (1998): 113–39; and C.G., Hepburn, R.-L. Franche, and L. Francis, "Successful Return to Work: The Role of Fairness and Workplace-based Strategies," *International Journal of Workplace Health Management* 3(2010): 7–24.

47. Ibid.

48. Ibid.

49. J.M. Eakin, "The Discourse of Abuse in Return to Work: A Hidden Epidemic of Suffering," in C.L. Peterson and C. Mayhew, eds., *Occupational Health and Safety: International Influences and the "New" Epidemics* (Amityville: Baywood, 2005), 159–74.

50. IAPA, "Performing a Physical Demands Analysis" (2009). Found at: http:// www.iapa.ca/main/documents/pdf/freedownloads_pda_intro.pdf (accessed June 14, 2016).

51. Occupational Health Clinics for Ontario Workers Inc. (OHCOW), "Physical Demands Analysis" (n.d.) Found at: http://www.ohcow.on.ca/uploads/ Resource/General%20Handouts/Physical%20Demands%20Analysis.pdfhttp:// www.ohcow.on.ca/uploads/Resource/General%20Handouts/Physical%20 Demands%20Analysis.pdf (accessed April 29, 2016).

52. D.P. Gross, and M.C. Battié, "Factors Influencing Results of Functional Capacity Evaluations in Workers' Compensation Claimants with Low Back Pain," *Physical Therapy*, *85*(4) (2005): 315–22.

53. C. Carroll, J. Rick, H. Pilgrim, J. Cameron, and J. Hillage, "Workplace Involvement Improves Return to Work Rates Among Employees with Back Pain on Long-Term Sick Leave: A Systematic Review of the Effectiveness and Cost-Effectiveness of Interventions," *Disability and Rehabilitation*, *32*(8) (2010): 607–21.

54. NIDMAR, Code of Practice.

55. Ibid.

56. Ibid.

57. Ibid.

58. Ibid.

59. Ibid.

60. IWH, "Seven 'Principles.'"

61. WorkplaceNL. "Leadership in Prevention Through Collaboration: A Workplace Injury and Illness Prevention Plan for Newfoundland and Labrador, 2015–2017. Found at: http://www.whscc.nl.ca/search.aspx?ss=leadership%20in%20 prevention (accessed April 28, 2016).

62. NIDMR, Code of Practice.

63. E. MacEachen, A. Kosny, S. Ferrier, and L. Chambers "The Toxic Dose of Systems Problems: Why Some Injured Workers Don't Return to Work as Expected," *Journal of Occupational Rehabilitation* 20(2010): 349–66.

64. N. Krause, L.K. Dasinger, L.J. Deegan, R.J. Brand, and L. Rudolph, "Psychosocial Job Factors and RTW After Low Back Injury: A Disability Phase-Specific Analysis," *American Journal of Industrial Medicine* 40 (2001): 374–92.

65. Krause and Lund, "Returning to Work After Occupational Injury."

66. Canada Life, "Disability Insurance." Found at: http://www.canadalife.com/ 003/Home/Products/DisabilityInsurance/index.htm (accessed June 14, 2016); Great-West Life, "Disability Insurance," http://www.greatwestlife.com/001/ Home/Individual_Products/Insurance/Disability_Insurance/index.htm (accessed June 14, 2016).

WORKPLACE WELLNESS: WORK–FAMILY AND HEALTH PROMOTION PROGRAMS

CHAPTER LEARNING OBJECTIVES

AFTER READING THIS CHAPTER, YOU SHOULD BE ABLE TO:

- discuss the concept of healthy workplaces
- describe the goals of worksite health promotion and family-friendly programs
- discuss the various types of worksite health promotion and family-friendly programs
- comment on the effectiveness of various types of worksite health promotion and family-friendly programs
- identify variables critical to the success of worksite health promotion and family-friendly programs
- discuss the importance of systematic evaluation of worksite health promotion and family-friendly policies

You snooze, you lose? Maybe not. Not that long ago, suggesting that someone was asleep on the job was a severe criticism. It implied that a person was lazy or not respectful of company time. Recent research on sleep deprivation suggests that a nap at work might be just what the doctor—and HR manager—ordered.

Today's busy workplaces and lifestyles are prompting many people to sacrifice their sleep hours to meet all their work and family demands. This strategy is detrimental to one's health. Not getting enough sleep is associated with a number of health problems, including hypertension, heart disease, and depression. A study in *Archives of Internal Medicine* demonstrated that afternoon naps are associated with a decreased risk for coronary mortality. From a business perspective, estimates suggest that sleep deprivation costs American employers $150 billion annually in reduced performance and safety incidents. A power nap might be the solution.

Sara Mednick's book *Take a Nap! Change Your Life* advocates naps at work. It prescribes a nap during a work shift as a potential remedy for the productivity and health and safety costs associated with a sleep-deprived workforce. A NASA study found that a short nap of less than 30 minutes was associated with improved alertness and performance. The idea that an afternoon nap is valuable is not new; after all, some cultures have siesta built into their work arrangements. Now some North American employers are taking notice and are providing nap rooms for sleep-starved employees. For example, The Huffington Post provides nap rooms to employees as do Uber and Google. The rooms at the Huffington Post have been dubbed NapQuest rooms and feature sleep pods that block light and sound. The afternoon power snooze might just be the coffee break of the future when it comes to revitalizing employees.

The "nap room" is a novel idea for employee health promotion. It can benefit both the employee and the employer in many ways. It will be interesting to see how this novel health promotion effort affects health and productivity in the companies that implement it. Some

© National Geographic Creative/Alamy Stock Photo

Nap pods or nap rooms are a growing trend in workplace health promotion. A short nap can help fatigued workers to revitalize and increase energy.

(*continued*)

companies report great success with their nap rooms, while others have found it harder to manage. The trick, it appears, is keeping the power naps short. In this chapter, we explore a variety of workplace wellness programs designed to improve employee health, well-being, and productivity.

Sources: S. Mednick and M. Ehrman, *Take a Nap! Change Your Life* (New York: Workman Publishing, 2006); A. Naska, E. Oikonomou, A. Trichopoulou, T. Psaltopoulou, and D. Trichopoulos, "Siesta in Healthy Adults and Coronary Mortality in the General Population," *Archives of Internal Medicine*, Vol. 167 (2007): 296–301; M. Rosekind, R.C. Graeber, D.F., Dinges, L.J. Connell, M.S. Rountree, C.L. Spinweber, and K.A. Gillen, "Crew Factors in Flight Operations 9: Effects of Planned Cockpit Rest on Crew Performance and Alertness in Long-Haul," NASA technical memorandum 108839, 1994. Found at: http://ntrs .nasa.gov/search.jsp?R=19950006379 (accessed June 16, 2016); Zoë Henry, "6 Companies (Including Uber) Where It's OK to Nap," *Inc.* (September 4, 2015). Found at: http://www.inc.com/zoe-henry/google-uber-and-other-companies-where-you-can-nap-at-the-office.html (accessed June 16, 2016); Chris Evans, "Do Nap Rooms Enhance Productivity? The Truth Behind a Nap Room and Increased Worker Effectiveness." Found at: http://ergonomics .about.com/od/Sleep_And_Ergonomics/a/Do_Nap_Rooms_Enhance_Productivity.htm (accessed June 16, 2016); Lisa Evans, "Why You Should Let Your Employees Nap at Work," *Entrepreneur* (August 24, 2014). Found at: https://www.entrepreneur.com/article/236755 (accessed June 16, 2016); Willa Frej, "Arianna: Office Nap Rooms Will Soon Be as Common as Conference Rooms," The Huffington Post (April 4, 2016). Found at: http://www.huffingtonpost .com/entry/arianna-huffington-office-nap-rooms-conference-rooms_us_57025cbfe4b0a06d58060ff1 (accessed June 16, 2016); Michelle Goodman, "Nap Rooms Gone Bad," BBC Capital (April 10, 2014). Found at: http://www.bbc.com/capital/story/20140409-nap-rooms-gone-bad (accessed June 16, 2016).

Given that people spend a substantial portion of their time at work, most would agree that active attempts should be made to ensure a healthy and safe work environment. Over the past couple of decades the concept of wellness at work emerged as an occupational health concern, augmenting organizations' more traditional concerns about employee safety. This interest in workplace wellness continues to grow. Some estimate that health-related programs are found in about 75% of American organizations with more than 50 employees and more than 90% of American companies with more than 200 employees. The most common interventions focus on exercise and weight loss.[1] The major motivators of this trend include a desire to reduce rising health care costs, improve productivity, and build a supportive organizational culture. Additionally, the Affordable Care Act in the United States emphasizes worksite health promotion.

Workplace wellness initiatives are also present in Canadian companies. Although estimates of prevalence vary somewhat from study to study, uptake for worksite health promotion programs is generally lower than in the United States. In one study of Canadian workplaces, employers reported an increasing offering of a range of wellness programs. Here are some of the more prevalent offerings. Among responding employers, 79% reported vaccination programs, 61% offered nutrition and fitness programs, 44% engaged in weight control programs, and 42% offered stress management support. Among the less prevalent offerings were preventive health screenings at 9% and chronic disease management at 21%.[2]

In contrast, in a survey of Canadian benefits programs, only 40% of plan members reported that their company offered wellness programming, with fitness programming being the most widely offered. Of members with access to wellness programming, almost half indicated they utilized these benefits. Not surprisingly, wellness programming was more common in larger than in smaller employers. Only 19% of plan members in companies with fewer than 50 employees had access to health promotion offerings, compared to 54% in companies with 500 of more employees.[3]

Why does the picture differ between Canada and the United States? Many suggest that because Canada has a public health care system, Canadian companies assume less of the cost for illness and therefore have less of a financial impetus to develop employee health initiatives. However, the focus on health at work is now rapidly growing in Canada. For instance, in 2013 the Canadian Standards Association released CSA-Z1003-13 a voluntary workplace standard for psychological health and safety in the workplace

FIGURE 14.1

FLOW CHART OF WORKPLACE WELL-BEING INITIATIVES

(see also chapters 1 and 7). This standard was developed in conjunction with the Mental Health Commission of Canada. The presence of a national standard on psychological health at work not only directs attention to the issue of psychological well-being at work, but also likely sets a new standard for organizations wanting to exercise due diligence in the provision of programs to promote psychologically healthy workplaces.[4]

Companies appear to be keeping pace with change and report increased intentions to increase wellness programming. The majority of Canadian companies (76%) included in a recent survey of workplace priorities and wellness reported that they intend to increase spending on health and wellness programming in the coming years. Among the priorities noted by Canadian employers were promoting employee mental health, growing employee engagement in health initiatives, and increasing health awareness among the workforce.[5]

It makes sense to focus on health at work. Employed adults spend a great deal of time in the workplace, so the worksite provides a convenient means of reaching many adults. Also, the health of employees affects their performance at work; therefore, companies should be interested in promoting worker health. In this chapter, we consider two broad categories of initiatives that companies can take to promote well-being at work: family-friendly policies and health promotion programs (see **Figure 14.1**). The **OH&S Today** boxes will highlight the successes and strategies of three Canadian organizations from very different sectors (financial, telecommunications, and steel production).

// WORK–FAMILY CONFLICT: FAMILY-FRIENDLY POLICIES IN THE WORKPLACE

Most people in today's workforce are attempting to balance work demands with non-work demands, such as family responsibilities. A recent large-scale study of work–life conflict in Canada, provided compelling evidence of the struggles to balance competing demands. This group of more than 25 000 working Canadians worked an average of 50 hours/week. About two-thirds were working parents, more than 60% reported elder

work–family conflict
a type of inter-role conflict in which the role pressures experienced in the work and family domains are incompatible

care obligations, and about one-third experienced both child care and elder care responsibilities.[6] We introduced work–family conflict in Chapter 7, where we learned that demographic realities such as the large proportion of working parents and the prevalence of dual-income families means that employees need to constantly balance work and family commitments. In this chapter we explore programs that organizations can provide to help employees manage their work and family commitments.

Work–family conflict is expensive for organizations. High work–family conflict is associated with reduced work performance and higher rates of absenteeism. The estimated costs associated with work–life conflict for Canadian organizations is staggering. For example, absenteeism stemming from work–family conflict costs in the range of $2 billion per year. One must also consider the estimated $2.8 billion in costs on the health care system for conditions that results from work–life conflict.[7]

Work–family conflict is also associated with substantial health and well-being costs for individuals. A high degree of work–family conflict, be it work demands interfering with family commitments or family demands interfering with work commitments, contributes to perceived stress, poorer physical health, decreased family functioning, increased mental health concerns (depression, anxiety, psychological distress), and increased alcohol use.[8] So it is important that individuals and organizations attempt to reduce this type of inter-role conflict. In the following sections, we examine some of the family-friendly policies that organizations have implemented in an effort to reduce work–family conflict and thereby avoid the resulting negative outcomes. Such policies are assuming greater importance as companies recognize that a growing number of employees have both child care and elder care responsibilities in addition to work responsibilities. The existence of these policies can help organizations recruit and retain employees. Most family-friendly policies are attempts to help employees balance their work and family responsibilities. Given that this chapter focuses on workplace policies and programs, we will be emphasizing organizational rather than individual efforts to reduce work–family conflict. We will consider three broad categories of family-friendly programs: flexible work arrangements, work leave systems, and family-friendly employee benefits.

Drawing on the preventive stress management framework introduced in Chapter 7, one could consider these programs as interventions designed to manage stressors related to work–family demands. Depending on the circumstances in which they are introduced, these programs can reflect primary, secondary, or tertiary interventions. For example, Ella uses a flexible work arrangement offered by her company as a primary intervention to help avoid her work demands becoming a stressor that disrupts her family life and vice versa. However, for Sylvia, who is experiencing high family stress because of a recent divorce, the flexible work arrangements offered by her workplace are helping her to manage her family stressors and avoid strain. In this case flexible work arrangements are being used as a secondary intervention.

flexible work arrangements (FWAs)
family-friendly policies that involve modifications to the traditional work schedule

compressed workweek
flexible work arrangement in which employees work full-time hours in fewer days per week

FAMILY-FRIENDLY POLICIES

FLEXIBLE WORK ARRANGEMENTS

Flexible work arrangements (FWAs) are modifications to the traditional work schedule. There are two basic versions of FWAs. First, some programs are designed to help mitigate work–family conflict by reducing the amount of *time* spent in the workplace. An example of this type of FWA is the compressed workweek. Under this option, employees can choose to work full-time hours in fewer days; for instance, 40 hours in four days rather than five. A modified version of work compression is to add a short amount of time to every work day to accrue hours for an earned day off. For example, Youssef works an extra 30 minutes per day and is able to take every third Friday off. The compressed work schedule can help employees reduce work–family conflict by allowing longer stretches of time at home, which also cuts down on commuting time.

Job sharing and job splitting programs also fall under this category of FWA. In *job sharing* programs, two employees share the responsibilities of a single position. In this case, the two employees have overlapping duties and must be sure to communicate with each other about all aspects of the work. For instance, Ellie and Anu job share a grade 1 teaching job, with Ellie working Monday, Wednesday, and Friday and Anu working Tuesdays and Thursdays. They share duties such as report cards and lesson planning. In *job splitting*, two employees split job responsibilities so that each takes sole responsibility for various components of the job. Kyle and Chen share the bookkeeping work at a construction organization. Kyle handles payroll and benefits and Chen manages accounts payable and receivable. Job sharing and job splitting arrangements typically benefit employees who want to work part-time hours. Job sharing and splitting options reduce the amount of time an employee must spend on work-related tasks and likely lead to a reduction in work role overload. As such, these types of arrangements may reduce the incidence of work–family conflict.

The second large category consists of FWA programs designed to increase the amount of *control* that individuals have over their work schedule. A common example of this type of arrangement is *flextime*. In flextime schedules, employees are permitted variable start and finish times to their workday. For instance, one employee at a company offering flextime may choose to work from 7 a.m. to 3 p.m. Another employee may opt to start work at 10 a.m. and work until 6 p.m. In this case, during several hours of the day all employees are at work and group or team-related matters can be dealt with. This degree of control over start and finish times can help employees better manage work and family demands. For instance, Edward, a working father who worries about his children being home alone after school, prefers to start early and finish at 3 p.m. so that he can supervise his children after school or help them get to and from after-school activities.

Flexplace work options offer a second example of this category of FWA. Flexplace work programs (also known as telecommuting, telework, or work-at-home programs) allow employees to complete their work assignments away from the office. The employee uses telecommunications technology to keep in touch with the worksite. This option can help some employees better blend their work and family responsibilities. For instance, a person who works from home can delay the start of the workday until children leave for school and then immediately start working without losing time to commuting. Flexplace arrangements may also be helpful for individuals who have elders living with them, as they are able to be at home in case of emergency. Some may choose to work away from the office to facilitate other goals or to build creativity. See **OH&S Today 14.1** to learn about ATB Financial's flexible working arrangements that reflect many of the concepts that we've considered in this section.

PERSONAL LEAVE SYSTEMS

Another broad category of family-friendly policies involves the provision of leave time to employees. Examples are maternity leave, parental leave, personal days, family leave, and sick leave. These leave programs are designed to help employees

job sharing
flexible work arrangement in which two employees share the responsibilities of a single position

job splitting
flexible work arrangement in which two employees divide the responsibilities of a single position

flextime
flexible work arrangement that permits employees to have variable start and finish times to their workday

flexplace
flexible work arrangement in which an employee regularly makes use of telecommunications technology to complete work assignments away from the office, usually at home

AWARDED FOR EXCELLENCE: ATB FINANCIAL

All across the country, organizations are excited about workplace wellness. More than ever, companies are making efforts to promote health and well-being among their employees. One Canadian company that has excelled at these efforts is ATB Financial and it is being recognized for its successes. For more than three-quarters of a century, ATB Financial has provided banking services to Albertans. It now employs more than 5200 people, and has more than 170 branches and more than $40 billion in assets. It is also considered a wonderful place to work. It has been recognized as one of the 50 Top Places to Work in Canada by Aon Hewlitt, noted as Top Employer in

Alberta (Mediacorp), named one of the 50 Most Engaged Workplaces in North America (Achievers), and credited as one of Canada's Passion Capitalists (Amrop/Knightsbridge). What makes a company a passion capitalist? It has strong values that create workplace culture and promote success. You just have to ask its employees. Employee reviews on the job site Glassdoor are highly favourable on dimensions from culture to work–life balance to career opportunities.

What are some of its programs? ATB Financial offers a customizable benefits package that can be tailored to meet individual needs, an employee recognition program, tuition supports, maternity/parental leaves (with potential salary top-ups), and a health care and a wellness spending account. It has flexible work options, including compressed weeks, flextime, and flexplace. Its Workplace 2.0 program includes funding to support home office equipment. Its head offices have healthy cafeteria choices, and an onsite gym.

ATB's commitment to its employees is not only a list of options but it is also embedded in its culture and is core to its values and strategy. Employee wellness is a pillar of its approach to corporate social responsibility. There is support for employee-focused wellness initiatives from the highest levels of organizational leadership. The initiatives are informed by employee input. ATB Financial's recruitment material highlights the quality of the work environment and benefits. Its Glassdoor page features a culture quiz about person–organization fit that highlights fun at work, meaningful work, professional/personal development, and innovation.

Paul Sutherland/Thinkstock

Organizations that promote a culture of wellness often provide opportunities for employees to take part in fun, team building, and fitness activities.

Sources: ATB Financial, "About Us, Awards, Corporate Social Responsibility, and Benefits." Found at: http://www.atb.com/about/Pages/default.aspx, http://www.atb.com/about/Pages/awards.aspx, http://www.atb.com/community/social-responsibility/Pages/default.aspx, and http://www.atb.com/careers/Pages/Benefits-at-ATB.aspx (accessed June 16, 2016); Workplace Wellness Online, "Best Practices and Success Stories." Found at: http://workplacewellnessonline.ca/success-stories.php (accessed June 16, 2016); R. Yerema and K. Leung, "ATB Financial: Recognized as One of ATB Financial's Top Employers (2016)," Mediacorp Canada. Found at: http://content.eluta.ca/top-employer-atb (accessed June 16, 2016); Glassdoor, "ATB Financial Rating Trends and Culture Quiz." Found at: https://www.glassdoor.ca/Reviews/ATB-Financial-Reviews-E331202.htm#trends-overallRating and https://www.glassdoor.ca/Overview/Working-at-ATB-Financial-EI_IE331202.11,24.htm#WhyWorkForUsTab-22876 (both accessed June 16, 2016); Knightsbridge Robertson Surette, "Canada's Passion Capitalists—Winners Announced" (November 25, 2013). Found at: http://www.kbrs.ca/news/canadas-passion-capitalists-winners-announced (accessed June 16, 2016).

meet their family demands, thereby reducing the occurrence of family-to-work conflict. Consider an employee who has a chronically ill child. This individual may use family leave and personal days to accompany the child on doctor's visits and to care for the child. The existence of such a leave program should reduce the incidence of unexcused absenteeism and tardiness. Maternity leave programs allow new mothers to take paid time away from work shortly before and for some time after the birth of a child. Parental leave programs permit new mothers and fathers to take a leave from work responsibilities when a child is born or placed with them through an adoption. In Canada, the federal government provides a one-year maternity and parental leave program that permits an individual to collect a portion of his or her regular earnings through the Employment Insurance program. Some companies have chosen to provide additional parental benefits that top up the amount the parent earns while on leave. For instance, a company may continue to pay employees a top-up amount so that their total earnings while on leave equal 95% of their regular earnings. Employment Insurance pays an employee 55% of insurable earnings. In 2016, the maximum insurable earnings was $50 800, thus the maximum employment insurance payment was $537 per week.

Leave-related benefits aim to reduce the amount of work–family conflict experienced by employees. Consider the case of a new parent: Having to return to work shortly after the birth of a child will probably result in a high degree of work–family conflict. The new parent is adjusting to newly increased family demands, and these demands can often interfere with work performance. The availability of company-sponsored financial benefits for parental leave also reduces the considerable financial strain that would otherwise prompt an individual to return to work earlier than initially planned.

FAMILY CARE BENEFITS

The final category of family-friendly policies we discuss in this chapter is family care benefit programs. Daycare and elder care benefits fall under this category. Employers can help employees who have children reduce their experience of work–family conflict by supporting daycare programs. This might involve an on-site daycare, which reduces the stress associated with dropping children off at various locations before arriving at work. Additionally, on-site daycares may reduce some of the stress associated with having children in nonparental care. When the daycare is at the work location, the working parent knows that he or she is nearby in case of an emergency. Additionally, the parent can drop in to see the child while at work. The parent may also have increased trust in the daycare provider, as it is a division of their own workplace. In some cases, employers who cannot provide on-site daycare can arrange to have daycare facilities near the worksite.

Another option under this category of family-friendly programs is subsidized dependant care. Here, organizations might provide employees with money to help cover the cost of elder care or child care, or to enroll elders or children in various programs. For instance, an employee who cares for an elderly parent might use this budget to enroll the parent in a seniors' program. As another example, an organization might sponsor summer camps for children of employees. In each case, we can see how these programs could reduce worries about responsibilities for dependant care.

Daycare benefits can help employees with young children reduce work–life conflict. Some companies are able to offer daycare services onsite.

// FAMILY-FRIENDLY POLICIES: AN EVALUATION

There are challenges associated with evaluating the effectiveness of family-friendly programs in Canadian workplaces. First, it is difficult to gauge how widely they are available to Canadian employees due a high degree of variability across different studies and data sources. A 2003 analysis of Statistics Canada's Workplace Employee Survey of more than 20 000 employees from more than 6000 employers indicated that flextime, the most prevalent family-friendly work option, was available to about one-third of employees. Rates for flexplace/telework and access to child care services were even lower, at about 5%.[9] In 2008, a large-scale report based on more than 30 000 Canadian workers indicated that flexible work arrangements were available to 49.4% of respondents, paid personal days to 42.2%, job sharing/part-time hours to 45.3%, and telework to 21.1%. Less than 10% had access to dependant care support or resources. More commonly available, accessible to 75% or more respondents, were reactive, emergency-driven programs such as unpaid days off.[10] More recently, a 2012 study reflected on the concerning fact that access to family-friendly work programs seemed to be declining in Canadian workplaces, with only 27% of a sample of more than 25 000 working Canadians indicating they had high levels of flexibility at work.[11]

It is also difficult to summarize family-friendly programming because the availability of programs and the types of programs differ across types of workplaces. For example, larger organizations often offer greater access to organized programs. From an industry perspective, certain sectors, such as health care, finance, and technology, appear to have the widest array of programs.[12]

The research that has been conducted on the effectiveness of the family-friendly policies described in this chapter is often inconclusive or methodologically flawed. Certainly, anecdotal evidence attesting to their effectiveness in reducing work–family conflict is readily available. However, the available research provides mixed results as to their *actual* impact on work–family conflict.[13] For example, flextime has been associated with an increase in the degree to which people feel they are in control of their work and family lives.[14] Yet, other studies report that flextime does *not* affect the occurrence of work–family conflict.[15] Still other studies report that flextime can possibly even increase work–life conflict.[16] Contradictions aside, the bulk of the meta-analytic evidence, that is evidence derived from studies that statistically summarize the literature, suggest that there are modest positive effects for family friendly programming. **OH&S Notebook 14.1** describes how organizations can use the programs described here to help employees with work–life balance. One possible explanation for the contradictory findings is that flexible work arrangements differentially affect work demands interfering with family commitments and family demands interfering with work commitments. One meta-analysis illustrated this point nicely. Work flexibility was associated with decreased work interference with family commitments, but not vice versa.[17]

Contextual and individual factors also seem to play a role in the outcomes of flexible work arrangements. For example, people who spent more of their working hours engaged in telework reported reduced work-to-family interference but *increased* family-to-work interference. Furthermore, those who had higher degrees of autonomy and flexibility in their jobs reported a greater positive effect of telework on their experiences of work–family conflict.[18] Gender may also moderate the relationships between family-friendly arrangements and various outcomes. For example, one study found that women used workplace flexibility to promote their work–life balance, whereas men used flexibility to increase work commitments.[19]

REDUCING WORK–LIFE CONFLICT: STRATEGIES FOR ORGANIZATIONS

A national study of work–life balance among Canadian employees paints a pictures of the conflict that workers experience. Tracking the Canadian workplace landscape since the early 1990s, authors Linda Duxbury and Christopher Higgins report that the demands of work have risen steadily, absenteeism has increased, and overall life satisfaction has decreased over two decades. Mental health among Canadian workers decreased through the 1990s and has stayed at concerning levels since that time. However, it appears that workplace supports for work–life balance by means of flexible work arrangements and supportive management have not improved since 2001.

To help employees reduce work–family conflict, employers are advised to *reduce demands* placed on employees and *increase the control* that employees have over their work. Here are some specific strategies that employers can engage to achieve these goals:

- Develop an organizational culture that values work–family balance.
- Recognize unrealistic work demands and acknowledge that such loads are not sustainable.
- Track the costs of understaffing and unrealistic work demands.
- Avoid reliance on overtime work; hire more people if the need arises.
- Track the direct and indirect costs of role overload and work–life conflict (absenteeism, overtime, employee assistance programs, turnover).
- Have policies about the use of office technology (e.g., change expectations about after-hours email).
- Offer "cafeteria-style" benefits programs so that employees can choose the services that benefit them.
- Support child- and dependant-care needs (paid leave, care options).
- Offer flexible work options and support employees who use them.
- Reduce the incidence of non-supportive management.

Sources: L. Duxbury and C. Higgins. "Revisiting Work–Life Issues in Canada: The 2012 National Study on Balancing Work and Caregiving in Canada" (2012). Found at: http://newsroom.carleton.ca/wp-content/files/2012-National-Work-Long-Summary.pdf (accessed June 16, 2016); L. Duxbury and C. Higgins, *Work–Life Conflict in Canada in the New Millennium: A Status Report, Final Report* (October 2003). Found at: http://publications.gc.ca/collections/Collection/H72-21-186-2003E.pdf (accessed March 8, 2013); C. Higgins, L. Duxbury, and S. Lyons, "Reducing Work–Life Conflict: What Works? What Doesn't?" (2008). Found at: http://www.hc-sc.gc.ca/ewh-semt/alt_formats/hecs-sesc/pdf/pubs/occup-travail/balancing-equilibre/full_report-rapport_complet-eng.pdf (accessed June 16, 2016).

Researchers have also examined the impact of family-friendly policies on organizations. Again, there are mixed results for the effectiveness of family-friendly initiatives. Flexible work has been associated with increased commitment to the organization and reduced intentions to quit.[20] It appears that flexible work options, such as flextime, telecommuting, and compressed work weeks have a positive impact on job satisfaction and performance.[21] One study reported a positive return on investment of $1.68 for every $1 invested in a particular work–life initiative.[22] However, the impact of these policies on organizational performance is uncertain: some studies report that flexible arrangements contribute to improved productivity; others report no significant effects.[23]

Given the mixed findings in the research literature, but the sustained use of family friendly programming in workplaces, additional research on the organizational and individual impacts of work–family policies is warranted. Specifically considering the type of work–family policy, the nature of the conflict (i.e., work-to-family versus family-to-work), and the influence of both organizational and national culture on work–life balance may help clarify the current inconsistencies.[24] Future work should also consider why companies choose to implement the particular family-friendly policies they do. The existing work on work–family policies as strategic human resource initiatives suggests that such programs may be important in terms of factors such as recruiting or retaining high-quality employees.[25]

Finally, future studies should distinguish between the availability of family-friendly policies and the extent to which employees actually use them or able to use them. Some employers who have family-friendly options make those programs available only to a select group of employees—for instance, people in a particular job classification—or at the manager's discretion.[26] Also, the data suggest that in some organizations, employees choose not to use family-friendly policies such as flextime because they fear that doing so will negatively affect their career progress or stigmatize them among their coworkers.[27] Clearly, the formal existence of a policy does not guarantee that employees will make use of it. People appear more likely to make greater use of family-friendly programs when their workgroups and organizations are truly supportive of these initiatives.[28] The importance of organizational support for family-friendly initiatives is clear. If employees fear that they will be looked down on or damage their career prospects, they may choose not to take advantage of available family-friendly programs.

// HEALTH PROMOTION PROGRAMS

health promotion
a combination of diagnostic, educational, and behavioural modification activities designed to support the attainment and maintenance of positive health

Wellness or health promotion programming is the active attempt to improve employee well-being through worksite interventions. The rationale for such programming is that many health-related concerns can be prevented through lifestyle changes such as diet, exercise, and smoking cessation. Given that employed adults spend many hours in the workplace and that the health of employees affects organizational and individual functioning, the workplace is a convenient and appropriate venue for reaching many adults. This is why more and more workplaces have launched health promotion programs. In **OH&S Notebook 14.2,** you can read about how healthy promotion programs are viable in even small organizations.

Health promotion efforts combine diagnostic, educational, and behavioural change initiatives with the goal of helping people attain and maintain positive health. In workplaces, health and productivity management programs promote the core value of employee health and integrate health promotion activities in ways that simultaneously increase employee well-being and decrease the organization's health-related costs, such as absenteeism and reduced work performance.[29] It would be useful here to trace the development of employee and family assistance plans (EFAPs) as the precursor to diverse array of health promotion programs (HPPs) we see in workplaces today.

employee and family assistance programs (EFAPs)
programs designed to help employees and members of their families with problems that may interfere with worker productivity, including alcohol and other drug abuse, emotional or behavioural problems among family members, and financial or legal problems

EMPLOYEE AND FAMILY ASSISTANCE PROGRAMS (EFAPs)

Employee and family assistance programs (EFAPs) provide counselling and assistance to members of an organization and to members of their families. Generally, these programs help individuals address personal concerns—such as alcoholism, drug use, and stress—that may affect their performance at work.[30] The roots of EFAPs date back to the 19th century and the social betterment movement. Initiatives included inexpensive housing, company-sponsored unions, sanitary working conditions, insurance, pension plans, banking, recreation, medical care, and education facilities. After the social

WELLNESS IN SMALL BUSINESSES

It's clear that the wellness programs program a company can offer will depend on a number of factors, including its size. Some might even ask if workplace health promotion is a reasonable effort for small businesses. The answer appears to be a resounding yes.

Some argue that wellness efforts might be even more important in small workplaces. When there are fewer employees, the impact of a team member who is absent or lower performing due to health concerns, work–life conflict, or lifestyle factors can be substantial. Creative workplace wellness activities for smaller budgets can be developed. Things like walking meetings, lunch and learn awareness sessions, or healthy lunch challenges don't have to cost a lot of money. Smaller workplaces might even have some advantages when it comes to worksite health promotion. Coworker cohesiveness and the visibility of leaders might lead to increased workplace participation.

The academic research supports the argument that wellness programs in small workplaces can thrive and carry substantial benefits for employees and employers. Companies with fewer than 50 employees have developed wellness programs with very high participation rates that result in improved health behaviour and life satisfaction. Small businesses can achieve a positive return on their investment in health promotion. Barriers such as lower budgets and time pressures can be overcome with the presence of a wellness champion in the organization and by consulting with a wellness consultant or facilitator external to the workplace.

Sources: S. Aldana, "Why Small Business Wellness Is the Future," Well Steps (January 27, 2016). Found at: http://wellnessprogramsblog.org/2016/01/27/small-business-wellness (accessed June 16, 2016); A Dwyer, "The Big Save. Wellness Programs Can Pump Up the Bottom Line," *The Globe & Mail* (October 16, 2015). Found at: http://www.theglobeandmail.com/report-on-business/wellness-programs-can-pump-up-the-bottom-line/article26825942 (accessed June 16, 2016); R.M. Merrill, "A Small Business Worksite Wellness Model for Improving Health Behaviors," *Journal of Occupational and Environmental Medicine*, 55 (2013): 895–900; R.M. Merrill, S.G. Aldana, J.E. Pope, D.R. Anderson, C.R. Coberley, T.P. Vyhlidal, G. Howe, and R.W. Whitmer, "Evaluation of a Best-Practice Worksite Wellness Program in a Small-Employer Setting Using Selected Well-being Indices," *Journal of Occupational & Environmental Medicine*, 53 (2011): 448–454; R.Z. Goetzel, M.Tabrizi, R.M. Henke, R. Benevent, C.V.S. Brockbank, K. Stinson, and L.S. Newman, "Estimating the Return on Investment from a Health Risk Management Program Offered to Small Colorado-Based Employers," *Journal of Occupational and Environmental Medicine/American College of Occupational and Environmental Medicine*, 56 (2014): 554–60; S.J. Williams and D.M. Snow, "Promoting Health in Small and Medium-sized Enterprises," *Journal of Small Business and Enterprise Development*, 19 (2012): 729–44.

betterment movement subsided in the 1920s and 1930s, personal counselling emerged. Management trained some shop workers to listen to workers' problems to reduce those problems' interference with productivity. For example, in 1917, Macy's Department Store established a program to assist employees who were dealing with personal problems. By 1920, one-third of the 431 largest companies in the United States had a full-time welfare secretary whose major role was as a counsellor.[31]

The 1940s saw the rise of the Occupational Alcohol Movement, generally acknowledged to be the direct predecessor of the EFAP.[32] Alcoholism was recognized as a serious impediment to productivity, and these programs sought to help workers troubled by this problem by offering alcohol-related and personal problem counselling. The 1970s were a period of rapid growth for EFAPs. In the 1980s, EFAPs expanded to include stress management. Today, EFAPs address all types of problems that may interfere with worker productivity, including alcohol and other drug abuse, emotional or behavioural problems among family members, and financial or legal problems.[33]

Today, workplace health promotion programs are viewed as subsuming the earlier EFAPs. The primary objectives of EFAPs are to help employees and their immediate family members address personal concerns that affect their workplace productivity.

These services are delivered in a manner respecting confidentiality and accessibility.[34]

Typically, health promotion programs include interventions aimed at *stress management* and *lifestyle changes* (e.g., diet, smoking cessation, physical fitness). We next turn our attention to these two classes of health promotion initiatives.

STRESS MANAGEMENT PROGRAMS

The goals of stress management programs are to educate workers about the causes and consequences of stress and to teach skills for managing physiological and psychological symptoms. Again, we can reflect back to the models of stress introduced in Chapter 7. Persistent exposure to stressors can contribute to the experience of stress. Likewise, prolonged or intense experiences of stress can contribute to symptoms of strain such as psychological concerns, physical health problems, or negative behaviours.

In terms of helping employees recognize the causes of stress, programs might draw attention to the pertinent workplace stressors such as workload and work pace, role stressors, and interpersonal relations. Programs that help people reduce their exposure to these stressors would be primary interventions. Other programs offer secondary interventions and focus on helping employees manage stress that they are experiencing. Still other programs are tertiary in nature and help people who are experiencing the symptoms of strain. There are several approaches to stress management including programs that promote cognitive-behavioural skills development, relaxation, increasing social support, and a growing area of mindfulness.

COGNITIVE-BEHAVIOURAL SKILLS TRAINING

Cognitive-behavioural programs are developed in terms of the cognitive model of stress, which posits that emotional responses to situations are largely determined by how they are thought about and interpreted. This training helps people think purposefully about events in new ways, be aware of how they are viewing stressful events, and adapt those thought patterns. Such programs can also help develop skills for coping with stress. The goal is to alter both one's thoughts about stressful events and behaviour toward them. For example, Akilah has been feeling excluded by her coworkers, leading to considerable stress and thoughts about leaving her job. In her cognitive talk therapy program provided through her EFAP, her counsellor is helping her rethink her attributions about why her coworkers do not invite her to lunch. She has always thought it is because they don't like her, but now she can generate other explanations, such as the fact she usually brings lunch and eats at her desk. In her sessions she will be trained in self-instruction, cognitive restructuring, and problem solving. The training program itself might use techniques such as role-playing or group sessions and classroom instruction. In a comprehensive review of stress management interventions, cognitive-behavioural interventions proved to be effective.[35]

RELAXATION TRAINING, MEDITATION, AND MINDFULNESS

Relaxation training teaches things such as progressive muscle relaxation and breathing exercises. If you have ever taken a class in yoga, martial arts, or even aerobics, you have probably experienced something similar to this. The instructor may ask you to lie down on the floor, close your eyes, and focus your mind on your body and your muscles.

Then, he or she may ask you to relax every muscle in your body, slowly working from the bottom up or the top down. For instance, part of Kasem's routine is to repeatedly make a fist and then release his grip while making cold calls to potential clients. This is a part of his job he finds stressful and a stress management counsellor at his work said this simple process can let go of tension. The purpose of this type of training is to provide people with skills to physically relax the body. Over time, individuals will learn to recognize the physical feelings associated with stress and to counteract these feelings by calling on the relaxation response. In doing so, they prevent stress leading to the type of strain reactions discussed earlier.

Relaxation training focuses on relaxing the physical body; meditation focuses on quieting the mind. There are many approaches to meditation, and you are probably familiar with at least some of them. Meditation helps individuals withdraw from a stressful situation and re-energize through mental exercise. A widely used form of meditation in the workplace involves sitting quietly for 20 minutes, repeating a single word on each exhalation.[36] Meditation practice can lead to positive outcomes for workers experiencing stress.[37] Similarly, relaxation training interventions seem to be moderately effective in reducing employee stress.[38]

Mediation can be based in a stress management technique known as mindfulness, which has gained popularity in the workplace. Mindfulness means to bring one's attention to the present moment in a purposeful and non-judgemental way.[39] In addition to meditation, bringing one's focus to the present can be accomplished by techniques such as focusing on the senses or focused breathing exercises. Mindfulness-based methods are proving to be a valuable tool to reduce workplace stress. For example, individuals' use of mindfulness techniques has been associated with reduced stress and improved performance. Importantly, workplace mindfulness interventions appear to be associated with reduced stress and burnout.[40]

INCREASING SOCIAL SUPPORT

A different strategy for reducing work-related stress is to provide a more supportive environment. One way of doing this is by training workers in how to seek social support and in how to create a more supportive workplace. For example, caregiver support programs are designed to help people deal with the stresses of providing care for others. Caregiver support programs are designed to teach employees the benefits of support systems, enhance their skills in mobilizing support, educate them about participatory problem-solving approaches, and show them how to build skills to implement these approaches in team meetings. Consider the case of Marisol, whose father has recently moved in with her and her three children because of his advancing dementia. Marisol joined a lunch-time caregiver support group offered at her work. Just talking with others who understood her challenges was helpful. She learned that there are several not-for-profit organizations that provide daytime services that could help her father. She also got some good ideas about ways to talk to her brothers about the type of help she needs.

EFFECTIVENESS OF STRESS MANAGEMENT TRAINING

Results are mixed regarding the effectiveness of stress management training programs. The lack of comprehensive, well-designed studies on workplace stress management interventions makes it difficult to assess the effectiveness of such programs.[41] Some programs appear to be effective at reducing the experience of job-related stress; others are not.

Review studies suggest that cognitive-behavioural interventions appear to be the most effective.[42] For example, in one study on stress management training, participants were exposed to a variety of stress management techniques, including cognitive restructuring, positive self-talk, deep muscle relaxation, autogenic instructions, and imagery exercises.[43] The training program included nine hours of instruction over six sessions. The researchers found that compared to a control group, those receiving training did not show a significant increase in learning or job satisfaction, or a significant decrease in blood pressure, somatic data, or anxiety. However, when a self-management module was included as part of the training, significant differences were found for all measures except job satisfaction. The self-management module included three hours of training in self-monitoring, specifying goals, evaluating behaviour against goals, and self-reinforcing. This study suggests that simply providing training is not enough to make a difference; participants must be provided with strategies to help them apply what they have learned.

WORKSITE HEALTH PROMOTION: A FOCUS ON LIFESTYLE CHANGES

Worksite health promotion programming can be classified into three categories: screening, education, and behavioural change. Many types of programs are being delivered in each of these various categories. The most common are those designed to affect an employee's health practices or physical lifestyle (e.g., in terms of exercise, eating habits, sleep patterns, weight control, alcohol use, smoking cessation, substance abuse). These efforts are often referred to as "lifestyle programming." It is generally thought that a healthy lifestyle helps promote physical and mental health on the job. Employers are trying to capitalize on this connection. A recent survey of Canadian companies reported that 40% of Canadian employers offer lifestyle-focused programming for their employees.[44] Some programs include activities designed to improve psychological aspects of an individual's lifestyle (e.g., social relations, intellectual activity, occupational conditions), but these programs are still the exception rather than the rule.

On-site programs may include fitness facilities, nutritional assessment and counselling, weight control groups, and smoking cessation help. Typically, these opportunities are available on a voluntary basis. Some may be offered only to individuals at a certain level in the organization (e.g., membership in an off-site health club for managers). Though the organization may provide incentives for using such programs, it would have difficulty mandating that employees alter their lifestyle. Though it is possible to make safety training (even stress reduction training) mandatory, it would be difficult to insist that all employees quit smoking or have a perfect body mass index. Indeed, doing so might violate human rights legislation. Instead of attempting to mandate such programs, organizations involved in worksite health promotion should develop cultures and environments that are highly supportive of healthful lifestyle practices.

Though health promotion programs are diverse, many are secondary-level interventions designed to help individuals who are feeling stress and who are at risk for illness. Worksite health promotion (WHP) programs typically include three steps:

Step 1: Physical or psychological assessment;

Step 2: Counselling concerning the assessment findings and recommendations about personal health promotion; and

Step 3: Referral to in-house or community-based resources.

If we focus on WHP programs that are more tertiary in nature—that is, those designed to help people who are currently experiencing symptoms or illness, such as alcohol and other substance abuse, hypertension, or psychological stress—the key components in such programs should include the following:

- The identification of currently symptomatic as well as high-risk individuals;
- The appropriate referral or treatment of individuals;
- Treatment directed at the symptoms, delivered by the appropriate professionals;
- Follow-up with the client to ensure the treatment was effective; and
- Evaluation of health improvement and cost efficacy.

Components of an effective employer-sponsored health promotion effort include employee education for health promotion or disease prevention; management training to raise awareness and identification of occupational health issues; EFAP services; redesigned benefit programs to provide easy access to interventions; a comprehensive data collection plan for use in program decision making; the integration of corporate health-related services; and greater attention to organizational health. We next turn our attention to some specific categories of WHP programs. In particular, we look at efforts focused on changing some aspect of an employee's lifestyle (i.e., lifestyle programming). As you read through, consider the benefits of a program like Rogers' bWell health online health assessment described in **OH&S Today 14.2**, which allows employees to identify their risk areas and generate an individualized plan for wellness.

OH&S TODAY 14.2

AWARDED FOR EXCELLENCE: ROGERS COMMUNICATIONS INC.

Rogers is a giant in Canadian telecommunications. Headquartered in Toronto, Ontario, it has business operations throughout Canada and employs 26 000 people. Rogers has put investment in employees as one of seven pillars of its strategic priorities program, Rogers 3.0. In doing so, the organization illustrates the value it places on employees and recognizes strategic benefits of building an engaged workforce.

Rogers' employee initiatives involve employee training and development opportunities for front-line and managerial employees. Rogers has family-friendly programming, including maternity/parental leave, salary top-ups, and flexible work arrangements. The organization also focuses on health promotion via bWell, an online resource and wellness program. Via this program, employees can chart their own health with a risk assessment, develop an action plan, and learn about health resources available to them as employees. There are employees who volunteer as health ambassadors to promote workplace health. The wellness program has support from the top. There is an executive champion for a healthy workplace and a steering committee for wellness.

Rogers' commitment to its employees is clear. Rogers 3.0 was developed following the President and CEO Guy Laurence's listening tour to gain feedback about the company. The strategic pillars grew from stakeholder feedback. Rogers also tracks its progress with identified indicators to illustrate development in each pillar of its strategic plan. For example, to assess its success in investing in employees, the company tracks employee engagement. Rogers has been widely recognized for its wellness offerings. It has been awarded by Excellence Canada with the Canada Award for Excellence (CAE), is recognized as one having of Canada's most engaged workforces, and is included on numerous Best Places to Work lists, including the Best Places to Work for Young Workers.

Sources: Rogers Company. Found at http://www.rogers.com/web/ir/overview/, http://about.rogers.com/about/corporate-social-responsibility/employee-experience/talent-management, http://about.rogers.com/about/corporate-social-responsibility/employee-experience/health-safety-wellness, and http://about.rogers.com/about/our-awards/great-canadian-employer (accessed June 16, 2016); Rogers Communication Inc., "What Matters Most: Rogers 2014 Corporate Social Responsibility Report." Found at: http://about.rogers.com/docs/default-source/csr-reports/2014-rogers-csr-report.pdf (accessed June 16, 2016); Canada's Top 100 Employers, "Rogers." Found at: http://content.eluta.ca/top-employer-rogers-communications (accessed June 16, 2016); Excellence Canada, "2015 CAE Recipient Profile—Rogers Communications." Found at: https://www.excellence.ca/en/awards/2015-cae-recipients/2015-cae-profiles/2015-caeprofile-rogers (accessed June 16, 2016).

SMOKING CESSATION

One of the most popular worksite health promotion interventions in recent years has been smoking cessation. As worksites have increasingly banned smoking, either voluntarily or because of legislation, more and more employers have seen the wisdom of helping employees quit smoking. Research has consistently documented that smokers are absent more than non-smokers; this provides employers with an economic incentive for smoking cessation programs. A recent quantitative review out of the United Kingdom showed that smokers were absent 2.74 more days per year than non-smokers with an estimated annual cost of 1.4 billion British pounds.[45] There are estimates that in Canada each smoker costs his or her workplace more than $4000/year in lost productivity due to unauthorized breaks and absenteeism.[46]

Smoking cessation programs may combine education, group support, counselling, nicotine replacement options, and behavioural change techniques. Other programs incorporate things like poster campaigns about the dangers of smoking. The success rates of such programs have varied between 25% and 60%. Several studies support the effectiveness of various targeted worksite interventions for reducing smoking.[47] A recent comprehensive review suggests that some types of programs are more successful than others. In particular, programs involving group or individual counselling, medication options, or a combination were more successful than program such as awareness campaigns or social support.[48] However, characteristics of individual smokers can influence their likelihood of success. For example, older smokers and those with respiratory concerns may have higher rates of success, and those with high dependency on nicotine and intense cravings lower rates of success.[49] Interestingly, organizational bans on smoking do not seem to be associated with reduced smoking behaviour among employees.[50]

ALCOHOL AND DRUG TESTING PROGRAMS

Research suggests that alcohol and drug use have negative effects in the workplace. For example, there are studies linking the prevalence of heavy drinkers in a workplace to increased incidence of gender harassment and the frequency of heavy drinking to increased absenteeism.[51] Furthermore, to the extent that alcohol and drug use may decrease alertness and quick thinking, they may lead to performance concerns, particularly relating to safety. As described earlier, EFAPs, both historically and currently, are avenues for employees to seek guidance and explore means of treatment for alcohol and drug addictions.

Because of the potentially severe outcomes associated with alcohol and drug use, some employers have introduced direct alcohol and drug testing programs to screen employees for recent drug or alcohol consumption. These programs are controversial. Some argue in support of drug testing because there is research to support the claim that workplace testing deters drug and alcohol use.[52] For example, a recent European study found that there were fewer accidents among employees subject to random alcohol testing compared to those who were not tested. That said, a recent systematic review of the literature found that the majority of studies on the topic suffer from methodological problems, limiting their interpretability.[53] Others argue against the practice for a variety of reasons, including the fact that drug testing detects exposure to a drug but not necessarily current impairment. Besides this, the practice violates employee privacy.[54]

Canadian employers are subject to the Canadian Human Rights Commission's policy on alcohol and drug testing. Under that policy, such testing is considered a discriminatory practice. The policy statement indicates that while drug testing can assess exposure, it does not assess ability impairment at the time of the screening. There are some apparent exceptions relating to alcohol screening for individuals who are in safety-sensitive positions because alcohol detection is indicative of impairment at the time of the test. If such alcohol screens are in place, employers must accommodate the needs of those who test positive and are identified as being dependent on alcohol. As with other discriminatory practices, Canadian employers can justify drug and alcohol testing if they can demonstrate that it is a *bona fide* occupational requirement. In those cases testing may occur for reasonable cause (e.g., the employee is unfit for work) or following a significant safety incident in which the employee is implicated.[55] This policy is available online for download.

Workplace health promotion programs can involve health screenings for common conditions such as hypertension or diabetes.

HYPERTENSION SCREENING

Hypertension, or high blood pressure, has been called the "silent killer." Individuals can have hypertension for a long time without knowing it or without experiencing symptoms. Hypertension is considered one of the major (and most easily controlled) risk factors in heart-related diseases. Workplace programs aimed at cardiovascular disease reduction, like hypertension screening, with medical and life style follow-ups, have numerous benefits.[56] Workplace programs aimed at addressing hypertension vary widely but typically consist of four interrelated steps:

> **hypertension**
> elevated blood pressure

1. *Education.* Employees are alerted to the dangers of hypertension and the benefits associated with treatment.
2. *Screening.* Employees are screened using blood pressure clinics in which participants have their blood pressure read by a medical professional.
3. *Referral.* Employees with elevated readings are referred to medical treatment.
4. *Follow-up.* Referred employees are followed up to verify the outcome of treatment and to monitor progress.

The incidence of hypertension is high in the Canadian population. More than 30% of individuals have blood pressure readings higher than their targeted levels, with an even higher incidence in those who also have diabetes. While people who are identified as having high blood pressure typically seek treatment, data suggests that 17% of Canadians are unaware that they are hypertensive.[57] In one study, a hypertension screening program targeted at taxi drivers was successful in getting individuals to seek follow-up medical care.[58] Thus, workplace screening programs can help those who are diagnosed monitor their condition and help to diagnose others.

NUTRITION AND WEIGHT CONTROL

Nutrition programs in the workplace typically take one of two forms. First, educational programs are aimed at providing instruction or information on the selection of foods, the basics of meal planning, and so on. Posters in the cafeteria promoting healthy eating are an example of educational programming. The second type of activity is to actually change the food available in the workplace. Providing healthy, low-fat alternatives in the cafeteria and changing the contents of vending machines in the workplace help employees maintain a healthy diet. There is empirical evidence for the effectiveness of some nutrition-focused worksite health promotion programs.[59]

Weight control programs are becoming increasingly popular and are often offered in conjunction with established weight-loss programs. Again, such programs rely on education, counselling, and group support. Workplaces are cautioned to treat all employees with respect as they engage in workplace weight-loss programs. Things like group weigh-ins and shared weight-lost amounts can be perceived as supportive by some people, but aversive to others. Some workplaces now offer online versions of weight-loss programs. Several studies indicate that worksite weight-loss programs can be effective; but program drop-out rates can be high and potentially influence the results. In other words, those who stay with the program may lose weight, but with a high attrition rate there are a large number of people for whom the programs are not effective. A trend in workplace weight management programs in the United States is financial incentives for weight loss. However, research suggests that this approach is not successful and in many ways undermines the collaborative approach to workplace wellness programming.[60]

PHYSICAL FITNESS PROGRAMS

Fitness programs in workplaces can take several forms. Some are simple and focus on *awareness* through programs like posters to encourage taking the stairs, health fairs in the workplace, and so forth. Others constitute organized programs aimed at changing behaviour. For instance, a company may sponsor lunch-time fitness programs or subsidize gym memberships. Some organizations take things a step further by creating a workplace that promotes a healthy lifestyle; for example, encouraging walking meetings, providing shower facilities for those who wish to work out at lunch time or run or bike to work, or offering onsite gym facilities.[61] Advancing technology introduces new elements to workplace fitness programs. For instance, fitness trackers are being incorporated into worksite wellness programs.

It seems that workplace physical activity programs are effective. Some studies report that workplace fitness programs are associated with important individual and workplace outcomes. These include increased physical activity, improved job satisfaction, decreased health care costs, decreased hospital admissions, and decreased absenteeism for those who take part.[62] That said, review studies report that the size of the change, while significant in a statistical sense, is nonetheless small. Research does show that individually tailored programs, those solidly based on theory, and motivational focus appear to be more successful than generic fitness programs.[63] Thus, additional high quality studies are needed to provide further evidence to the efficacy of workplace fitness programming.

DEVELOPING A SUCCESSFUL WORKSITE HEALTH PROMOTION PROGRAM

A worksite health promotion (WHP) program will succeed only if employees are making use of what it offers. See **OH&S Today 14.3** and ArcelorMittal Dofasco Inc.'s programs and the high degree of employee participation. Research on worksite health

AWARDED FOR EXCELLENCE: ARCELORMITTAL DOFASCO

ArcelorMittal Dofasco Inc. is a Hamilton-based company that is one of the most profitable steelmakers in North America. Further, it has been recognized by *The Globe and Mail* as one of Canada's best places to work and was awarded Excellence Canada's Canadian Award for Excellence as recognition of its healthy workplace strategy. Its longstanding slogan—"Our Product Is Steel. Our Strength Is People"—reflects ArcelorMittal Dofasco's emphasis on employee engagement and well-being. As part of its Healthy Lifestyles programs, ArcelorMittal Dofasco provides numerous family-friendly and health-focused options, including employee access to a multi-sport recreation and learning centre and several health promotion initiatives such as on-site, subsidized weight management meetings, smoking cessation programs, first aid training, a comprehensive employee assistance program, and health assessments. ArcelorMittal Dofasco is active in its support of mental health awareness in the workplace. This company's high investment in employees has been a success. There is a high degree of program participation and attendance among employees. From a financial perspective, there has been a marked reduction in lost-time injuries, workers' compensation premiums, and incidence of non-work-related injuries since the health programs were initiated. ArcelorMittal Dofasco's commitment to its people gives it a recruitment and retention advantage and makes it a good place to work.

Sources: ArcelorMittal. Found at: http://www.dofasco.ca (accessed June 17, 2016); D. Jermyn, "Many of Canada's Top Employers Have Staying Power," *The Globe and Mail* (November 25, 2015). Found at: http://www.theglobeandmail.com/report-on-business/careers/top-employers/many-of-canadas-top-100-employers-have-staying-power/article27484362 (accessed June 17, 2016); Excellence Canada, "2014 CAE Recipient Profile—ArcelorMittal Dofasco." Found at: https://www.excellence.ca/en/awards/2014-cae-recipients/2014-cae-profiles/2014-caeprofile-amd; J. Paterson, "ArcelorMittal Dofasco Reinforces Focus on Employee Mental Health," *Benefits Canada* (January 26, 2016). Found at: http://www.benefitscanada.com/benefits/health-wellness/arcelormittal-dofasco-reinforces-focus-on-employee-mental-health-76317 (accessed June 17, 2016); R. Wright, "Injury Prevention Program: Decreasing the Risk of Musculoskeletal Injuries," *Rehab and Community Care Medicine* (February 25, 2015). Found at: http://www.rehabmagazine.ca/healthcare/workplace-health/corporate-wellness (accessed June 17, 2016).

promotion efforts has provided some key evidence-based insights on the best practices that contribute to successful program implementation. The following key practices were identified in a comprehensive review.[64]

1. The health program should be in line with the workplace's goals and values.
2. Multiple factors that influence health, including those at the individual, cultural, and policy factors should be considered.
3. The program should target a range of health issues.
4. The program should be tailored to meet specific needs,
5. Efforts need to be made to achieve high participation.
6. Thorough evaluation is necessary.
7. Program success must be communicated to the stakeholders.

These program elements are considered best practices across several review studies. One expert noted the importance of engaging but relentless communication about the program to employees and that the program must develop over time. Others have noted that leaders play a particular role in the success of WHPs, but that success must also be achieved in partnership with employee groups. The importance of rigorous evaluation is widely noted.[65] You can learn some evaluation pointers in **OH&S Notebook 14.3**.

USING EVALUATION TO BUILD A BUSINESS CASE FOR HEALTH PROMOTION AND FAMILY-FRIENDLY PROGRAMS

For OH&S professionals and HR managers to make a strong business case for continued or increased funding for workplace wellness and family-friendly programs, they need to demonstrate that the programs work. The outcomes associated with such programs should be subjected to careful study via well-designed evaluation studies. How does one conduct a thorough evaluation study? Here are factors to keep in mind:

1. *Good evaluation studies include assessments of relevant important outcome factors.* You must ask, what are the variables the intervention should influence? These might be individual factors like weight loss, perceived stress, or life satisfaction. They should also be workplace issues such as absenteeism, workers' compensation rates, injury data, turnover rates, or productivity. The evaluation for some interventions might call for biological data that can be gathered by researchers who invite participants to use equipment such as blood pressure monitors or activity trackers. It is important to emphasize that employees' privacy must be respected during the evaluation process. Some information is clearly available to the organization. For example, whether or not an employee was absent is tracked by many workplaces. However, organizations have less right to know about the particular illness prompting the absence. If sensitive or personal data such as blood pressure or health symptoms are being tracked as part of the evaluation process, this information can be submitted confidentially, noting only whether or not the individual in question took part in the program and not his or her name. To track such information over time, employees can be assigned an evaluation identification number, rather than their names or employee IDs, that they can use to submit their information to the evaluators. Researchers who are conducting evaluation studies, whether they are internal or external to the organization, must be aware of and respect privacy laws and adhere to any research ethics protocols relevant to their organizations.

2. *Good evaluation studies include pre-intervention and post-intervention assessments of the outcome factors.* You need to have a baseline to assess the extent of improvement experienced by the program participants and the organization. Thus, intervention studies require planning. These variables need to be identified and the pre-intervention information gathered during the planning stages of the study.

3. *Good evaluation studies include reliable and valid measures of important variables.* These measures should consider different aspects of the participants' experience in the program. You should ask formative questions about the participants' reactions to the program. Formative questions would be things like whether the program met the participants' needs and if they liked the program. There should be process questions that tap into participants' experiences in taking part. For example, were there barriers to taking part in the intervention? Finally there must be outcome evaluation to determine if the program achieved its initial goals, be it weight loss, reduced job stress, fewer smokers, etc.

4. *Good intervention studies have long-term follow-up on the important outcome factors.* To really know how successful the program is, you need to ask whether people maintain their weight loss, their improved mood, or increased work engagement etc. over time. Ideally, there should also be multiple post-intervention assessments to allow researchers to gain an understanding of the long-term effectiveness of the program.

5. *Good evaluation studies consider the extent to which employees joined, participated in, or abandoned the program.* This information can help you understand the study results. For example, if there does not appear to be improvement in important variables, you can determine if the lack of change is related to low participation or attrition. You might also gain insight into whether this is the type of program that employees want.

(continued)

6. *Good intervention studies include a control group.* Really good intervention studies have control groups and intervention groups that are assigned at random Control groups are people who are not taking part in the program. You can then compare the outcomes of those employees who took part in the program with a comparable group. If you see improvements in those who took part (i.e., the intervention group), but not in the control group, you have evidence that your wellness intervention is effective.

Sources: Region of Waterloo Project Health, "Evaluation Tools for Workplace Wellness Activities." Found at: http://www.projecthealth.ca/sites/default/files/files/Evaluation%20Tools%20for%20Workplace%20Wellness%20Activities.pdf (accessed June 17, 2016); CDC, "Workplace Health Promotion: Evaluation." Found at: http://www.cdc.gov/workplacehealthpromotion/tools-resources/workplace-health/evaluation.html (accessed April 16, 2016).

UNINTENDED CONSEQUENCES OF WHP PROGRAMS

The goal of health promotion is to reduce costs to the organization in terms of health care, lost time, turnover, and so on. However, some unintended consequences of WHP programs need to be considered. First, the reduction of health care utilization by employees (offered through benefits plans) may lead to a higher unit cost for those employees who do use health and medical benefits. The individual cost of offering certain benefits decreases with a high enrolment rate because the risk to insurance companies of having to pay out on claims is reduced with a large subscription. Reduced enrolment in some aspects of a cafeteria-style benefits plan (in which employees have some options concerning the coverage they want in areas such as medical, dental, life insurance, etc.) may make it prohibitive for those employees who need access to those benefits. A second potential consequence is that participation in exercise or fitness programs may cause work disruptions, increase fatigue, lower performance, and increase accidents among those who are beginning such a program.

Also, health promotion can cause friction among workers. For example, smoking restrictions may produce conflict between smokers and non-smokers, produce negative attitudes about smoking, and reduce productivity among smokers if they must leave the workstation to smoke. Finally, the diagnosis of previously unknown risk factors may contribute to absenteeism (e.g., doctor's appointments). For example, individuals who did not know they were hypertensive may exhibit increased absenteeism as a result of being informed of their condition.

OVERALL EVALUATION

How successful are worksite health promotion programs? Once again, we find "success" to be a difficult thing to assess. To quote the authors of a recent review of the literature on workplace health promotion: "… it appears that some programs work some of the time, with some people, for some criteria."[66] Some studies show that these programs can be effective. In fact, in one study evaluating a multifaceted worksite health promotion program's effect on absenteeism reported that program participants were absent an average of three fewer days per year than nonparticipants. The associated cost savings for the organization was $15.60 returned for every $1 initially invested in the program.[67] An ongoing Canadian evaluation of wellness programs, the Sunlife-Ivey Canadian Wellness Return on Investment Study, is showing supportive results. Its preliminary literature review concluded that wellness programs reduce absenteeism, saving organizations 1.5–1.7 lost days per worker each year. As part of this study, several organizations implemented a wellness program. The results show that employees taking part in the program show improved physical activity, nutrition, and energy.[68] So, for every dollar spent on program expenses such as extra staff to run the program, advertisements for the program, or equipment and facilities to support the program, companies can experience substantial cost savings by way of factors such as reduced absenteeism, benefits costs, or health care costs.

However, not all studies support the success of WHP programs. In fact, some authors argue that there is simply not enough systematic research on the various categories of WHP programs to reach a definitive conclusion about their efficacy.[69] Some point out that evaluation studies often have methodological weaknesses—lacking vital elements such as control groups, randomization of participants, and well-defined outcome measures-measures—that can inflate the estimate financial success of the program. That said, when looking at studies high in methodological rigour, it appears the return on investment estimates remain positive, but are smaller in magnitude.[70]

// SUMMARY

A broad array of programs can be offered in organizations under the rubric of work–family and worksite health promotion programming. For the most part, the jury is still out on whether these programs offer significant benefits to organizational outcomes. However, some evidence shows that work–family programs have *some* positive impact on the experience of work–family conflict. Similarly, health promotion programming can succeed in changing individual behaviour to enhance health. One positive spinoff of the programs for organizations is the general increase in employee morale (e.g., satisfaction, commitment) that is associated with making health promotion and family-friendly programs available in the workplace.

KEY TERMS

compressed workweek 348
employee and family assistance programs (EFAPs) 354
flexible work arrangements (FWAs) 348
flexplace 349
flextime 349
health promotion 354
hypertension 361
job sharing 349
job splitting 349
work–family conflict 348

DISCUSSION QUESTIONS

1. EFAPs often have two routes of entry. An individual can voluntarily contact the EFAP for assistance with a problem, or a supervisor can refer the individual. In the latter case, a supervisor who notes a decline in performance can insist that an

individual seek assistance or be disciplined (including dismissal). Is this degree of coercion justified? Is it likely to facilitate a change in behaviour?

2. The logic of health promotion programs in the workplace is based on the observation that the workplace provides a convenient way to reach large segments of the population. Yet many individuals wonder whether organizations have the right to get involved in employees' lifestyle choices. What do you think? Should organizations be involved in these programs?

3. What benefits would you expect to see from implementing a physical fitness program (e.g., paid memberships in the local health club) in your workplace?

4. Is stress management training an effective approach to dealing with workplace stress? Why or why not?

5. Generate some strategies that a dual-income couple might use to help them manage work and family demands more effectively. How might their employers help them enact some of these strategies?

USING THE INTERNET

1. Visit the websites of a number of companies representing a variety of job sectors (e.g., manufacturing, high tech, communications, medical). Search the sites to find information on the types of health promotion programs (e.g., smoking cessation, fitness) and family-friendly policies (e.g., flextime, telecommuting) they offer.

   a. Identify the proportion of the companies that offer health promotion programs or family-friendly policies.

   b. Which health promotion programs and family-friendly policies appear to be most commonly available?

   c. What are some of the company characteristics that appear to be related to the programs they offer? For instance, are companies in a particular sector or of a particular size more likely to offer health promotion and family-friendly programs?

   d. Discuss with your classmates the extent to which the availability of health promotion and family-friendly programs is important to them when they are looking for a job. Which programs appear to be the most desirable to job seekers?

2. Health promotion programs are more likely to succeed if they are based on a thorough needs assessment (i.e., assessments of the needs of the organization and its employees). Design a needs assessment instrument for measuring the need for health promotion programming in your current or a former workplace. If your work experience does not provide a suitable example for this Internet exercise, interview someone about his or her workplace and develop a needs assessment instrument for that work environment. The Internet will be very helpful in this task. Search the Internet using keywords such as "wellness" and "health promotion." This search will help you identify many components of such a needs assessment instrument.

3. Search the Internet to learn details about government-sponsored mandatory parental or maternal leave benefits in different countries (e.g., Canada, the United States, the United Kingdom). Compare the policies in each country. Also, search the

websites of various organizations that have operations in each of the countries you chose to determine whether they provide additional parental leave benefits to their employees. Afterward, discuss the following issues in class:

a. What impact would the policies in each of these countries and companies have on a new parent's experience of work–family conflict? Would these policies help a working parent balance work and family roles?

b. What are the advantages and disadvantages of these programs for the person taking the leave?

c. What are the advantages and disadvantages of these programs for the organizations that have employees taking leave?

d. What are the advantages and disadvantages of these programs for families?

4. Each year, *Report on Business* magazine releases a ranking of the Best Employers in Canada. Access a Best Employers list from a recent year, and search the websites of five of these top employers. Assess the extent to which they offer work/family-friendly and worksite health promotion programs. Describe some of the programs they offer.

EXERCISES

1. With a small group of classmates, discuss the following scenario: Imagine your current work hours are Monday to Friday, 9 to 5. At present, the start time of 9 a.m. is strictly enforced. However, the company is considering implementing a new flextime approach to work scheduling. Under this program, employees will be able to start their eight-hour workday any time between 7 a.m. and 11 a.m. However, each employee must work a continuous shift (i.e., there is no flexibility midday).

Each person in the group should reflect on how such a change would benefit or disadvantage him or her, given current circumstances. Additionally, discuss how the move to flextime might affect the following individuals or groups:

a. a working parent who has young school-aged children.

b. someone who is not a morning person

c. a person who commutes a long distance to work

d. an individual who has substantial elder care responsibilities

e. coworkers of individuals who opt to use the flextime arrangement

f. the organization implementing the change

What other types of flexible scheduling might help some of these people manage their multiple responsibilities to work and family?

2. In this chapter we have discussed the importance of evaluating health promotion programs. For any program, a number of outcome variables might offer insight into the success or failure of the program. One approach would apply the four types of strain introduced in Chapter 7 (psychological, physical, behavioural, organizational). With your classmates, brainstorm some of the pertinent outcome variables relating to each of these broad categories; then incorporate those variables into each of the

following types of health promotion programs. The group should also consider how they might measure each of these variables:

a. smoking cessation
b. on-site physical fitness centre
c. lunchtime Weight Watchers program
d. off-site, call-in EFAP
e. subsidized yoga classes

OH&S IN ACTION

As the OHS director at financial institution, you want to help your organization celebrate its success in family-friendly and wellness programming. The company has invested considerably and the employees participate at high rates in the wellness fairs and employee fitness challenge (including the pedometer race to 1 000 000 steps), and love the priority placement at the daycare centre a block aware. You are applying for an award that has three criteria: employee engagement, employee health and physical activity, and work–life balance. Write a one page "intent to apply" letter advising the award organizers why your company receives an A+ in wellness. (You are free to make assumptions and embellish details about the particular company, programs, and indicators you are tracking).

CASE STUDY 1   MANDATORY AEROBICS

As a new manager, Jean McDonald is eager to improve morale and productivity in the work group. Believing that people will work better if they feel better, Jean has scheduled a group aerobics class in which all group members must participate. Several group members object to enforced exercise and have approached you (as Jean's immediate supervisor) with their concerns. What do you tell the employees? What do you tell Jean?

CASE STUDY 2   EVALUATING THE BENEFITS OF WHPS

Quan Dar is the human resource manager of a mid-sized insurance firm. A faltering economy has resulted in the need to re-examine all current expenditures and to find areas in which to cut costs. Senior management is questioning the amount of money the firm spends on health promotion programs. Currently, the firm offers weight loss clinics, subsidized smoking cessation products, an on-site fitness program, regular stress prevention training programs, and an employee assistance program. Quan feels that these programs have value and add significant worth to the firm. However, senior management demands evidence. Quan has approached you for advice—how can he demonstrate the value of these programs to the firm?

Sherry and Marco are highly skilled marketing managers at a large telecommunications firm. In their time with the company, Marco and Sherry have worked very long hours. Indeed, they have worked well as a team to design several large-scale, successful advertising campaigns for new products and services. However, both are now parents of young children, and are feeling the pressure of competing work and family demands. Of late, both have expressed concerns about their ability to keep up with the fast pace of their home and work responsibilities and have mentioned the possibility of either cutting back their time at work or leaving their jobs altogether. As the director of human resources, you don't want to lose such valuable talent in the marketing department. You think that Sherry and Marco might be ideal candidates for the company's new job-sharing program. How might you facilitate a job-sharing arrangement for Sherry and Marco? What types of working arrangement might you suggest to them?

// NOTES

1. S. Mattke, C. Schnyer, and K.R. Van Busum. "A Review of the U.S. Workplace Wellness Market" *RAND Health* (2012).

2. Towers Watson. *2013/2014 Staying@Work Report—Canada Summary* (2014). Found at: https://www.towerswatson.com/en-CA/Insights/IC-Types/Survey -Research-Results/2014/02/2013-2014-staying-at-work-report-canada-summary (accessed July 6, 2016).

3. Sanofi Canada, "The Sanofi Canada Health Care Survey" (2012). Found at: http://www.sanofi.ca/l/ca/en/layout.jsp?cnt=65B67ABD-BEF6-487B-8FC1 -5D06FF8568ED (accessed July 6, 2016).

4. CSA Group, "CAN/CSA-Z1003-13 Psychological Health and Safety in the Workplace—Prevention, Promotion, and Guidance to Staged Implementation" (January 2013).

5. Towers Watson. *2013/2014 Staying@Work Report—Canada Summary*.

6. L. Duxbury and C. Higgins. "Revisiting Work–Life Issues in Canada: The 2012 National Study on Balancing Work and Caregiving in Canada" (2012). Found at: http://newsroom.carleton.ca/wp-content/files/2012-National-Work -Long-Summary.pdf (accessed July 6, 2016).

7. C. Higgins, L. Duxbury, and S. Lyons, "Reducing Work–Life Conflict: What Works? What Doesn't?" (2008). Found at http://www.phac-aspc.gc.ca/ publicat/work-travail/index.html (accessed April 16, 2016).

8. G. Grennhaus and T.D. Allen, "Work–Family Balance: A Review and Extension," in J.C. Quick and L.E. Tetrick, eds., *Handbook of Occupational Health Psychology, 2nd ed.* (Washington: APA, 2011), 165–83.

9. D. Comfort, K. Johnson, and D. Wallace, "Part-Time Work and Family-Friendly Practices in Canadian Workplaces," Statistics Canada, Human

Resources Development Canada (2003). Found at http://www.statcan.gc.ca/pub/71-584-m/71-584-m2003006-eng.pdf (accessed April 27, 2010).

10. C. Higgins, L. Duxbury, and S. Lyons, "Reducing Work–Life Conflict: What Works? What Doesn't?"

11. L. Duxbury and C. Higgins. "Revisiting Work–life Issues in Canada: The 2012 National Study on Balancing Work and Caregiving in Canada" (2012). Found at: http://newsroom.carleton.ca/wp-content/files/2012-National-Work-Long-Summary.pdf (accessed April 16, 2016).

12. R. Ireson, B. Sethi, and A. Williams, "Availability of Caregiver-friendly Workplace Policies (CFWPs): An International Scoping Review," *Health & Social Care in the Community* (2016).

13. T.D. Allen, R.C. Johnson, K.M. Kiburz, and K.M. Shockley, "Work–Family Conflict and Flexible Work Arrangements: Deconstructing Flexibility," *Personnel Psychology*, 66(2) (2013): 345–76.

14. H.H. Nijp, D.G. Beckers, S.A. Geurts, P. Tucker, and M.A. Kompier, "Systematic Review on the Association Between Employee Worktime Control and Work–Non-Work Balance, Health and Well-Being, and Job-Related Outcomes," *Scandinavian Journal of Work, Environment & Health* (2012): 299–313.

15. L.M. LaPierre and T.D. Allen, "Work-Supportive Family, Family-Supportive Supervision, Use of Organizational Benefits, and Problem-Focused Coping: Implications for Work–life Conflict and Employee Well-Being," *Journal of Occupational Health Psychology* 11 (2006): 169–81.

16. C. Higgins, L. Duxbury, and M. Julien, "The Relationship Between Work Arrangements and Work–Life Conflict," *Work*, 48(1) (2014): 69–81; S.J. Goff, M.K. Mount, and R.L. Jamieson, "Employer Supported Child Care, Work/Family Conflict, and Absenteeism: A Field Study," *Personnel Psychology* 43 (1990): 793–809; L.M. LaPierre and T.D. Allen, "Work-Supportive Family, Family-Supportive Supervision, Use of Organizational Benefits, and Problem-Focused Coping: Implications for Work–Life Conflict and Employee Well-Being," *Journal of Occupational Health Psychology* 11 (2006): 169–81.

17. T.D. Allen, R.C. Johnson, K.M. Kiburz, and K.M. Shockley "Work–Family Conflict and Flexible Work Arrangements: Deconstructing Flexibility," *Personnel Psychology*, 66(2) (2013): 345–76.

18. T.D. Golden, J.F. Veiga, and Z. Simsek, (2006). "Telecommuting's differential impact on work-family conflict: Is there no place like home?," *Journal of Applied Psychology* 91(6) (2006): 13–40.

19. D. Hofäcker and S. König, "Flexibility and Work–Life Conflict in Times of Crisis: A Gender Perspective," *International Journal of Sociology and Social Policy*, 33(9/10) (2013): 613–35.

20. T.D. Golden, "Avoiding Depletion in Virtual Work: Telework and the Intervening Impact of Work Exhaustion on Commitment and Turnover Intentions," *Journal of Vocational Behavior* 69 (2006): 176–87.

21. M.M. Butts, W.J. Casper, and T.S. Yang, "How Important Are Work–Family Support Policies? A Meta-Analytic Investigation of Their Effects on Employee Outcomes," *Journal of Applied Psychology*, 98(1) (2013): 1; C.D. Cotti, M.R. Haley, and L.A. Miller, "Workplace Flexibilities, Job Satisfaction and Union Membership in the US Workforce," *British Journal of Industrial Relations*,

52(3) (2014): 403–25; J.C. Latona, "Flextime and the Compressed Work Week: Possible Strategies for Smaller Firms to Increase Employee Performance and Satisfaction. *Journal of Small Business Strategy*, *3*(2) (2015): 67–72.

22. C. Barbosa, J.W. Bray, W.N. Dowd, M.J. Mills, P. Moen, B. Wipfli et al., "Return on Investment of a Work–Family Intervention: Evidence From the Work, Family, and Health Network," *Journal of Occupational and Environmental Medicine*, *57*(9) (2015): 943–51.

23. L.M. de Menezes and C. Kelliher, "Flexible Working and Performance: A Systematic Review of the Evidence for a Business Case," *International Journal of Management Reviews*, 13 (2011): 452–74. doi: 10.1111/j.1468-2370.2011.00301.x.

24. T.D. Allen, R.C. Johnson, K.M. Kiburz, and K.M. Shockley, "Work–Family Conflict and Flexible Work Arrangements: Deconstructing Flexibility," *Personnel Psychology*, *66*(2) (2013): 345–76; A.D. Masuda, S.A. Poelmans, T.D. Allen, P.E. Spector, L.M. Lapierre, C.L.Cooper, et al. "Flexible Work Arrangements Availability and Their Relationship with Work-to-Family Conflict, Job Satisfaction, and Turnover Intentions: A Comparison of Three Country Clusters," *Applied Psychology*, *61*(1) (2012): 1–29; T. Kim and L.B. Mullins, "How Does Supervisor Support and Diversity Management Affect Employee Participation in Work/Family Policies," *Review of Public Personnel Administration 36*(1) (2016): 80–105.

25. R.J. Thompson, S.C. Payne, and A.B. Taylor, "Applicant Attraction to Flexible Work Arrangements: Separating the Influence of Flextime and Flexplace," *Journal of Occupational and Organizational Psychology*, *88* (2015): 726–49, doi: 10.1111/joop.12095.

26. V.L. Brescoll, J. Glass, and A. Sedlovskaya, "Ask and Ye Shall Receive? The Dynamics of Employer-Provided Flexible Work Options and the Need for Public Policy. Journal of Social Issues," 69 (2013): 367–388. doi: 10.1111/josi.12019.

27. Christin L. Munsch, Cecilia L. Ridgeway, and Joan C. Williams, "Pluralistic Ignorance and the Flexibility Bias: Understanding and Mitigating Flextime and Flexplace Bias at Work," *Work and Occupations* vol. 41(1) (2014): 40–46; Christin L. Munsch, "Flexible Work, Flexible Penalties: The Effect of Gender, Child Care, and Type of Request on the Flexibility Bias," *Social Forces* (2016): 122.

28. M. Blair-Loy and A.S. Wharton, "Employees' Use of Work–life Policies and the Workplace Social Context," *Social Forces* 80 (2002): 813–45.

29. R.Z. Goetzel, D. Shechter, R.J. Ozminkowski, P.F. Marmet, M.J. Tabrizi, and E.C. Roemer, "Promising Practices in Employer Health and Productivity Management Efforts: Findings from a Benchmarking Study," *Journal of Occupational and Environmental Medicine*, *49*(2) (2007): 111–30; and S. Sullivan, "Making the Business Case for Health and Productivity Management," *Journal of Occupational and Environmental Medicine*, *46*(6) (2004): S56–61.

30. C.L. Cooper, P. Dewe, and M. O'Driscoll, "Employee Assistance Programs," in J.C. Quick and L.E. Tetrick, eds., *Handbook of Occupational Health Psychology*, 2nd ed. (Washington: APA, 2011), 357–72.

31. P.R. Popple, "Social Work in Business and Industry," *Social Services Review* 6 (1981): 257–69.

32. M.T. Matteson and J.M. Ivancevich, "Health Promotion at Work," in C.L. Cooper and I.T. Robertson, eds., *International Review of Industrial and Organizational Psychology, 1988* (Chichester: Wiley, 1988), 279–306.

33. C.L. Cooper, P. Dewe, and M. O'Driscoll, "Employee Assistance Programs," in J.C. Quick and L.E. Tetrick, eds., *Handbook of Occupational Health Psychology,* 2nd ed. (Washington: APA, 2011), 357–72.

34. Practice Guidelines of the Canadian Employee Assistance Program Association. Found at http://www.ceapaonline.com/practiceguidelines.htm (accessed July 6, 2016).

35. K.M. Richardson and H.R. Rothstein, "Effects of Occupational Stress Management Intervention Programs: A Meta-Analysis," *Journal of Occupational Health Psychology, 13*(1) (2008): 69–93.

36. R.E. Quillian-Wolever and M.E. Wolever, "Stress Management at Work," in J.C. Quick and L.E. Tetrick, eds., *Handbook of Occupational Health Psychology* (Washington: APA, 2003), 355–75.

37. R. Manocha, D. Black, J. Sarris, and C. Stough, "A Randomized, Controlled Trial of Meditation for Work Stress, Anxiety and Depressed Mood in Full-Time Workers," *Evidence-based Complementary and Alternative Medicine,* vol. 2011. doi:10.1155/2011/960583.

38. Richardson and Rothstien, "Effects of Occupational Stress Management Training Intervention Programs."

39. U.R. Hülsheger, H.J. Alberts, A. Feinholdt, and J.W. Lang, "Benefits of Mindfulness at Work: The Role of Mindfulness in Emotion Regulation, Emotional Exhaustion, and Job Satisfaction," *Journal of Applied Psychology, 98* (2) (2013): 310–25; J. Kabat-Zinn, "Mindfulness-based Interventions in Context: Past, Present, and Future," *Clinical Psychology: Science and Practice, 10*(2) (2013): 144–56; P. Collard and J. Walsh, "Sensory Awareness Mindfulness Training in Coaching: Accepting Life's Challenges," *Journal of Rational-Emotive & Cognitive-Behavior Therapy, 26*(1) (2008): 30–37.

40. P. Collard and J. Walsh, "Sensory Awareness Mindfulness Training in Coaching: Accepting Life's Challenges"; E. Dane, and B.J. Brummel, "Examining Workplace Mindfulness and Its Relations to Job Performance and Turnover Intention," *Human Relations (67)* (2014): 105–28, doi. 10.1177/0018926713487753; U.R. Hülsheger, H.J. Alberts, A. Feinholdt and J.W. Lang, "Benefits of Mindfulness at Work: The Role of Mindfulness in Emotion Regulation, Emotional Exhaustion, and Job Satisfaction," *Journal of Applied Psychology, 98*(2) (2013): 310–25; J. Kabat-Zinn, "Mindfulness-based Interventions in Context: Past, Present, and Future," *Clinical Psychology: Science and Practice, 10*(2) (2003): 144–56; M. Virgili, "Mindfulness-based Interventions Reduce Psychological Distress in Working Adults: A Meta-Analysis of Intervention Studies," *Mindfulness, 6*(2) (2015): 326–37.

41. D.T. Kenny and C. Cooper, "Introduction: Occupational Stress and Its Management," *International Journal of Stress Management* 10 (2003): 275–79.

42. Richardson and Rothstien, "Effects of Occupational Stress Management Training Intervention Programs"; Kamaldeep S. Bhui, Sokratis Dinos, Stephen A. Stansfeld, and Peter D. White, "A Synthesis of the Evidence for Managing Stress at Work: A Review of the Reviews Reporting on Anxiety, Depression,

and Absenteeism," *Journal of Environmental and Public Health*, vol. 2012. doi:10.1155/2012/515874.

43. J.A. Thomason and S.B. Pond, "Effects of Instruction on Stress Management Skills and Self-Management Skills Among Blue-Collar Employees," in L.R. Murphy, J.J. Hurrell, Jr., L. Sauter, and G.P. Keita, eds., *Job Stress Interventions* (Washington: APA, 1995), 7–20.

44. Towers Watson, "Pathway to Health and Productivity: 2011/2012 Staying@work™ Survey Report, North America."

45. S.F. Weng, S. Ali, and J. Leonardi-Bee, "Smoking and Absence from Work: Systematic Review and Meta-Analysis of Occupational Studies," *Addiction* 108 (2013): 307–19. doi: 10.1111/add.12015.

46. Conference Board of Canada, "Workplaces Can Cut the Number of Smokers Sharply with Smoking Cessation Programs" (October 29, 2013). Found at: http://www.conferenceboard.ca/press/newsrelease/13-10-29/up_in_smoke _smokers_cost_their_employers_more_than_4_000_each_per_year.aspx FE (accessed July 6, 2016).

47. H. Moshammer and M. Neuberger, "Long-Term Success of Short Smoking Cessation Seminars Supported by Occupational Health Care," *Addictive Behaviors* 32 (2007): 1486–93; I. Nerín, A. Crucelaegui, A. Más, J.A. Villalba, D. Guillén, and A. Gracia, "Results of a Comprehensive Workplace Program for the Prevention and Treatment of Smoking Addiction," *Archivos de Bronconeumologia* 41 (2005): 197–201.

48. K. Cahill and T. Lancaster, "Workplace Interventions for Smoking Cessation," *Cochrane Database of Systematic Reviews* 2014, Issue 2, Art. No.: CD003440. doi: 10.1002/14651858.CD003440.pub4.

49. D. Stolz, A. Scherr, B. Seiffert, M. Kuster, A. Meyer, K. Fagerström, and M. Tamm, "Predictors of Success for Smoking Cessation at the Workplace: A Longitudinal Study," *Respiration* 2014 (87):18–25.

50. J. Goldgruber and D. Ahrens, "Effectiveness of Workplace Health Promotion and Primary Prevention Interventions: A Review," *Journal of Public Health* 18 (2010): 75–88.

51. S.B. Bacharach, P.A. Bamberger, and M. Biron, "Alcohol Consumption and Workplace Absenteeism: The Moderating Effect of Social Support," *Journal of Applied Psychology* 95 (2010): 334–48; S.B. Bacharach, P.A. Bamberger, and V.M. McKinney, "Harassing Under the Influence: The Prevalence of Male Heavy Drinking, the Embeddedness of Permissive Workplace Drinking Norms, and the Gender Harassment of Female Coworkers," *Journal of Occupational Health Psychology* 12 (2007): 232–50.

52. C.S. Carpenter, "Workplace Drug Testing and Worker Drug Use," *Health Services Research* 42 (2007): 795–810; M.T. French, M.C. Roebuck, and P.K. Alexandre, "To Test or Not to Test: Do Workplace Drug Testing Programs Discourage Employee Drug Use?" *Social Science Research* 33 (2004): 45–63.

53. P.H. Marques, V. Jesus, S.A. Olea, V. Vairinhos, and C. Jacinto, "The Effect of Alcohol and Drug Testing at the Workplace on Individual's Occupational Accident Risk," *Safety Science, 68* (2014): 108–20; and K. Pidd and A.M. Roche, "How Effective Is Drug Testing as a Workplace Safety Strategy? A Systematic Review of the Evidence," *Accident Analysis & Prevention, 71* (2014): 154–65.

54. D.R. Comer, "A Case Against Workplace Drug Testing," *Organization Science* 5 (1994): 259–67; H.M. Trice and P.D. Steele, "Impairment Testing: Issues and Convergence with Employee Assistance Programs," *Journal of Drug Issues* 25 (1995): 471–503.

55. Canadian Human Rights Commission, "Canadian Human Rights Commission's Policy on Alcohol and Drug Testing" (2009). Found at http://www.chrc-ccdp.gc .ca/sites/default/files/padt_pdda_eng.pdf (accessed April 12, 2016).

56. R. Arena, M. Guazzi, P.D. Briggs, L.P. Cahalin, J. Myers, L.A. Kaminsky et al, "Promoting Health and Wellness in the Workplace: A Unique Opportunity to Establish Primary and Extended Secondary Cardiovascular Risk Reduction Programs," *Mayo Clinic Proceedings*, Vol. 88, No. 6 (June 2013): 605–17.

57. N.R. Campbell, F.A. McAlister, H. Quan, and H.O.R.T. Force, "Monitoring and Evaluating Efforts to Control Hypertension in Canada: Why, How, and What It Tells Us Needs to Be Done about Current Care Gaps," *Canadian Journal of Cardiology*, 29(5) (2013): 564–70.

58. Francesca Gany, Sehrish Bari, Pavan Gill, Rebecca Loeb, and Jennifer Leng, "Step On It! Impact of a Workplace New York City Taxi Driver Health Intervention to Increase Necessary Health Care Access," *American Journal of Public Health*, vol. 105, no. 4 (April 2015): 786–92. doi: 10.2105/ AJPH.2014.302122.

59. A. Carnie, J. Lin, B. Aicher, B. Leon, A.B. Courville, N.G. Sebring et al. "Randomized Trial of Nutrition Education Added to Internet-based Information and Exercise at the Work Place for Weight Loss in a Racially Diverse Population of Overweight Women," *Nutrition & Diabetes* 3(12) (2013): e98.; and S. Mache, S. Jensen, R. Jahn, M., Steudtner, E. Ochsmann, and G. Preuß, "Worksite Health Program Promoting Changes in Eating Behavior and Health Attitudes," *Health Promotion Practice* (2015). doi: 1524839915596310.

60. K.M. Carpenter, J.C. Lovejoy, J.M. Lange, J.E. Hapgood, and S.M. Zbikowski, "Outcomes and Utilization of a Low Intensity Workplace Weight Loss Program," *Journal of Obesity*, 201 (2014); J. Cawley and J.A. Price "A Case Study of a Workplace Wellness Program that Offers Financial Incentives for Weight Loss," *Journal of Health Economics* 32(5) (2013): 794–803; T. Kyle, "How Healthy Are Employer Wellness Programs? *Conduit* (2015). Found at: http://www.obesitynetwork.ca/files/CONDUIT-Spring2015-Whole_Book -F.pdf (accessed April 14, 2015); and M.S. Patel, D.A. Asch, A.B. Troxel, M. Fletcher, R. Osman-Koss, J. Brady et al, "Premium-based Financial Incentives Did Not Promote Workplace Weight Loss in a 2013–15 Study," *Health Affairs*, 35(1) (2016): 71–79.

61. L.M. Anderson, T.A. Quinn, K. Glanz, G. Ramirez, L.C. Kahwati, D.B. Johnson, et al, "The Effectiveness of Worksite Nutrition and Physical Activity Interventions for Controlling Employee Overweight and Obesity: A Systematic Review," *American Journal of Preventive Medicine*, 37(4)(2009): 340–57; D.L. Gebhardt and C.E. Crump, "Employee Fitness and Wellness Programs in the Workplace," *American Psychologist*, 45(2): 262.

62. S.G. Aldana, R.M. Merrill, K. Price, A. Hardy, and R. Hager, "Financial Impact of a Comprehensive Multisite Workplace Health Promotion Program," *Preventive Medicine* 40 (2005): 131–37; S.H. Malik, H. Blake, and L.S. Suggs, "A Systematic Review of Workplace Health Promotion Interventions for

Increasing Physical Activity," *British Journal of Health Psychology*, *19*(1) (2014): 149–80; N. Taylor, M. Conner, and R. Lawton, "The Impact of Theory on the Effectiveness of Worksite Physical Activity Interventions: A Meta-Analysis and Meta-Regression," *Health Psychology Review*, *6*(1) (2012): 33–73.

63. A.D. Hutchinson, and C. Wilson, "Improving Nutrition and Physical Activity in the Workplace: A Meta-Analysis of Intervention Studies," *Health Promotion International*, *27*(2) (2012): 238–49; N. Taylor, M. Conner, and R. Lawton, "The Impact of Theory on the Effectiveness of Worksite Physical Activity Interventions: A Meta-Analysis and Meta-Regression," *Health Psychology Review*, *6*(1) (2012): 33–73; K.I. Proper, V.H. Hildebrandt, A.J. Van der Beek, J.W.R. Twisk, and W. Van Mechelen, "Effect of Individual Counseling on Physical Activity Fitness and Health: A Randomized Controlled Trial in a Workplace Setting," *American Journal of Preventive Medicine* 24 (2003): 218–26.

64. R.Z. Goetzel, D. Shechter, R.J. Ozminkowski, P.F. Marmet, M.J. Tabrizi, and E.C. Roemer, "Promising Practices in Employer Health and Productivity Management Efforts: Findings from a Benchmarking Study," *Journal of Occupational and Environmental Medicine*, *49*(2) (2007): 111–30.

65. N. Pronk, "Best Practice Design Principles of Worksite Health and Wellness Programs," *ACSM's Health & Fitness Journal*, *18*(1) (2014): 42–46; N. Freundlich, "Making Workplace Health Promotion (Wellness) Programs "Work" (February 11, 2015). Johns Hopkins Bloomberg School of Public Health. Institute for Health and Productivity Studies. Found at: http://www .jhsph.edu/research/centers-and-institutes/institute-for-health-and-productivity -studies/ihps-blog/making-workplace-health-promotion-wellness-programs -work (accessed July 6).

66. A. Day and T. Helson, *Workplace Health Promotion–The Wiley Blackwell Handbook of the Psychology of Occupational Safety and Workplace Health*, S. Clarke, T.M. Probst, F. Guldenmund, and J. Passmore, eds. (Chichester: Sussex: Wiley, 2016), 377–413.

67. S.G. Aldana, R.M. Merrill, K. Price, A. Hardy, and R. Hager, "Financial Impact of a Comprehensive Multisite Workplace Health Promotion Program," *Preventive Medicine* 40 (2005): 131–37.

68. Sun Life-Ivey Canadian Wellness Return on Investment Study. "Overview of Phase 2 Results: Making the Case for Wellness Programs" (December 14, 2015). Found at: http://www.ivey.uwo.ca/news/news-ivey/2015/12/making -the-case-for-wellness-programs/ (accessed July 6, 2016).

69. D. Lerner, A.M. Rodday, J.T. Cohen, and W.H. Rogers, "A Systematic Review of the Evidence Concerning the Economic Impact of Employee-focused Health Promotion and Wellness Programs," *Journal of Occupational and Environmental Medicine*, *55*(2) (2013): 209–22.

70. S. Baxter, K. Sanderson, A.J. Venn, C.L. Blizzard, and A.J. Palmer, "The Relationship Between Return on Investment and Quality of Study Methodology in Workplace Health Promotion Programs," *American Journal of Health Promotion*, *28*(6) (2014): 347–63.

GLOSSARY

accident proneness the notion that some individuals are inherently more likely than others to be involved in accidents, as a result of individual characteristics, 7

act a federal, provincial, or territorial law that constitutes the basic regulatory mechanism for occupational health and safety, 31

active transactional leadership a form of leadership based on the foundation that leaders actively communicate to followers the tasks that are required to meet expectations, 256

administrative control management involvement, training of employees, rotation of employees, environmental sampling, and medical surveillance to protect individuals, 95

aerosols airborne respirable contaminants, such as liquid droplets or solid particulate, dispersed in air, that are of a fine enough particle size (0.01 to 100 micrometres) to remain suspended for a time, 138

agents any substances—chemical, biological, or physical—to which a human may be exposed at work or at home, 135

aggression behaviour by an individual or individuals within or outside an organization that is intended to physically or psychologically harm a worker or workers and that occurs in a work-related context, 190

alveoli tiny air sacs, 141

ambient all-encompassing condition associated with a given environment, being usually a composite of inputs from sources all around us, 111

amotivation complete lack of motivation, 252

assault cycle a model suggesting that violence occurs only after a period of escalation, 196

assumption of risk the belief that a worker accepted the risks of employment when he or she accepted a job, 7

attenuated reduction of noise at one location compared to another farther from the source, 117

autonomous motivation self-directed motivation reflecting an individual's free will, 252

behavioural involvement the amount of time a person spends in a particular role, 178

biohazards hazards created by exposure to infectious microorganisms, proteins, or nucleic acids, 134

boiling point temperature at which the vapour pressure of a liquid equals atmospheric pressure, 143

brown lung a disease of the lungs caused by excessive inhalation of dust; the disease is in the pneumoconiosis family and often afflicts textile workers, 7

buffer a variable that protects people from the negative effects of stress, 167

bullying aggressive, nonphysical behaviours perpetrated by organizational members over a prolonged period of time, 190

chain of infection the process and conditions by which biological agents are spread from one host to another, 136

chemical agent hazards created by exposure to chemicals, 134

close call a series of events that could have led to a safety incident but did not, 234

cognitive failure a mistake or failure in the performance of an action that an individual is normally capable of performing, 306

collective liability where all employers in a class or other rate group are liable for the costs of any or all accidents and occupational diseases that occur in the operations of those employers, 52

compressed workweek flexible work arrangement in which employees work full-time hours in fewer days per week, 348

conduction heat transfer occurring when two surfaces are in contact, 123

confined space any space that is enclosed or partially enclosed and restricts entrance and exit by the location and size, and is potentially deficient in oxygen or could contain toxic gases, 100

consequences the results or severity of the injury, 84

constructor in health and safety legislation, a person or company that oversees the construction of a project and that is ultimately responsible for the health and safety of all workers, 35

contingent reward a form of active transactional leadership in which leaders reward employees who meet their communicated expectations, 256

controlled motivation motivation based in response to pressure, 252

convection heat transfer occurring when one surface adds heat to the surroundings, 123

critical incident stress debriefing (CISD) a post-trauma intervention focused on providing victims with an opportunity to discuss their experiences and reactions to a traumatic event, 286

decalcification loss of lime salts (calcium) in the bones, 120

dermatitis the inflammation of the skin from any cause, 143

disability management proactive employer practices with the goals of preventing or reducing workplace disability, intervening early in the face of risk or injury, and providing coordinated management and rehabilitation functions to promote workers' recovery and safe and timely return to work, 325

distributive justice the perceived fairness of outcomes, 173

domino theory the theory that every incident results from a series of events, 303

due diligence an expected standard of conduct that requires employers to take every reasonable precaution to ensure safety, 11

duty to accommodate legislated responsibility of employers to accommodate workers who are attempting to return to work following an injury or illness via changes in job tasks and/or the work environment to enable workers with a temporary or permanent disability to perform work productively, 322

early warning change a deterioration of hearing in the upper frequency—the earliest detectable sign of noise-induced hearing loss, 114

emergency a sudden, generally unexpected occurrence or set of circumstances demanding immediate action, 275

emotional abuse another term for bullying, 190

employee and family assistance programs (EFAPs) programs designed to help employees and members of their families with problems that may interfere with worker productivity, including alcohol and other drug abuse, emotional or behavioural problems among family members, and financial or legal problems, 354

engineering control modification of work processes, equipment, and materials to reduce exposure to hazards, 91

extrinsic motivation motivation rooted in instrumental reasons for acting, 252

family-to-work conflict a form of work–family conflict in which family demands interfere with the fulfillment of work responsibilities, 177

fault tree an illustration of things that can go wrong, 82

fire a chemical process in which fuel, oxygen, and heat are combined, 281

flexible work arrangements (FWAs) family-friendly policies that involve modifications to the traditional work schedule, 348

flexplace flexible work arrangement in which an employee regularly makes use of telecommunications technology to complete work assignments away from the office, usually at home, 349

flextime flexible work arrangement that permits employees to have variable start and finish times to their workday, 349

free-burning stage the stage at which flames first appear, 282

functional ability assessment a standardized assessment of an injured or ill worker's ability to perform job tasks that is completed by a member of the health care professional, 332

gender harassment comments or actions seen as creating a hostile environment based on gender, 190

general adaptation syndrome the body's way of gearing up for fight or flight (i.e., to confront or run away from a predator), 166

general duty a primary duty directly articulated in the occupational health and safety act. The general duty provision requiring employers to take every reasonable precaution to ensure employee safety is represented in health and safety acts across Canada, 34

GHS an international standard for the classification and labelling of chemicals being adopted by countries around the world, 40

gradual work exposure a type of light-duty accommodation where job demands slowly increase until the workers are performing the full requirement of their pre-injury jobs, 330

guidelines and policies more specific rules that are not legally enforceable unless referred to in a regulation or act, 31

harassment engaging in annoying or embarrassing conduct against a worker in a workplace—conduct that is known or ought reasonably to be known to be unwelcome, 190

hazard analysis an orderly, analytical technique that examines a system for the most probable hazards having the severest consequences, for the purpose of establishing corrective or control mechanisms, 82

hazard any object, action, or condition that can be a source of potential adverse health effect, damage, or harm to people, processes, or equipment within the workplace, 78

hazard control the program or process used to establish preventative and corrective measures, 89

health promotion a combination of diagnostic, educational, and behavioural modification activities designed to support the attainment and maintenance of positive health, 354

high-reliability organizations organizations in hazardous industries that maintain a high safety record over time, 306

homeostasis the balance of heat generation, 123

human factor when a worker causes an incident by commission, poor judgment, or omission (failing to do something), 79

hyperreflexia the condition of unusually quick reaction by the nerves to some external stimulus, 116

hypertension elevated blood pressure, 361

imminent risk the short-term risk of violence occurring in the current situation, 196

incident an event or occurrence that had or could have had a negative impact on people, property, or processes, 78

incipient stage a source of ignition and fuel come together, 282

incivility rude or discourteous behaviour, 190

injury any trauma, physical or mental, direct or indirect, acute or chronic, experienced by a human being, 85

instructional systems design (ISD) model of training a general model of the training process that incorporates needs analysis, training design and delivery, and training evaluation and that notes the interdependencies among the three major components of the training process, 221

interactional justice the perceived fairness of interpersonal treatment, 173

internal responsibility system (IRS) the system of shared responsibility for health and safety that is the basis for most Canadian OH&S legislation, 13

intrinsic motivation motivation based on one's interest and enjoyment, 252

job description the content and hierarchy specific to a particular job, 81

job sharing flexible work arrangement in which two employees share the responsibilities of a single position, 349

job specifications the requirements necessary to perform the various functions of a job (e.g., ability to lift weight, education level), 81

job splitting flexible work arrangement in which two employees divide the responsibilities of a single position, 349

job/task analysis a component of the training needs analysis process during which the jobs and specific job tasks that are in need of training are identified and studied, 225

kickback action of having a work piece suddenly thrown backward into the operator, 94

latency period the time between exposure to a cause and development of a disease, 62

light-duty work workplace accommodation where workers return to a job that is less demanding than their previous job, 330

loss of functional capacity limit of ability or dexterity depending on the seriousness of an injury, 59

lost-time injury a workplace injury that results in the employee missing time from work, 4

machine guarding protection for workers from the hazards and energies created by moving machinery, 92

management by exception (active) a form of active transactional leadership in which leaders monitor workers' actions and step in with corrective action when needed to prevent serious problems from occurring, 256

mobbing a term used mainly in Europe to refer to bullying, 190

mode of transmission the means or channel by which an agent is carried from one host to another, 136

moderator a variable that changes the relationship between two other variables, 167

necrosis death or decay of tissue, 120

needs analysis the initial stage of the training development process, intended to identify employee and organizational deficiencies that can be addressed with training and to recognize potential obstacles to the success of a training program, 222

negative affectivity a dispositional dimension reflecting persistent individual differences in the experience of negative emotion, 167

net earnings salary after mandatory deductions (income tax, Canada pension, and employment insurance), 57

normal incidents the theory that incidents are expected outcomes of interactive complexities, 306

occupational health and safety (OH&S) the identification, evaluation, and control of hazards associated with the work environment, 5

occupational health and safety management system (OHSMS) reflect an interactive collection of strategic organizational approaches and programs focused on identifying, achieving, and maintaining desired occupational health and safety targets, 257

occupational illness any abnormal condition or disorder caused by exposure to environmental factors associated with employment, 6

occupational injury any cut, fracture, sprain, or amputation resulting from a workplace accident, 6

organizational analysis an analysis of the entire organization designed to examine its resources, strategy, and environment in order to assess the organization's support for training, 222

overexertion injuries injuries resulting from excessive physical effort, repetitive motions, and, possibly, awkward working positions, 86

overt traumatic injuries injuries resulting from coming into contact with an energy source, 85

person analysis a component of the training needs analysis process during which individual employees' behaviour is studied to identify gaps in performance, 225

physical agents sources of energy that may cause injury or disease, 111

physical demands analysis a standardized evaluation of the physical and cognitive demands of a job completed by a person familiar with the job, 331

physical rehabilitation the steps taken to restore, fully or partially, the worker's physical function, 61

point-of-contact control managing hazards at the point of contact with the worker, 89

portal of entry the path by which a biohazardous agent gains access to a new host, 136

portal of exit the path by which a biohazardous agent leaves its host, 136

positive tree shows, graphically, how a job should be done, 82

postcontact control manages the escalation of an incident and ensures further harm or damage does not occur, 89

precontact control addressing issues before an incident or accident occurs, 89

prescribed duty under OH&S legislation, a duty to be undertaken because of health and safety regulation, 34

preventive maintenance the orderly, continuous, and scheduled protection and repair of equipment and buildings, 99

preventive stress management an approach to managing stress in the workplace that emphasizes that the health of an organization and its employees are interdependent; encourages the reduction of stressors in the workplace as well as the recognition and management of occupational stress and strain, 170

primary interventions stress interventions that involve the reduction or removal of actual stressors, 171

probability the chance or likelihood that an event will occur and will result in harm or loss, 83

procedural justice the perceived fairness of decision-making processes, 173

psychological involvement the degree to which a person identifies with a particular role and sees the role as a central component of his or her self-concept, 178

psychologically healthy and safe workplace a workplace that promotes workers' psychological well-being and actively works to prevent harm to workers' psychological health including in negligent, reckless, or intentional ways, 162

psychosocial model of health approach to the study of health that highlights the importance of both the social environment and psychological factors, 162

RAC program a hazard recognition, assessment, and control program; a key element in most health and safety programs, 292

radiation heat transfer occurring when energy is transmitted by electromagnetic waves, 123

reactive materials cause a violent, explosive reaction when they comes in contact with another material, such as acetylene with water, or bleach with chlorinated cleaner, 283

re-enactment a simulation designed to recreate the circumstances leading up to an incident, 300

regulations explain how the general intent of the act will be applied in specific circumstances, 31

reservoir the home or environment where the biological agent grows and multiplies, 136

resonance the effect that occurs when an object reacts strongly to some particular frequency, 121

return-to-work coordinator person who is responsible for return-to-work case management, 328

return-to-work plan a collaboratively developed individualized plan that identifies an injured or ill worker's return-to-work goals, 329

risk factor a variable that increases the negative effects of stress, 167

risk perception an individual's interpretation of the potential for harm based on values, beliefs, and experience with a hazard, 78

risk the probability or the extent to which a hazard is likely to cause harm to people, processes, or equipment, 78

safety behaviours behaviours leading to safe performance of a particular job, 245

safety climate employees' shared perceptions of the importance of safety in the workplace, 224

safety compliance the extent to which employees follow safety rules and procedures, 246

safety leadership organizational leadership that is actively focused on and promotes occupational health and safety, 255

safety motivation an individual's willingness to exert effort to enact safety behaviour and the valence associated with those behaviours, 247

safety participation the extent to which employees go beyond compliance and engage proactively and voluntarily to actively improve safety, 246

safety sampling a systematic survey procedure undertaken by safety personnel who record their observations of unsafe practices on a sampling document, 81

secondary interventions stress intervention techniques that focus on minimizing negative consequences once a person is feeling stress, 172

segmental vibration vibrations that affect only parts of the body, 120

sexual coercion the attempt to extort sexual cooperation; can take the form of subtle or explicit job-related threats, 190

sexual harassment intentional, persistent, and unwelcome sexual conduct or remarks that occur despite resistance from the victim, 190

smouldering stage fuel, oxygen, and heat are present and are causing the heat to rise through limited chain reaction, 282

social rehabilitation the psychological and practical services that help workers with severe disabilities cope with daily life, 61

standards and codes design-related guides established by agencies such as the CSA or the ILO, 31

strain the result of stress; it is classified into four categories of reactions: psychological, physical, behavioural, and organizational, 168

stress an individual's internal response to, or evaluation of, stressors; often characterized by negative feelings of arousal, 166

stressor an objectively verifiable event that occurs outside the individual that has the potential to cause stress, 163

supported and sheltered work modified work arrangements designed to help those with permanent disabilities who have either not been successful in competitive work environments or require substantial support to return to work, 331

surfactant layer layer of liquids in the digestive tract and elsewhere (e.g., the cardiovascular system) that modify or reduce the surface tension within the conductors—intestine, blood vessels—to allow material—blood, food, stools, and so on—to move easily, 142

susceptible host an individual or animal that becomes infected with a biohazardous agent, 137

systems approach an approach to disability management that emphasizes the work and organizational context, 325

target organs tissues or organs that are most affected by exposure to a particular substance, 142

tertiary interventions stress intervention techniques that are used to help those individuals who have not been able to manage workplace stress effectively and who are now experiencing symptoms of strain, 173

three Es a traditional approach to occupational health and safety that emphasized engineering, education, and enforcement, 20

toxicity ability to cause injury to human biological tissue, 137

train the trainer programs designed to offer subject matter experts in various content areas skills in program delivery and communication, 228

training evaluation a component of the ISD training model designed to assess the value added for individuals and organizations following the implementation of a training program, 232

training objectives statements regarding the knowledge, skills, and behavioural changes that trainees should acquire in the training program, 227

transformational leadership highly effective approach to leadership that emphasizes employee well-being and is characterized by idealized influence, inspirational motivation, intellectual stimulation, and individualized consideration, 256

turbinates spiral or spongy sections of the respiratory system that have a centrifugal effect to help remove aerosols, 140

Type A behaviour action–emotion complex that can be observed in any person who is aggressively involved in a chronic, incessant struggle to achieve increasingly more in increasingly less time, 167

Type I violence violence committed by someone with no legitimate relationship to the organization, often while committing another criminal act, 192

Type II violence violence committed by clients or customers of the organization, 192

Type III violence violence committed by coworkers (e.g., other employees of the organization), 192

Type IV violence violence committed by the spouse or partner of the victim, 193

uncontrolled fire stage fire is out of control and major property damage is under way, 282

undue hardship aspect of human rights legislation that means that employers must accommodate the needs of a disabled worker unless the necessary modifications would lead to health and safety difficulties or present unsustainable economic or efficiency costs, 322

unsafe act a deviation from standard job procedures or practices that increases a worker's exposure to a hazard, 78

unwanted sexual attention persistent and unwelcome sexual comments or attention, 190

vasoconstriction the process of causing a constriction of the blood vessels, 116

violence an actual physical assault or threat of an assault, 190

vocational rehabilitation the steps undertaken by WCBs to help injured workers return to their place of employment or find similar or suitable work elsewhere, 61

walkthrough inspection of the incident scene to get a picture of the total environment, 298

walk-through survey a survey in which a safety professional walks through a worksite and notes hazards, 81

WHMIS Workplace Hazardous Materials Information System; a legislated training program in the handling of potentially hazardous chemicals in the workplace that ensures Canadian workers recognize hazardous materials and are knowledgeable in emergency procedures following a chemical spill, 230

whole-body vibration vibrations that affect the whole body as a unit, 120

work trials a form of accommodation where workers return to work on a trial basis, 331

work–family conflict a type of inter-role conflict in which the role pressures experienced in the work and family domains are incompatible, 348

workplace accommodation modifications to the arrangement of work that promote early and safe return to work for injured, ill, or disabled workers, 329

work-to-family conflict a form of work–family conflict in which work demands interfere with the fulfillment of family responsibilities, 177

INDEX

Note: Following a page number, *f* denotes a figure and a *t* denotes a table.

A

A1 Manufacturing, 240
ABC model, 253
accident investigation. *See* incident investigation
accident proneness, 7, 249
act, 31, 42, 149, 207, 261
active transactional leadership, 256, 257
activity sampling, 81
acute stressors, 163, 285
administrative control, 95, 114, 122, 125, 128, 149, 155. *See also* engineering control; hazard control
    housekeeping, 97–98
    HR practitioner, 95–96
    preventive maintenance, 99–102
    safety awareness, 96–97
administrative interventions, 245
aerosols, 138, 144, 150
agency, 301, 302
agents, 135, 154, 155, 301
aggression, 190. *See also* workplace aggression
    policy, 211
alcoholism, 354–355
alcohol testing programs, 360–361
aldehydes, 147*t*
aliphatic hydrocarbons, 147*t*
alkalines, 146
alveolar ducts, 141
alveoli, 141, 142
ambient, 111
American Conference of Governmental Industrial Hygienists (ACGIH), 31
amotivation, 252
ArcelorMittal Dofasco Inc., 363
Archives of Internal Medicine, 345
aromatic hydrocarbons, 147*t*

asphyxiants, 144
assault cycle, 196, 197
assessments, 64
    calculating injury frequency and severity rates, 65
    experience rating, 65–67
    illustrative industry rates, 64
Association of Workers' Compensation Boards of Canada (AWCBC), 17
assumption of risk, 7
ATB Financial, 350
attention, 231
attenuation, 117
auditing, 104
auto-ignition temperature, 146
autonomous motivation, 252, 253
awkward working positions, 89

B

bakers' asthma, 139
Berdahl, Jennifer, 208
barrier guards, 93–94
barriers to return to work, 334–336
behavioural interventions, 245
behavioural involvement, 178
behavioural strain, 169
behaviour-based safety program. *See also* safety behaviours
    elements, 249
    risky side, 249–250
behaviourist approach, 230–231
behaviour modification approaches, 248
behaviour sampling, 81
Bill C-45, 41, 239
billboards, 96
biohazards, 134, 147, 148, 154, 157
biological agents, 135*t*. *See also* chemical agents
    administrative controls, 149
    chain of infection, 136*f*
    control of exposures, 147
    Ebola outbreak, 134

    engineering controls, 147–148*t*
    needlestick injuries, 154
    personal hygiene practices, 156
    physical hazards, 134–135
    portal of entry, 136–137
    PPE, 155
    unexpected gas, 158
    WHMIS, 149–154
    work practices and procedures, 154–155
biological terrorism, 289
boiling point, 138, 143
bona fide occupational requirement, 361
bow-tie analysis, 305*f*
British Columbia (BC), 54
brown lung, 7
buffers, 167, 168
bullying, 164, 189, 190, 204–205

C

CAD-7, 66
CAL/OSHA framework, 193–194
Canada's compensation system, 60
Canada's Healthy Workplace Month (CHWM), 9
Canadian Centre for Occupational Health and Safety (CCOHS), 14, 84, 87
    CCOHS Young Workers Zone, 97
Canadian data, 191–192
Canadian legislation and OH&S programs, developments in, 8
Canadian Registered Safety Professional (CRSP®), 19
Canadian Standards Association (CSA), 31
Canadian standards for safety, 31
cancer
    carcinogens, 145
    firefighters and, 158
    occupational, 84, 140
carcinogens, 145
cardiopulmonary resuscitation course (CPR course), 285

Carpal tunnel syndrome, 174

catastrophic stressors, 163, 274

caught in, under, or between machinery (CIUB machinery), 86

CCINFOWEB online information service, 14

Center for Disease Control (CDC), 134

central nervous system (CNS), 144

Certificate of Recognition (COR), 56

chain of infection, 136, 157

chemical agents, 134, 137, 147–148, 155. *See also* biological agents
    administrative controls, 149
    bakers' asthma, 139
    contaminants types, 138
    control of exposures, 147
    engineering controls, 147–148*t*
    needlestick injuries, 154
    personal hygiene practices, 156
    physical state, 137–138
    PPE, 155
    WHMIS, 149–154
    work practices and procedures, 154–155
    workplace health hazard, 138–139

chemical asphyxiants, 144

chemical hazards, 5

chemical spills, 284

chlorinated solvents, 142

chromic acid (H_2CrO_4), 146

chronic stressor, 163

civility, respect, and engagement process (CREW process), 206

classic heat stroke, 125

close call, 78, 234, 235, 294
    incident, 78

closed circuit televisions, 198

cognitive-behavioural skills training, 356

cognitive failures, 306

cognitive interviewing, 299

cold-related injuries and illnesses, 126–127

collective liability, 52, 64

community-focused safety groups, 17

compliance with safety standards, 266

compressed workweek, 348–349

conduction, 123

conductive hearing loss, 115

confined space, 96, 100, 101, 102*f*

confined-space entry, 100–102*f*

consequences, 60, 78, 82, 84, 161, 163, 248, 253, 274, 356, 365

constructor, 35

contact control *See also* hazard control; postcontact control; precontact control
    fire plan, 281
    fire prevention and suppression, 281–284
    first aid and medical attention, 284–285
    irritant, 144
    legislated first aid requirements, 285

contaminants types, 138

contingent reward, 256

contractor duties, 35

controlled motivation, 252

convection, 123

coronary heart disease (CHD), 169

corporate liability for OH&S under Criminal Code, 41–42

corporate social responsibility (CSR), 43

cost motivation, 21–22

Criminal Code, corporate liability for OH&S under, 41–42

critical incident stress debriefing (CISD), 286

CSA-Z1003-13 national standard, 9, 346

cyber-aggression, 205

cyber-bullying, 205

D

daily stressors, 163

daycare benefits, 351, 351*f*

decalcification, 120

decibels (db), 115

defatting process, 142

dermatitis, 84, 135, 137, 142, 143

digital safety, 223

dimethyl sulphoxide, 142

direct costs of injury, 10

disability management, 319, 324
    assessing programs, 325–326
    barriers to return to work, 334–336
    early intervention, 327
    education, 327
    high-profile style, 320–321

    integrated claims management and monitoring systems, 328–329
    memory impairment in restaurant, 338
    motives, 321–324
    people-focused climate, 326
    practices, 326
    prevention focus, 326–327
    return-to-work case management, 327–328
    return-to-work planning, 329–332
    stakeholders, 332–334
    WidgIT, 339

disaster, 16
    natural, 286
    rail, 2

distributive justice, 173

domino theory, 303
    Heinrich's domino model, 304*f*

drug testing programs, 360–361

due diligence, 11–12, 117, 162, 221

duties
    of contractors, 35
    of employees, 33
    of employers, 33, 34, 74
    for stakeholders, 33
    of supervisors, 35
    of workers, 35–36

duty to accommodate, 322–324

E

early warning change, 114

earnings loss, 58

Ebola Virus Disease (EVD), 134

economic consideration, 10–11

educating, 20

education, 327

elder care benefits, 351
    electromagnetic radiation, 112
    eye absorption properties for, 113*f*

emergency, 277, 278, 285

emergency measures organizations (EMOs), 274, 277

emergency operations centres (EOCs), 280

emergency planning, 272, 277
    biological terrorism, 289
    contact, 281–285
    Fort McMurray, 272

emergency planning (*continued*)

    getting back to normal, 286–287

    Norwalk outbreak at Mount Allison, 276

    postcontact, 285–286

    precontact, 277–280

    preparedness, 275

emergency response plans (ERPs), 201, 277, 279

emotional abuse, 190

employee and family assistance plans (EFAPs), 172*t*, 354–356

employee assistance programs (EAPs), 275

employees, 15

    training, 199

employers, 14–15, 64

    duties, 34, 74

enclosure guards, 93–94

enforcing, 20

engineering, 20

    interventions, 245

    solutions, 20

engineering control, 95, 113, 122, 125, 128, 148. *See also* administrative control; hazard control

    equipment design, 95

    machine guarding, 92–94

    process modification, 92

    substitution, ventilation, and isolation, 91–92

environmental factors, 80, 297

environmental legislation, 42–44

ergonomics, 17

esters, 147*t*

ethers, 147*t*

evacuation plan, 278–279

exertional heat stroke, 125

experience rating in workers' compensation, 65–67

experiential learning, 231

external regulation, 252

extremely low frequency radiation (ELF radiation), 112

extrinsic motivation, 252

eyeball resonance, 121

F

falls, 86, 97

    injuries from, 10

    preventing, 98

family care benefits, 351

family-friendly policies. *See also* health promotion programs; work–family conflict

    evaluation, 352–354

    family care benefits, 351

    FWAs, 348–349

    personal leave systems, 349–351

    using evaluation to build business case, 364–365

family-to-work conflict, 177, 178

fault tree, 82, 83*f*

federal laws, 31

feeding tools, 94

financial motives, 321–322

fire, 282

    chemical spills, 284

    classes, 283*t*

    plan, 281

    prevention and suppression, 281

    tetrahedron, 282*f*

    toxic fumes, 283

    triangle, 281*f*

firefighters and cancer, 158

first aid training, 236–237

flexible work arrangements (FWAs), 348–349, 352

flexplace, 349, 352

flextime, 349, 352, 354

Fort McMurray, 272, 287

free-burning stage, 282

Freedom Six to Six program, 175

free field effect, 117

frequency rates calculation, 65

frostnip, 126

functional ability assessment, 332

G

gender harassment, 190

general adaptation syndrome, 166

general duty, 33–35

global positioning system (GPS), 198

Global Harmonized System (GHS), 40, 135, 149

glycols, 147*t*

goal setting theory, 251

government, 13. *See also* human resources

    employees, 15

    employers, 14–15

    organized labour, 15

gradual hearing loss, 116

gradual work exposure, 330

gross domestic product (GDP), 11

guidelines and policies, 31

H

halogenated hydrocarbons, 147*t*

hand–arm vibration syndrome (HAVS), 121

hand-removal devices, 94

harassment, 189, 190, 204–205

hazard, 6, 77–78, 137

    analysis, 82

    evaluation, 277

hazard control, 77, 89–91, 104, 108, 276. *See also* administrative control; engineering control

    point-of-contact control, 90

    postcontact control, 90–91

    precontact control, 89–90

hazard recognition, 77

    administrative control, 95–102

    audits and reports, 81–82

    components, 81

    control, 77, 89–91

    danger in grocery store, 108

    engineering control, 91–95

    environment, 79–80

    equipment, 79

    follow-up, 85

    hazard analysis, 82

    hazard control, 108

    and identification, 78

    identification programs, 80

    industrial hazard assessment, 107

    materials, 80

    monitoring/auditing, 104

    people, 78–79

    PPE, 102–103

    processes, 80

    record keeping, 104

    risk assessment, 82

    source–path–human controls, 103–104

    task and job inventory, 81

    terminology, 78

    types of injuries, 85

Hazardous Products Act (HPA), 149
Hazardous Products Regulations (HPR), 149
health and safety training programs, 221
    needs analysis, 222–226
    training content, 227
    training design and delivery, 226
    training evaluation, 232–235
    training logistics, 227–232
health care organizations, 162
health promotion, 345, 354, 356, 365
health promotion programs (HPPs), 354. *See also* family-friendly policies
    EFAPs, 354–356
    stress management programs, 356–357
    stress management training effectiveness, 357–358
    WHP programs, 358–366, 369
healthy workplace movement, 9
hearing loss, 115. *See also* noise
    auditory system, 116
    noise exposure standards and hearing conservation programs, 117
hearing protection types, 131
hearing protectors, 119
heat fainting, 125
heat hyperpyrexia, 125
heat stroke, 125
heat syncope, 125
heating, ventilation, air conditioning unit (HVAC), 92
heat-related illnesses, 124–125
Heinrich's domino model, 304*f*
Hertz (Hz), 114
hexane, 145
high blood pressure. *See* hypertension
high-reliability organizations, 306
homeostasis, 123
hostile environment, 208
housekeeping, 97–98
human factor, 79
human hearing response, 115
human immunodeficiency virus (HIV), 142
human resources, 20, 33
    safety decreasing costs, 21
    safety integration in other functions, 20–21
    safety requiring legislative compliance, 21

hydrochloric acid (HCl), 146
hyperreflexia, 116
hypertension, 169, 361
hypertension screening, 361
hyperthermic, 123
hypothermia, 127
hypothermic, 123

I

identified regulation, 252
illnesses
    assessment form, 315–316*f*
    cold-related, 126–127
    heat-related, 124–125
    occupational, 6–7, 11, 285, 333
immersion foot, 126
imminent risk, 196–197
incident, 3, 54, 78, 79, 82, 234, 237, 294, 296, 303
incident investigation, 291, 308
    analysis, 302–303
    critical factors in investigative process, 293–294
    domino theory, 303–304
    environmental factors, 297
    forms, 309
    human factors, 295–296
    investigative tools, 301
    long report, 311*f*–314*f*
    numerous individuals, 297
    office incident, 308
    physician's report, 315*f*–316*f*
    psychology, 306
    rationale for incident investigation, 292–293
    reports, 301
    short report, 310*f*
    situational factors, 296–297
    steps, 295
    Swiss cheese model, 305–306
    types of information collected, 294
    witness report, 317*f*
    workplace fatality investigation, 292
incipient stage, 282
incivility, 190
increasing social support, 357

indirect costs of injury, 10
individual evaluation, 233–234
industrial hazard assessment, 107
industrial hearing protection types, 131*t*
infrared radiation (IR), 112
inhalation, 140–142, 155
inhaled irritants, 144
injury, 85
    direct costs of, 10
    indirect costs of, 10
    lost-time, 4, 10, 204, 235, 308, 320, 335
    musculoskeletal, 174–175, 326, 330
    needlestick, 154
    non-freezing, 126
    occupational, 6–7, 11, 223, 224
    overexertion, 86–89
    overt traumatic, 86
    types of, 85
    workplace, 85–86
inorganic solvents, 146
instructional systems design (ISD) model of training, 221, 222*f*
integrated claims management, 328–329
integrated regulation, 252
interactional justice, 173
internal responsibility system (IRS), 13, 33, 37
    philosophy, 36
International Labour Organization (ILO), 11, 31
International Organization for Standardization (ISO), 31
intimate partner violence, 193
intrinsic motivation, 252
introjected regulation, 252
investigative methods, 297. *See also* incident investigation
    analysis of incident, 298
    interviews, 298–299
    observation, 298
    re-enactments, 300s
investigative process, critical factors in, 293
    legal requirements, 294
    severity, 293–294
    timing, 293
investigative tools, 301
ionizing radiation, 112

irritants, 144

isolation, 91–92

J

job description, 81, 225

job sharing programs, 349, 370

job specifications, 81

job splitting, 349

job/task analysis, 225

joint health and safety committees, 36–37

K

ketones, 147*t*

kickback, 94

L

Labour Code, 208

labour legislation and standards, 33

latency period, 62

leadership

    active transactional, 256

    safety, 20, 245, 255

    transformational, 256–257

learning theory, 230–231

leave-related benefits, 351

legal consideration, 11–12

legal motives, 322–324

legislative framework

    Canadian standards for safety, 31

    corporate liability for OH&S under Criminal Code, 41–42

    environmental legislation, 42–44

    OH&S acts, 33–40

    OH&S legislation in Canada, 30

    scope of OH&S legislation, 32–33

    small fishing vessel regulations, 29

    transportation of dangerous goods, 44–45

    WHMIS, 40

    workplace tragedy, 47

    work refusal at regional hospital, 47

liability, changing perspectives on, 7

lifestyle changes, focus on, 358–362

lifestyle programming, 358

lifting activities, 87

lifting guidelines, 87

light-duty work, 325, 330

local fire department, 281

lockout procedures, 99–100

loss of functional capacity, 59

lost-time injury, 4, 10, 204, 235, 308, 320, 335

    by jurisdiction (2014), 4*f*

lower explosion limit (LEL), 145

lower flammability limit (LFL). See lower explosion limit (LEL)

M

machine guarding, 89, 92–94

macrophages, 142

maintenance hazard analysis, 99

management by exception (active), 256

management commitment to OH&S, 253

    improving safety climate, 254–255

    peer learning and support to create safety change, 254

    safety leadership, 255–257

material safety data sheets (MSDSs), 14, 40, 237

maternity leave programs, 351

meditation, 356–357

memory, 231

    impairment in restaurant, 338

Mental Health Commission of Canada, 162, 165

Merit Adjusted Premium (MAP), 66

mindfulness, 356–357

mobbing, 190, 230

mode analysis, 99

mode of transmission, 136

moderators, 167–168

monitoring systems, 104, 328–329

Montreal, Maine & Atlantic (MMA), 2

moral consideration, 12

moral motives, 322

motivation, 231, 243

    amotivation, 252

    autonomous, 252, 253

    compliance with safety standards, 266

    controlled, 252

    cost, 21–22

    extrinsic, 252

    financial, 321–322

    increasing opportunity for safety behaviour, 253–257

    intrinsic, 252

    legal, 322–324

    moral and social, 322

    motivating safety behaviour, 247–253

    organizational health and safety management systems, 257–263

    safety, 247, 257, 266

    safety behaviour, 245–247

motor control, 231

Mount Allison University, 276

mucus, 140

musculoskeletal injuries, 174

mutagens, 145

N

"nap room," 345–346

National Institute for Occupational Safety and Health (NIOSH), 31, 161, 170

National Institute of Disability Management and Research (NIDMAR), 328

natural disasters, 286

natural radiation, 112

Natural Sciences and Engineering Research Council (NSERC), 104

near-miss incident, 78

necrosis, 120

needlestick injuries, 154

needs analysis, 221, 222, 226

    digital safety, 223

    job/task analysis, 225

    organizational analysis, 222–224

    person analysis, 225–226

negative affectivity, 167, 168

net earnings, 57

New Experimental Experience Rating Program (NEER), 66

nitro-hydrocarbons, 147*t*

noise, 114

    control, 117–119

    hearing loss types, 115–117

    hearing protectors, 119

    response of human ear, 115

    in workplace, 118

noise-induced hearing loss (NIHL), 115

non-freezing injuries, 126

non-ionizing radiation, 112

    eye absorption properties for, 113*f*

normal incidents, 306

Nova Scotia, 190

    mine explosion, 41

nutrition control, 361–362

O

Occupational Alcohol Movement, 355

occupational diseases, 62–63

Occupational health psychology, 166

occupational health and safety (OH&S), 5, 6, 29

    acts, 33

    barriers, 15–16

    changing perspectives on risk and liability, 7

    under Criminal Code, corporate liability for, 41–42

    developments in Canadian legislation, 8

    economic consideration, 10–11

    government, 13–15

    health and safety, 24

    human resources, 20–21

    imperatives for, 10

    joint health and safety committees, 36–37

    legal consideration, 11–12

    legislation, 30, 32–33, 37

    moral consideration, 12

    occupational injuries and illnesses, 6–7

    partnerships, 16–19

    production or safety, 24

    professionals, 19–20

    programs, 6

    stakeholders, 12*t*, 12–13, 34–36

    stop-work provisions, 39–40

    training, 219–221

    work refusals, 37–39

Occupational Health and Safety Council of Ontario (OHSCO), 203

Occupational health and safety management system (OHSMS), 244–245, 251, 255, 257–258, 260

    CSA-Z1000-06 Plan-Do-Check-Act Model, 260*f*

primary elements, 258–259

occupational illnesses, 6–7, 11, 285, 333

occupational injuries, 6–7, 11, 223, 224

OCTranspo, 189

off-the-job training, 229

office incident, 308

offsite harassment, 212

on-site daycares, 351

on-site programs, 358

on-the-job training, 229

Ontario Human Rights Code, 208

Operations Integrity Management System (OIMS), 259

organic solvents, 146, 147*t*

organizational analysis, 222–224

organizational evaluation, 234–235

organizational health and safety management systems, 257

    CSA standard, 261

    CSA-Z1000-06 Plan-Do-Check-Act model, 260*f*

    Imperial Oil, 259

    policy checklist, 262–263

    primary elements, 258–259

organizational policies and programs, 203–204

organizational strain, 169–170

organized labour, 15

original equipment manufacturer (OEM), 308

ototoxic effects, 139

overexertion injuries, 86

    awkward working positions, 89

    repetitive strain injuries, 87–88

    workers, 86–87

overt traumatic injuries, 56, 85

P

parental leave programs, 351

Passport to Safety, 220

people-focused climate, 326

peripheral neuropathy, 145

permanent threshold shift (PTS), 116

person analysis, 225–226

personal leave systems, 349–351

personal protective equipment (PPE), 90, 102–103, 114, 118, 155

photoelectric eye, 94

physical agents, 40, 111

    blue light effects, 111

    expensive jewellery, 130

    hearing protection types, 131

    noise, 114–119

    radiation, 111–114, 129–130

    thermal stress condition, 123

    vibration, 120–122

physical demands analysis, 331–332

physical fitness programs, 362

physical hazards, 5, 134–135

physical rehabilitation, 61

physical strain, 169

Plan-Do-Check-Act model, 260–261

point-of-contact control, 89, 90, 113, 114

policy statement, 201

portal of entry, 136–137

portal of exit, 136

portfolio, 20

positive health, 354

positive safety climate, 254–255, 257

positive tree, 82

postal shootings, 189

postcontact control, 89, 113, 285. *See also* contact control; hazard control; precontact control

    business continuity planning, 287

    CISD, 286

    stress and, 285–286

post-traumatic stress, 285–286

post-traumatic stress disorder (PTSD), 54

potassium hydroxide (KOH), 146

precontact control, 89–90, 277. *See also* contact control; hazard control; postcontact control

    drills, 280

    emergency plan, 277

    EOCs, 280

    ERP, 277–278

    evacuation plan, 278–279

    futureproofing, 277

    hazard evaluation, 277

    manager, 280

    notification of authorities, 279–280

    pandemic planning, 278

    supplies, 280

prescribed duties, 34

preventive maintenance, 96, 99, 155
    confined-space entry, 100–102
    lockout procedures, 99–100
    work permits, 100

preventive stress management, 170–171, 348

primary interventions, 171–172, 356

primary irritants. *See* irritants

probability, 67, 78, 82, 83

procedural justice, 173

psychological abuse, 191

psychological involvement, 178

psychologically healthy and safe workplace, 162

psychological strain, 168–169

psychology of incidents, 306

psychosocial hazards
    Mental Health Commission of Canada, 162
    preventive stress management, 170–171
    primary interventions, 171–172
    psychological first aid, 161
    psychologically healthy and safe workplace, 162
    recognizing, assessing, and managing, 170
    secondary interventions, 172–173
    spotlight on stressor, 173–178
    strain, 168–170
    stress, 166–168
    stressful job, 182
    stressors, 163–165
    technology at work, 183
    tertiary interventions, 173
    toxic workplace, 183

psychosocial model of health, 162

Q

quantitative risk assessments, 83

"quid pro quo" harassment. *See* sexual coercion

R

radiation, 111, 123, 129–130
    controlling radiation, 113–114
    ionizing radiation, 112

non-ionizing radiation, 112
    types, 111–112

radio frequency (RF), 112

rail disaster at Lac-Mégantic, 2

rate group method, 52

rationale for incident investigation, 292–293

Raynaud's phenomenon, 121

reactive materials, 283

recognition, assessment, and control program (RAC program), 292

record keeping, 99, 104, 155

re-enactments, 300, 301

registered occupational hygienist technologists, 19

regulations, 2, 29–32, 34, 36, 53, 149, 152, 285

rehabilitation, 60–61

reinforcement theory, 248
    elements of behaviour-based safety program, 249
    risky side of behaviour-based safety programs, 249–250

relaxation training, 356–357

repetitive strain injury (RSI), 87–88
    awareness day, 88

reporting requirements, 67
    employer incident report, Manitoba, 68*f*–71*f*
    noncompliance, 72

reservoir, 136

resonance, 121

respiration, 140–142

respiratory system, 141*f*

return-to-work case management, 327–328

return-to-work coordinator, 323, 327, 328, 333

return-to-work planning, 326, 329, 331, 338
    functional ability assessment, 332
    physical demands analysis, 331–332
    workplace accommodation, 329–331

risk, 78
    changing perspectives on, 7
    risk factors, 166, 167, 169, 198, 203, 204, 332, 361, 365
    risk mitigation, 201
    young workers at, 17–18

risk assessment, 77, 82, 84*t*, 201
    probability, 83–84
    risk level of hazard, 84–85
    risk perceptions, 78, 82–83
    sample hazard inventory and risk evaluation, 85*t*

Rogers Communications Inc., 359

Royal Newfoundland Constabulary Association (RNCA), 51

S

safety, 13
    associations, 59
    in bakery, 266
    climate, 20, 224, 254–255
    compliance, 246, 253, 256, 257
    culture, 255
    decreasing costs, 21
    integration in other human resource functions, 20–21
    motivation, 247, 257
    participation, 246
    performance, 246, 247
    requiring legislative compliance, 21
    sampling, 81
    training initiatives, 236–237

safety awareness, 96–97
    awards and incentives, 97
    CCOHS Young Workers Zone, 97
    special events, 96–97
    visible reminders, 96

safety behaviours, 245, 248, 254, 257, 361
    ability, motivation, opportunity, 247*f*
    goal setting, 251
    increasing opportunity, 253
    management commitment to OH&S, 253–257
    motivating, 247
    proper use of PPE, 246
    reinforcement theory, 248–250
    self-determination theory, 252–253

safety data sheets (SDS), 149, 152–153

safety leadership, 20, 245, 255
    active transactional leadership, 256
    transformational leadership, 256–257

safety management systems, 3, 258

Second Injury and Enhancement Fund (SIEF), 60

secondary interventions, 171–173, 348

segmental vibration, 120, 122

selective hearing, 116

self-determination theory, 252

    levels and types, 253*t*

sensitizers, 145

sensorineural hearing loss, 115

severe acute respiratory syndrome (SARS), 273

severity, 293–294

    rates calculation, 65

sexual coercion, 190, 191, 208

sexual harassment, 189, 190, 207. *See also* workplace harassment

    as health and safety issue, 208–209

    prototypical cases of, 208

short-duration noise, 115

signal detection, 275

"silent killer". *See* hypertension

simple asphyxiant, 144

situational factors, 296–297

slips, preventing, 98

small fishing vessel regulations, 29

SmithCorp, 183

smoking cessation, 360

smouldering stage, 282

snoozing on job, 345–346

social goals of workers' compensation, 60

    provision for second injuries, 60

    rehabilitation, 60–61

social learning, 231

social motives, 322

social rehabilitation, 61

Social Sciences and Humanities Research Council (SSHRC), 104

sodium chloride (NaCl), 146

sodium hydroxide (NaOH), 146

solvents

    characteristics and properties of, 143

    flammability, 143–145

    inorganic solvents, 146

    organic solvents, 146, 147*t*

    toxic substances, 144–145

    vaporization, 146

sound pressure level. *See* decibels (db)

source–path–human controls, 103–104

stakeholders, 12*t*, 13

    contractors, 35

    in disability management, 332–334

    duties and responsibilities, 34

    employers, 34

    philosophy of internal responsibility system, 36

    supervisors, 35

    workers, 35

standards and codes, 31

statutes awareness to OH&S in Canada, 44

stop-work provisions, 39–40

strain, 168

    behavioural strain, 169

    organizational strain, 169–170

    physical strain, 169

    psychological strain, 168–169

stress, 166, 285–286

    intervention strategies, 172*t*

    moderators, 167–168

    occupational health psychology, 166

    psychologists, 167

stressful job, 74, 182

stress management programs, 356

    cognitive-behavioural skills training, 356

    increasing social support, 357

    relaxation training, meditation, and mindfulness, 356–357

    training effectiveness, 357–358

stress-related disabilities, 62

stressor(s), 163

    categories of, 163*t*

    injustice at work, 173–174

    mental health at work, 165

    technology, 174–175

    technology-related stressors, 175–176

    work–family conflict, 176–178

    in workplace, 164–165

subjective risk assessments, 83

substandard practice. *See* unsafe act

substitution, 91–92

sulphuric acid (H_2SO_4), 146

supervisor, 297

    duties, 35

supported and sheltered work, 331

surfactant layer, 142

surveillance systems, 200*f*

susceptible host, 136–137

Swearing, Agitation, Volume, Threat (SAV-T), 195, 197

sweep away devices, 94

Swiss cheese model, 305

    bow-tie analysis, 305*f*

    normal incidents, 306

systems approach, 325

T

table salt. *See* sodium chloride (NaCl)

target hardening strategies, 199

target organs, 142

task analysis, 81

technology at work, 183

technology-based training, 229

technology-related stressors, 175–176

temporary threshold shift (TTS), 116

teratogens, 145

tertiary interventions, 173, 348

thermal stress condition, 123. *See also* physical agents

    body as machine system, 123*f*

    cold environments, 125

    cold-related injuries and illnesses, 126–127

    controlling cold, 128

    controlling heat, 125

    heat-related illnesses, 124–125

    measurement, 124

    men and women in cold, 126

    signs and symptoms of hypothermia, 127

thermodynamic theory, 123

three Es, 20

threshold of hearing, 115

timing, incident investigation, 293

toxic

    fumes, 283

    workplace, 183

toxicity, 137

    terminology, 140

toxicology, 139. *See also* chemical agents

    ingestion, 142

    ototoxic effects, 139

    penetration, 142

toxicology (*continued*)

   respiration, 140–142

   skin absorption, 142

   toxicity terminology, 140

"train the trainer" program, 228

training, 218

   classroom training, 218*f*

   content, 227

   delivery, 230–231

   health and safety training programs, 221–235

   objectives, 227

   OH&S training, 219–221

   safety training initiatives, 236–237

training evaluation, 221, 232

   individual evaluation, 233–234

   organizational evaluation, 234–235

training logistics, 227

   learning theory and training delivery, 230–231

   off-the-job training, 229

   safety training literature, 232

   "train the trainer" program, 228

   WHMIS, 230

transformational leadership, 256–257

Transportation Safety Board of Canada (TSB), 2, 29, 77

turbinates, 140

Type A behaviour, 167–168

Type I violence, 192, 198–199

Type II violence, 192, 199

   behavioural/interpersonal strategies, 201–202

   environmental strategies, 200

   organizational/administrative strategies, 200–201

   surveillance systems, 200*f*

Type III violence, 192–193, 202

Type IV violence, 193, 202–203

U

ulcer, 62

ultraviolet radiation (UV), 112

uncontrolled fire stage, 282

undue hardship, 51, 322, 324

unexpected gas, 158

unintended consequences of WHP programs, 365

unsafe act, 78–79, 81, 248, 284, 298, 301, 305

unwanted sexual attention, 190

upper explosion limit (UEL), 145

upper flammability limit (UFL). *See* upper explosion limit (UEL)

U.S. prevalence data, 191

V

Vancouver International Airport (YVR), 244

vasoconstriction, 116

ventilation, 91–92

vibration, 120

   controlling vibration, 122

   HAVS, 121

   health effects of, 120

   vibration effects diagnosis, 121

vibration-induced white finger (VWF), 121

violence, 190

visible light, 111

vocational rehabilitation, 61

W

wage loss, 58

wage loss benefits, 58

walk-through survey, 81

walkthrough, 298, 301

web-based training, 230

weight control, 361–362

wellness programming, 346

Westray mine disaster, 8

wet bulb globe temperature (WBGT) index, 124

whole-body vibration, 120

worker duties, 35

workers' compensation, 51

   administration and responsibilities, 53–54

   assessments, 64–67

   in Canada, 53

   compensation rates and methods, 57–59

   firefighters battling and police fighting, 51

   historical roots, 52–53

   medical aid and incident prevention, 59

   occupational diseases, 62–63

   premiums, 55

   prevention, 55–57

   reporting requirements, 67–72

   social goals, 60–61

   system in Canada, 64

   at work, 61–62

   workplace stress, 62–63

Workers Compensation Appeals Tribunal (WCAT), 59

Workers' Compensation Board (WCB), 52, 55, 62

   claims process, 63

   contact information for provincial and territorial, 56–57

work–family conflict, 164, 176–178, 347–348

   family-friendly policies, 348–354

   reducing work–life conflict, 353

work hardening, 330

working to change safety, 266

work–life balance, 177

work permits, 100

   scaffold use permit, 101*f*

workplace

   fatalities in Canada, 3*f*

   injury statistics, 11

   stress, 62–63

workplace accommodation, 326, 329

   gradual work exposure, 330

   light-duty work, 330

   supported and sheltered work, 331

   work trials, 331

workplace aggression, 190

   assault cycle, 196*f*

   Canadian data, 191–192

   prevalence by source, 194

   prevalence of, 190

   risk factors for, 195–197

   sources of workplace violence, 192–194

   U.S. prevalence data, 191

workplace harassment, 189, 204–205. *See also* sexual harassment

   investigation of incidents, 206

   respectful workplaces, 206–207

Workplace Hazardous Materials Information System (WHMIS), 8, 40, 135, 149, 230
    education and training, 153–154
    hazard classes and categories, 149–150
    labels, 150
    SDS, 152–153
    supplier labels, 151–152
    training, 237
    WHMIS 2015–pictograms, 153
    WHMIS classes and categories, 150
    WHMIS supplier label, 151
Workplace Safety Insurance Appeals Tribunal (WSIAT), 63
Workplace Safety and Insurance Board (WSIB), 254
Workplace Safety and Prevention Services (WSPS), 223
workplace violence, 190
    intimate partner violence, 193
    organizational policies and programs, 203–204

    prevention, 198
    sources of, 192–194
    Type I violence, 198–199
    Type II violence, 199–202
    Type III violence, 202
    Type IV violence, 202–203
workplace wellness
    family-friendly policies, 347–354
    health promotion programs, 354–366
    initiatives, 346, 347*f*
    job sharing in telecommunications firm, 370
    mandatory aerobics, 369
    in small businesses, 355
work refusals, 37–39
worksite health promotion programs (WHP programs), 358–360, 369
    alcohol and drug testing programs, 360–361
    development, 362, 363
    using evaluation to build business case, 364–365

    hypertension screening, 361
    nutrition control, 361–362
    overall evaluation, 365–366
    physical fitness programs, 362
    smoking cessation, 360
    unintended consequences, 365
    weight control, 361–362
work-to-family conflict, 177, 178
work trials, 331
World Health Organization, 275

X

X-radiation, 112

Y

Young Worker Awareness Program, 18
young worker's quandary, 240
Yukon Workers' Compensation Health and Safety Board (YWCHSB), 54